A Manual of

ENGINEERING DRAWING

for Students and Draftsmen

THE ENGINEERING DRAWING SERIES

FRENCH AND VIERCK   Engineering Drawing
Eighth Edition, 715 pages, 6 x 9, 1288 illustrations

McGRAW-HILL TEXT-FILMS FOR ENGINEERING DRAWING
A Series of Directly Correlated
Motion Pictures and Filmstrips (8 films)

VIERCK, COOPER,   Engineering Drawing Problems
AND MACHOVINA   Series 2, 11 x 17
Engineering Drawing—Basic Problems
Series A, 8½ x 11

LEVENS AND EDSTROM   Problems in Engineering Drawing
Series III, 8½ x 11 (Series IV in preparation)

RUSS   Quiz Questions to Accompany Engineering Drawing

FRENCH AND TURNBULL   Lessons in Lettering
Book I—Vertical Single Stroke Lettering
Third Edition, 40 pages, 9 x 6
Book II—Inclined Single Stroke Lettering
Third Edition, 40 pages, 9 x 6

FRENCH AND SVENSEN   Mechanical Drawing
Fifth Edition, 437 pages, 6 x 9, 618 illustrations

McGRAW-HILL TEXT-FILMS FOR MECHANICAL DRAWING
A Series of Directly Correlated Motion
Pictures and Filmstrips

LEVENS AND EDSTROM   Problems in Mechanical Drawing
Problems in Mechanical Drawing, Second Course

A Manual of

ENGINEERING
DRAWING

for Students and Draftsmen

by THOMAS E. FRENCH

Late Professor of Engineering Drawing, The Ohio State University

and CHARLES J. VIERCK

Professor of Engineering Drawing, The Ohio State University

with the assistance of

Charles D. Cooper   Ralph S. Paffenbarger

Paul E. Machovina   Hollie W. Shupe

of the Department of Engineering Drawing, The Ohio State University

EIGHTH EDITION

McGRAW-HILL BOOK COMPANY, INC.

NEW YORK   TORONTO   LONDON

1953

A MANUAL OF ENGINEERING DRAWING
FOR STUDENTS AND DRAFTSMEN

Library of Congress Catalog Card Number: 52-13455

VI

First Edition (August, 1911)
Ten Printings, 35,000 copies

Second Edition (July, 1918)
Twelve Printings, 108,000 copies

Third Edition (May, 1924)
Ten Printings, 96,000 copies

Fourth Edition (June, 1929)
Ten Printings, 106,000 copies

Fifth Edition (April, 1935)
Sixteen Printings, 148,000 copies

Sixth Edition (May, 1941)
Fourteen Printings, 439,700 copies

Seventh Edition (August, 1947)
Seven Printings, 291,099 copies

Eighth Edition (March, 1953)
Six Printings, 156,000 copies

Total Issue 1,379,799

THE MAPLE PRESS COMPANY, YORK, PA.

Preface to the Eighth Edition

Again, as in previous editions, the basic plan has been to bring the text and problems up to date by eliminating the obsolete material, and to use new subject matter consistent with current standards and practices. This edition represents a complete revision. Almost every chapter has been altered or rewritten, and figures have been changed or redrawn to increase the over-all usefulness of the text.

The text has been arranged to follow a more logical pattern and meet the preference of a majority of users. The material on projections has been expanded for better coverage. Also, the division into shorter chapters simplifies reading assignments. All the chapters on projections, including pictorial, intersections, and developments, have been grouped in the front portion of the book. This portion is then followed by dimensioning. Next, the basic machine elements, such as screw threads, fasteners, pipe, gears, etc., are discussed, which are followed by the chapter on Working Drawings. In the latter portion is grouped the specialties, architectural, structural, topographic drawing, etc.

The various chapters also have been altered in their coverage. Chapter 1 now outlines the whole field of engineering drawing and contains some information that was formerly in Chapter 6. It is hoped that the new chapter on Reading will be useful. Also, the chapter on Auxiliary Views, which formerly contained the material on revolution, has been split into three chapters having a better coverage. The term *revolution* has been changed to *rotation*, a more accurate descriptive word for the operations involved.

The chapter on Screw Threads follows the new Unified Standard and presents this new material in a way that it is hoped will be easily usable and effective. The former chapter, containing information on screw threads, threaded fasteners, keys, rivets, and springs, is now given in three separate chapters.

The chapter on Welding Drawings has been revised to conform to the latest ASA Standard, and new material has been added to the chapter on Gears and Cams. The chapters on Structural Drawing and Architectural Drawing have been completely revised.

In this edition, the favorite problems of the previous edition have been retained and many new ones, representing current design, have been added. Some new problems have been arranged in "exploded" form and many of the older ones rearranged to make for greater flexibility in their choice. It is hoped that the new material in the text and the rearrangement and expansion will not only make a better book for class use, but also a more valuable book for the engineer's technical library.

Again available with this edition are the McGraw-Hill Text-Films, designed especially for, and correlated with, the text and problems. Two new titles, "Developments" and "Pictorial Sketching," are being added to the previously available series. These visual materials, consisting of motion pictures and filmstrips, have a very high teaching value and illustrate certain features more effectively than is possible by the use of a textbook alone. Thus, these films added to the previously available series of textbooks, problem books, and lettering books, further extend the coverage of teaching needs.

The helpful suggestions, encouraging comment, and valuable ideas received from the teachers of engineering drawing and from engineers in industry throughout the country, many of whom are personal friends, are recorded with appreciation, as are the contributions of Dale O. Miller, of the Rochester Gear Works, to the chapter on Gears and Cams; and of G. A. Johnson, of the Frederick Post Company; L. A. Miller, Jr., of the Dietzgen Company; Frank E. Oppenheimer, of the Gramercy Import Company; M. G. Thomas, of the Keuffel and Esser Company; and F. E. Vaughn, of the V. and E. Manufacturing Company to the chapter on The Selection of Instruments.

Professors Theodore T. Aakhus, Alfred S. Gaskell, Frank A. Heacock, Kenneth Holderman, and B. Leighton Wellman supplied prerevision reviews. Professors Albert S. Levens and James S. Rising reviewed the final manuscript. Professor John M. Russ has supplied a very complete list of corrections and suggestions for clarifying text and problems. All of these products are highly valued.

Several engineering equipment manufacturers have supplied drawings and parts from which problems were made up. Credit lines appear with the various items used.

The assistance of Clyde H. Kearns, Jr., on Charts, Graphs, and Diagrams, the help of Alfred J. Philby in obtaining new problems, the contributions of Fairfax E. Watkins to the chapters on Structural Drawing, Gearing, and Piping Drawings, and the work of Wilma E. Russell in preparing the manuscript are greatly esteemed.

Charles J. Vierck

Columbus, Ohio
November, 1952

Preface to the First Edition

There is a wide diversity of method in the teaching of engineering drawing, and perhaps less uniformity in the courses in different schools than would be found in most subjects taught in technical schools and colleges. In some well-known instances the attempt is made to teach the subject by giving a series of plates to be copied by the student. Some give all the time to laboratory work; others depend principally upon recitations and homework. Some begin immediately on the theory of descriptive geometry, working in all the angles; others discard theory and commence with a course in machine detailing. Some advocate the extensive use of models; some condemn their use entirely.

Different courses have been designed for different purposes, and criticism is not intended, but it would seem that better unity of method might result if there were a better recognition of the conception that drawing is a real language, to be studied and taught in the same way as any other language. With this conception it may be seen that except for the practice in the handling and use of instruments, and for showing certain standards of execution, copying drawings does little more in the study as an art of expression of thought than copying paragraphs from a foreign book would do in beginning the study of a foreign language.

And it would appear equally true that good pedagogy would not advise taking up composition in a new language before the simple structure of the sentence is understood and appreciated; that is, "working drawings" would not be considered until after the theory of projection has been explained.

After a knowledge of the technic of expression, the "penmanship and orthography," the whole energy should be directed toward training in constructive imagination, the perceptive ability which enables one to think in three dimensions, to visualize quickly and accurately, to build up a clear mental image, a requirement absolutely necessary for the designer who is to represent his thoughts on paper. That this may be accomplished more readily by taking up solids before points and lines has been demonstrated beyond dispute.

It is then upon this plan, regarding drawing as a language, the universal graphical language of the industrial world, with its varied force of expression, its grammar and its styles, that this book has been built. It is not a "course in drawing," but a textbook, with exercises and problems in some variety from which selections may be made.

Machine parts furnish the best illustrations of principles, and have been used freely, but the book is intended for all engineering students. Chapters on architectural drawing and map drawing have been added, as in the interrelation of the professions every engineer should be able to read and work from such drawings.

In teaching the subject, part of the time, at least one hour per week, may profitably be scheduled for class lectures, recitations, and blackboard work, at which time there may be distributed "study sheets" or home plates of problems on the assigned lesson, to be drawn in pencil and returned at the next corresponding period. In the drawing-room period, specifications for plates, to be approved in pencil and some finished by inking or tracing, should be assigned, all to be done under the careful supervision of the instructor.

The judicious use of models is of great aid, both in technical sketching and, particularly, in drawing to scale, in aiding the student to feel the sense of proportion between the drawing and the structure, so that in reading a drawing he may have the ability to visualize not only the shape but the size of the object represented.

In beginning drawing it is not advisable to use large plates. One set of commercial drafting-room sizes is based on the division of a 36" x 48" sheet into 24" x 36", 18" x 24", 12" x 18", and 9" x 12". The size 12" x 18" is sufficiently large for first year work, while 9" x 12" is not too small for earlier plates.

Grateful acknowledgment is made of the assistance of Messrs. Robert Meiklejohn, O. E. Williams, A. C. Harper, Cree Sheets, F. W. Ives, W. D. Turnbull, and W. J. Norris of the staff of the Department of Engineering Drawing, The Ohio State University, not only in the preparation of the drawings, but in advice and suggestion on the text. Other members of the faculty of this University have aided by helpful criticism.

The aim has been to conform to modern engineering practice, and it is hoped that the practical consideration of the draftsman's needs will give the book permanent value as a reference book in the student's library.

The author will be glad to cooperate with teachers using it as a textbook.

Thomas E. French

Columbus, Ohio
June, 1911

Contents

1

Introductory

1.1 The language of the engineer. Engineering drawing is the graphic language used in the industrial world by engineers and designers to express and record the ideas and information necessary for the building of machines and structures.

As distinguished from drawing as a fine art, practiced by artists in pictorial representation, engineering drawing is a descriptive graphical language, whereas drawing as a fine art is a means of aesthetic expression. The artist strives to produce, either from the model or landscape before him or through his creative imagination, a picture which will impart to the observer the same mental impression as that produced by the object itself, or the object's visualization in the artist's mind. By employing color, gradation of tone in monotone light and shade, or line combinations in black and white, he is able to suggest his meanings and to depend upon the observer's imagination to visualize the effect of perspective foreshortening and to supply the lack of complete detail.

The engineering draftsman has a more exacting task. Limited usually to outline alone (shading is not often used, except for illustrations), he may not depend upon suggested meanings, but must give precise and positive information regarding every detail of the machine or structure existing in his imagination. Thus, drawing to him is more than pictorial representation; it is a complete graphical language, by whose aid he may describe minutely every operation necessary and may keep a complete record of the work for duplication and repairs. By a logical system of related "views," intricate and complicated shapes are clearly shown, exact and detailed sizes are given without ambiguity, individual parts are identified for assembly and are located in the machine in their correct functional position. In addition, descriptive notes and specifications give materials, finishes, and directions for manufacture and assembly.

In the artist's case, the result can be understood in greater or less degree by anyone. The draftsman's result does not show the object as it would appear to the eye when finished; consequently, his drawing can be read and understood only by one trained in the language.

Thus, as the foundation upon which all designing and subsequent manufacture are based, engineering drawing becomes, with the possible exception of mathematics, the most important single branch of study in a technical school. Every engineering student must know how to make and how to read drawings. The subject is essential in all types of engineering practice. The drafting room is often the entering gateway into industry, but even one who may never have to make drawings must be able to inter-

1

pret them and to know whether or not a drawing is correct.   An engineer
without a working knowledge of the engineer's language would be professionally illiterate.

1.2   Methods of expression.   To serve the many purposes for which
drawings may be made, the engineering draftsman has at his disposal
several different methods by which he may convey information.   For the
great bulk of engineering work, the orthographic system (Chaps. 6 to 15)
will be employed, and this method, with its variations and the necessary
symbols and abbreviations, constitutes a most important portion of this
book.   However, for presentation drawings, illustrations, some working
drawings and others, principally used by the layman, one of the pictorial
methods (Chaps. 16 to 18) may be better suited to the purpose.

The well-trained engineer, therefore, must be thoroughly familiar with
all methods and must be able to specify their use with assurance regarding
the final result; the accomplished engineering draftsman must be able, as
well, to follow the engineer's directions and produce work of professional
grade.

The following outline classifies the various projective systems according
to their theory.   Also included are chapter references.

Systems of Projection

		Two-view drawings	Chap. 6
		Three-view drawings	Chap. 6
		Orthographic reading	Chap. 7
	Multiplanar	Auxiliary views	Chap. 10
	(Two or more	Oblique views	Chap. 11
Orthographic	planes)	Rotation	Chap. 12
Projection		Sectional views	Chap. 13
(Projectors		Intersections	Chap. 14
perpendicular		Developments	Chap. 15
to planes of		Isometric projection	Chap. 16
projection)	**Uniplanar**	Isometric drawing	Chap. 16
	(One plane)	Dimetric drawing	Chap. 16
		Trimetric drawing	Chap. 16
		Axonometric projection from orthographic views	Chap. 16
Oblique		Cavalier projection	Chap. 16
Projection		Cavalier drawing	Chap. 16
(Projectors	**Uniplanar**	Cabinet drawing	Chap. 16
oblique to		Various oblique positions	Chap. 16
plane of		Oblique projection from orthographic views	Chap. 16
projection)			
Perspective			
Projection			
(Projectors	**Uniplanar**	Parallel perspective	Chap. 17
converging		Angular perspective	Chap. 17
to a station			
point)			

Included also as an important part of the method of expression is a study of the description of *size*, including special notes and specifications. The accomplished draftsman must also understand the special practices peculiar to the separate sections of engineering work. The principal difference between specialized fields is that there is not any variation fundamentally in the methods of projection, but that the dimensioning and notes will be made in accordance with the accepted standards for each field.

The following outline lists dimensioning practice from the standpoint of drawing type.

Dimensioning Practice

1.3 Technique. To write the graphic language easily and accurately, the aid of drawing instruments is required. When these implements are used, it is called "instrument drawing." When done with the unaided hand, without the assistance of instruments or appliances, it is known as "freehand drawing." Training in both of these methods is necessary for the engineer, the first to develop accuracy and manual dexterity, the second to develop comprehensive observation and to give control and mastery of form and proportion.

In this study, then, we must become familiar with the technique of expression, and an important requirement is the ability to use the drawing instruments correctly. Continued practice will develop a facility in their use that will free the mind from any thought of the means of expression.

The following subjects are classed as dealing with technique, although some theory may also be included.

Drawing Technique

1.4 Objectives. Our object, then, is to study this language so that we may write it, express ourselves clearly to one familiar with it, and read it readily when written by another. To do this we must know its basic theory, its composition, and be familiar with its accepted conventions and abbreviations. This language is universal, as its principles are essentially the same throughout the world, and one trained in the practices of one nation can readily adapt himself to the practices of another.

This new language is entirely a graphical or written one. It cannot be read aloud, but must be interpreted by acquiring a visual knowledge of the subject represented; and the student's success in it will be indicated not alone by his skill in execution, but also by his ability to interpret his impressions and to visualize clearly in space.

It is not a language to be learned only by the comparatively few draftsmen who will be professional writers of it but, as already indicated, should be understood by all connected with, or interested in, technical industry. The training its study gives in quick, accurate observation and the power of reading description from lines is of a value quite unappreciated by those not familiar with it.

TEXT-FILMS

A brief description of each McGraw-Hill Text-Film available for use with this textbook is given at the end of the chapter with which the film is correlated.

The following Text-Film is designed as an orientation film to be used in conjunction with Chap. 1:

According to Plan: Introduction to Engineering Drawing (10-min. sound motion picture).

This film is designed for use at the beginning of the course to introduce the student to the subject of engineering drawing. It shows that engineering drawing is the working language of the engineer, indicates why it is important, and gives an insight into the relation between modern methods of production and engineering drawing.

2

Lettering

To give all the information necessary for the complete construction of a machine or structure there must be added to the "graphical language" of lines describing its shape, the figured dimensions, notes on material and finish, and a descriptive title, all of which must be lettered, freehand, in a style that is perfectly legible, uniform and capable of rapid execution. So far as its appearance is concerned there is no part of a drawing so important as the lettering. A good drawing may be ruined, not only in appearance but in usefulness, by lettering done ignorantly or carelessly, as illegible figures are very apt to cause mistakes in the work.

2.1 The paragraph above refers to the use of lettering on engineering drawings. In a broad sense, the subject of lettering is a distinct branch of design. There are two general classes of persons who are interested in its study: (1) those who have to use letters and words to convey information on drawings; and (2) those who use lettering in applied design, such as art students, artists, and craftsmen. The first group is concerned mainly with legibility and speed, the second with beauty of form and composition. Architects come under both classes, as they not only have to letter their working drawings but also have to design inscriptions and tablets to be executed in stone or bronze.

The engineering student takes up lettering as his first work in drawing and continues its practice throughout his course, becoming more and more skillful and proficient.

In the art of lettering there are various forms of alphabets used, each appropriate for some particular purpose. The parent of all these styles is the "Old Roman" of the classic Roman inscriptions. This beautiful letter is the basic standard for architects and artists, although they have occasional appropriate use for other forms, such as the gothic of the Middle Ages, one form of which is popularly known as **"Old English."** A variation known as Modern Roman is used by civil engineers in finished map and topographical drawing.   For working drawings the simplified forms called commercial gothic are used almost exclusively.

There are two general divisions of lettering: *drawn* or *built-up* letters, and *written* or *single-stroke* letters.   Roman letters are usually drawn in outline and filled in; commercial gothic, except in the larger sizes, are generally made in single stroke.

Lettering is *not* mechanical drawing.   Large, carefully drawn letters are often made with instruments, but the persistent use by some draftsmen of mechanical caricatures known as "geometrical letters," "block letters," etc., made up of straight lines ruled in with T square and triangle is to be condemned entirely.

2.2   General proportions.   There is no one standard for the proportions of letters, but there are certain fundamental points in design and certain characteristics of individual letters that must be thoroughly learned by study and observation before composition into words and sentences may be attempted.   Not only do the widths of letters in any alphabet vary, from *I*, the narrowest, to *W*, the widest, but different alphabets vary as a whole. Styles narrow in their proportion of width to height are called **"COMPRESSED LETTERS"** and are used when space is limited.   Styles wider than the normal are called **"EXTENDED LETTERS."**

The   proportion   of   the   thickness   of   stem   to   the   height   varies widely, ranging all the way from one-third to one-twentieth.   Letters with heavy stems are called **boldface** or **blackface,** those with thin stems LIGHTFACE.

2.3   The rule of stability.   In the construction of letters, the well-known optical illusion in which a horizontal line drawn across the middle of a rectangle appears to be below the middle must be provided for.   In order to give the appearance of stability, such letters as *BEKSXZ* and the figures *3* and *8* must be drawn smaller at the top than at the bottom.   To see the effect of this illusion turn a printed page upside down and notice the letters mentioned.

2.4   Single-stroke lettering.   By far the greatest amount of lettering on drawings is done in a rapid single-stroke letter, either vertical or inclined, and every engineer must have absolute command of these styles.   The ability to letter well can be acquired only by continued and careful practice, but it can be acquired by anyone with normal muscular control of his fingers who will practice faithfully and intelligently and take the trouble to observe carefully the shapes of the letters, the sequence of strokes in making them, and the rules for their composition.   It is not a matter of artistic talent, or even of dexterity, in handwriting.   Many draftsmen who write very poorly letter well.

The terms "single-stroke" or "one-stroke" do not mean that the entire letter is made without lifting the pencil or pen, but that the width of the stroke of the pencil or pen is the width of the stem of the letter.

2.5 Guide lines. Light guide lines for both tops and bottoms of letters should always be drawn, using a sharp pencil. Figure 2.1 shows a method of laying off a number of equally spaced lines of letters. Draw the first base line, and above it mark the desired height of the letters; then set the bow spacers to the distance wanted between base lines and step off the required number of base lines. With the same setting, step down again from the upper point, thus obtaining points for the tops of each line of letters.

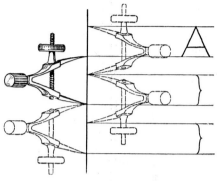

Fig. 2.1. Spacing lines.

The Braddock-Rowe triangle, Fig. 2.2, and the Ames lettering instrument, Fig. 2.3, are convenient devices for spacing lines of letters. A sharp pencil is inserted in the proper row of countersunk holes, and the instrument, guided by a T-square blade, is drawn back and forth by the pencil.

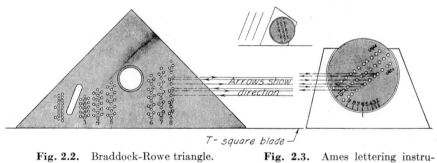

Fig. 2.2. Braddock-Rowe triangle.   **Fig. 2.3.** Ames lettering instrument.

The holes are grouped for capitals and lower case, the numbers indicating the height of capitals in thirty-seconds of an inch; thus No. 6 spacing means that the capitals will be $\frac{6}{32}$ or $\frac{3}{16}$ in. high.

2.6 Lettering in pencil. In the previous chapter the necessity for good technique in drawing was mentioned. This is equally true for lettering, either as finished work to be reproduced by one of the printing processes, or as part of a pencil drawing to be inked. In the first case the penciling will be clean, firm, and opaque, while in the second case it may be lighter. The lettering pencil should be selected carefully by trial on the paper. In one case the same grade as that used for the drawing may be chosen, in another case a grade or two softer may be preferred. Sharpen the pencil to a long conical point, then round the lead slightly on the end so that it is not so sharp as a point used for drawing.

The first requirement in lettering is the correct holding of the pencil or pen. Figure 2.4 shows the pencil held comfortably with the thumb, fore-finger, and second finger on alternate flat sides, and the third and fourth fingers on the paper. Vertical, slanting, and curved strokes are drawn with

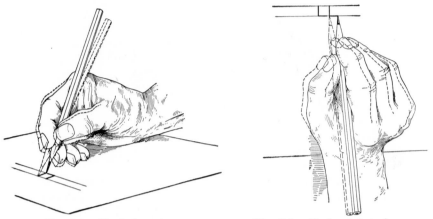

Fig. 2.4. Vertical strokes.   Fig. 2.5. Horizontal strokes.

a steady, even, finger movement; horizontal strokes are made similarly, but with some pivoting of the hand at the wrist, Fig. 2.5. Exert a firm, uniform pressure, but not so heavy as to cut grooves in the paper. To keep the point symmetrical, the habit of rotating the pencil after every few strokes should be formed.

 2.7 Lettering pens. There are many steel writing pens either adaptable to, or made especially for, lettering. The sizes of the strokes of a few

LEONARDT 516 F: 506 F
HUNT 512: ESTERBROOK 968
Esterbrook 1000   Spencerian No. 1
Gillott 404: Gillott 303 For very fine lines Gillott 170 and 290 or Esterbrook 356 and 355

Fig. 2.6. Pen strokes, full size.

popular ones are shown in full size in Fig. 2.6. Several special pens made in sets of graded sizes have been designed for single-stroke lettering, among which are those illustrated in Fig. 2.7. These are particularly useful for large work. The ink-holding reservoir of the Henry tank pen, Fig. 2.8, assists materially in maintaining uniform weight of line. A similar device may be made by bending a brass strip from a paper fastener, a piece of annealed watch spring or, perhaps best, a strip cut from a piece of shim brass into the shape shown in Fig. 2.9 and inserting it in the penholder so that the curved end just touches the nibs of the pen. The rate of feed can be increased by moving the end closer to the point of the pen.

Always wet a new pen and wipe it thoroughly before using to remove the oil film. Some draftsmen prepare a new pen by holding it in a match flame

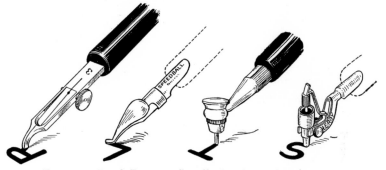

Fig. 2.7. Barch-Payzant, Speedball, Edco and Leroy pens.

Fig. 2.8. Henry tank pen.   **Fig. 2.9.** Ink holder.

for 2 or 3 sec. A lettering pen well broken in by use is worth much more than a new one. It should be kept with care and never lent. A pen that has been dipped into writing ink should never be put into drawing ink. When in use, a pen should be wiped clean frequently with a cloth penwiper. The use of a ruling pen for freehand lettering is not recommended.

2.8 Using the pen. A penholder with cork grip (the small size) should be chosen and the pen set in it firmly. Many prefer to ink the pen with the quill filler, touching the quill to the underside of the pen point, rather than to dip it into the ink bottle. If the

Fig. 2.10. Too much ink.   **Fig. 2.11.** Holding the pen.

pen is dipped, the surplus ink should be shaken back into the bottle or the pen touched against the neck of the bottle as it is withdrawn. Lettering with too much ink on the pen is responsible for results of the kind shown in Fig. 2.10.

With the penholder in the position shown in Fig. 2.11, it should be held in the fingers firmly but without pinching. The strokes of the letters should be made with a steady, even motion and a slight uniform pressure on the paper that will not spread the nibs of the pen.

2.9 Single-stroke vertical capitals. The vertical single-stroke commercial gothic letter is a standard for titles, reference letters, etc. As to the proportion of width to height, the general rule is that the smaller the letters the more extended should they be in width. A low extended letter is more legible than a high compressed one and, at the same time, makes a better appearance.

The basic requirement is to learn the form and peculiarity of each of the letters. Too many persons think that lettering is simply "printing" of the childish kind learned in the primary grades. There is an individuality in lettering often nearly as marked as in handwriting, but it must be based on a careful regard for the fundamental letter forms.

2.10 Order of strokes. In the following figures an alphabet of slightly extended vertical capitals has been arranged in family groups. The shape of each letter, with the order and direction of the strokes forming it, must be studied carefully and the letter repeatedly practiced until its form and construction are perfectly familiar. The first studies should be made in pencil to large size, perhaps ⅜ in. high, afterward to smaller size, and finally directly in ink.

To aid in seeing the proportions of widths to heights and in learning the subtleties in the shapes of the letters, they are shown against a square background with its sides divided into sixths. It will be noted that several of the letters in this alphabet, such as *A*, *T*, etc., fill the square, that is, they are as wide as they are high; while some others, such as *H*, *D*, etc., are approximately five spaces wide, or five-sixths of their height. *These proportions must be learned visually* so well that letters of various heights can be drawn in correct proportion without hesitation.

The IHT group. Fig. 2.12. The letter *I* is the foundation stroke. It may be found difficult to keep the stems vertical. If so, direction lines may be drawn lightly an inch or so apart, to aid the eye. The *H* is nearly square

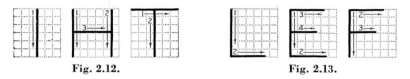

Fig. 2.12.   Fig. 2.13.

(five-sixths) and, in accord with the rule of stability, the crossbar is just above the center. The top of the *T* is drawn first to the full width of the square and the stem started accurately at its middle point.

The LEF group. Fig. 2.13. The *L* is made in two strokes. Note that the first two strokes of the *E* are the same as the *L*, that the third or upper stroke is slightly shorter than the lower, and that the last stroke is two-thirds as long and just above the middle. *F* has the same proportions as *E*.

The NZXY group. Fig. 2.14. The parallel sides of *N* are generally drawn first, but some prefer to make the strokes in consecutive order. *Z* and *X* are both started inside the width of the square on top and run to full width on the bottom. This throws the crossing point of the *X* slightly above the center. The junction of the *Y* strokes is at the center.

Fig. 2.14.   Fig. 2.15.

The VAK group. Fig. 2.15. *V* is the same width as *A*, the full breadth of the square. The *A* bridge is one-third up from the bottom. The second stroke of *K* strikes the stem one-third up from the bottom; the third stroke branches from it in a direction starting from the top of the stem.

The MW group. Fig. 2.16. These are the widest letters. *M* may be made either in consecutive strokes, or by drawing the two vertical strokes first, as with the *N*. *W* is formed of two narrow *V*'s, each two-thirds of the square in width. Note that with all the pointed letters the width at the point is the width of the stroke.

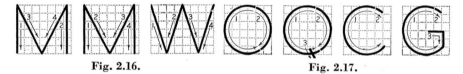

Fig. 2.16.   Fig. 2.17.

The OQCG group. Fig. 2.17. In this extended alphabet the letters of the *O* family are made as full circles. The *O* is made in two strokes, the left side a longer arc than the right, as the right side is harder to make. Make the kern of the *Q* straight. A large-size *C* and *G* can be made more accurately with an extra stroke at the top, while in smaller letters the curve is made in one stroke, Fig. 2.25. Note that the bar on the *G* is half-way up and does not extend past the vertical stroke.

The DUJ group. Fig. 2.18. The top and bottom strokes of *D* must be horizontal. Failure to observe this is a common fault with beginners. *U* in larger letters is formed of two parallel strokes to which the bottom stroke is added. For smaller letters it may be made in two strokes curved at the bottom to meet. *J* has the same construction as *U*, with stroke 1 omitted.

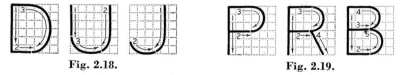

Fig. 2.18.   Fig. 2.19.

The PRB group. Fig. 2.19. With *P*, *R*, and *B*, the number of strokes used depends upon the size of the letter. For large letters the horizontal

lines are started and the curves added, but for smaller letters only one stroke
for each lobe is needed.   The middle lines of *P* and *R* are on the center line,
that of *B* observes the rule of stability.

The S83 group.   Fig. 2.20.   The *S*, *8*, and *3* are closely related in form,
and the rule of stability must be observed carefully.   For a large *S*, three
strokes may be used, for a smaller one, two strokes, and for a very small
size, one stroke only is best.   The *8* may be made on the *S* construction in
three strokes, or in "head and body" in four strokes.   A perfect *3* should
be capable of being finished into an *8*.   The *3* with flat top, sometimes seen,
should not be used, on account of the danger of mistaking it for a *5*.

Fig. 2.20.   Fig. 2.21.

The 069 group.   Fig. 2.21.   The cipher is an ellipse five-sixths the width
of the letter *O*.   The backbones of the *6* and *9* have the same curve as the
cipher, and the lobes are slightly less than two-thirds the height of the figure.

The 257& group.   Fig. 2.22.   The secret in making the *2* lies in getting
the reverse curve to cross the center of the space.   The bottom of *2* and the

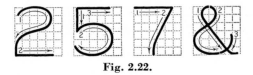

Fig. 2.22.

tops of *5* and *7* should be horizontal straight lines.   The second stroke of *7*
terminates directly below the middle of the top stroke.   Its stiffness is
relieved by curving it slightly at the lower end.   The ampersand (&) is
made in three strokes for large letters and two for smaller ones, and must be
carefully balanced.

The fraction group.   Fig. 2.23.   Fractions are always made with horizontal bar.   Integers are the same height as capitals.   The total fraction

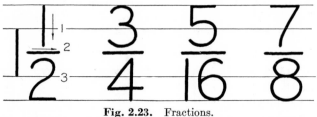

Fig. 2.23.   Fractions.

height is best made twice the height of the integer.   The numerator and
denominator will be about three-fourths the height of the integer.   Be careful to leave a clear space above and below the horizontal bar.   Guide lines

for fractions are easily obtained with lettering instruments by using the set of uniformly spaced holes, or by drawing the integer height above and below the center, the position of the horizontal bar.

2.11 Vertical lower case. The single-stroke, vertical lower-case letter is not commonly used on machine drawings but is used extensively in map drawing. It is the standard letter for hypsography in government topographical drawing. The bodies are made two-thirds the height of the capitals, with the ascenders extending to the cap line and the descenders dropping the same distance below. The basic form of the

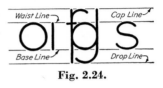

Fig. 2.24.

letter is the combination of a circle and a straight line, Fig. 2.24. The alphabet with some alternate shapes is shown in Fig. 2.25, which also gives the capitals in alphabetical order.

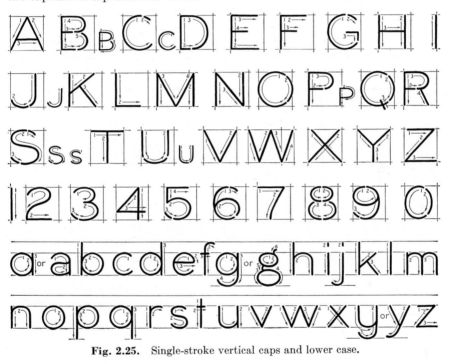

Fig. 2.25. Single-stroke vertical caps and lower case.

2.12 Single-stroke inclined caps. The inclined or slant letter is used in preference to the upright by many draftsmen. The order and direction of strokes are the same as in the vertical form.

After ruling the guide lines, slanting "direction lines" should be drawn across the sheet to aid the eye in keeping the slope uniform. These slope lines may be drawn with a special lettering triangle of about $67\frac{1}{2}°$, or the slope of 2 to 5 may be fixed on the paper by marking two units on a horizontal line and five on a vertical line and using T square and triangle as shown in Fig. 2.26.   The Braddock-Rowe triangle and the Ames instrument both provide for the drawing of slope lines, Figs. 2.2 and 2.3.   The form taken by the rounded letters when inclined is illustrated in Fig. 2.27, which shows that curves are sharp in all upper right-hand and lower left-hand

Fig. 2.26.   Slope guide lines.

Fig. 2.27.   Fig. 2.28.

Fig. 2.29.   Single-stroke inclined caps and lower case.

corners and flattened in the other two corners.   Particular care must be observed with the letters having sloping sides, such as *A*, *V*, and *W*.   The sloping sides of these letters must be drawn so that they appear to balance about a slope guide line passing through the intersection, as in Fig. 2.28. The alphabet is given in Fig. 2.29.   Study the shape of each letter carefully.

The snap and swing of professional work are due to three things: (1) to keeping to a uniform slope, (2) to having the letters full and well shaped, and (3) to keeping them close together. The beginner's invariable mistake is to cramp the individual letters and space them too far apart.

2.13 Single-stroke inclined lower case. The inclined lower-case letters, Fig. 2.29, have the bodies two-thirds the height of the capitals, with the ascenders extending to the cap line and the descenders dropping the same distance below the base line. This letter is generally known among older engineers, particularly among civil engineers, as the Reinhardt letter, in honor of Charles W. Reinhardt, who first systematized its construction. It is very legible and effective and, after its swing has been mastered, can be made very rapidly. The lower-case letter is suitable for notes and state-

Fig. 2.30. The straight-line letters.

ments on drawings for the two reasons indicated: (1) it is much more easily read than all caps, since we read words by the word shapes; and (2) it can be done much faster.

All the letters of the Reinhardt alphabet are based on two elements: the straight line and the ellipse, and have no unnecessary hooks on append-ages. They may be divided into four groups as shown in Figs. 2.30 to 2.33.

Fig. 2.31. The loop letters.

Fig. 2.32. The ellipse letters. 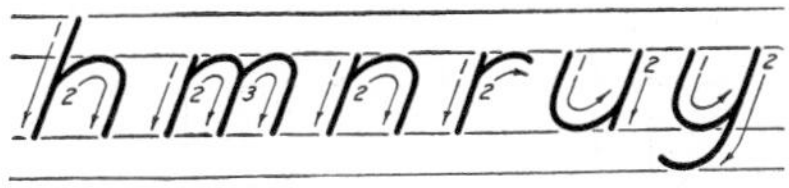   **Fig. 2.33.** The hook letters.

The dots of *i* and *j* and the top of the *t* are on the "*t* line" halfway between the waistline and the cap line. The loop letters are made with an ellipse, whose long axis is inclined about 45°, in combination with a straight line. In lettering rapidly, this ellipse tends to assume a pumpkin-seed form that should be guarded against.

The *c*, *e*, and *o* are based on an ellipse of the shape of the capitals, but not inclined quite so much as the loop-letter ellipse. In rapid, small work the *o* is often made in one stroke, as are also *e*, *v*, and *w*. The *s* is similar to the capital but, except in letters more than ⅛ in. high, is made in one stroke. In the hook-letter group, note particularly the shape of the hook.

The single-stroke letter may, if necessary, be very much compressed and still be clear and legible, Fig. 2.34. It is also used sometimes in extended form.

COMPRESSED LETTERS ARE USED
when space is limited. Either vertical
or inclined styles may be compressed

EXTENDED LETTERS OF A
given height are more legible

Fig. 2.34. Compressed and extended letters.

2.14 For left-handers only. The order and direction of strokes in the preceding alphabets have been designed for right-handed persons. The principal reason that left-handers sometimes find lettering difficult is that, whereas the right-hander progresses away from the body, the left-hander progresses toward the body; consequently his pencil and hand partially hide the work he has done, making it harder to join strokes and to preserve uniformity. Also, in the case of inclined lettering, the slope direction, instead of running toward his eye, runs off into space to the left of his body, making this style so much harder for him that the left-hander is strongly advised to *use vertical letters exclusively.*

Fig. 2.35. Strokes for left-handers.

For the natural left-hander whose writing position is the same as a right-hander except reversed left for right, a change in the sequence of strokes of some of the letters will obviate part of the difficulty caused by interference with the line of sight. Figure 2.35 gives an analyzed alphabet with an alternate for some letters.   In E the top bar is made before the bottom bar, and M is drawn from left to right, to avoid having strokes hidden by the pencil or pen.   Horizontal curves are easier to make from right to left; hence the starting points for O, Q, C, G, and U differ from the standard right-hand stroking. S is the perfect letter for the left-hander and is best made in a single smooth stroke. 6 and 9 are difficult and require extra practice.   In the lower-case letters a, d, g, and q, it is better to draw the straight line before the curve even though it makes spacing a little harder.

The hook-wrist left-handed writer, who pushes his strokes from top to bottom, finds vertical lettering more difficult than does the natural left-hander.   In Fig. 2.35, where alternate strokes are given for some of the letters, the hook-wrist writer will probably find the stroking of the second one easier for him than that of the first.   Some prefer to reverse *all* the strokes, drawing vertical strokes from bottom to top and horizontal strokes from right to left.

By way of encouragement it may be said that many left-handed draftsmen letter beautifully.

2.15 Composition.   Composition in lettering has to do with the selection, arrangement, and spacing of appropriate styles and sizes of letters. On engineering drawings, the selection of the style is practically limited to vertical or inclined single stroke, so that composition here means arrangement into pleasing and legible form.   After the shapes and strokes of the individual letters have been learned, the entire practice should be on composition into words and sentences, since proper spacing of letters and words does more for the appearance of a block of lettering than the forms of the letters themselves.   Letters in words are not spaced at a uniform distance from each other but are arranged so that the areas of white spaces (the irregular backgrounds between the letters) are approximately equal, thus making the spacing *appear* approximately uniform.   Figure 2.36 illustrates these background shapes.   Each letter is spaced with reference to its shape and the shape of the letter preceding it.   Thus, adjacent letters with straight

Fig. 2.36.   Background areas.

COMPOSITION IN LETTERING
REQUIRES CAREFUL SPACING, NOT ONLY
OF LETTERS BUT OF WORDS AND LINES

Fig. 2.37.   Word composition.

sides would be spaced farther apart than those with curved sides.   Sometimes combinations such as LT or AV may even overlap.   Definite rules for spacing are not successful; it is a matter of the draftsman's judgment and sense of design.   Figure 2.37 illustrates word composition.   The sizes of letters to use in any particular case may be determined better by sketching them lightly than by judging from the guide lines alone. A finished line of letters always looks larger than the guide lines would indicate. Avoid the use of a coarse pen for small sizes, and one that makes thin wiry lines for large sizes. When caps and small caps are used, the height of the small caps should be about four-fifths that of the caps.

In spacing words, a good method is to leave the space that would be taken by an assumed letter *I* connecting the two words into one, as in Fig. 2.38. The space would never be more than the height of the letters.

WORDSISPACEDIBYISKETCHINGIANIIIBETWEEN

WORDS SPACED BY SKETCHING AN I BETWEEN
Fig. 2.38. Word spacing.

The clear distance between lines may vary from ½ to 1½ times the height of the letter but, for appearance sake, should not be exactly the same as the letter height. The instruments of Figs. 2.2 and 2.3 provide spacing two-thirds the letter height. Paragraphs should always be indented.

2.16 Titles. The most important problem in lettering composition that the engineering draftsman will meet is the design of titles. Every drawing has a descriptive title giving the necessary information concerning it, which is either all hand-lettered or filled in on a printed form. This information, of course, is not the same for all kinds of drawings (see working-drawing titles, Chap. 28; architectural titles, Chap. 31; structural titles, Chap. 30; map titles, Chap. 32).

The usual form of lettered title is the *symmetrical title*, which is balanced or "justified" on a vertical center line and designed with an elliptical or oval outline. Sometimes the wording necessitates a pyramid or inverted pyramid ("bag") form. Figure 2.39 illustrates several shapes into which

Fig. 2.39. Shapes in symmetrical composition.

titles can be composed. The lower right-hand corner of the sheet is, from long custom and on account of convenience in filing, the usual location for the title, and in laying out a drawing this corner is reserved for it. The space allowed is a matter of judgment and depends on the size and purpose of the drawing. On an 11 by 17 in. working drawing the title may be about three inches long.

2.17 To draw a title. When the wording has been determined, write out the arrangement on a separate piece of paper as in Fig. 2.40 (or, better, typewrite it). Count the letters, including the word spaces, and make a mark across the middle letter or space of each line. The lines must be displayed for prominence according to their relative importance as judged from the point of view of the persons who will use the drawing. Titles are usually made in all caps. Draw the base line for the most important line of the title and mark on it the approximate length desired. To get the letter height, divide this length by the number of letters in the line, and

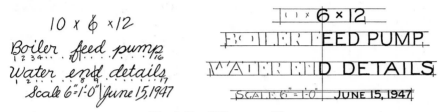

Fig. 2.40. Title composition.

draw the cap line. Start at the center line and sketch very lightly the last half of the line, drawing only enough of the letters to show the space each will occupy. Lay off the length of this right half on the other side and sketch that half, working either forward or backward. When this line is satisfactory in size and spacing, draw the remainder in the same way. Study the effect, shift letters or lines if necessary, and complete in pencil. Use punctuation marks only for abbreviations.

2.18 The scratch-paper methods. Sketch each line of the title separately on a piece of scratch paper, using guide lines of determined height. Find the middle point of each of these lines, fold the paper along the base line of the letters, fit the middle point to the center line on the drawing, and draw the final letters directly below the sketches. *Or* draw the letters along the edge of the scratch paper, using either the upper or the lower edge as one of the guide lines. *Or* letter the title on scratch paper, cut apart and adjust until satisfactory, and then trace it.

2.19 The proportional method. On account of the varying widths of roman letters, it is sometimes difficult to space a word or line to a given length by counting letters. Figure 2.41 illustrates the method of spacing by the principle of similar triangles. Suppose it is necessary to put the word "ROMAN" on the line to the length ab. A line ac is drawn from a at any angle (say 30°) and a second line de parallel to it, then the word is sketched in this space, starting at a and spacing each letter with reference to the one before it, allowing the word to end where it will. The end of the last letter, at c, is con-

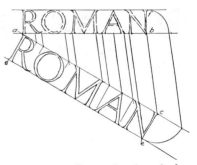

Fig. 2.41. Proportional method.

nected with b, and lines parallel to cb are drawn from each letter, thus dividing ab proportionately. The height bf is obtained from ce by the construction shown, after which the word can be sketched in its final position.

2.20 Outlined commercial gothic. Thus far the so-called "gothic" letter has been considered only as a single-stroke letter. For sizes larger than, say $\frac{5}{16}$ in., or for boldface letters, it is drawn in outline and filled in solid. For a given size, this letter is readable at a greater distance than

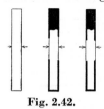

Fig. 2.42.

any other style; hence it would be used in any place where legibility is the principal requirement. The stems may be one-tenth to one-fifth of the height, and much care must be exercised in keeping them to uniform width at every point on the letter. In inking a penciled outline, keep the *outside* of the ink line on the pencil line, Fig. 2.42; otherwise the letter will be heavier than expected.

Making two strokes in place of one, the general order and direction of penciling large commercial gothic letters is similar to the single-stroke analysis, as shown in the typical examples of Fig. 2.43. Free ends, such

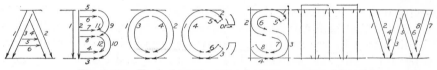

Fig. 2.43. Typical construction for large commercial gothic.

as on C, G, and S, are cut off perpendicular to the stem. The stiffness of plain letters is sometimes relieved by finishing the ends with a slight spur, as in Fig. 2.44. The complete alphabet in outline, with stems one-sixth of the height, is given in Fig. 2.45. The same scale of widths may be used

Fig. 2.44. Compressed commercial gothic.

for drawing lighter face letters. Figure 2.44 illustrates a commercial gothic alphabet compressed to two-thirds the normal width. In this figure the stems are drawn one-seventh of the height, but the scale is given in sixths, as in Fig. 2.45.

Fig. 2.45. Large commercial gothic construction.

Fig. 2.46. Old Roman capitals.

2.21 The roman letter. The roman letter has been mentioned as the parent of all the styles, however diversified, which are in use today. Although there are many variations of it, there may be said to be three general forms: (1) the early or classic, (2) the Renaissance, (3) the Modern. The first two are very similar in effect, and the general term "Old Roman" is used for both.

The roman letter is composed of two weights of lines, corresponding to the downstroke and the upstroke of the broad reed pen with which it was

Fig. 2.47. Old Roman lower case.

originally written. It is an inexcusable fault to shade a roman letter on the wrong stroke.

Rule for shading. All horizontal strokes are light. All vertical strokes are heavy except in M, N, and U. To determine the heavy stroke in letters containing slanting sides, trace the shape of the letter from left to right in one stroke and note which lines were made downward. Figure 2.46 is an Old Roman alphabet with the width of the body stroke one-tenth of the height of the letter and the light lines slightly over one-half this width. For inscriptions and titles, capitals are generally used, but sometimes the lower case, Fig. 2.47, is needed. This example is drawn with the waistline six-tenths high and the width of the stems one-twelfth of the cap height.

The Old Roman is the architect's one general-purpose letter. A single-stroke adaptation of it, Fig. 2.48, is generally used on architectural drawings.

ABCDEFGHIJKLMNOPQRS
TUVWXYZ& 1234567890
abcdefghijklmnopqrstuvwxyz
Compressed Italic for Limited Space
Sans-serif for Speed & Simplicity

Fig. 2.48.   Single-stroke roman and italic.

2.22   Modern Roman.   Civil engineers in particular must be familiar with the Modern Roman, as it is the standard letter for finished map titles and the names of civil divisions, such as countries and cities.   It is a difficult letter to draw and can be mastered only by careful attention to details. The heavy or "body" strokes are one-sixth to one-eighth the height of the letter.   Those in Fig. 2.49 are one-seventh.   A paper scale made by

Fig. 2.49.   Modern Roman capitals.

dividing the height into seven parts will aid in penciling. Modern lower case, Fig. 2.50, is used on maps for names of towns and villages. Notice the difference in the serifs of Figs. 2.50 and 2.47.

The order and direction of strokes used in drawing Modern Roman letters are illustrated in the typical letters of Fig. 2.51. The serifs on the

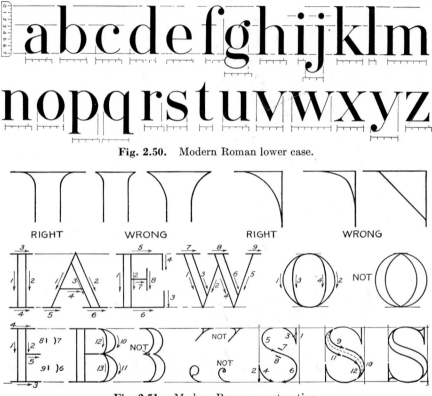

Fig. 2.50. Modern Roman lower case.

Fig. 2.51. Modern Roman construction.

MAP SHOWING

IRON ORE DEPOSITS

IN THE

WESTERN STATES

SCALE–MILES

Fig. 2.52. A roman-letter title.

ends of the strokes extend one space on each side and are joined to the main stroke by small fillets. It will be noticed that the curved letters are flattened slightly on their diagonals. A title in roman letters is illustrated in Fig. 2.52.

The roman letter may be extended or compressed, as shown in Fig.

2.53. For these, a scale for widths may be made longer or shorter than the normal scale. For example, the compressed letters of Fig. 2.53 are made with a scale three-fourths of the height divided into sevenths.

EXTENDED ROMAN
BCGHJKLPQSUVW

COMPRESSED ROMAN-BHKTWG

Fig. 2.53. Modern Roman, extended and compressed.

*A B C D E F G H I
J K L M N O P Q R
S T U V W X Y Z &
a b c d e f g h i j k l m n o
p q r s t u v or v w or w x y or y z
1 2 3 4 5 6 7 8 9 0*

Fig. 2.54. Inclined roman and stump letters.

2.23 Inclined roman. Inclined letters are used for water features on maps. An alphabet of inclined roman made to the same proportions as the vertical of Fig. 2.49 is shown in Fig. 2.54. The slope may be 65° to 75°. Those shown are inclined 2 to 5. The lower-case letters in this figure are known as stump letters. For small sizes their lines are made with one stroke of a fine flexible pen, while larger sizes are drawn and filled in.

EXERCISES

The following exercises are designed for a 5- by 7-in. working space. Lettering practice should be done in short intensive periods.

Series I. Single-stroke vertical capitals

1. Large letters in pencil, for careful study of the shapes of the individual letters. Starting $\frac{9}{16}$ in. from the top border draw guide lines for five lines of $\frac{3}{8}$-in. letters. Draw each of the straight-line letters *I H T L E F N Z Y V A M W X* four times in pencil only, studying carefully Figs. 2.12 to 2.16. Figure 2.55 is a full-sized reproduction of a corner of this exercise.

2. Same as Exercise 1 for the curved line letters *O Q C G D U J B P R S*. Study Figs. 2.17 to 2.20.

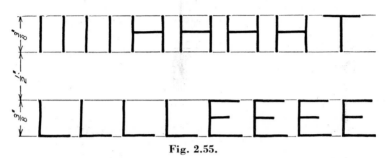

Fig. 2.55.

3. Same as Exercise 1 for figures 3, 8, 6, 9, 2, 5, $\frac{1}{2}$, $\frac{3}{4}$, $\frac{5}{8}$, $\frac{7}{16}$, $\frac{9}{32}$. Study Figs. 2.21 to 2.23.

4. Composition. Same layout as for Exercise 1. Read paragraph on composition, then letter the following five lines in pencil (1) WORD COMPOSITION, (2) TOPO-GRAPHIC SURVEY, (3) TOOLS AND EQUIPMENT, (4) BRONZE BUSHING, (5) JACK-RAFTER DETAIL.

5. Quarter-inch vertical letters in pencil and ink. Starting $\frac{1}{4}$ in. from top, draw guide lines for nine lines of $\frac{1}{4}$-in. letters. In the group order given, draw each letter first four times in pencil, then four times directly in ink, as in Fig. 2.56.

6. Composition. Make a three-line design of the quotation from Benjamin Lamme on the Lamme Medals: "THE ENGINEER VIEWS HOPEFULLY THE HITHERTO UNATTAINABLE."

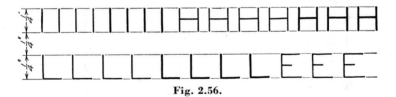

Fig. 2.56.

7. Eighth-inch vertical letters. Starting $\frac{1}{4}$ in. from top, draw guide lines for 18 lines of $\frac{1}{8}$-in letters. Make each letter and numeral eight times directly in ink. Fill the remaining lines with a portion of paragraph 2.15 on composition.

8. Composition. Letter the following definition: "Engineering is the art and science of directing and controlling the forces and utilizing the materials of nature for the benefit of man. All engineering involves the organization of human effort to attain these ends. It also involves an appraisal of the social and economic benefits of these activities."

Series II. Single-stroke inclined capitals

9 to 16. Same spacing and specifications as for Series I, Exercises 1 to 8, but for inclined letters. Study paragraph 2.12 and Figs. 2.26 to 2.29.

Series III.   Single-stroke inclined lower case

17. Large letters in pencil for use with ⅜-in. caps.   The bodies are ¼ in., the ascenders ⅛ in. above, and the descenders ⅛ in. below.   Starting ⅜ in. from top, draw guide lines for seven lines of letters.   This can be done quickly by spacing ⅛ in. uniformly down the sheet and bracketing cap and base lines.   Make each letter of the alphabet four times in pencil only.   Study Figs. 2.29 to 2.33.

18. Lower case for ³⁄₁₆-in. caps.   Starting ½ in. from top, draw cap, waist, and base lines for 13 lines of letters (Braddock or Ames No. 6 spacing).   Make each letter six times in pencil, then six times in ink.

19. Composition.   Same spacing as Exercise 18.   Letter opening paragraph of this chapter.

20. Letter the first 10 lines of paragraph 2.4.

Series IV.   Titles

21. Design a title for the assembly drawing of a rear axle, drawn to the scale of 6 in. = 1 ft, as made by the Chevrolet Motor Co., Detroit.   The number of the drawing is C82746.   Space allowed, 3 by 5 in.

22. Design a title for the front elevation of a powerhouse, drawn to quarter-inch scale by Burton Grant, Architect, for the Citizens Power and Light Company of Punxsutawney, Pennsylvania.

3

The Selection of Instruments

3.1 In the selection of instruments and materials for drawing, the only general advice that can be given is to secure the *best* that can be afforded. For one who expects to do work of professional grade, it is a great mistake to buy inferior instruments. Sometimes a beginner is tempted by the suggestion that he get cheap instruments for learning, with the expectation of getting better ones later. With reasonable care a set of good instruments will last a lifetime, while poor ones will be an annoyance from the start and will be worthless after short usage. As poor instruments look so much like good ones that an amateur is unable to distinguish them, trustworthy advice should be sought before buying.

This chapter will be devoted to a short description of the instruments usually necessary for drawing. Mention of some others not in everyday use, but convenient for special work, will be found in Chap. 35.

3.2 Instrument joints. Modern high-grade instruments are made with some form of pivot joint, originally patented by Theodore Alteneder in 1850 and again in 1871. Older instruments, and some cheap modern ones made

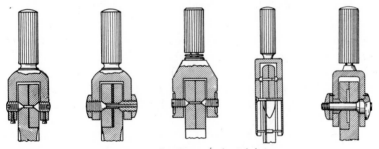

Fig. 3.1. Sections of pivot joints.

with tongue joints and through bolt or pin, are unsatisfactory, as wear of the tongue and pin results in lost motion which, after a time, renders the instrument unfit for use. In the pivot joint, however, the wear is on adjustable conical or spherical surfaces. The Alteneder joint and several modifications of it are shown in Fig. 3.1.

The handle attached to the yoke, although not essential to the working of the joint, is very convenient. Not all instruments with handles, however, are pivot-joint instruments. Several straightener devices for keeping the handle erect have been made, but some designs are not good, as pressure upon the handle may change the setting of the instrument.

3.3 Instrument patterns. The development of the various instrument patterns has followed a definite historical sequence, influenced by the methods of manufacture. The oldest in common use today is known as the "square type," Fig. 3.2*A*. First used because the legs were of square cross section, this term is now applied to practically all compasses and dividers cut from solid metal and of angular cross section. More than three hundred years ago, instruments of this type were hand-filed in a vise from brass and steel bars, but most of the work is now done by milling machines.

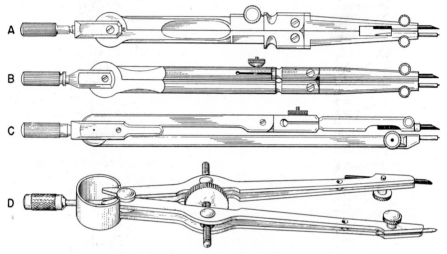

Fig. 3.2. Instrument patterns (compasses).

The round and flat types were so developed from the square type as to take advantage of modern manufacturing methods. Most of the forming of the legs of the round type, shown in Fig. 3.2*B*, is done on a lathe.

The legs of compasses and dividers of the flat type, Fig. 3.2*C*, are made from hard-rolled nickel-silver bars by machining, or by forging and machining.

A newer pattern known as the "open-truss" type combines great strength with light weight, Fig. 3.2*D*. Its outstanding feature is that each leg consists of two stampings from steel, welded together just above the clamp that holds the pencil or steel point. The upper ends bear upon a hinge pin and are well separated to ensure strength and alignment. This structure is used in both bow and friction compasses and dividers.

3.4 Compasses. Compasses are generally made with the lower portion of the pencil leg removable to be replaced, when needed, with the pen leg. Thus one instrument serves for both penciling and inking. When circles larger than about 5 in. radius are to be drawn, the lengthening bar is attached, by which means the radius may be increased to about 8 in. Four different compasses are shown in Fig. 3.2.

Friction compasses can be tested for accuracy by bending the knuckle joints, as in Fig. 3.3. The points should come together. Bow compasses are tested by drawing very small circles. There should be no trouble in going down to a diameter of ⅛ in.

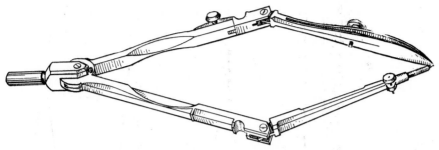

Fig. 3.3. Test for alignment.

3.5 Dividers. These instruments are made following the various patterns already referred to in paragraph 3.3, but they are further differentiated according to whether they are "plain," Fig. 3.4*A*, "hairspring," Fig. 3.4*B*, or "bow," Fig. 3.4*C*. The hairspring type, having a screw for fine adjustment, is occasionally convenient and is to be preferred. Bow dividers have adjusting screws and hold their settings securely.

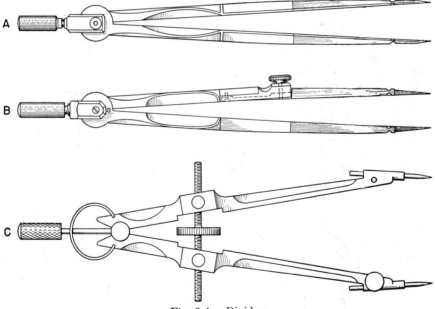

Fig. 3.4. Dividers.

3.6 Spring bow instruments. The conventional set of three spring bow instruments includes bow divider or spacer, bow pencil, and bow pen. There are numerous designs, and they vary in over-all length from 3¼ to

$4\frac{1}{2}$ in.   A standard set of side-screw bow instruments is shown in Fig. 3.5*A*, *B*, and *C*.   At *D* is illustrated the hoop-spring type, also known as the ring-head bow.   Both standard and ring-head types are also made as center-screw instruments, illustrated by the center-screw bow pen at *E*.

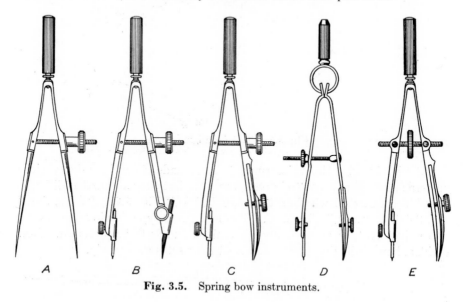

Fig. 3.5.   Spring bow instruments.

3.7   Ruling pens.   Ruling pens are made in a variety of forms, Fig. 3.6. The two most popular ones are the simple spring blade *A*, which opens sufficiently wide for cleaning when the thumbscrew is completely released, and the jackknife *D*, which may be cleaned without changing the setting.

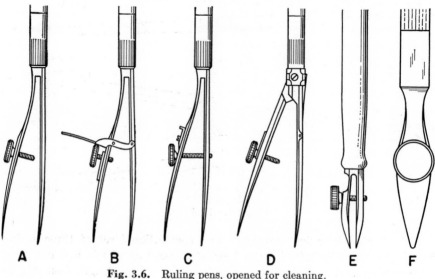

Fig. 3.6.   Ruling pens, opened for cleaning.

B and *C* show special devices for opening the blades. A recent development is shown at *E*. The form shown at *F* is known as a "detail pen," or "Swedish pen," and is a desirable instrument for drawing very long or very heavy lines.

A really good pen can be made only at considerable expense. The nibs should be shaped as shown in Fig. 4.23. They should be ground to smooth curves.

3.8 Composition of sets. For half a century prior to the Second World War, the three-bow set was rather firmly established as standard equipment for most draftsmen. A typical set of this type, Fig. 3.7, would include:

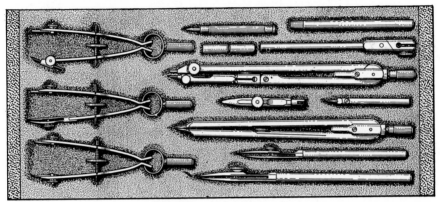

Fig. 3.7.   A three-bow set.

6-in. compass with detachable pencil holder; pen attachment for compass, interchangeable with pencil holder; lengthening bar for compass; 6-in. hairspring divider; 4-in. bow divider; 4-in. bow pen; 4-in. bow pencil; 4½-in. ruling pen; 5½-in. large ruling pen; metal box with extra leads and metal points; screw driver and miscellaneous small wrenches. In addition to the foregoing, many draftsmen had, to meet their particular needs, one or more of the following: drop bow compass, broad Swedish-type detail pen, beam compass, contour pen, and railroad pen.

Just as the development of the all-pencil technique has greatly influenced the construction of drawing instruments, so also has it influenced the composition of instrument sets. Fewer instruments are now required, but these must possess greater strength. In a general way, a modern set must afford the utmost in convenience and also withstand the severe service of making finished drawings in pencil. It should also provide for inking in case of need. However, just what constitutes a properly balanced set is a matter of some controversy, and we find a considerable variety of instrument combinations in use. One widely used combination, Fig. 3.8, includes: 6½-in. bow compass, 4½-in. bow compass, 6½-in. friction divider, pen attachment for compass, 5½-in. ruling pen, metal box with extra leads and steel points.

When drawing instruments from Germany and Switzerland began to arrive after the Second World War, they were, for the most part, made up as the conventional three-bow sets built around frictional compasses and

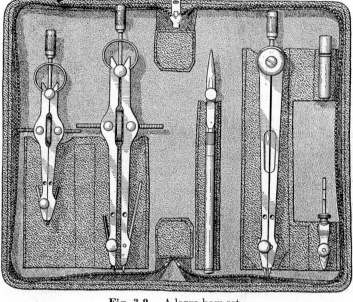

Fig. 3.8.　A large-bow set.

dividers; but since 1948 there has been a marked trend toward the set composition described in the foregoing paragraph and the suggested variations featuring large bow compasses and having fewer pieces than formerly.

An altogether different combination of instruments has found favor in some industries, particularly in the automotive industry, where many of the

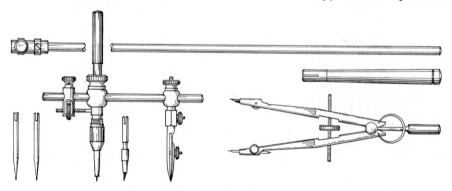

Fig. 3.9.　A detailer's set.

pieces to be drawn are rather large, but can still be drawn natural size. An example is shown in Fig. 3.9. It consists of a large bow compass with pencil lead holder, beam compass with lead holder, beam-compass extension bar for drawing very large circles, slip-handle penholder, pen attachment interchangeable between beam compass and slip handle, divider points for beam compass.   The utility of this set has done a great deal toward making the beam compass popular, and as a result, we now find many sets that include either complete beam compasses or beam attachments for bow compasses.   An example of this is afforded by a combination of instruments, as shown in Fig. 3.8, together with a beam compass and extension beam.   A set of essentially the same composition is shown in Fig. 3.10.

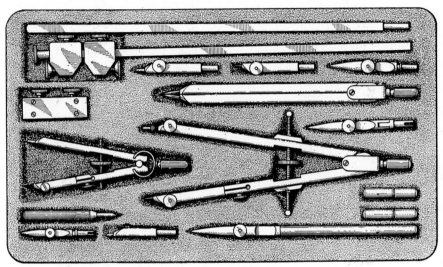

Fig. 3.10.   A large-bow and beam-compass set.

While no combination of drawing instruments has universal acclaim as the "perfect set," it is quite evident that, at the present time, there is a set for every need.

3.9   Drawing boards.   The drawing surface may be either the table top itself or a separate board.   In either case, the working surface should be made of well-seasoned clear white pine or basswood, cleated to prevent warping.   The working edge must be straight and should be tested with a steel straightedge.   Some boards and table tops are supplied with a hardwood edge or a steel insert on the working edge, thus ensuring a better wearing surface.

3.10   The T square.   The fixed-head T square, Fig. 3.11A, is used for all ordinary work.   It should be of hardwood, and the blade should be perfectly straight.   The transparent-edged blade is much the best.   A draftsman will have several fixed-head squares of different lengths and will find an adjustable-head square (B) of occasional use.   A T-square blade may be tested for straightness by drawing a sharp line through two points and then turning the square over and with the same edge drawing another line through the points, as shown in Fig. 3.12.

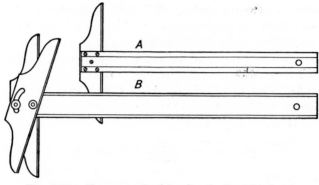

Fig. 3.11.   T squares, fixed head and adjustable head.

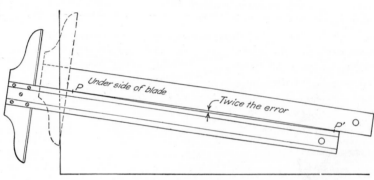

Fig. 3.12.   To test a T square.

3.11   Triangles.   Triangles are made of transparent celluloid (fiberloid) or plastic material.   Through internal strains, they sometimes lose their accuracy.   They should, therefore, be tested periodically by drawing a

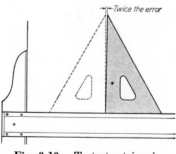

Fig. 3.13.   To test a triangle.

perpendicular line, then reversing the triangle and drawing another perpendicular, as shown in Fig. 3.13.   For ordinary work a 6- or 8-in. 45° and a 10-in. 30-60° are good sizes.   Triangles should always be kept flat to prevent warping.

3.12 Scales. Scales are made in a variety of types to meet the requirements of many different kinds of work. For convenience, scales are classified according to their most common uses:

1. *Mechanical engineer's scales,* divided and numbered so that fractions of inches represent inches. The most common ranges are ⅛, ¼, ½, and 1 in. *to the inch.* These scales are also known as the *size* scales, because the designated reduction also represents the ratio of size, as, for example, *one-eighth size.* A full and half-size scale is illustrated in Fig. 3.14. Mechanical

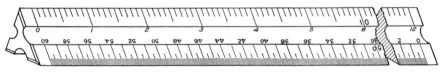

Fig. 3.14. A mechanical engineer's full- and half-size scale.

engineer's scales are almost always "full divided," that is, the smallest divisions run throughout the entire length. These scales are also often graduated with the marked divisions numbered from right to left, as well as from left to right, as shown in Fig. 3.14. Mechanical engineer's scales are used mostly for drawings of machine parts and small structures where the drawing size is never less than one-eighth the size of the actual object.

2. *Civil engineer's scales,* divided in decimals with 10, 20, 30, 40, 50, 60, and 80 divisions to the inch, Fig. 3.15. Such a scale is usually full divided

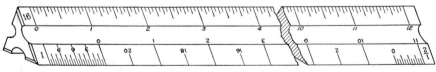

Fig. 3.15. A civil engineer's scale.

and is sometimes numbered both left to right and right to left. These scales are most used for plotting and drawing maps, although they are also very useful for any work where divisions of the inch in tenths is required.

3. *Architect's scales,* divided in proportional feet and inches, with divisions indicating ⅛, ¼, ⅜, ½, ¾, 1½, and 3 in. *to the foot,* Fig. 3.16.

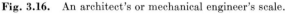

Fig. 3.16. An architect's or mechanical engineer's scale.

These are usually "open divided," that is, the units are shown along the entire length, but only the end units are subdivided into inches and fractions. These scales are much used by all engineers, mechanical, industrial, chemical, etc., for both machine and structural drawings and are sometimes also called *mechanical engineer's* scales.

Scales are made having various cross-sectional shapes, as shown in

Fig. 3.17. The triangular form either *A* or *B* has long been favored, because it carries six scales as a unit and is very stiff. However, many draftsmen prefer the flat types as being easier to hold flat to a board, and as having any particular working scale more readily available. The "opposite bevel," scale *E*, is easier to pick up than the "flat bevel," scale *D*; moreover, it shows only one graduation at a time. The "double-bevel," scale *F*, in the shorter lengths is convenient as a pocket scale, but it can be had in lengths up to 24 in.

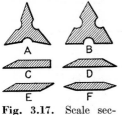

Fig. 3.17. Scale sections.

Practically all drafting scales of good quality were formerly made of boxwood, either plain or with white edges of celluloid. Although metal scales have been available for more than thirty years, they were seldom used until about 1935, when drafting machines equipped with metal scales made rather important gains in popularity. Extruded medium-hard aluminum alloys are the preferred materials. The cross section shown at *D* is the most common, but some modifications, as hollowing out the underside, are also used. The Second World War brought a period of considerable experimentation with various types of plastics for all kinds of drafting scales. Up to the present time the white-edge scale has retained a large measure of its popularity. Another type of scale is now getting considerable attention, a metal scale having a white plastic coating, which carries the graduations. Both magnesium and aluminum have been used successfully. These scales have all the reading advantages of a white-edge boxwood scale, together with the stability afforded by metal.

3.13 Lettering devices. The Ames lettering instrument and the Braddock-Rowe triangle, Figs. 2.2 and 2.3, are convenient devices used in drawing guide lines for lettering.

3.14 Curves. Curved rulers, called "irregular curves" or "french curves," are used for curved lines other than circle arcs. The patterns for

Fig. 3.18. Irregular curves.

these curves are laid out in parts of ellipses and spirals or other mathematical curves in various combinations. For the student one ellipse curve of the general shape of Fig. 3.18*A* or *D* and one spiral, either a log spiral *B* or one similar to the one used in Fig. 4.36, will be sufficient. C is a useful small curve.

3.15 Drawing pencils. The manufacturers grade drawing pencils by numbers and letters from 6B, very soft and black, through 5B, 4B, 3B, 2B, B, and HB, to F, the medium grade; then H, 2H, 3H, 4H, 5H, 6H, 7H, and 8H, to 9H, the hardest. The soft (B) grades are used primarily for sketching and rendered drawings, and the hard (H) grades for instrument drawings. Some draftsmen prefer a holder using standard-size drawing-lead fillers.

3.16 Pencil pointer. After the wood of the ordinary pencil is cut away with a pocketknife or mechanical sharpener, the lead must be formed to a long conical point. A lance-tooth file about six inches long is fine for the purpose. Some draftsmen prefer the standard sandpaper pencil-pointer pad, Fig. 4.1.

3.17 Erasers. The Ruby pencil eraser, large size with beveled ends, is the standard. This eraser not only removes pencil lines effectively, but is much better for ink than the so-called ink eraser, as it will remove the ink perfectly without seriously damaging the surface of paper or cloth. A good metal erasing shield aids in getting clean erasures.

Artgum or a *soft* rubber eraser is useful for cleaning paper and cloth of finger marks and smears that spoil the appearance of the completed drawing.

3.18 Penholders and pens. The penholder should have a grip of medium size, small enough to enter the mouth of a drawing-ink bottle easily, yet not so small as to cramp the fingers while in use. A size slightly larger than the diameter of a pencil is good.

An assortment of pens for lettering, grading from coarse to fine, may be chosen from those listed in Chap. 2.

A penwiper of lintless cloth or thin chamois skin should always be at hand for both lettering and ruling pens.

3.19 Drawing ink. Drawing ink is finely ground carbon in suspension, with natural or synthetic gum added to render the mixture waterproof. Nonwaterproof ink flows more freely, but smudges very easily. Drawing ink diluted with distilled water, or Chinese ink in stick form rubbed up with water in a slate slab, is used in making wash drawings and for very fine line work.

Bottleholders prevent the possibility of ruining the drawing table or floor by ink from an upset bottle. They are made in various patterns, one of which is illustrated in Fig. 3.19. As a temporary substitute, the lower half of the paper container in which the ink was sold may be fastened to the table with a thumbtack, or a strip of paper or cloth with a hole for the neck of the bottle may be tacked down over the bottle.

Fig. 3.19. Bottle-holder.

3.20 Drafting tape. Scotch drafting tape is usually used as the means of fastening paper to the drawing board. It may be used either by sticking a short piece across each corner, or by taping the entire edge of the paper. There is a distinction between "drafting tape" and "masking tape" (made by the same company) in that the latter has a heavier coating of adhesive and does not come off the drawing paper so cleanly as the former.

3.21 Thumbtacks. The best thumbtacks have thin heads with steel points screwed into them. Cheaper ones are made by stamping. Tacks with tapering pins of small diameter should be chosen. Flat-headed (often colored) map pins should not be used, as the heads are too thick and the pins rather large.

3.22 Drawing paper. Paper for drawing purposes is made in a variety of qualities with varying prices and may be had in either sheets or rolls. White drawing papers that will not turn yellow with age or exposure are used for finished drawings, maps, charts, and drawings for photographic reproduction. For pencil layouts and working drawings, cream or buff detail papers are easier on the eyes, do not show soil so quickly as white papers, and are therefore preferred. In general, paper should have sufficient grain or "tooth" to take the pencil, be agreeable to the eye, and have a hard surface not easily "grooved" by the pencil, with good erasing qualities. Formerly, imported papers were considered superior to American-made products, but our mills are now making practically all the paper used in this country. The cheap manila papers should be avoided. A few cents more per yard is well spent in the increased satisfaction gained from working on good paper.

3.23 Tracing papers. Tracing papers are thin papers, either *natural* or *transparentized*, through which drawings are traced, either in pencil or ink, and from which blueprints or similar contact prints can be made. In most drafting rooms, original drawings are being penciled on tracing papers and blueprints made directly from these drawings, a practice increasingly successful because of the improvements both in papers and in printing. Tracing papers vary widely in color, thickness, surface, etc., and the grade of pencil and the technique must be adjusted to suit the paper. With the proper combination, however, good resulting prints may be obtained.

3.24 Tracing cloth. Finely woven cloth coated with a special starch or plastic is used for making drawings in either pencil or ink. The standard tracing cloth is used for inked tracings, and specially made pencil cloth for pencil drawings or tracings. The advantage of cloth is that it will stand more handling than paper and is thus more permanent. Tracing and duplicating processes are described in Chap. 28.

3.25 The slide rule. Although not a drawing instrument, the slide rule is essentially an engineer's tool, and proficiency in its use is a requirement of every modern drafting room. A good way for a beginner to learn to use a slide rule is in connection with a drawing course. Its use facilitates the rapid calculations of volumes and weights as an aid in reading drawings or, later, as an essential part of drafting work. Of the several varieties of slide rules, those recommended for prospective engineers are a Polyphase Duplex Trig,[1] a Polyphase Duplex Decitrig,[1] a Log Log Duplex Trig,[1] a Log Log Duplex Decitrig,[1] or a Versilog[1] in 10-in. size.

3.26 Check list of instruments and materials

1. Set of drawing instruments, including at least: 6-in. compasses with fixed needle-point leg, removable pencil and pen legs, and lengthening bar; 6-in. hair-spring dividers; $3\frac{1}{2}$-in. bow pencil, bow pen, and bow dividers; two ruling pens; box of leads; *or* large bow set containing: $6\frac{1}{2}$-in. bow compass, $4\frac{1}{2}$-in. bow compass, $6\frac{1}{2}$-in. friction divider, pen attachment for compass; $5\frac{1}{2}$-in. ruling pen, beam compass with extension beam; box for extra leads and points.

2. Drawing board.
3. T square.
4. 45° and 30°-60° triangles.
5. Three mechanical engineer's scales, flat pattern, or the equivalent triangular scale.
6. Lettering instrument or triangle.
7. French curves.
8. Drawing pencils, 6H, 4H, 2H, H, and F.
9. Pocketknife or pencil sharpener.
10. Pencil pointer (file or sandpaper).
11. Pencil eraser (Ruby).
12. Artgum or cleaning rubber.
13. Penholder, pens for lettering, and penwiper.
14. Bottle of drawing ink and bottleholder.
15. Scotch drafting tape or thumbtacks.
16. Drawing paper to suit.
17. Tracing paper and cloth.
18. Dusting cloth or brush.

To these may be added:

19. Civil engineer's scale.
20. Protractor.
21. Erasing shield.
22. Slide rule.
23. Six-foot steel tape.
24. Clipboard or sketchbook.
25. Hard Arkansas oilstone.
26. Piece of soapstone.
27. Cleaning powder or pad.

The student should mark all his instruments and materials plainly with his initials or name as soon as they have been purchased and approved.

3.27 Additional instruments. The instruments and materials described in this chapter are all that are needed for ordinary practice and are, as a rule, with the exception of such supplies as paper, pencils, ink, erasers, etc., what a draftsman is expected to take with him into a drafting room.

There are many other special instruments and devices which are not necessary in ordinary work, but with which, nevertheless, the draftsman should be familiar, as they may be very convenient in some special cases and are often found as a part of the drafting-room equipment. Some are described in Chap. 35.

[1] Registered trade-marks.

4

The Use of Instruments

4.1   In beginning the use of drawing instruments, particular attention should be paid to the correct method of handling them.   Read carefully the instructions given and observe strictly all the details of the technique.

Facility will come with continued practice, but from the outset *good form* must be insisted upon.   One might learn to write fairly well holding the pen peculiarly between the fingers or gripped in the closed hand, but it would be poor form.   Bad form in drawing is distressingly common and may be traced in every instance to lack of care or knowledge at the beginning, and the consequent formation of bad habits.   These habits, when once formed, are most difficult to overcome.

All mechanical drawings serve incidentally for practice in the use of instruments, but it is best for the beginner to make a few drawings solely to become familiar with the handling and "feel" of the instruments so that, later, in working a drawing problem, there may be no loss of time on account of faulty manipulation.   With practice, the correct skillful use of the instruments will become a subconscious habit.

The requirements of good drawing ability are *accuracy* and *speed*, and in commercial work neither is worth much without the other.   Accurate penciling is the first consideration.   Inking should not be attempted until real proficiency in penciling has been attained.   A good instructor knows that it is a mistaken kindness to the beginner to accept faulty or careless work.   The standard held at the start will be carried through his professional life, and the beginner should learn that a *good* drawing can be made just as quickly as a *poor* one.   Erasing is expensive, and most of it can be avoided.   The student allowed to continue in a careless way will grow to regard his erasers as the most important tools in his kit.   The draftsman, of course, erases occasionally, and instructions in making corrections should be given, but the beginner should strive for sheets without blemish or inaccuracy.

4.2   Preparation for drawing.   The drawing table should be set so that the light comes from the left and should be adjusted to a convenient height, that is, 36 to 40 in., for use while sitting upon a standard drafting stool, or while standing.   One may draw with more freedom standing than sitting, especially on large drawings.   The board, for use in this manner, should be inclined at a slope of about 1 to 8.   Nevertheless, it is more tiring to draw while standing, and many modern drafting rooms use tables made so that the board may be used in an almost vertical position and may be raised or lowered so that the draftsman may use a lower stool with swivel seat and a backrest, thus working with comfort and even greater freedom than when an almost horizontal board is used.

The instruments should be placed within easy reach either on the table or on a special tray or stand beside the table. The table, board, and instruments should be wiped with a dustcloth before starting to draw.

4.3 The pencil and its use. The grade of pencil must be selected carefully, with reference to the surface of the paper used, as well as the line quality desired. For a pencil layout on detail paper of good texture, a pencil as hard as 5H or 6H may be used, while for finished pencil drawings on the same paper 2H, 3H, or 4H pencils give the blacker line needed. For finished pencil drawings or tracings on vellum, softer pencils, H to 3H, are employed to get printable lines. The F pencil is much used for technical sketching, and the H is popular for lettering. In every case the pencil chosen must be hard enough not to blur or smudge, but not so hard as to cut grooves in the paper under reasonable pressure.

To sharpen a pencil, cut away the wood from the unlettered end with a penknife to make a long conical point, as shown in Fig. 4.1*A*, and then

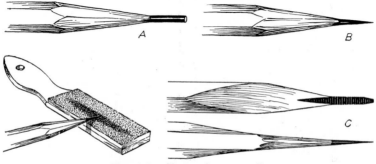

Fig. 4.1. Sharpening a pencil.

sharpen the lead as at *B* by twirling the pencil as the lead is rubbed with long even strokes against the sandpaper pad or file.

A flat or wedge point will not wear away in use so fast as a conical point, and on that account is preferred by some draftsmen for straight-line work. The long wedge point illustrated at *C* is made by first sharpening as at *A*, then making the two long cuts on opposite sides, as shown, then flattening the lead on the sandpaper pad or file, and finishing by touching the corners to make the wedge point narrower than the diameter of the lead.

Have the sandpaper pad within easy reach and *keep the pencils sharp.* Some hang the pad or file on a cord attached to the drawing table. The professional draftsman sharpens his pencil every few minutes. After sharpening the lead, wipe off excess graphite dust before using the pencil. Form the habit of sharpening the lead as often as you might dip a writing pen into the inkwell. Most commercial and many college drafting rooms are equipped with Dexter or other pencil sharpeners to save the draftsman's time.

Not only must pencil lines be clean and sharp, but, for pencil drawings and tracings to be blueprinted, it is absolutely necessary that all the lines of each kind be uniform, firm, and opaque. This means a very careful choice of pencils and the proper use of them. The attempt to make a dark line with too hard a pencil results in cutting deep grooves in the paper. Hold the pencil firmly, yet with as much ease and freedom as possible.

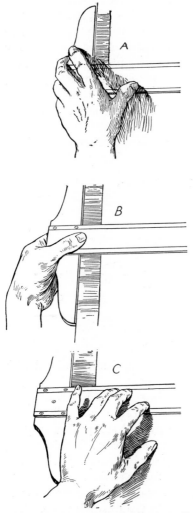

Keep an even constant pressure on the pencil, and, when using a conical point, rotate the pencil as the line is drawn so as to keep both the line and pencil sharp. Use a draftsman's brush or soft cloth occasionally to dust off excess graphite from the drawing.

Too much emphasis cannot be given to the importance of clean, careful, accurate penciling. Never entertain the thought that poor penciling can be corrected in tracing.

4.4 Placing the paper. Since the T-square blade is more rigid near the head than toward the outer end, the paper, if much smaller than the size of the board, should be placed close to the left edge of the board (within an inch or so) with its lower edge several inches from the bottom of the board. With the T square against the left edge of the board, square the top of the paper; hold in this position, slipping the T square down from the edge, and put a thumbtack in each upper corner, pushing it in up to the head so that the head aids in holding the paper. Now move the T square down over the paper to smooth out possible wrinkles, and put thumbtacks in the other two corners. Drafting tape may be used instead of thumbtacks.

Fig. 4.2. Manipulating the T Square.

4.5 Use of the T square. The T square is used with its head against the left edge of the drawing board. Manifestly, the T square is used for drawing horizontal lines and is manipulated as follows: holding the head of the tool, as shown at *A*, Fig. 4.2, the draftsman slides it along the edge of the board to a spot very near the position desired. Then, for closer adjustment, he changes his hold either to that shown at *B*, in which the thumb remains on top of the T-square head and the other fingers press against the underside of the board, or more often, to that shown at *C*, in which the fingers remain on the T square and the thumb is placed on the board.

Figure 4.3 shows the position of the hand and pencil for drawing horizontal lines. Note that the pencil is inclined in the direction the line is drawn, that is, toward the right, and also inclined slightly away from the body, so as to bring the pencil point as close as possible to the T-square blade.

In drawing lines, great care must be exercised to keep them accurately parallel to the guiding edge of the T square. The pencil should be held

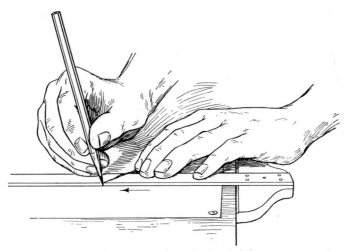

Fig. 4.3. Drawing a horizontal line.

lightly, but close against the edge, and the angle should not vary during the progress of the line. These lines should always be drawn from left to right.

4.6 Use of the triangles. Vertical lines are drawn with the triangle set against the T square, with the perpendicular edge nearest the head of the square and thus toward the light, Fig. 4.4. These lines are always drawn upward, from bottom to top.

In drawing vertical lines, the T square is held in position against the left edge of the board by the thumb and little finger of the left hand while the other fingers of this hand adjust and hold the triangle. One may be sure that the T square is in contact with the board by hearing the little double click as the two come together, and slight pressure of the thumb and little finger toward the right will maintain the position. As the line is drawn, pressure against the board of all the fingers will hold the T square and triangle firmly in position.

As explained before for horizontal lines, care should be exercised to keep the line accurately parallel to the guiding edge. Note the position of the pencil in Fig. 4.4.

In both penciling and inking, the triangles should always be used in contact with a guiding straightedge.   To ensure accuracy, never work to the extreme corner of a triangle; to avoid having to do so, keep the T square below the lower end of the line to be drawn.

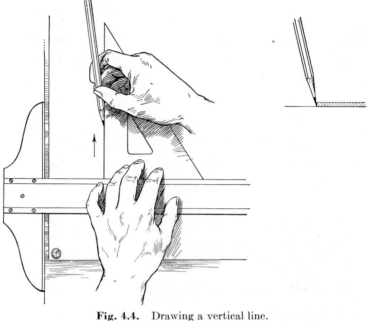

Fig. 4.4.   Drawing a vertical line.

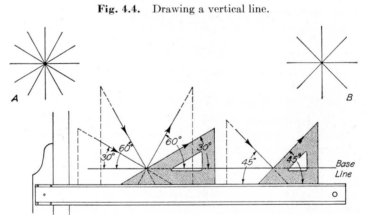

Fig. 4.5.   To draw angles of 30°, 45°, and 60°.

With the T square against the edge of the board, lines at 45° may be drawn with the standard 45° triangle, and lines at 30 and 60° with the 30-60° triangle, as shown in Fig. 4.5.   With vertical and horizontal lines included, lines at increments of 45° may be drawn with the 45° triangle as at *B*, and lines at 30° increments with the 30-60° triangle as at *A*, Fig. 4.5.

The two triangles are used in combination for angles of 15, 75, 105°, etc., Fig. 4.6. Thus any multiple of 15° can be drawn directly, and a circle can be divided with the 45° triangle into 8 parts, with the 30-60° triangle into 12 parts, and with both into 24 parts.

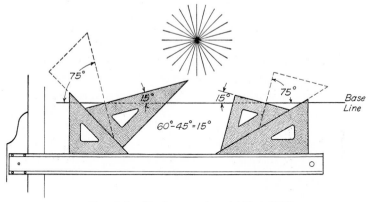

Fig. 4.6. To draw angles of 15° and 75°.

To draw one line parallel to another, Fig. 4.7, adjust to the given line a triangle held against a straightedge (T square or triangle), hold the guiding edge in position, and slip the triangle on it to the required position.

To draw a perpendicular to any line, Fig. 4.8A, place a triangle with one edge against the T square (or another triangle) and move the two until the hypotenuse of the triangle is coincident with the line; hold the T square in position and turn the triangle, as shown, until its other side is against the T square; the hypotenuse will then be perpendicular to the original line.

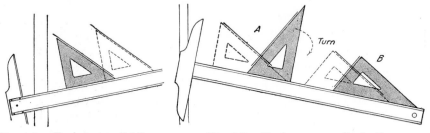

Fig. 4.7. To draw parallel lines.   Fig. 4.8. To draw perpendicular lines.

Move the triangle to the required position. *Or* a quicker method is to set the triangle with its hypotenuse against the guiding edge, fit one side to the line, slide the triangle to the required point, and draw the perpendicular, as shown at *B*.

Never attempt to draw a perpendicular to a line with only one triangle by placing one leg of the triangle along the line.

4.7 The left-handed draftsman reverses the T square and triangles left for right as compared with the regular right-handed position. The head of the T square is used along the right edge of the board. Horizontal lines are drawn from right to left. The triangle is placed with its vertical edge to the right, and the line is drawn from bottom to top. The drawing table should be placed with the light coming from the right.

4.8 Use of the scale. Scale technique is governed largely by the requirements of accuracy and speed. Before a line can be drawn, its relative position must be found by scaling, and the speed with which the scale measurements can be made will greatly affect the total drawing time.

Precise layouts, developments, etc., made for the workmen to scale, must be very accurately drawn, at the expense of speed; conversely, drawings having figured dimensions need not be quite so carefully scaled, and better speed may be attained.

To make a measurement, place the scale on the drawing where the distance is to be laid off, align the scale in the direction of the measurement, and make a *light* short dash with a sharp pencil at the proper graduation mark,

Fig. 4.9. Making a measurement.

Fig. 4.9. In layout work where extreme accuracy is required, a "pricker," or needle point set in a wood handle, may be substituted for the pencil, and a *small* hole pricked into the paper in place of the pencil mark.

Measurements should not be made on a drawing by taking distances off the scale with dividers, as this method is time-consuming and no more accurate than the regular methods.

To avoid cumulative errors, successive measurements on the same line should, if possible, be made without shifting the scale.

4.9 Scale drawings. In representing objects that are larger than can be drawn to their natural or full size, it is necessary to reduce the size of the drawing in some regular proportion, and for this purpose some one of the standard mechanical engineer's, civil engineer's, or architect's scales is used. Standard scales are given in Fig. 4.10.

The first reduction is to *half size*, or to the scale of $6'' = 1'\text{-}0''$. In other words, $\frac{1}{2}$ in. on the drawing represents a distance of 1 in. on the object. Stated in terms used for the architect's scales, a distance of 6 in. on the drawing represents 1 ft on the object. This scale is used even if the object is only slightly larger than could be drawn full size. If this reduction is not sufficient, the drawing is made to *quarter size*, or to the scale of $3'' = 1'\text{-}0''$. If the quarter size scale is too large, the next reduction is *eighth size*, or $1\frac{1}{2}'' = 1'\text{-}0''$, the smallest proportion usually supplied on standard mechanical engineer's scales, but the architect's scales are used down to $\frac{3}{32}'' = 1'\text{-}0''$, as shown by the listings in Fig. 4.10.

In stating the scale used on a drawing, the information should be given in accordance with the scale used to make the drawing. Thus, if a standard mechanical engineer's scale is employed, the statement may read: Scale, (a) *full size*, (b) *half size*, (c) *quarter size*, or (d) *eighth size*. These scales may also be given as (a) $1'' = 1''$, (b) $\frac{1}{2}'' = 1''$, (c) $\frac{1}{4}'' = 1''$, or (d) $\frac{1}{8}'' = 1''$. If a standard architect's scale has been used, the statement will be given in terms of inches to the foot. Examples are (a) $3'' = 1'\text{-}0''$, (b) $1\frac{1}{2}'' = 1'\text{-}0''$, (c) $1'' = 1'\text{-}0''$. It should be remembered that, in stating the scale, the first figure always refers to the drawing and the second to the object. Thus, scale $3'' = 1'\text{-}0''$ means that 3 in. on the *drawing* represents 1 ft on the *object*.

Drawings to odd proportions, such as $9'' = 1'\text{-}0''$, $4'' = 1'\text{-}0''$, etc., are used only in rare cases when it is desired to make it difficult or impossible for a workman to measure them with an ordinary rule.

The scale $\frac{1}{4}'' = 1'\text{-}0''$ is the usual one for ordinary house plans and is often called by architects the "quarter scale." This term should not be confused with the term "quarter size," as the former means $\frac{1}{4}$ in. to 1 ft and the latter $\frac{1}{4}$ in. to 1 in.

Scales

Mechanical Engineer's

Full size ($1'' = 1''$) Half size ($\frac{1}{2}'' = 1''$)
Quarter size ($\frac{1}{4}'' = 1''$) Eighth size ($\frac{1}{8}'' = 1''$)

Architect's or Mechanical Engineer's

$12'' = 1'\text{-}0''$	(Full size)	$\frac{1}{2}'' = 1'\text{-}0''$	($\frac{1}{24}$ size)
$6'' = 1'\text{-}0''$	($\frac{1}{2}$ size)	$\frac{3}{8}'' = 1'\text{-}0''$	($\frac{1}{32}$ size)
$3'' = 1'\text{-}0''$	($\frac{1}{4}$ size)	$\frac{1}{4}'' = 1'\text{-}0''$	($\frac{1}{48}$ size)
$1\frac{1}{2}'' = 1'\text{-}0''$	($\frac{1}{8}$ size)	$\frac{3}{16}'' = 1'\text{-}0''$	($\frac{1}{64}$ size)
$1'' = 1'\text{-}0''$	($\frac{1}{12}$ size)	$\frac{1}{8}'' = 1'\text{-}0''$	($\frac{1}{96}$ size)
$\frac{3}{4}'' = 1'\text{-}0''$	($\frac{1}{16}$ size)	$\frac{3}{32}'' = 1'\text{-}0''$	($\frac{1}{128}$ size)

Civil Engineer's

10, 20, 30, 40, 50, 60, or 80 divisions to the inch representing: feet, 10 ft, 100 ft, rods, miles, or any other necessary unit.

Fig. 4.10. Standard scales.

The size of a circle is generally stated by giving its diameter, while to draw it the radius is necessary. In drawing to half size, it is, thus, often convenient to lay off the amount of the diameter with a quarter-size scale and use this distance as the radius.

Small pieces are often made "double size," and very small mechanisms, such as drawings of watch parts, are drawn to greatly enlarged sizes: 10 to 1, 20 to 1, 40 to 1, and 50 to 1, using special enlarging scales.

For plotting and map drawing, the civil engineer's scale of decimal parts, with 10, 20, 30, 40, 50, 60, and 80 divisions to the inch, is used. This scale is not used for machine or structural work, but is used in certain aircraft drawings.

The important thing in drawing to scale is to think of, and speak of, each dimension in its full size and not in the reduced (or enlarged) size it happens to be on the paper.

4.10 Reading the scale. Reading the standard mechanical engineer's scales is rather simple, because the scale is plainly marked in inches and the smaller graduations are easily recognized as the regular divisions of the inch into ½, ¼, ⅛, and 1/16. Thus the scales for *half size, quarter size,* and *eighth size* are employed in exactly the same manner as a full-size scale.

The architect's scales, however, being open divided and to stated reductions, such as 3″ = 1'-0″, may require some study by the beginner in order to prevent confusion and mistakes. As an example, consider the scale of 3″ = 1'-0″. This is the first reduction scale of the usual triangular scale; on it the distance of 3 in. is divided into 12 equal parts, and each of these is subdivided into eighths. This distance should be thought of not as 3 in., but as a foot divided into inches and eighths of an inch. Notice that the divisions start with the zero on the inside, the inches of the divided foot running to the left and the open divisions of feet to the right, so that dimensions given in feet and in inches may be read directly, as 1'-0½″, Fig. 4.11.

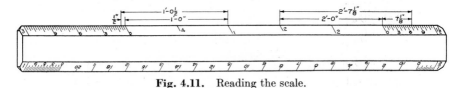

Fig. 4.11. Reading the scale.

On the other end will be found the scale of 1½″ = 1'-0″, or "eighth size," with the distance of 1½ in. divided on the right of the zero into 12 parts and subdivided into quarter inches, with the foot divisions to the left of the zero coinciding with the marks of the 3-in. scale. The other scales, such as ¾″ = 1'-0″, ¼″ = 1'-0″, are divided in a similar way, the only difference being in the value of the smallest graduations. The scale of 3/32″ = 1'-0″, for example, can be read only to the nearest 2 in.

4.11 "Laying out" the sheet. The paper is usually cut somewhat larger than the desired size of the drawing and is trimmed to size after the work is finished. Suppose the finished size is to be 11 by 17 in. with a ½-in. border inside. Lay the scale down on the paper close to the lower edge and measure 17 in., marking the distance with the pencil; at the same time mark ½ in. inside at each end for the border line. Use a short dash forming a continuation of the division line on the scale in laying off a dimension. Do not bore a hole with the pencil. Near the left edge mark 11-in. and ½-in. borderline points. Through these four marks on the left edge draw horizontal lines with the T square, and through the points on the lower edge draw vertical lines, using the triangle against the T square.

4.12 Use of the dividers. The dividers are used for transferring measurements and for dividing lines into any number of equal parts. Facility in the use of this instrument is most essential, and quick and absolute control of its manipulation must be gained. It should be opened with one hand by pinching the chamfer with the thumb and second finger.

This will throw it into correct position with the thumb and forefinger outside the legs and the second and third fingers inside, with the head resting just above the second joint of the forefinger, Fig. 4.12. It is thus under perfect control, with the thumb and forefinger to close it and the other two to open it. This motion should be practiced until an adjustment to the smallest fraction can be made. In coming down to small divisions, the second and third fingers must be gradually slipped out from between the legs while they are closed down upon them. Notice that the little finger is not used in manipulating the dividers.

Fig. 4.12. Handling the dividers.

4.13 To divide a line by trial. In bisecting a line, the dividers are opened at a guess to, roughly, one-half the length. This distance is stepped off on the line, holding the instrument by the handle with the thumb and forefinger. If the division is short, the leg should be thrown out to one-half the remainder (estimated by the eye) without removing the other leg from the paper and the line spaced again with this new setting, Fig. 4.13. If the

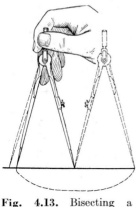

Fig. 4.13. Bisecting a line.

result should not come out exactly, the operation may be repeated. With a little experience a line may be divided very rapidly in this way. Similarly, a line, either straight or curved, may be divided into any number of equal parts, say five, by estimating the first division, stepping this lightly along the line, with the dividers held vertically by the handle, turning the instrument first in one direction and then in the other. If the last division falls short, one-fifth of the remainder should be added by opening the dividers, keeping the one point on the paper. If the last division is over, one-fifth of the excess should be taken off and the line respaced. If it is found difficult to make this small adjustment accurately with the fingers, the hairspring may be used. It will be found more convenient to use the bow spacers instead of the dividers for small or numerous divisions. Avoid pricking unsightly holes in the paper. The position of a small prick point may be preserved, if necessary, by drawing a small circle around it with the pencil. For most work, and until one is very proficient, it is best to divide a line into a number of parts with the scale, as explained on page 76.

Proportional dividers, Fig. 35.2, are sometimes used to divide both straight lines and circles.

4.14 Use of the compasses. The compasses have the same general shape as the dividers and are manipulated in a similar way. First of all,

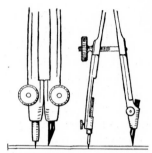

Fig. 4.14.   Adjusting the needle point.   **Fig. 4.15.**   Adjusting the pencil lead.

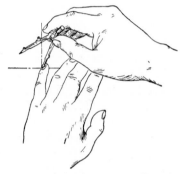

Fig. 4.16.   Setting the compasses to radius   **Fig. 4.17.**   Guiding the needle point.
size.

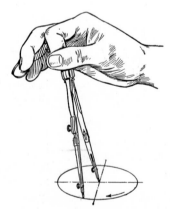

Fig. 4.18.   Starting a circle.   **Fig. 4.19.**   Completing a circle.

the needle should be permanently adjusted.   Insert the pen in place of the pencil leg, turn the needle with the shoulder point out, and set it a trifle longer than the pen, Fig. 4.14; replace the pencil leg, sharpen the lead to a long bevel, as in Fig. 4.15, and adjust it to the needle point.

     To draw a circle, set the compass on the scale, as shown in Fig. 4.16, and adjust it to the radius needed; then place the needle point at the center on the drawing, guiding it with the left hand, Fig. 4.17.   Now raise the fingers to the handle and draw the circle in one sweep, rolling the handle with the thumb and forefinger, inclining the compass slightly in the direction of the line, Fig. 4.18.

The position of the fingers after the rotation is illustrated in Fig. 4.19. The pencil line may be brightened, if necessary, by making additional turns. Circles up to perhaps 3 in. in diameter may be drawn with the legs of the compasses straight, but for larger sizes, both the needle-point leg and the pencil or pen leg should be bent at the knuckle joints so as to be perpen-

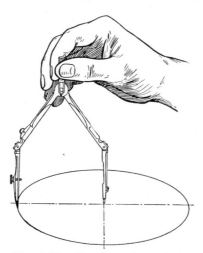

Fig. 4.20. Drawing a large circle.

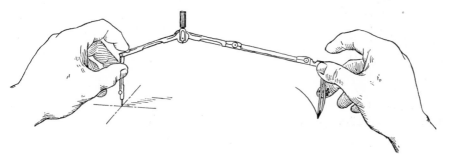

Fig. 4.21. Use of lengthening bar.

dicular to the paper, Fig. 4.20. The 6-in. compasses may be used in this way for circles up to perhaps 10 in. in diameter; larger circles are made by using the lengthening bar, as illustrated in Fig. 4.21, or by using the beam compasses, Fig. 3.9. In drawing concentric circles, the *smallest* should always be drawn *first*, before the center hole has become worn.

The bow instruments are used for small circles, particularly when a number are to be made of the same diameter. To avoid wear (on side-wheel instruments), the pressure of the spring against the nut may be relieved in changing the setting by holding the points in the left hand and spinning the nut in or out with the finger. Small adjustments should be made with one hand with the needle point in position on the paper, Fig. 4.22.

When several concentric circles are to be drawn, a saving in time may

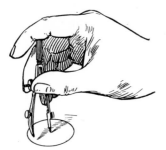

be had by marking off the several radii on the paper from the scale, and then setting the compass to each mark as the circles are made. In some cases it may be advantageous to measure and mark the radius on the paper instead of setting the compass directly on the scale. This method must be used whenever the radius is greater than the length of the scale.

When *extreme accuracy* is required, the compass is set, a light circle is drawn on the paper,

Fig. 4.22.   Adjusting the bow pen.

and the diameter is checked with the scale; if the size is not satisfactory, the compass is adjusted and the operation repeated until the size needed is obtained.

4.15   The ruling pen.   The ruling pen is for inking straight lines and noncircular curves. Several types are illustrated in Fig. 3.6. The important feature is the shape of the blades; they should have a well-designed ink space between them, and their points should be rounded (actually elliptical in form) equally, as in Fig. 4.23. If pointed, as in Fig. 4.24, the ink will

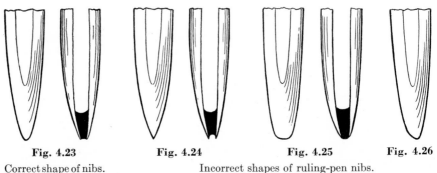

| Fig. 4.23 | Fig. 4.24 | Fig. 4.25 | Fig. 4.26 |

Correct shape of nibs.   Incorrect shapes of ruling-pen nibs.

arch up as shown and will be provokingly hard to start. If rounded to a blunt point, as in Fig. 4.25, the ink will flow too freely, the result being bulbs and overruns at the ends of the lines. Pens in constant use become dull and worn, as illustrated in Fig. 4.26. It is easy to tell whether or not a pen is dull by looking for the reflection of light that travels from the side and over the end of the point when the pen is turned in the hand. If the reflection can be seen all the way the pen is too dull. A pen in poor condition is an abomination, but a well-sharpened one is a delight to use. Every draftsman should be able to keep his pens in fine condition.

High-grade pens usually come from the makers well sharpened. Cheaper ones often need sharpening before they can be used.

4.16 To sharpen a pen. The best stone for the purpose is a hard Arkansas knife piece. It is well to soak a new stone in oil for several days before using. The ordinary carpenter's oilstone is too coarse for drawing instruments.

The nibs must first be brought to the correct shape, as in Fig. 4.23. Screw the nibs together until they touch and, holding the pen as in drawing a line, draw it back and forth on the stone, starting the stroke with the handle at 30° or less with the stone, and swinging it up past the perpendicular as the line across the stone progresses. This will bring the nibs to exactly the same shape and length, leaving them very dull. Then open them slightly and sharpen each blade in turn, *on the outside only*, until the bright spot on the end has just disappeared. Now, as in Fig. 4.27, hold the pen

Fig. 4.27. Sharpening a pen.

at a small angle with the stone and rub it back and forth with a slight oscillating or rocking motion to conform to the shape of the blade. A stone 3 or 4 in. long held in the left hand with the thumb and fingers gives better control than one laid on the table. A pocket magnifying glass may be of aid in examining the points. The blades should not be sharp enough to cut the paper when tested by drawing a line across it without ink. If oversharpened, the blades should again be brought to touch, and a line swung very lightly across the stone as in the first operation. When tested with ink, the pen should be capable of drawing clean sharp lines down to the finest hairline. If these finest lines are ragged or broken, the pen is not perfectly sharpened. It should not be necessary to touch the inside of the blades unless a burr has been formed, which might occur if the metal is very soft, the stone too coarse, or the pressure too heavy. To remove such a burr or wire edge, draw a strip of detail paper between the nibs, or open the pen wide and lay the entire inner surface of the blade flat on the stone and move it with a very light touch.

4.17 Use of the ruling pen. The ruling pen is always used in connection with a guiding edge, T square, triangle, straightedge, or curve. The T square and triangle should be held in the same positions as for penciling.

To fill the pen, take it to the bottle and touch the quill filler between the nibs, being careful not to get any ink on the outside of the blades. Not more than $\frac{3}{16}$ to $\frac{1}{4}$ in. of ink should be put in, or the weight of the ink will cause it to drop out in a blot. The pen should be held in the fingertips, as illustrated in Fig. 4.28, with the thumb and second finger against the sides of the nibs and the handle resting on the forefinger. This hold should be observed carefully, as the tendency will be to bend the second finger to the position used when a pencil or writing pen is held. The position illus-

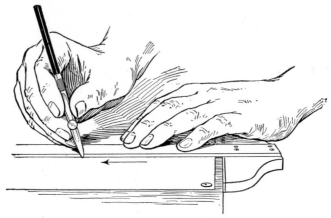

Fig. 4.28.   Correct position of ruling pen.

trated aids in keeping the pen at the proper angle and the nibs aligned with the ruling edge.

The pen should be held against the straightedge, with the blades parallel to it, the screw being on the outside and the handle inclined slightly to the right and always kept in a plane passing through the line and perpendicular to the paper. The pen is thus guided by the upper edge of the ruler, as illustrated in actual size in Fig. 4.29. If the pen point is thrown out from the perpendicular, it will run on one blade and a line ragged on one side will result. If turned in from the perpendicular, the ink is very apt to run under the edge of the ruler and cause a blot.

Fig. 4.29. Correct pen position.

A line is drawn with a steady, even arm movement, the tips of the third and fourth fingers resting on, and sliding along, the straightedge, keeping the angle of inclination constant. Just before the end of the line is reached, the two guiding fingers on the straightedge should be stopped and, without stopping the motion of the pen, the line finished with a finger movement. Short lines are drawn with this finger movement alone. When the end of the line is reached, lift the pen quickly and move the straightedge away from the line. The pressure on the paper should be light, but sufficient to give a clean-cut line, and will vary with the kind of paper and the sharpness of the pen. The pressure against the T square, however, should be only enough to guide the direction.

If the ink refuses to flow, it may be because it has dried in the extreme point of the pen. If pinching the blades slightly or touching the pen on the finger does not start it, the pen should immediately be wiped out and fresh ink supplied. Pens must be wiped clean after using.

In inking on either paper or cloth, the full lines will be much wider than the pencil lines, and thus the beginner must be very careful to have the center of the ink line cover the pencil line, as shown in Fig. 4.30.

Fig. 4.30. Inking a pencil line.

Instructions in regard to the ruling pen apply also to the compasses. The instrument should be slightly inclined in the direction of the line, and both nibs of the pen kept on the paper, bending the knuckle joints, if necessary, to effect this.

It is a universal rule in inking that *circles and circle arcs must be inked first.* It is much easier to connect a straight line to a curve than a curve to a straight line.

4.18 Tangents. It should be noted particularly that two lines are tangent to each other when the center lines of the lines are tangent and not simply when the lines touch each other; thus, at the point of tangency, the width will be equal to the width of a single line, Fig. 4.31. Before inking

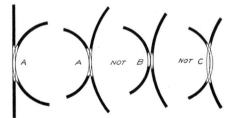

Fig. 4.31. Correct and incorrect tangents.

tangent lines, the point of tangency should be marked in pencil. For an arc tangent to a straight line, this point will be on a line through the center of the arc and perpendicular to the straight line, and for two circle arcs will be on the line joining their centers, as described in paragraphs 5.11 to 5.28.

4.19 The alphabet of lines. As the basis of drawing is the line, a set of conventional symbols covering all the lines needed for different purposes may properly be called an "alphabet of lines." Figure 4.32 shows the alphabet of lines adopted by the American Standards Association (ASA) as applied

1. To layout drawings in pencil on detail paper to be traced on tracing paper or cloth.

2. To drawings either made directly or traced in pencil on tracing paper or pencil cloth, from which blueprints or other reproductions are to be made.

3. To tracings in ink on tracing cloth or tracing paper and to inked drawings on white paper for display or photoreproductions.

The ASA recommends three widths of lines: thick, medium, and thin, for finished drawings, as follows: *thick* for visible outlines, cutting-plane, and short-break lines; *medium* for hidden outlines; and *thin* for section, center, extension, dimension, long-break, adjacent parts, alternate position, and repeat lines.   The actual widths of the three weights of lines, on average drawings, should be about as given in Fig. 4.32.   A convenient line gage

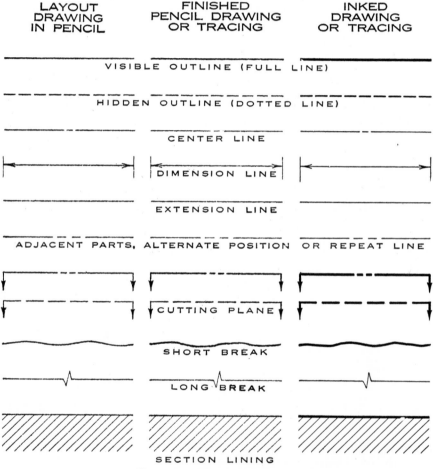

Fig. 4.32. The alphabet of lines.

is illustrated in Fig. 4.33.   If applied to Fig. 4.32, this gage would show the heavy lines in ink to be between $\frac{1}{40}$ and $\frac{1}{50}$ in., the medium lines $\frac{1}{80}$ in., and the fine lines $\frac{1}{200}$ in. in width.   To use the line gage, draw a line about $1\frac{1}{2}$ in. wide in pencil or ink on a piece of the drawing paper and apply to the center of the gage.   By this method a very good comparison can be made.   Figure 4.34 shows the application of the alphabet of lines.

4.20 Line practice. After reading the preceding several paragraphs, the beginner had best take a blank sheet of paper and practice making straight lines and circles in all the forms, full, dotted, etc., shown in Fig.

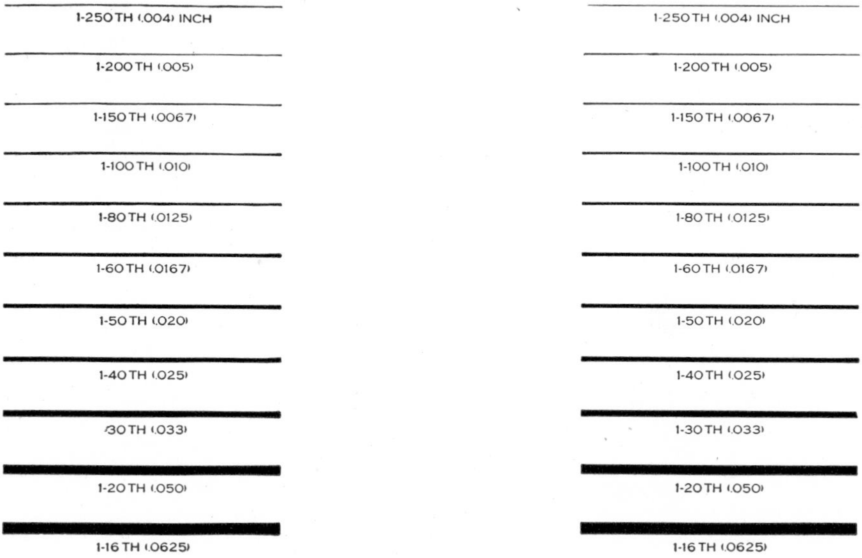

1-250 TH (.004) INCH
1-200 TH (.005)
1-150 TH (.0067)
1-100 TH (.010)
1-80 TH (.0125)
1-60 TH (.0167)
1-50 TH (.020)
1-40 TH (.025)
30 TH (.033)
1-20 TH (.050)
1-16 TH (.0625)
1-250 TH (.004) INCH
1-200 TH (.005)
1-150 TH (.0067)
1-100 TH (.010)
1-80 TH (.0125)
1-60 TH (.0167)
1-50 TH (.020)
1-40 TH (.025)
1-30 TH (.033)
1-20 TH (.050)
1-16 TH (.0625)

Fig. 4.33. Line gage.

Extension line
Section lines (Cross hatching)
Alternate position
Cutting plane
A
A
10"
Center line
3-0"
Dimension line
Visible outline
Hidden outline
Short break
Wood
Adjacent part
C I Base
Long break

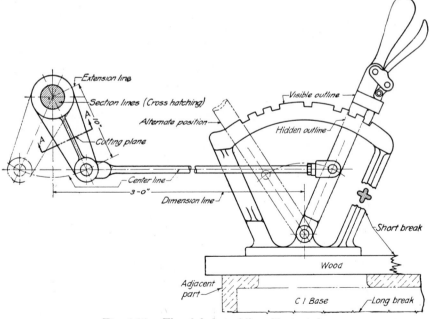

Fig. 4.34. The alphabet of lines illustrated.

4.32.   The practice should include starting and stopping lines, with special attention to tangents and corners.

In pencil, try to get all the lines uniform in width and color for each type. Circle arcs and straight lines should match exactly at tangent points.

In ink, proceed as for pencil practice and pay particular attention to the weight of lines and to the spacing of dashed-in dotted lines and center lines.

If inked lines appear imperfect in any way, the reason should be ascertained immediately.   It may be the fault of the pen, the ink, the paper, or the draftsman, but with the probabilities greatly in favor of the last.

Figure 4.35 illustrates the characteristic appearance of several kinds of faulty lines.   The correction in each case will suggest itself.

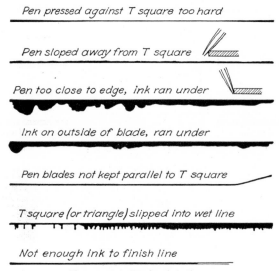

Fig. 4.35.   Faulty ink lines.

4.21   Use of the french curve.   The french curve, as has been stated on page 38, is a rule for noncircular curves.   When sufficient points have been determined, it is best to sketch in the line lightly in pencil, freehand, without losing the points, until it is clean, smooth, continuous, and satisfactory to the eye.   The curve should then be applied to it, selecting a part that will fit a portion of the line most nearly and seeing to it, particularly, that the curve is so placed that the direction in which its curvature increases is the direction in which the curvature of the line increases, Fig. 4.36.   In drawing that part of the line matched by the curve, *always* stop a little short of the distance in which the ruler and the line seem to coincide.   After drawing this portion, the curve is shifted to find another place that will coincide with the continuation of the line.   In shifting the curve, care should be taken to preserve smoothness and continuity and to avoid breaks or cusps.   This may be done if, in its successive positions, the curve is always adjusted so that it coincides for a short distance with the part of the line already drawn. Thus, at each juncture, the tangents will coincide.

If the curved line is symmetrical about an axis, marks locating this axis, after it has been matched accurately on one side, may be made in pencil on the curve and the curve then reversed. In such a case exceptional care must be taken to avoid a "hump" at the joint. It is often better to stop a line short of the axis on each side and close the gap afterward with another setting of the curve.

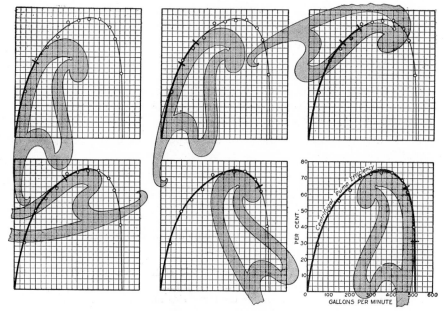

Fig. 4.36. Use of the french curve.

When using the curve in inking, the pen should be held perpendicular and the blades kept parallel to the edge. Inking curves will be found to be excellent practice.

Sometimes, particularly at sharp turns, a combination of circle arcs and curves may be used; in inking a long narrow ellipse, for example, the sharp curves may be inked by selecting a center on the major axis by trial, drawing as much of an arc as will practically coincide with the ends of the ellipse, and then finishing the ellipse with the curve. The experienced draftsman will sometimes ink a curve that cannot be matched accurately by varying the distance of the pen point from the ruling edge as the line progresses.

4.22 Erasing. The manner of erasing both pencil lines and ink lines is a necessary technique to learn. A designer, working freely but lightly, uses a soft pencil eraser when changing some detail so as not to damage the finish of the paper. Heavier lines are best removed by a Ruby pencil eraser.   If the paper has been grooved by the line, it may be rubbed over with a burnisher, or even with the back of the thumbnail.   In erasing an ink line, hold the paper down firmly and, with a Ruby pencil eraser, rub lightly and patiently, first along the line, then across it, until the ink is removed. A triangle slipped under the paper or cloth gives a good backing surface.

When an erasure is to be made close to other lines, select an opening of the best shape on the erasing shield and rub through it, holding the shield down firmly, first seeing that both of its sides are clean.   Wipe off the eraser crumbs from the paper with a dustcloth or brush.   Never scratch out a line or a blot with a knife or razor blade, and use so-called ink erasers very sparingly, if at all.   A skilled draftsman sometimes uses a sharp blade to trim a thickened spot or overrunning end on a line.   For extensive erasing, an electric erasing machine is a great convenience.   Several successful models are on the market.

4.23   Special instruments.   Various instruments, such as drafting machines, parallel rules, pantographs, lettering machines, and proportional dividers, not in the usual draftsman's outfit, are used in commercial drafting work.   A description of a number of these special instruments is given in Chap. 35.

4.24   Exercises in the use of instruments.   The following may be used as progressive exercises for practice in using the instruments, doing them either as finished pencil drawings, or in pencil layout to be inked.   Line work should conform to that given in the alphabet of lines, Fig. 4.32.

The problems in Chap. 5 afford excellent additional practice in accurate penciling.

1. An exercise for the T square, triangle, and scale.   Fig. 4.37.   Through the center of the space draw a horizontal and a vertical line.   Measuring on these lines as diameters lay off a 4-in. square.   Along the lower side and upper half of the left side measure ½-in. spaces with the scale.   Draw all horizontal lines with the T square and all vertical lines with the T square and triangle.

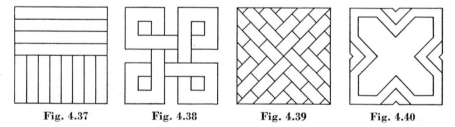

Fig. 4.37   Fig. 4.38   Fig. 4.39   Fig. 4.40

2. An interlacement.   Fig. 4.38.   For T square, triangle, and dividers.   Draw a 4-in. square.   Divide the left side and lower side into seven equal parts with dividers. Draw horizontal and vertical lines across the square through these points.   Erase the parts not needed.

3. A street-paving intersection.   Fig. 4.39.   For 45° triangle and scale.   An exercise in starting and stopping short lines.   Draw a 4-in. square.   Draw its diagonals with 45° triangle.   With the scale, lay off ½-in. spaces along the diagonals from their intersection.   With 45° triangle, complete the figure, finishing one quarter at a time.

4. A square pattern. Fig. 4.40. For 45° triangle, dividers, and scale. Draw a 4-in. square and divide its sides into three equal parts with dividers. With 45° triangle, draw diagonal lines connecting these points. Measure ⅜ in. on each side of these lines and finish the pattern as shown.

5. An acoustic pattern. Fig. 4.41. For 45° triangle, T square, and scale. Draw two intersecting 45° diagonals 4 in. long to form a field. With the scale lay off ½-in. spaces from their intersection. Add the narrow border ³⁄₁₆ in. wide. Add a second border ½ in. wide. The length of the border blocks are projected from the corners of the field blocks.

6. Five cards. Fig. 4.42. Visible and hidden lines. Five cards 1¾ by 3 in. are arranged with the bottom card in the center, the other four overlapping each other and placed so that their outside edges form a 4-in. square. Hidden lines indicate edges covered.

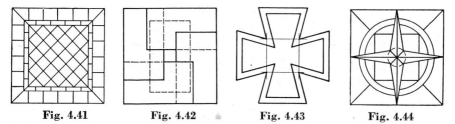

Fig. 4.41   Fig. 4.42   Fig. 4.43   Fig. 4.44

7. A Maltese cross. Fig. 4.43. For T square, spacers, and both triangles. Draw a 4-in. square and a 1⅜-in. square. From the corners of inner square draw lines to outer square at 15° and 75°, with the two triangles in combination. Mark points with spacers ¼ in. inside each line of this outside cross, and complete the figure with triangles in combination.

8. Insigne. Fig. 4.44. For T square, triangles, scale, and compasses. Draw the 45° diagonals and the vertical and horizontal center lines of a 4-in. square. With compasses, draw a ¾-in. diameter construction circle and a 2¾- and 3¼-in. circle. Complete the design by adding a square and pointed star as shown.

9. A six-pointed star. Fig. 4.45. For compasses and 30°-60° triangle. Draw a 4-in. construction circle and inscribe the six-pointed star with the T square and 30°-60° triangle. Accomplish this with four successive changes of position of the triangle.

10. A stamping. Fig. 4.46. For T square, 30°-60° triangle, and compasses. In a 4-in. circle draw six diameters 30° apart. Draw a 3-in. construction circle to locate the centers of ⁵⁄₁₆-in. radius circle arcs. Complete the stamping with perpendiculars to the six diameters as shown.

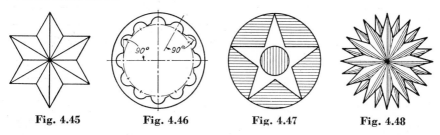

Fig. 4.45   Fig. 4.46   Fig. 4.47   Fig. 4.48

11. Aircraft insigne. Fig. 4.47. This device is a white star with a red center on a blue background. Draw a 4-in. circle and a 1¼-in. circle. Divide the large circle into five equal parts with the dividers and construct the star by connecting alternate points as shown. Red is indicated by vertical lines and blue by horizontal lines. Space these by eye approximately ¹⁄₁₆ in. apart.

12. A 24-point star. Fig. 4.48. For T square and triangles in combination. In a 4-in. circle draw 12 diameters 15° apart, using T square and triangles singly and in combination. With the same combinations, finish the figure as shown.

13. Concentric circles. Fig. 4.49. For compasses (legs straight) and scale. Draw a horizontal line through the center of a space. On it, mark off radii for eight concentric circles ¼ in. apart. In drawing concentric circles, always draw the smallest first.

14. A four-centered spiral. Fig. 4.50. For accurate tangents. Draw a ⅛-in. square and extend its sides as shown. With the upper right corner as center, draw quadrants with ⅛- and ¼-in. radii. Continue with quadrants from each corner in order until four turns have been drawn.

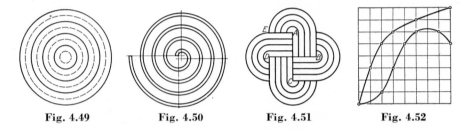

Fig. 4.49   Fig. 4.50   Fig. 4.51   Fig. 4.52

15. A loop ornament. Fig. 4.51. For bow compasses. Draw a 2-in. square, about center of space. Divide AE into four ¼-in. spaces with scale. With bow pencil and centers, A, B, C, and D, draw four semicircles with ¼-in. radius, and so on. Complete the figure by drawing the horizontal and vertical tangents as shown.

16. A rectilinear chart. Fig. 4.52. For french curve. Draw a 4-in. field with ½-in. coordinate divisions. Plot points at the intersections shown, and through them sketch a smooth curve very lightly in pencil. Finish by marking each point with a ¹⁄₁₆-in. circle and drawing a smooth bright line with the french curve.

17. Scale practice. Fig. 4.53. *a.* Measure lines A to G to the following scales: A, full size; B, half size; C, $3'' = 1'\text{-}0''$; D, $1'' = 1'\text{-}0''$; E, ¾$'' = 1'\text{-}0''$; F, ¼$'' = 1'\text{-}0''$; G, ³⁄₁₆$'' = 1'\text{-}0''$.

b. Lay off distances on lines H to N as follows: H, $3³⁄₁₆''$, full size; I, $7''$, half size; J, $2'\text{-}6''$, scale $1½'' = 1'\text{-}0''$; K, $7'\text{-}5½''$, scale ½$'' = 1'\text{-}0''$; L, $10'\text{-}11''$, scale ⅜$'' = 1'\text{-}0''$; M, $28'\text{-}4''$, scale, ⅛$'' = 1'\text{-}0''$; N, $40'\text{-}10''$, scale ³⁄₃₂$'' = 1'\text{-}0''$.

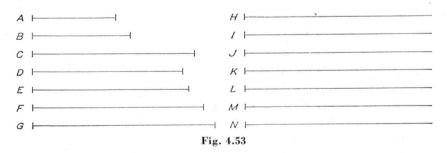

Fig. 4.53

c. For engineer's scale. Lay off distances on lines H to N as follows: H, $3.2''$, full size; I, $27'\text{-}0''$, scale $1'' = 10'\text{-}0''$; J, $66'\text{-}0''$, scale $1'' = 20'\text{-}0''$; K, $105'\text{-}0''$, scale $1'' = 30'\text{-}0''$; L, $156'\text{-}0''$, scale $1'' = 40'\text{-}0''$; M, $183'\text{-}0''$, scale $1'' = 50'\text{-}0''$; N, $214'\text{-}0''$, scale $1'' = 60'\text{-}0''$.

18. A telephone dial plate. Fig. 4.54. Draw double size from the dimensions given.

19. A film-reel stamping. Fig. 4.55. Draw to scale of $6'' = 1'\text{-}0''$.

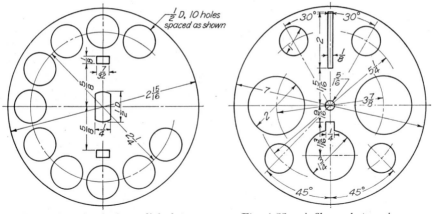

Fig. 4.54. A telephone dial plate.   **Fig. 4.55.** A film-reel stamping.

20. Box cover. Make one-view drawing for rectangular stamping 3 by 4 in., corners rounded with $\frac{1}{2}$-in. radius. Four holes, one in each corner, $\frac{3}{16}$-in. diameter, 3 and 2 in. center to center, for fasteners. Rectangular hole in center, $\frac{3}{8}$ by 1 in., with 1-in. side parallel to 4-in. side. Two slots $\frac{1}{4}$ in. wide, 2 in. long with semicircular ends, located midway between center and 4-in. edges, with 2-in. side parallel to 4-in. side and centered between 3-in. edges.

21. Spacer. Make one-view drawing for circular stamping 4 in. OD, 2 in. ID. Six $\frac{1}{4}$-in.-diameter holes equally spaced on 3-in.-diameter circle, with two holes on vertical center line. Two semicircular notches 180° apart made with $\frac{3}{8}$-in. radius centered at intersections of horizontal center line and 4-in.-OD circle.

22. Blank for wheel. Make a one-view drawing for stamping 5 in. OD; center hole $\frac{1}{2}$-in. diameter; eight spokes $\frac{3}{8}$ in. wide connecting $1\frac{1}{2}$-in.-diameter center portion with $\frac{1}{2}$-in. rim. Eight $\frac{1}{4}$-in.-diameter holes with centers at intersection of center lines of spokes and $4\frac{1}{2}$-in. circle, $\frac{1}{8}$-in. fillets throughout to break sharp corners.

23. Cover plate. Make a one-view drawing for rectangular stamping 3 by 4 in., corners beveled $\frac{1}{2}$ in. each way. Four holes, one in each corner, $\frac{1}{4}$-in. diameter, 3 and 2 in. center to center, for fasteners. Rectangular hole in center, $\frac{1}{2}$ by 1 in. with 1-in. side parallel to 4-in. side. Two holes, $\frac{3}{4}$-in. diameter, located midway between the slot and short side of rectangle on center line through slot.

A List of Cautions

Never use the scale as a ruler.
Never draw horizontal lines with the lower edge of the T square.
Never use the lower edge of the T square as a horizontal base for the triangles.
Never cut paper with a knife and the edge of the T square as a guide.
Never use the T square as a hammer.
Never put either end of a pencil into the mouth.
Never work with a dull pencil.
Never sharpen a pencil over the drawing board.
Never jab the dividers into the drawing board.
Never oil the joints of compasses.
Never use the dividers as reamers or pincers or picks.
Never use a blotter on inked lines.
Never screw the pen adjustment past the contact point of the nibs.
Never leave the ink bottle uncorked.
Never hold the pen over the drawing while filling.

Never put into the drawing-ink bottle a writing pen which has been used in ordinary writing ink.

Never try to use the same thumbtack holes in either paper or board when putting paper down a second time.

Never scrub a drawing all over with an eraser after finishing.   It takes the life out of the lines.

Never begin work without wiping off the table and instruments.

Never put instruments away without cleaning.   This applies with particular force to pens.

Never put bow instruments away without opening to relieve the spring.

Never work with the table cluttered with unneeded instruments or equipment.

Never fold a drawing or tracing.

5

Applied Geometry

5.1 With the aid of a straightedge and compasses, all pure geometry problems may be solved. The principles of geometry are constantly used in mechanical drawing, but as the geometrical solution of problems and construction of figures differ in many cases from the draftsman's method, equipped as he is with instruments for gaining time and accuracy, all constructions are not included here.   However, the application of these geometrical methods is occasionally necessary in work where the usual drafting instruments could not be used, as in laying out full-size sheet-metal patterns on the floor or in lofting work.   It is assumed that students using this book are familiar with the elements of plane geometry and will be able to apply their knowledge.   If the solution of a particular problem is not remembered, it may readily be referred to in any of the standard handbooks.   There are some constructions, however, with which the draftsman should be familiar, as they will occur more or less frequently in his work.   The constructions in this chapter are given on this account and for the excellent practice they afford in the accurate use of instruments as well.

It must always be remembered that the results obtained will be only as accurate as the skill of the draftsman makes them accurate.   Therefore, care (and in some cases, extreme care) in measuring, drawing, and the use of the instruments must be observed.

As an aid in recalling the names of various geometrical figures, see Fig. 5.84 at the end of this chapter.

5.2 To draw a line through two points. *Draftsman's methods—first method.* Fig. 5.1. Place the point of the pencil at Q, bring the triangle

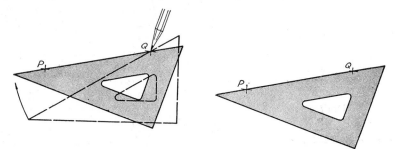

Fig. 5.1 **Fig. 5.2**

Figs. 5.1 and 5.2.   To draw a line through two points, draftsman's methods.

or straightedge against the point of the pencil, then using this point as a pivot swing the triangle until its edge is in alignment with point P. Then, draw the line.

Second method. Fig. 5.2. Align the straightedge or triangle with the given points *P* and *Q* and then draw the line.

5.3   To draw a straight line through a point parallel to another straight line. *Draftsman's method.* Fig. 5.3. Adjust a triangle to the given line *AB* with a second triangle as a base. Slide the aligned triangle to its position at point *P* and draw the required line.

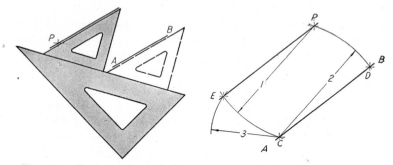

Fig. 5.3. Draftsman's method.   **Fig. 5.4.** Geometric method.
Figs. 5.3 and 5.4.   Parallel lines.

Geometric method. Fig. 5.4. With *P* as the center and a radius of sufficient length, draw an arc *CE* intersecting the line *AB* at *C*. With *C* as the center and the same radius, draw the arc *PD*. With center *C* and radius *DP*, draw an arc intersecting *CE* at *E*. Then *EP* is the required line.

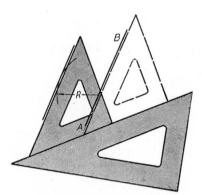
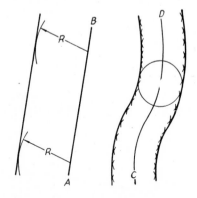

Fig. 5.5   **Fig. 5.6**   **Fig. 5.7**
Draftsman's method   Geometric method
Figs. 5.5, 5.6 and 5.7.   Parallel lines.

5.4   To draw a line parallel to another at a given distance from it.
(1) For straight lines—draftsman's method. Fig. 5.5. With the given distance *R* as a radius and any point on the given line as a center, draw an arc. Adjust a triangle to the given line *AB*, with a second triangle as a base. Slide the aligned triangle to its position tangent to the circle arc and draw the required line.

(2) *For straight lines—geometric method.* Fig. 5.6. With the given distance as a radius and two points on the given line as centers (as far apart as convenient), draw two arcs. A line tangent to these arcs will be the required line.

(3) *For curved lines—geometric method.* Fig. 5.7. Draw a series of arcs with centers along the line. Draw tangents to these arcs with a french curve, see Fig. 4.36.

5.5   To erect a perpendicular to a given straight line. *Draftsman's method—first method, given line horizontal.* Fig. 5.8. With the T square as a base and the triangle in the position shown, draw the required perpendicular.

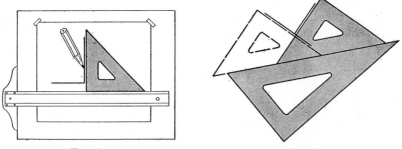

Fig. 5.8   **Fig. 5.9**
Figs. 5.8 and 5.9.   Perpendiculars, draftsman's methods.

Second method. Fig. 5.9. Set a triangle with its hypotenuse against a guiding edge. Fit one side to the line, slide the triangle to the required point, and draw the perpendicular.

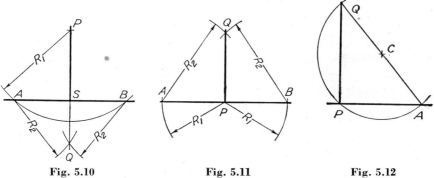

Fig. 5.10   **Fig. 5.11**   **Fig. 5.12**
Figs. 5.10 to 5.12.   Perpendiculars, geometric method.

5.6   To erect a perpendicular from a point to a given straight line. *Geometric method.* Fig. 5.10. With point P as the center and any convenient radius R_1, draw a circle arc intersecting the given line at A and B. With any convenient radius R_2 and with centers at A and B, draw intersecting arcs locating Q. The required perpendicular is PQ, with S the intersection of the perpendicular and given line.

5.7 To erect a perpendicular from a point on a given straight line. *Geometric first method.* Fig. 5.11. With point P on the line as center and any convenient radius R_1, draw circle arcs to locate points A and B equidistant from P. With any convenient radius R_2 longer than R_1, and with centers at A and B, draw intersecting arcs locating Q. PQ is the required perpendicular.

5.8 To erect a perpendicular from a point on a given straight line. *Geometric second method.* Fig. 5.12. With any convenient center C and radius CP, draw somewhat more than a semicircle from the intersection of the circle arc with the given line at A. Draw AC extended to meet the circle arc at Q. PQ is the required perpendicular.

5.9 To locate the center of a circle. Fig. 5.13. Draw any chord AB; then draw AC and BD perpendicular to AB. Then AD and BC are diameters of the circle and cross at center O.

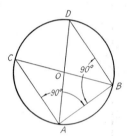

Fig. 5.13. Circle center.

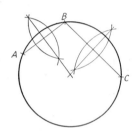

Fig. 5.14. Circle through three points.

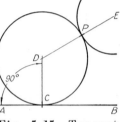

Fig. 5.15. Tangent points.

5.10 To draw a circle arc through three given points. Fig. 5.14. Given the points A, B, and C. The intersection of the perpendicular bisectors of lines AB and BC will be the center of the required circle.

5.11 Tangents. One of the most frequent geometrical operations in drafting is the drawing of tangents to circle arcs and the drawing of circle arcs tangent to straight lines or other circles. These should be constructed accurately, and on pencil drawings that are to be inked or traced, the points of tangency should be located by short cross marks to show the stopping points for the ink lines. The method of finding these points is indicated in the following constructions.

5.12 To locate tangent points. *First case.* Fig. 5.15. To find the point of tangency for line AB and a circle with the center at D. Draw DC perpendicular to line AB. Point C is the tangent point.

Second case. Fig. 5.15. To find the point of tangency for two circle arcs. Draw the line DE joining the centers of the given arcs. Point P is the tangent point.

5.13 To draw a circle of given size tangent to a line and passing through a point. *Geometric method.* Fig. 5.16. Draw a line AB, the given radius distance R away from and parallel to the given line; cut line AB at O with the given radius, using the given point S as center; O is the center of the circle.   Note that there are two possible positions for the circle.

5.14   To draw a circle tangent to a line at a point and passing through a second point. *Geometric method.*   Fig. 5.17.   Connect the two points P and S and draw the perpendicular bisector AB; where AB crosses a perpendicular to the given line at P is the center O of the required circle.

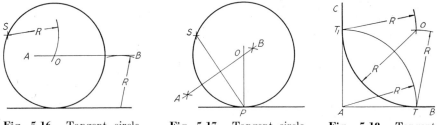

Fig. 5.16. Tangent circle.   **Fig. 5.17.** Tangent circle.   **Fig. 5.18.** Tangent arc.

5.15   To draw a circle arc of given radius tangent to two lines at right angles to each other. *Geometric method.*   Fig. 5.18.   Draw an arc of radius R, with center at corner A, cutting the lines AB and AC at T and T_1; then with T and T_1 as centers and with the same radius R, draw arcs intersecting at O, the center of the required arc.

5.16   To draw an arc tangent to two straight lines. *Draftsman's method.*   Figs. 5.19 and 5.20.   Given the lines AB and CD to draw a tangent arc of radius R.   Set the compass to radius R, and at any convenient

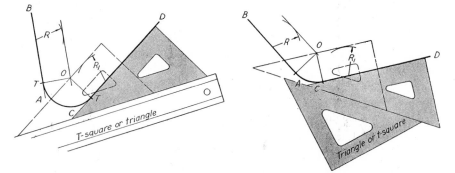

Fig. 5.19. Tangent arc, acute angle,   **Fig. 5.20.** Tangent arc, obtuse angle,
draftsman's method.   draftsman's method.

point on the given lines, draw the arcs R and R_1.   With the method of Fig. 5.3, draw parallels to the given lines through the limits of the arcs. These parallels are the loci of the centers of all circles of radius R tangent to the lines AB and CD, and their intersection at point O will be the center of the required arc.   Find the tangent points by erecting perpendiculars, as in Fig. 5.9, to the given lines through the center O.   Figure 5.19 is for an acute angle and Fig. 5.20 for an obtuse angle.

5.17   To draw a tangent to a circle at a point on the circle.   *Draftsman's method.*   Fig. 5.21.   Given the arc ACB, draw a tangent at the point C. Arrange a triangle in combination with the T square (or another triangle) so that its hypotenuse passes through center O and point C.   Holding the T square firmly in place, turn the triangle about its square corner and move it until the hypotenuse passes through C; the required tangent then lies along the hypotenuse.   (For small constructions, or with a large triangle, this may be done a little quicker by setting the hypotenuse of the triangle on the T square, as in Fig. 4.8 at B.)

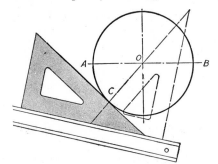

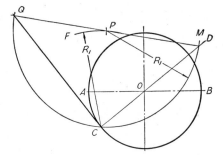

Fig. 5.21.   Drawing a tangent, draftsman's method.

Fig. 5.22.   Drawing a tangent, geometric method.

5.18   To draw a tangent to a circle at a point on the circle.   *Geometric method.*   Fig. 5.22.   Given the arc ACB to draw a tangent at point C. Draw the diameter CD and locate point M, then with any convenient radius R_1, locate point P equidistant from C and M; now with the same radius R_1, draw somewhat more than a semicircle and draw the line MPQ.   The line QC is a tangent to the circle at point C.   (See also Fig. 5.12.)

5.19   To draw a tangent to a circle from a point outside.   *Draftsman's method.*   Fig. 5.23.   Given the arc ACB and point P to draw a tangent from point P to the given arc.   Arrange a triangle in combination with another triangle (or T square) so that one side passes through point P and is tangent to the circle arc at C.   Now, slide the triangle until the right

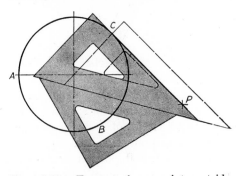

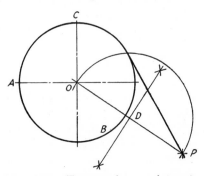

Fig. 5.23.   Tangent from point outside, draftsman's method.

Fig. 5.24.   Tangent from point outside, geometric method.

angle side passes through the center of the circle and mark, lightly, the tangent point C. Then, bring the triangle back to its original position and draw the tangent line.

5.20 To draw a tangent to a circle from a point outside. *Geometric method.* Fig. 5.24. Connect the point P with the center of the circle O. Then draw the perpendicular bisector of OP, and with the intersection at D, draw a semicircle. Its intersection with the given circle is the point of tangency. Draw tangent line from P.

5.21 To draw a tangent to two circles. *First case, open belt—draftsman's method.* Fig. 5.25. Arrange a triangle in combination with a T square or triangle so that one side is in the tangent position. Move to positions 2 and 3, marking lightly the tangent points T_1 and T_2. Return to the original position and draw the tangent line.

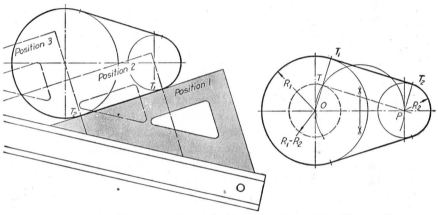

Fig. 5.25. Tangent lines, open belt, draftsman's method.   **Fig. 5.26.** Tangent lines, open belt, geometric method.

5.22 To draw a tangent to two circles. *First case, open belt—geometric method.* Fig. 5.26. At center O draw a circle with a radius $R_1 - R_2$. From P draw a tangent to this circle by the method of Fig. 5.24. Extend OT to T_1 and draw PT_2 parallel to OT_1. Join T_1 and T_2.

5.23 To draw a tangent to two circles. *Second case, crossed belt—draftsman's method.* Fig. 5.27. Arrange a triangle in combination with a

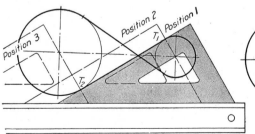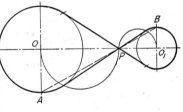

Fig. 5.27. Tangent lines, crossed belt, draftsman's method.   **Fig. 5.28.** Tangent lines, crossed belt, geometric method.

T square or triangle so that one side is in the tangent position. Move to positions 2 and 3, marking lightly the tangent points T_1 and T_2. Return to the original position and draw the tangent line. Repeat for the other side.

5.24 To draw a tangent to two circles. *Second case, crossed belt— geometric method.* Fig. 5.28. Draw OA and O_1B perpendicular to OO_1. From P, where AB crosses OO_1, draw tangents as in Fig. 5.24.

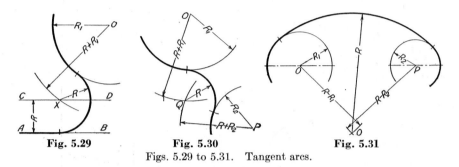

Fig. 5.29   Fig. 5.30   Fig. 5.31

Figs. 5.29 to 5.31.   Tangent arcs.

5.25 To draw a circle of radius R tangent to a given circle and a straight line. Fig. 5.29. Let AB be the given line and R_1 the radius of the given circle. Draw a line CD parallel to AB at a distance R from it. With O as a center and radius $R + R_1$, swing an arc intersecting CD at X, the desired center. The tangent point for AB will be on a perpendicular to AB from X; the tangent point for the two circles will be on a line joining their centers X and O. Note that when two circles are tangent to each other the point of tangency must be on a line through their centers.

5.26 To draw a circle of radius R tangent to two given circles. *First case.* Fig. 5.30. For this case the centers of the given circles are outside the required circle. Let R_1 and R_2 be the radii of the given circles having centers O and P, respectively. With O as a center and a radius $R + R_1$, describe an arc. With P as a center and a radius $R + R_2$, swing another arc intersecting the first arc at Q, which is the center sought. Mark the tangent points in line with OQ and QP.

Second case. Fig. 5.31. For this case the centers of the given circles are inside the required circle. With O and P as centers and radii $R - R_1$ and $R - R_2$, describe arcs intersecting at the required center Q.

5.27 To draw a reverse or ogee curve. Fig. 5.32. Given two parallel lines AB and CD. Join B and C by a straight line. Erect perpendiculars at B and C. Any arcs tangent to lines AB and CD at B and C must have their centers on these perpendiculars. On the line BC assume point E, the point through which it is desired that the curve shall pass. Bisect BE and EC by perpendiculars. Any arc to pass through B and E must have its center somewhere on the perpendicular from the middle point. The intersection, therefore, of these perpendicular bisectors with the first two perpendiculars will be the centers for arcs BE and EC. This line might be the center line for a curved road or pipe. The construction may be checked by drawing the line of centers, which *must* pass through E. Figure 5.33 illustrates the principle of reverse-curve construction in various combinations.

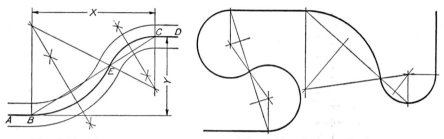

Fig. 5.32. Ogee curve.   **Fig. 5.33.** Ogee applications.

5.28 To draw a reverse curve tangent to two lines and to a third secant line at a given point. Fig. 5.34A, B, and C. Given two lines AB and CD cut by the line EF at points E and F. Through a given point P on EF, draw a perpendicular JH to EF. With E as a center and radius EP, intersect CD at G. Draw a perpendicular from G intersecting JH at H. With F as the center and a radius FP, intersect AB at K. Draw a perpendicular to AB from K intersecting JH at J. H and J will be the centers for arcs tangent to the three lines.

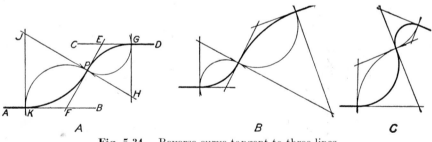

Fig. 5.34. Reverse curve tangent to three lines.

5.29 To lay out a given angle. *Tangent method.* Fig. 5.35. The trigonometrical tangent of an angle is the ratio of the side opposite divided by the side adjacent. Thus, $Y/X = \tan A$, or $X \tan A = Y$. To lay out a given angle, obtain the value of the tangent from a table of natural tangents, assume any convenient distance X, and multiply X by the tangent to get distance Y. Note that the angle between the sides X and Y must be a right angle.

5.30 To lay out a given angle. *Chordal method.* Fig. 5.36. If the length of the chord is known for an arc of given radius and included angle, the angle may be accurately laid out. Given an angle in degrees, to lay out the angle: Obtain the chord length for a 1-in. circle arc from the table on page 649, Appendix. Select any convenient arc length *R* and multiply the

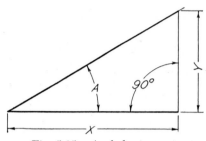

Fig. 5.35. Angle by tangent.

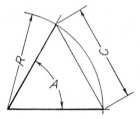

Fig. 5.36. Angle by chord.

chord length for a 1-in. arc by this distance, thus obtaining the chord length *C* for the radius distance selected. Lay out the chord length on the arc with compasses or dividers and complete the sides of the angle.

The chord length for an angle may be had from a sine table by taking the sine of half the given angle and multiplying by two.

5.31 To divide a line. *First method.* Fig. 5.37. To divide a line *AB* into, say, five equal parts, draw any line *BC* of indefinite length; on it measure, or step off, five divisions of convenient length; connect the last point with *A* and, using triangles and a straightedge as shown in Fig. 4.7, draw lines through the points parallel to *CA* intersecting *AB*.

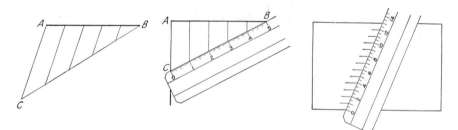

Fig. 5.37   Fig. 5.38   Fig. 5.39
Figs. 5.37 to 5.39. To divide a line.

Second method. Figs. 5.38 and 5.39. First, draw a perpendicular *AC* from *A*; then place a scale so that five convenient equal divisions are included between *B* and the perpendicular, as in Fig. 5.38. With a triangle and T square draw perpendiculars through the points marked, thus dividing the line *AB* as required. Figure 5.39 illustrates an application in laying off

stair risers. This method may be used for dividing a
line into any series of proportional parts.

**5.32 To construct a triangle having given the
three sides.** Fig. 5.40. Given the lengths A, B,
and C. Draw one side A in the desired position.
With its ends as centers and radii B and C, draw
two intersecting arcs as shown. This construction
is used extensively in developments by triangulation.

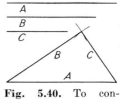

Fig.   5.40. To construct a triangle.

5.33 To transfer a polygon to a new base. *By triangulation.* Fig. 5.41.
Given polygon $ABCDEF$ and a new position of base $A'B'$. Consider each
point as the vertex of a triangle whose base is AB. With centers A' and
B' and radii AC and BC, describe intersecting arcs locating the point C'.
Similarly, with radii AD and BD locate point D'. Connect $B'C'$ and $C'D'$
and continue the operation always using A and B as centers.

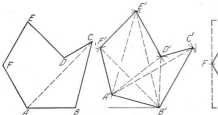

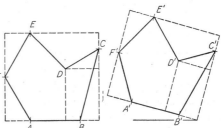

Fig. 5.41. To transfer a polygon—by
triangulation.

Fig. 5.42. To transfer a polygon—box or
offset method.

Box or offset method. Fig. 5.42. Enclose the polygon in a rectangular
"box." Draw the box on the new base (method of Fig. 4.8), locate the
points $ABCEF$ on this box; then set point D by rectangular coordinates as
shown.

5.34 Uses of the diagonal. The diagonal may be used in many ways
to simplify construction and save drafting time. Figure 5.43 illustrates the

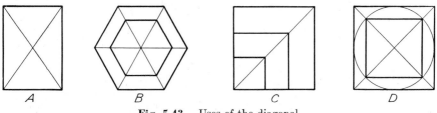

Fig. 5.43. Uses of the diagonal.

diagonal used at A for locating the center of a rectangle, at B for enlarging
or reducing a geometrical shape, at C for producing similar figures having the
same base, and at D for drawing inscribed or circumscribed figures.

5.35 To construct a regular hexagon, given the distance across corners.
First method. Fig. 5.44. Draw a circle on AB as a diameter. With the same radius and A and B as centers, draw arcs intersecting the circle and connect the points.

Second method (without compasses). Draw lines with the 30°-60° triangle in the order shown in Fig. 5.45.

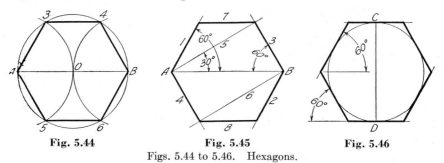

Fig. 5.44   Fig. 5.45   Fig. 5.46
Figs. 5.44 to 5.46. Hexagons.

Given the distance across flats. The distance across flats is the diameter of the inscribed circle. Draw this circle, and with the 30°-60° triangle draw tangents to it as in Fig. 5.46.

5.36 To inscribe a regular pentagon in a circle. Fig. 5.47. Draw a diameter AB and a radius OC perpendicular to it. Bisect OB. With this point D as center and a radius DC, draw arc CE. With center C and radius CE, draw arc EF. CF is the side of the pentagon. Step off this distance around the circle with the dividers. Instead of using this geometrical method, most draftsmen prefer to guess at CF and divide the circle by trial as described in paragraph 4.13.

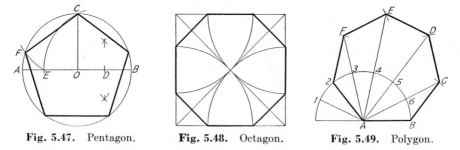

Fig. 5.47. Pentagon.   Fig. 5.48. Octagon.   Fig. 5.49. Polygon.

5.37 To draw a regular octagon in a square. Fig. 5.48. Draw the diagonals of the square. With the corners of the square as centers and a radius of half the diagonal, draw arcs intersecting the sides of the square and connect these points.

5.38 To construct a regular polygon, given one side. Fig. 5.49. Let the polygon have seven sides. With the side AB as a radius and A as the center, draw a semicircle and divide into seven equal parts with dividers. Through the second division from the left draw radial line A-2. Through points 3, 4, 5, and 6 extend radial lines as shown. With AB as the radius and B as the center, cut line A-6 at C. With C as the center and the same radius, cut A-5 at D, and so on at E and F. Connect the points *or*, after A-2 is found, draw the circumscribing circle.

5.39   To lay off on a straight line the approximate length of a circle arc. Fig. 5.50. Given the arc AB. At A draw the tangent AD and the chord

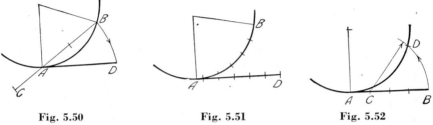

Fig. 5.50   **Fig. 5.51**   **Fig. 5.52**

Figs. 5.50 to 5.52.   Lengths of arcs.

produced, BA. Lay off AC equal to half the chord AB. With center C and radius CB, draw an arc intersecting AD at D; then AD will be equal in length to the arc AB (very nearly).[1] If the given arc is between 45° and 90°, a closer approximation will result by making AC equal to the chord of half the arc instead of half the chord of the arc.

The usual way of rectifying an arc is to set the dividers to a space small enough to be practically equal in length to the corresponding arc. Starting at B, step along the arc to the point nearest A and, without lifting the dividers, step off the same number of spaces on the tangent, as shown in Fig. 5.51.

5.40   To lay off on a given circle the approximate length of a straight line. Fig. 5.52. Given the line AB tangent to the circle at A. Lay off AC equal to one-fourth AB. With C as a center and a radius CB, draw an arc intersecting the circle at D. The arc AD is equal in length to AB (very nearly).[1] If arc AD is greater than 60°, solve for one-half AB.

5.41   Conic sections. In cutting a right circular cone (a cone of revolution) by planes at different angles, four curves called *conic sections* are obtained, Fig. 5.53. These are the *circle*, cut by a plane perpendicular to the

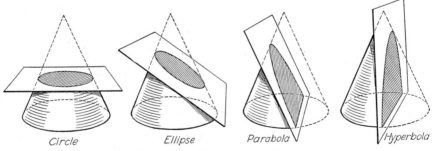

Circle   Ellipse   Parabola   Hyperbola

Fig. 5.53.   The conic sections.

[1] In this (Professor Rankine's) solution, the error varies as the fourth power of the subtended angle. For 60° the line will be $\frac{1}{900}$ part short, while at 30° it will be only 1/14,400 part short.

axis; the *ellipse*, cut by a plane making a greater angle with the axis than do the elements; the *parabola*, cut by a plane making the same angle with the axis as do the elements; the *hyperbola*, cut by a plane making a smaller angle than do the elements. These curves are studied mathematically in analytic geometry, but may be drawn without a knowledge of their equations by knowing something of their characteristics.

5.42 The ellipse—major and minor axes. Fig. 5.54. An ellipse is the plane curve generated by a point moving so that the sum of its distances from two fixed points (F_1 and F_2), called "focuses," is a constant equal to the long diameter, or major axis AB.

The minor axis, or short diameter, DE is the line through the center perpendicular to the major axis. The focuses may be determined by cutting the major axis with an arc having its center at an end of the minor axis and a radius equal to one-half the major axis.

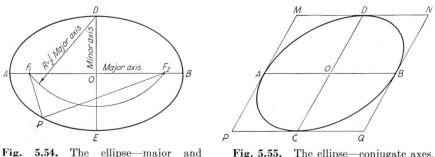

Fig. 5.54. The ellipse—major and minor axes.

Fig. 5.55. The ellipse—conjugate axes.

Aside from the circle, the ellipse is met with in practice much more often than any of the other conics, and draftsmen should be able to construct it readily; hence several methods are given for its construction, both as a true ellipse and as an approximate curve made by circle arcs. In the great majority of cases when this curve is required, its long and short diameters, that is, its major and minor axes, are known.

5.43 The ellipse—conjugate axes. Fig. 5.55. Any line through the center of an ellipse may serve as one of a pair of conjugate axes. A property of conjugate axes is that each is parallel to the tangents to the curve at the extremities of the other. AB and CD are a pair of conjugate axes having AB parallel to the tangents MN and PQ and CD parallel to the tangents MP and NQ. A given ellipse may have an unlimited number of pairs of conjugate axes. Also, either one of a pair of conjugate axes bisects all the chords parallel to the other.

To determine the major and minor axes of a given ellipse, a pair of conjugate axes being given. First method. Fig. 5.56. Given the conjugate axes CN and JG. With a center O and radius OJ, draw a semicircle intersecting the ellipse at P. The major and minor axes will be parallel to the chords GP and JP, respectively.

Second method when the curve is not given. Fig. 5.57.   Given the conjugate axes *CN* and *JG*.   With a center *O* and radius *OJ*, describe a circle and draw the diameter *QR* at right angles to *JG*.   Bisect the angle *QCR*. The major axis will be parallel to this bisector and equal in length to *CR* + *CQ*.   The length of the minor axis will be *CR* − *CQ*.

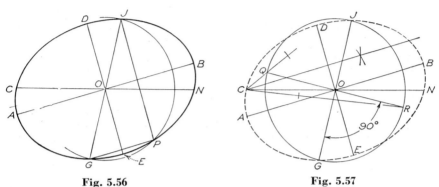

Fig. 5.56   **Fig. 5.57**

Figs. 5.56 and 5.57.   The ellipse—conjugate axes.

5.44   Ellipse—pin-and-string method.   This well-known method, sometimes called the "gardener's ellipse," is often used for large work and is based on the definition of the ellipse.   Drive pins at the points *D*, F_1, and F_2, Fig. 5.54, and tie an inelastic thread or cord tightly around the three pins. If the pin *D* is removed and a marking point moved in the loop, keeping the cord taut, it will describe a true ellipse.

5.45   Ellipse—trammel method, for major and minor axes.   *First method.*   Fig. 5.58.   On the straight edge of a strip of paper, thin cardboard,

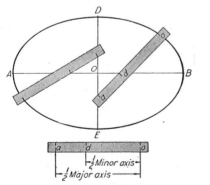

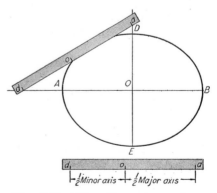

Fig. 5.58. The ellipse—trammel, first method.

Fig. 5.59. The ellipse—trammel, second method.

or sheet of celluloid, mark the distance *ao* equal to one-half the major axis and *do* equal to one-half the minor axis.   If the strip is moved, keeping *a* on the minor axis and d on the major axis, o will give points on the ellipse. This method will be found very convenient, as no construction is required, but for accurate results, great care must be taken to keep the points a and d exactly on the axes. The ellipsograph, Fig. 35.6, is constructed on the principle of this method.

Second method. Fig. 5.59. On some suitable material as in the first method, mark the distance do equal to one-half the minor axis and oa equal to one-half the major axis. If this strip is moved, keeping a on the minor axis and d on the major axis, o will give points on the ellipse. This arrangement is preferred where the ratio between the major and minor axes is small.

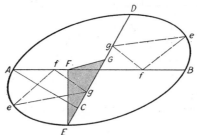

Fig. 5.60. The ellipse—triangle trammel for conjugate axes.

5.46 Ellipse—triangle trammel, for conjugate axes. Fig. 5.60. Given the conjugate axes AB and DE. Erect the perpendicular AC to the axis ED and lay off distance AC from E to locate point G. Erect the perpendicular EF to the axis AB. Transfer to a piece of paper, thin cardboard, or sheet of celluloid and cut out the triangle EFG. If this triangle is moved keeping f on AB and g on ED, e will give points on the ellipse. Extreme care must be used to keep points f and g on the axes.

5.47 Ellipse—concentric-circle method, for major and minor axes. Fig. 5.61. This is perhaps the most accurate method for determining points

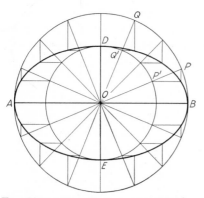

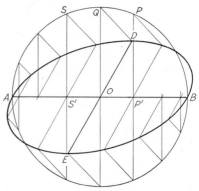

Fig. 5.61. The ellipse—concentric-circle method.

Fig. 5.62. The ellipse—circle method.

on the curve. On the two principal diameters, which intersect at O, describe circles. From a number of points on the outer circle, as P and Q, draw radii OP, OQ, etc., intersecting the inner circle at P', Q', etc. From P and Q draw lines parallel to OD, and from P' and Q' draw lines parallel to OB. The intersection of the lines through P and P' gives one point on the ellipse, the intersection of the lines through Q and Q' another point, and so on. For accuracy, the points should be taken closer together toward the major axis. The process may be repeated in each of the four quadrants and the curve sketched in lightly freehand; or one quadrant only may be constructed and the remaining three repeated by marking the french curve.

5.48 Ellipse—circle method, for conjugate axes. Fig. 5.62. Given the conjugate axes AB and DE. On the conjugate axis AB describe a circle, then from a number of points as P, Q, and S draw perpendiculars as QO to the axis AB. From S and P, etc., draw lines parallel to QD, and from S' and P' draw lines parallel to OD. The intersection of the lines through P and P' gives one point on the ellipse, the intersection of the lines through S and S' another point, and so on.

5.49 Ellipse—parallelogram method. Figs. 5.63 and 5.64. This method may be used either with the major and minor axes or with any pair

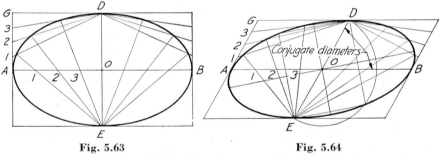

Fig. 5.63   Fig. 5.64

Figs. 5.63 and 5.64.   The ellipse—parallelogram method.

of conjugate axes. On the axes construct a parallelogram. Divide AO into any number of equal parts and AG into the same number of equal parts, numbering points from A. Through these points draw lines from D and E, as shown. Their intersections will be points on the curve.

5.50 To draw a tangent to an ellipse. (1) *At a point P on the curve.* Fig. 5.65. Draw lines from the point to the focuses. The line bisecting the exterior angle of these focal radii is the required tangent.

(2) *Parallel to a given line GH.* Fig. 5.65. Draw F_1E perpendicular to GH. With F_2 as the center and a radius AB, draw an arc

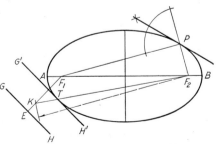

Fig. 5.65.   Tangents to an ellipse.

cutting F_1E at K. The line F_2K cuts the ellipse at the required point of tangency T, and the required tangent passes through T parallel to GH.

(3) *From a point outside.* Fig. 5.66. Find the focuses F_1 and F_2. With given point P and a radius PF_2, draw the arc RF_2Q. With F_1 as the center and a radius AB, strike an arc cutting this arc at Q and R. Connect QF_1 and RF_1. The intersections of these lines with the ellipse at T_1 and T_2 will be the tangent points of tangents to the ellipse from P.

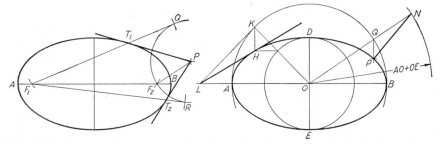

Fig. 5.66. Tangent from point outside. **Fig. 5.67.** Tangent and normal to an ellipse.

(4) *Concentric-circle method.* When the ellipse has been drawn by the concentric-circle method, Fig. 5.67, a tangent at any point H may be drawn by drawing a line perpendicular to AB from the point to the outer circle at K and drawing the auxiliary tangent KL to the outer circle, cutting the major axis at L. From L draw the required tangent LH.

5.51 To draw a normal to an ellipse. Fig. 5.67. From point P on the curve, project a parallel to the minor axis to intersect the major axis circle at Q. Draw OQ extended to intersect (at N) an arc with center at O and radius $AO + OE$. NP is the required normal.

Or, normals may be drawn perpendicular to the tangents of Figs. 5.65 and 5.66.

5.52 Approximate four-centered ellipse. Fig. 5.68. Join A and D. Lay off DF equal to $AO - DO$. Bisect AF by a perpendicular crossing AO at G and intersecting DE produced (if necessary) at H. Make OG' equal

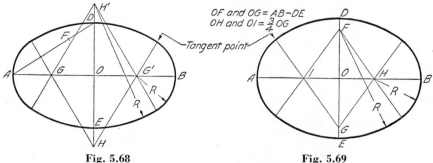

Fig. 5.68   **Fig. 5.69**
Figs. 5.68 and 5.69. Approximate ellipses, four centers.

to OG and OH' equal to OH. Then G, G', H, and H' will be centers for four tangent circle arcs forming a curve approximating the shape of an ellipse.

Another method is shown in Fig. 5.69. This should be used only when the minor axis is at least two-thirds the length of the major axis.

5.53 Approximate eight-centered ellipse. Fig. 5.70. When a closer approximation is desired, the eight-centered ellipse, the upper half of which is known in masonry as the "five-centered arch," may be constructed. Draw the rectangle $AFDO$. Draw the diagonal AD and the line from F perpendicular to it, intersecting the extension of the minor axis at H. Lay off OK equal to OD and, on AK as a diameter, draw a semicircle intersecting the extension of the minor axis at L. Make OM equal to LD. With a center H and radius HM, draw the arc MN. From A, along AB, lay off AQ equal to OL. With P as the center and a radius PQ, draw an arc intersecting MN at N; then P, N, and H are centers for one-quarter of the eight-centered approximate ellipse.

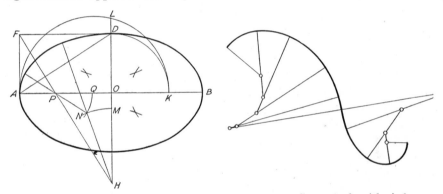

Fig. 5.70. Approximate ellipse, 8 centers.   **Fig. 5.71.** Curve made with circle arcs.

It should be noted that an ellipse is changing its radius of curvature at every successive point and that these approximations are therefore not ellipses, but simply curves of the same general shape and, incidentally, not nearly so pleasing in appearance.

5.54 Any noncircular curve may be approximated by tangent circle arcs, as follows: select a center by trial, draw as much of an arc as will practically coincide with the curve, and then, changing the center and radius, draw the next portion, remembering always that, *if arcs are to be tangent, their centers must lie on the common normal at the point of tangency.* Draftsmen sometimes prefer to ink curves in this way rather than to use irregular curves. Figure 5.71 illustrates the construction.

5.55 The parabola. The parabola is a plane curve generated by a point so moving that its distance from a fixed point, called the *focus*, is always equal to its distance from a straight line, called the *directrix*. Among its practical applications are included searchlights, parabolic reflectors, some loud-speakers, road sections, and certain bridge arches.

When the focus F and the directrix AB are given, Fig. 5.72, draw the axis through F perpendicular to AB. Through any point D on the axis, draw a line parallel to AB. With the distance DO as radius and F as a center, draw an arc intersecting the line, thus locating a point P on the curve. Repeat the operation as many times as needed.

To draw a tangent at any point P. Draw PQ parallel to the axis and bisect the angle FPQ.

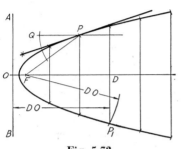 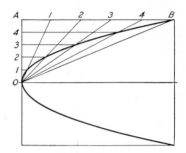

Fig. 5.72   Fig. 5.73

Figs. 5.72 and 5.73.   Methods of drawing the parabola.

5.56 Parabola—parallelogram method. Usually when a parabola is required, the dimensions of the enclosing rectangle, that is, the width and depth of the parabola (or span and rise), are given, as in Fig. 5.73. Divide OA and AB into the same number of equal parts. From the divisions on AB, draw lines converging at O. The intersections of these with the lines from the corresponding divisions on OA that are drawn parallel to the axis will be points on the curve.

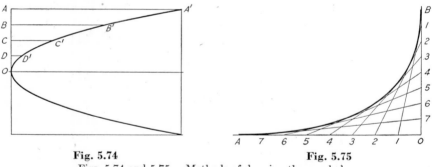

Fig. 5.74   Fig. 5.75

Figs. 5.74 and 5.75.   Methods of drawing the parabola.

5.57 Parabola—offset method. Given the enclosing rectangle, the parabola, Fig. 5.74, may be plotted by computing the offsets from the line OA. These offsets vary in length as the square of their distances from O. Thus, if OA is divided into four parts, DD' will be one-sixteenth of AA'; CC', since it is twice as far from O as DD' is, will be four-sixteenths of AA'; and BB', nine-sixteenths. If OA had been divided into five parts, the relations would be $\frac{1}{25}$, $\frac{4}{25}$, $\frac{9}{25}$, and $\frac{16}{25}$, the denominator in each case being the square of the number of divisions. This method is the one generally used by civil engineers in drawing parabolic arches.

5.58 Parabolic envelope. Fig. 5.75. This method of drawing a pleasing curve is often used in machine design. Divide OA and OB into the same number of equal parts. Number the divisions from O and B and connect corresponding numbers. The tangent curve will be a portion of a parabola, but a parabola whose axis is not parallel to either ordinate.

5.59 The hyperbola. The hyperbola is a plane curve generated by a point moving so that the difference of its distances from two fixed points, called the "focuses," is a constant. (Compare this definition with that of the ellipse.)

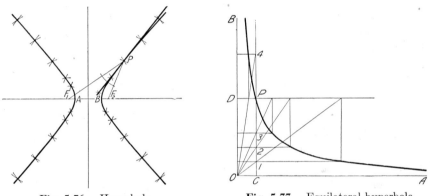

Fig. 5.76. Hyperbola.   **Fig. 5.77.** Equilateral hyperbola.

To draw a hyperbola when the focuses F_1F_2 and the transverse axis AB (constant difference) are given. Fig. 5.76. With F_1 and F_2 as centers and any radius greater than F_1B, as F_1P, draw arcs. With the same centers, and radius $F_1P - AB$, strike arcs intersecting these arcs, giving points on the curve.

To draw a tangent at any point P, bisect the angle F_1PF_2.

5.60 Equilateral hyperbola. The case of the hyperbola of commonest practical interest to the engineer is the equilateral, or rectangular, hyperbola referred to its asymptotes. With it the law $pv = c$, connecting the varying pressure and volume of a portion of steam or gas, can be graphically presented.

To draw the equilateral hyperbola. Fig. 5.77. Let OA and OB be the asymptotes of the curve, and P any point on it (this might be the point of cutoff on an indicator diagram). Draw PC and PD. Mark any points 1, 2, 3, etc., on PC and through these points draw a system of lines parallel to OA, and a second system through the same points converging to O. From the intersections of these lines of the second system with PD extended, draw perpendiculars to OA. The intersections of these perpendiculars with the corresponding lines of the first system give points on the curve.

5.61   Cycloidal curves.   A cycloid is the curve generated by the motion of a point on the circumference of a circle rolled in a plane along a straight line.   If the circle is rolled on the outside of another circle, the curve generated is called an "epicycloid"; if rolled on the inside, it is called a "hypocycloid."   These curves are used in drawing the cycloid system of gear teeth.

To draw a cycloid.   Fig: 5.78.   Divide the rolling circle into a convenient number of parts (say, eight) and, using these divisions, lay off on the tangent *AB* the rectified length of the circumference.   Draw through *C* the line of

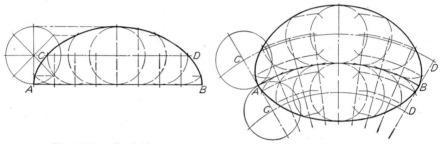

Fig. 5.78.   Cycloid.   **Fig. 5.79.**   Epicycloid and hypocycloid.

centers *CD*, and project the division points up to this line by perpendiculars to *AB*.   About these points as centers, draw circles representing different positions of the rolling circle, and project in order the division points of the original circle across to these circles.   The intersections thus determined will be points on the curve.   The epicycloid and hypocycloid may be drawn similarly, as illustrated in Fig. 5.79.

5.62   The involute.   An involute is the spiral curve traced by a point on a taut cord unwinding from around a polygon or circle.   Thus, the

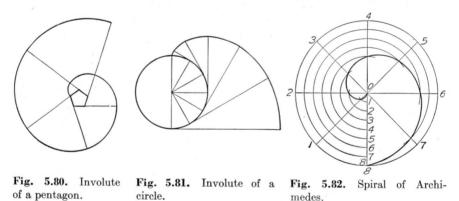

Fig. 5.80. Involute   **Fig. 5.81.** Involute of a   **Fig. 5.82.** Spiral of Archi-
of a pentagon.   circle.   medes.

involute of any polygon may be drawn by extending its sides, as in Fig. 5.80, and, with the corners of the polygon as successive centers, drawing arcs terminating on the extended sides.

In drawing a spiral in design, as, for example, of bent ironwork, the easiest way is to draw it as the involute of a square.

A circle may be conceived as a polygon of an infinite number of sides. Thus, to draw the involute of a circle, Fig. 5.81, divide it into a convenient number of parts, draw tangents at these points, lay off on these tangents the rectified lengths of the arcs from the point of tangency to the starting point, and connect the points by a smooth curve. The involute of the circle is the basis for the involute system of gearing.

5.63   The spiral of Archimedes.   The spiral of Archimedes is the plane curve generated by a point moving uniformly along a straight line while the line revolves about a fixed point with uniform angular velocity.

To draw a spiral of Archimedes that makes one turn in a given circle, Fig. 5.82, divide the circle into a number of equal parts, drawing the radii and numbering them.   Divide the radius *0-8* into the same number of equal parts, numbering from the center.   With *0* as a center, draw concentric arcs intersecting the radii of corresponding numbers, and draw a smooth curve through these intersections.   The Archimedean spiral is the curve of the heart cam used for converting uniform rotary motion into uniform reciprocal motion.

5.64   The helix.   The helix is a space curve generated by a point moving uniformly along a straight line while the line revolves uniformly about another line as an axis.   If the moving line is parallel to the axis, it will generate a cylinder.   The word "helix" alone always means a cylindrical helix.   If the moving line intersects the axis at an angle less than 90°, it will generate a cone, and the curve made by the point moving on it will be a "conical helix."   The distance parallel to the axis through which the point advances in one revolution is called the "lead."   When the angle becomes 90°, the helix degenerates into the Archimedean spiral.

5.65   To draw a helix.   Fig. 5.83.   Draw the two views of the cylinder and measure the lead along one of the contour elements.   Divide this lead

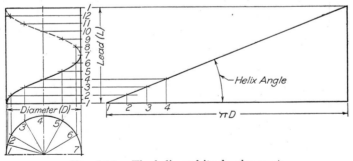

Fig. 5.83.   The helix and its development.

into a number of equal parts (say, 12), and the circle of the front view into the same number.   Number the divisions on the top view starting at point 1, and the divisions on the front view starting at the front view of point 1.

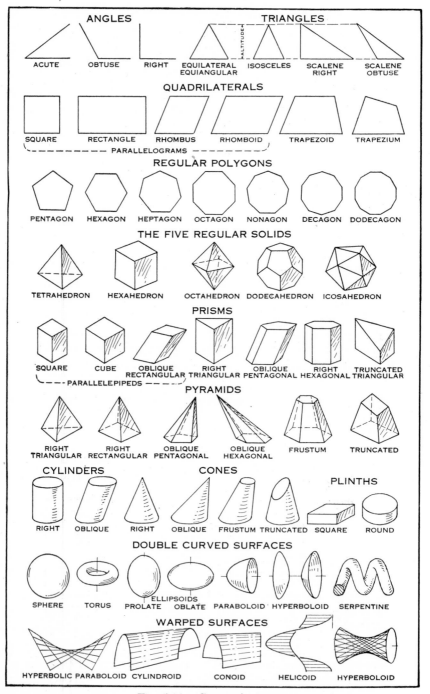

Fig. 5.84. Geometric shapes.

When the generating point has moved one-twelfth of the distance around the cylinder, it has also advanced one-twelfth of the lead; when halfway around the cylinder, it will have advanced one-half the lead. Thus, points on the top view of the helix may be found by projecting the front views of the elements, which are points on the circular front view of the helix, to intersect lines drawn across from the corresponding divisions of the lead. The conical helix is drawn similarly, the lead being measured along the axis. If the cylinder is developed, the helix will appear on the development as a straight line inclined to the base at an angle, called the "helix angle," whose tangent is $L/\pi D$, where L is the lead and D the diameter.

PROBLEMS

To be of value both as drawing exercises and as solutions, geometrical problems should be worked very accurately. The pencil must be kept very sharp, and comparatively light lines must be used. A point should be located by two intersecting lines, and the length of a line should be indicated by short dashes across the line. The following problems are dimensioned to fit in a space of not over 5 by 7 in., except as noted. Thus, either one or two may be drawn on a standard 8½- by 11-in. sheet, and either two or four on an 11- by 17-in. sheet.

Lines and Plane Figures

1. Near the center of the space, draw a horizontal line 4½ in. long. Divide it into seven equal parts by the method of Fig. 5.38.

2. Draw a vertical line 1 in. from the left edge of the space and 3⅞ in. long. Divide it into parts proportional to 1, 3, 5, and 7.

3. Construct a polygon as shown in Fig. 5.85, drawing the horizontal line AK, of indefinite length, ⅝ in. above the bottom of the space. From A draw and measure AB. Proceed in the same way for the remaining sides. The angles may be obtained by proper combinations of the two triangles, see Figs. 4.5 and 4.6.

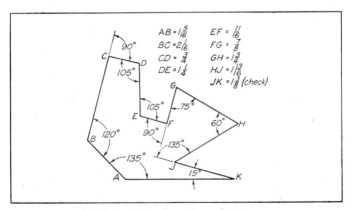

Fig. 5.85. Irregular polygon.

4. Draw line AK making an angle of 15° with the horizontal. With this line as a base, transfer the polygon of Fig. 5.85.

5. Draw a regular hexagon having a distance across corners of 4 in.

6. Draw a regular hexagon, distance across flats 3⅜ in.

7. Draw a regular dodecagon, distance across flats 3⅜ in.

Tangent Problems

These problems are given for practice in the accurate joining of tangent lines.   Read carefully paragraphs 5.11 and 5.28 before beginning.

8. Draw the offset swivel plate, Fig. 5.86.

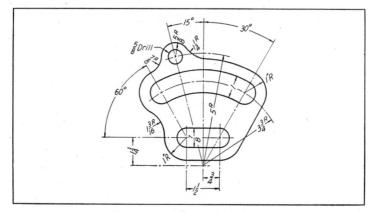

Fig. 5.86.   Offset swivel plate.

9. Draw two lines AB and AC making an included angle of 30°.   Locate point P, 4 in. from A and $\frac{1}{2}$ in. from line AB.   Draw a circle arc through point P and tangent to lines AB and CD.   Two solutions.

10. Construct an ogee curve joining two parallel lines AB and CD as in Fig. 5.32, making $X = 4$ in., $Y = 2\frac{1}{2}$ in., and $BE = 3$ in.   Consider this as the center line for a rod $1\frac{1}{4}$ in. in diameter and draw the rod.

11. Make the contour view of the bracket shown in Fig. 5.87.   In the upper ogee curve, the radii R_1 and R_2 are equal.   In the lower one, R_3 is twice R_4.

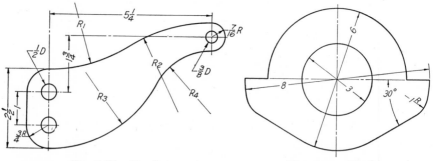

Fig. 5.87.   Bracket.   **Fig. 5.88.**   Washer.

12. Draw an arc of a circle having a radius of $3^{13}\!/_{16}$ in., with its center $\frac{1}{2}$ in. from the top of the space and $1\frac{1}{4}$ in. from the left edge.   Find the length of an arc of 60° by construction; compute the length arithmetically and check the result.

13. Front view of *washer*, Fig. 5.88.   Draw half size.

14. Front view of *shim*, Fig. 5.89.   Draw full size.

15. Front view of *rod guide*, Fig. 5.90.   Draw full size.

16. Front view of a *star knob*, Fig. 5.91.   Radius of circumscribing circle $2\frac{3}{8}$ in. Diameter of hub $2\frac{1}{2}$ in.   Diameter of hole $\frac{3}{4}$ in.   Radius at points $\frac{3}{8}$ in.   Radius of fillets $\frac{3}{8}$ in.   Mark tangent points in pencil.

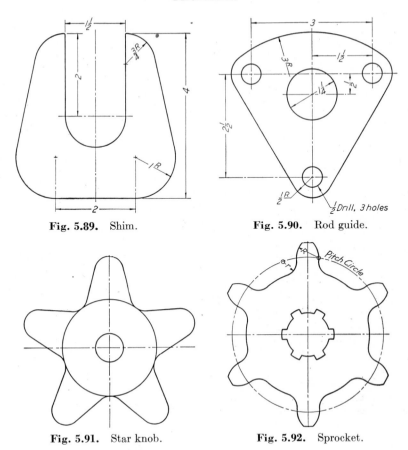

Fig. 5.89. Shim.

Fig. 5.90. Rod guide.

Fig. 5.91. Star knob.

Fig. 5.92. Sprocket.

17. Front view of a *sprocket*, Fig. 5.92. Outside diameter 4¾ in., pitch diameter 4 in., root diameter 3¼ in., bore 1¼ in. Thickness of tooth at the pitch line is 9/16 in. Splines ¼ in. wide by ⅛ in. deep. Mark tangent points in pencil.

18. Front view of a *fan*, Fig. 5.93. Draw full size to dimensions given (9- by 9-in. space).

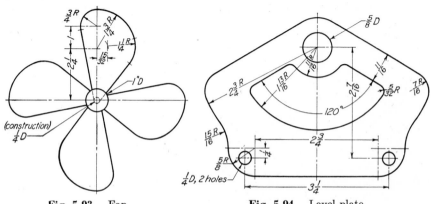

Fig. 5.93. Fan.

Fig. 5.94. Level plate.

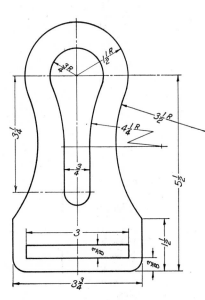

Fig. 5.95.   Eyelet.

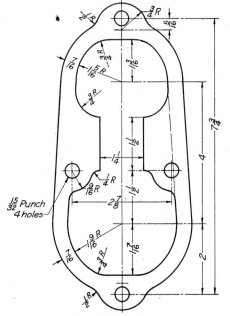

Fig. 5.96.   Stamping.

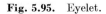

Fig. 5.97.   Cam.

Fig. 5.98.   Fan base.

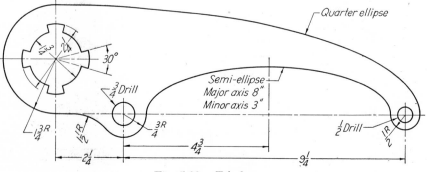

Fig. 5.99.   Trip lever.

19. Front view of a *level plate*, Fig. 5.94.   Draw to full size.

20. Front view of an *eyelet*, Fig. 5.95.   Draw to dimensions given (5- by 8-in. space).

21. Front view of a *stamping*, Fig. 5.96.   Draw to dimensions given (5- by 9-in. space).

22. Front view of a *cam*, Fig. 5.97.

23. Front view of a drawn-metal *fan base*, Fig. 5.98.   The curve profile is a parabolic envelope.   Refer to Fig. 5.75.

24. Front view of *trip lever*, Fig. 5.99.   Draw half size.

25. Front view of *spline lock*, Fig. 5.100.

26. Front view of gage *cover plate*, Fig. 5.101.

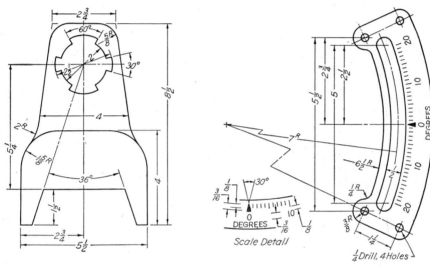

Fig. 5.100.   Spline lock.   **Fig. 5.101.**   Gage cover plate.

Curve Problems

In locating a curve, the number of points to be determined will depend upon the size of the curve and the rate of change of curvature.   More points should be found on the sharp turns.   For most of the following problems, points may average about $\frac{1}{4}$ in. apart.

27. Draw an ellipse having a major axis of $4\frac{1}{2}$ in. and minor axis of 3 in., using the trammel method as explained in paragraph 5.45, *first method*.

28. Draw an ellipse having a major axis of $4\frac{1}{2}$ in. and minor axis of 4 in., using the trammel method as explained in paragraph 5.45, *second method*.

29. Draw an ellipse having a major axis of $4\frac{5}{8}$ in. and minor axis of $1\frac{1}{2}$ in., using the concentric-circle method as explained in paragraph 5.47.

30. Draw an ellipse on a major axis of 4 in.   One point on the ellipse is $1\frac{1}{2}$ in. to the left of the minor axis and $\frac{7}{8}$ in. above the major axis.

31. Draw an ellipse whose minor axis is $2\frac{3}{16}$ in. and distance between focuses is $3\frac{1}{4}$ in.   Draw a tangent at a point $1\frac{3}{8}$ in. to the right of the minor axis.

32. Draw an ellipse, major axis 4 in.   A tangent to the ellipse intersects the minor axis $1\frac{3}{4}$ in. from the center, at an angle of 60°.

33. Draw a five-centered arch with a span of 5 in. and a rise of 2 in.   Refer to paragraph 5.53.

34. Draw an ellipse having conjugate axes of $4\frac{3}{4}$ in. and $2\frac{3}{4}$ in. making an angle of 75° with each other.   Determine the major and minor axes.

35. Draw the major and minor axes for an ellipse having a pair of conjugate diameters 60° apart, one horizontal and $6\frac{1}{4}$ in. long, the other $3\frac{1}{4}$ in. long.

36. Draw an ellipse having a pair of conjugate axes, one making 15° with the horizontal and 6 in. long, the other making 60° with the first axis and $2\frac{1}{2}$ in. long, using the *circle method* as explained in paragraph 5.48.

37. Draw an ellipse having a pair of conjugate axes 60° apart, one horizontal and 6 in. long, the other 4 in. long, using the *triangle trammel method* as explained in paragraph 5.46.

38. Draw an ellipse having a pair of conjugate axes 45° apart, one making 15° with the horizontal and 6 in. long, the other 3 in. long, using the triangle trammel method as explained in paragraph 5.46.

39. Draw a parabola, axis vertical, in a rectangle 4 by 2 in.

40. Draw a parabolic arch, with 6-in. span and $2\frac{1}{2}$-in. rise, by the offset method, dividing the half span into eight equal parts.

41. Draw an equilateral hyperbola passing through a point P, $\frac{1}{2}$ in. from OB and $2\frac{1}{2}$ in. from OA. (Reference letters correspond to Fig. 5.77.)

42. Draw two turns of the involute of a pentagon whose circumscribed circle is $\frac{1}{2}$ in. in diameter.

43. Draw one-half turn of the involute of a circle $3\frac{1}{4}$ in. in diameter whose center is 1 in. from the left edge of space. Compute the length of the last tangent and compare with the measured length.

44. Draw a spiral of Archimedes making one turn in a circle 4 in. in diameter.

45. Draw the cycloid formed by a rolling circle 2 in. in diameter. Use 12 divisions.

46. Draw the epicycloid formed by a 2-in.-diameter circle rolling on a 15-in.-diameter directing circle. Use 12 divisions.

47. Draw the hypocycloid formed by a 2-in.-diameter circle rolling inside a 15-in.-diameter directing circle. Use 12 divisions.

6

Orthographic Projection

6.1   The previous chapters have been preparatory to the real subject
of engineering drawing as a language.   In Chap. 1 attention was directed
to the difference between the representation of an object by the artist, in
which he seeks to convey certain impressions or emotions, and the representation by the engineer, where the main intent is to convey information.
The facts required from the engineer include the description of the *shape*
of the object and the specification of the *size* of every detail.   In this
chapter we are concerned with the method of describing *shape*.

Orthographic projection provides a means of describing the exact shape
of any material object.   Practically, the drawing is made up of a set of
separate views of the object taken by the observer from different positions

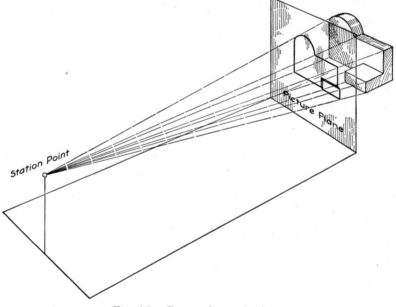

Fig. 6.1.   Perspective projection.

and arranged relative to each other in a definite way.   Each of these views
will show the shape of the object for a particular view direction, and a
combination of two or more views will completely describe the object.

6.2   Fundamental theory.   On the supposition that a transparent plane
may be set up between an object and the station point of an observer's eye,
Fig. 6.1, the intersection of this plane with the rays formed by lines of sight

97

from the eye to all points of the object will give a picture that will be practically the same as the image formed in the eye of the observer.

If the observer will then imagine himself as walking backward from the station point until he reaches a theoretically *infinite* distance, the rays formed by lines of sight from his eye to the object will grow longer and finally become infinite in length, *parallel to each other*, and perpendicular to the picture plane. The picture so formed on the picture plane is what is known as orthographic projection. See Fig. 6.2.

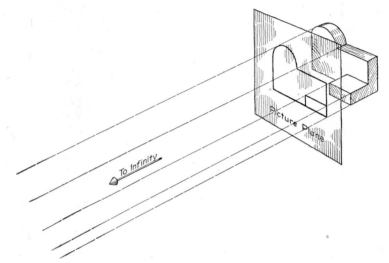

Fig. 6.2. Orthographic projection (projection on a plane with station point at infinity).

6.3 Definition. Basically, orthographic[1] projection could be defined as any single projection made by dropping perpendiculars to a plane. However, it has been accepted through long usage and common consent to mean the combination of two or more such views, hence the following definition: *Orthographic projection is the method of representing the exact shape of an object in two or more views on planes generally at right angles to each other, by extending perpendiculars from the object to the planes.* (The term orthogonal[2] is sometimes used for this system of drawing.)

6.4 Orthographic views. As stated in the definition just given, the rays from the picture plane to infinity, as described in paragraph 6.3, may be discarded and the picture or "view" thought of as being found by extending perpendiculars to the plane from all points of the object as shown in Fig. 6.3. This picture, or projection on a frontal plane, will show the shape of the object when viewed from the front, but it will not tell the shape or distance from front to back; hence more than one projection will be required to describe the object.

---

[1] Right-writing.
[2] Right-angled.

In addition to the frontal plane, another transparent plane is then imagined as placed horizontally above the object, as in Fig. 6.4. The projection on this plane, found by extending perpendiculars to it from the object, will give the appearance of the object as if viewed from directly above, and will show the distance front to rear. If this horizontal plane is now revolved into coincidence with the vertical plane, as in Fig. 6.5, the

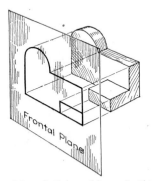

Fig. 6.3. Orthographic projection.

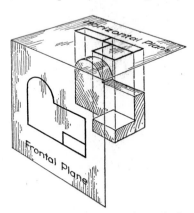

Fig. 6.4. Frontal and horizontal planes of projection.

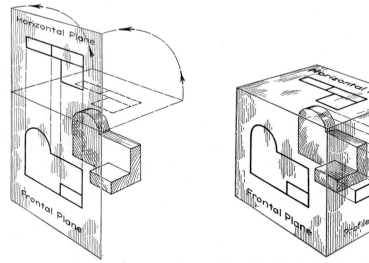

Fig. 6.5. The horizontal plane revolved.　　Fig. 6.6. The three planes of projection.

two views of the object will then be in the same plane, as if on a sheet of paper. A third plane, called a profile plane, may be imagined, perpendicular to the first two, Fig. 6.6, and on it a third view may be projected. The third view will show the shape of the object when viewed from the side and the distance bottom to top and front to rear. The horizontal and profile planes are shown revolved into the same plane as the frontal plane (again thought of as the plane of the drawing paper), in Fig. 6.7; moreover, thus related in the same plane, they will correctly give the three-dimensional shape of the object.

In orthographic projection, the picture planes are called *planes of projection* and the perpendiculars, *projecting lines* or *projectors*.

In looking at these theoretical projections, or views, the observer should not think of the views as being flat surfaces on the transparent planes, but should imagine himself as looking *through* the transparent planes at the object itself.

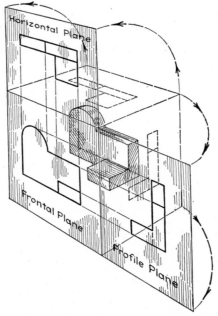

Fig. 6.7. The horizontal and profile planes revolved.

6.5 The six principal views. If now we consider the fact that the object can be entirely surrounded by a set of six mutually perpendicular planes, as shown by Fig. 6.8, views may be obtained by looking at the object from the top, front, right side, left side, bottom, and rear.

The six sides, or planes, of the box are then thought of as being opened up, as illustrated in Fig. 6.9, into one plane, the plane of the paper. The front is considered to be originally in the plane of the paper, and the other sides are considered to be hinged and rotated into position as shown. The projection on the front plane is known as the *front view, vertical projection,* or *front elevation;* that on the horizontal plane, the *top view, horizontal projection,* or *plan;* that on the side or "profile" plane the *side view, profile projection, side elevation,* or sometimes *end view* or *end elevation.* By reversing the direction of sight, a *bottom view* will be obtained instead of a *top view*, or a *rear view* instead of a *front view*. In comparatively rare cases, either a bottom view or a rear view or both may be required to show some

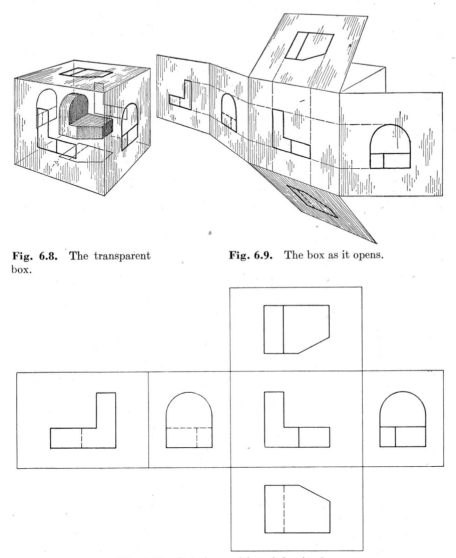

Fig. 6.8. The transparent box.

Fig. 6.9. The box as it opens.

Fig. 6.10. Relative position of the six views.

detail of shape or construction. Figure 6.10 shows the relative positions of the six views as set by the ASA. In actual work, there is rarely ever an occasion where all six principal views would be needed on one drawing, but no matter how many are required, their positions relative to each other would be as given in Fig. 6.10. All these views are principal views. Each one of the six views shows two of the three dimensions of height, width, and depth.

6.6 Combination of views. The most usual combination selected from the six possible views consists of the *top*, *front*, and *right-side* views, as shown in Fig. 6.11, which, in this case, best describes the shape of the given block. Sometimes the left-side view will help describe an object more clearly than the right side would. Figure 6.12 shows the arrangement of *top*, *front*, and *left-side* views (in this case the right-side view would be preferred as it has no hidden lines). Note that the *side view of the front face of the object is adjacent to the front view*, and that the side view of any

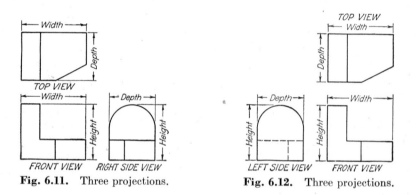

Fig. 6.11. Three projections.   **Fig. 6.12.** Three projections.

point will be the same distance from the front surface as is its distance from the front surface on the top view. The combination of *front, right-side,* and *bottom views* is shown in Fig. 6.13 and that of *front, top, left-side,* and *rear* views in Fig. 6.14.

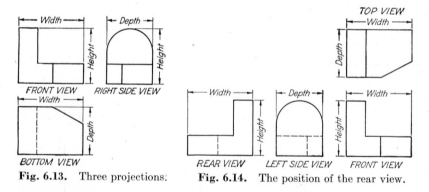

Fig. 6.13. Three projections.   **Fig. 6.14.** The position of the rear view.

6.7 "Alternate-position" views. The top of the enclosing transparent box may be thought of as in a fixed position with the front, rear, and sides hinged as illustrated in Fig. 6.15, thus bringing the sides in line with the top

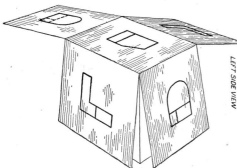

Fig. 6.15. The box opening for alternate position.

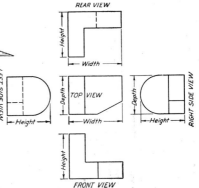

Fig. 6.16. Alternate position views.

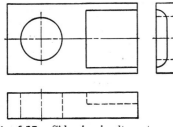

Fig. 6.17. Side view in alternate position.

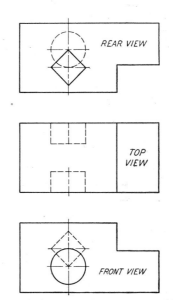

Fig. 6.18. Rear view in alternate position.

view and the rear view above the top view, Fig. 6.16. This alternate-position arrangement is of occasional use in drawing a broad flat object, Fig. 6.17, as it saves space on the paper. The alternate position for the rear view may be used if this arrangement makes the drawing easier to read, Fig. 6.18.

6.8 The three space dimensions. As all material objects from single pieces to complicated structures are definitive and measurable by three space dimensions,[1] it is desirable for drawing purposes to define these dimensions and to fix their direction.

Height is the difference in elevation between any two points, measured as the perpendicular distance between a pair of horizontal planes that contain the points, Fig. 6.19. Edges of the object may or may not correspond

---

[1] *Space dimensions* and *dimensions of the object* should not be confused. The primary function of orthographic projection is to show the shape. Size is not established until the figured dimensions and/or the scale is placed on the drawing. Space dimensions are *only* the measure of three-dimensional space.

with the height dimensions.   Edge AB corresponds with the height dimension, while edge CD does not, but the space height of A and C are the same,
as are B and D.   Height is always measured in a vertical direction and has
no relationship whatever to the shape of the object.

Width is the positional distance of left to right, between any two points
measured as the perpendicular distance between a pair of profile planes

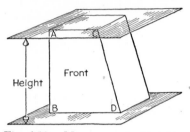

Fig. 6.19.   Measurement of height.

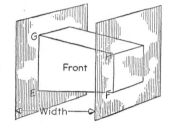

Fig. 6.20.   Measurement of width.

containing the points.   The relative width between points E and G on the
left and H and F on the right of an object is shown by the dimension marked
width, Fig. 6.20.   The object edge EF is parallel to the width direction and
corresponds with the width dimension, but edge GH slopes downward from
G to H, thus making the actual object edge longer than the width separating
points G and H.

Depth[1] is the positional distance, front to rear, between any two points
measured as the perpendicular distance between two frontal planes containing the points.   Figure 6.21 shows two frontal planes, one at the front of the
object containing points J and L, the other at the rear containing points K

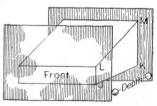

Fig. 6.21.   Measurement of depth.

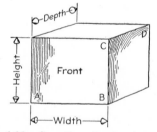

Fig. 6.22.   Location of points in space.

and M.   The relative depth separating the front and rear of the object is
the perpendicular distance between the planes as shown.

Any point may be located in space by giving its height, width, and depth
relative to some other known point.   Figure 6.22 shows a cube with four
identified corners A, B, C, and D.   Assuming that the plane containing
points A and B is the front of the object, height, width, and depth would be
as marked.   Assuming also that point A is fixed in space, point B may be
located from point A by giving the width dimension, including the statement that height and depth measurements are zero. C may be located from

---

[1] The term "depth" is used in the civil engineering sense, as the depth of a lot.

A by giving width, height, and zero depth. *D* may be located from *A* by giving width, height, and depth measurements.

6.9   The relationship of planes, view directions, and space dimensions. Under the theory explained in paragraphs 6.4 and 6.5, the object to be drawn may be thought of as surrounded by transparent planes upon which the actual views are projected. The three space dimensions, height, width, and depth, and the planes of projection are unchangeably oriented and connected with each other and with the view directions, Fig. 6.23. Each of the planes of projection is perpendicular, respectively, to its own view direction. Thus, the frontal plane is perpendicular to the front-view direction, the horizontal plane is perpendicular to the top-view direction, and the profile plane is perpendicular to the side-view direction. The two

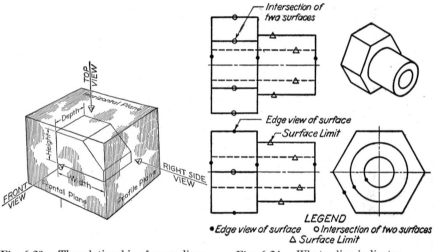

Fig. 6.23.   The relationship of space directions and the planes of projection.

Fig. 6.24.   What a line indicates.

space measurements for a view are parallel to the plane of that view and perpendicular to the view direction. Therefore height and width are parallel to the frontal plane and perpendicular to the front-view direction; width and depth are parallel to the horizontal plane and perpendicular to the top-view direction; height and depth are parallel to the profile plane and perpendicular to the side-view direction. Note that the three planes of projection are *mutually* perpendicular as are the three space measurements, and also the three view directions. Carefully study the views of Figs. 6.11 to 6.17 and note the space dimensions marked on each figure.

6.10   Representation of lines. Although uniform in appearance, the lines on a drawing may indicate three different types of directional change on the object. An *edge view* is a line showing the edge of a receding surface (a surface perpendicular to the plane of projection). An *intersection* is the line formed by the meeting of two surfaces. A *surface limit* is the reversal element line of a curved surface (or the series of points of reversal on a warped surface). Figure 6.24 illustrates the different line meanings.

6.11 Hidden features. To describe an object completely, a drawing should contain lines representing all the edges, intersections, and surface limits of the object. *In any view there will be some parts of the object that cannot be seen from the position of the observer, as they will be covered by portions of the object closer to the observer's eye.* The edges, intersections, and surface limits of these hidden parts are indicated by a line made up of short dashes, sometimes called "dotted lines" by draftsmen. In Fig. 6.25, the drilled hole[1] that is visible in the right-side view is hidden in the top and front

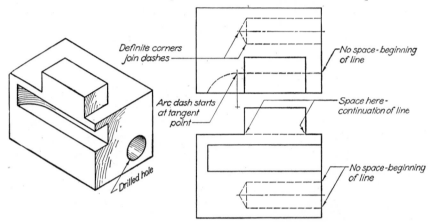

Fig. 6.25. Dotted line treatment of hidden features.

views, and therefore it is indicated by a dotted line showing the hole and the shape as left by the drill point. The milled slot (see Glossary) is visible in the front and side views, but is hidden in the top view.

The beginner must pay particular attention to the execution of these dotted lines. If carelessly drawn, they not only will ruin the appearance of a drawing, but will make it much harder to read. The line is drawn lighter than the full lines, of short dashes uniform in length, with the space between them very short, about one-fourth the length of the dash. It is important that they start and stop correctly. A dotted line always starts with a dash except when it would form a continuation of a full line, in which case a space is left, as shown in Fig. 6.25. Dashes always meet at corners. An arc must start with a dash at the tangent point, except when it would form a continuation of a full line straight or curved. The number of dashes used in a tangent arc should be carefully judged to maintain a uniform appearance, Fig. 6.26. Study carefully all dotted lines in Figs. 6.25 and 6.27.

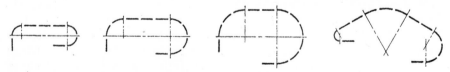

Fig. 6.26. Dotted arcs (actual size).

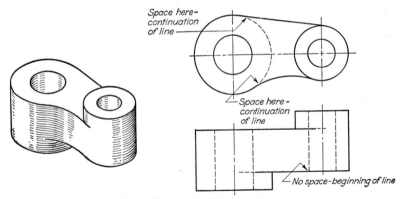

Fig. 6.27.   Dotted lines and arcs.

6.12   Center lines.   In general, the first lines to be drawn in the layout of an engineering drawing are the center lines, thereby forming the axes of symmetry for all symmetrical views or portions of views: (1) Every part with an axis, as a cylinder or a cone, will have the axis drawn as a center line before the part is drawn.   (2) Every circle will have its center at the intersection of two center lines.

The standard symbol for center lines on finished drawings is a fine line made up of alternate long and short dashes, as shown in the alphabet of lines, Fig. 4.32.   They are always extended slightly beyond the outline of the view, or portion of view, to which the center line applies.   Center lines form the skeleton construction of the drawing, from and to which the important measurements are made and dimensions given.   Study the center lines in Figs. 9.73 and 9.74.

6.13   Precedence of lines.   In any view there is likely to be a coincidence of lines.   Hidden portions of the object may project identically with visible portions.   Center lines may likewise occur where there is the visible or hidden outline of some part of the object.

As the physical features of the object *must* be represented, full and dotted lines take precedence over all other lines.   As the visible outline is more prominent by space position, full lines take precedence over dotted lines. A full line could cover up a dotted line, but a dotted line could not cover a full line.   It is evident, also, that a dotted line could not occur as one of the boundary lines of a view.

When a center line and cutting-plane line coincide, the one that is more important for the readability of the drawing should take precedence over the other.

Break lines should be placed so that they do not spoil the readability of the over-all view.

Dimension and extension lines must always be placed so as not to coincide with other lines of the drawing.

The following list gives the order of precedence of lines:

1. Full line.
2. Dotted line.
3. Center line or cutting plane.
4. Break lines.
5. Dimension and extension lines.
6. Crosshatch lines.

Note the coincident lines in Fig. 6.28.

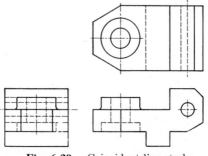

Fig. 6.28.   Coincident-line study.

6.14 Object orientation.   An object may, of course, be drawn in any of several possible positions. *The simplest position should be used*, with the object oriented so that the principal faces are perpendicular to the sight directions for the views and parallel to the planes of projection as shown in Fig. 6.29.   Any other position with the faces of the object at some angle to the planes of projection would complicate the drawing, foreshorten the object faces, and make the drawing difficult to make and to read.

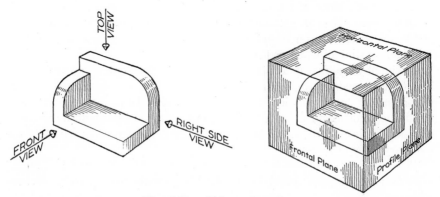

Fig. 6.29.   Object orientation.

6.15 Selection of views.   In practical work, it is very important to choose the combination of views that will describe the shape of an object in the best and most economical way.   Often only two views are necessary as, for example, a cylindrical shape, which, if on a vertical axis, would require only a front and top view and, if on a horizontal axis, only a front and side view. Conical and pyramidal shapes also may be described in two views. Figure 6.30 illustrates two-view drawings. On the other hand, some shapes will need more than the three regular views for adequate description.

Objects may be thought of as being made up of combinations of simple geometrical solids, principally cylinders and rectangular prisms, and the views necessary to describe any object would be determined by the directions from which it would have to be viewed to see the characteristic contour

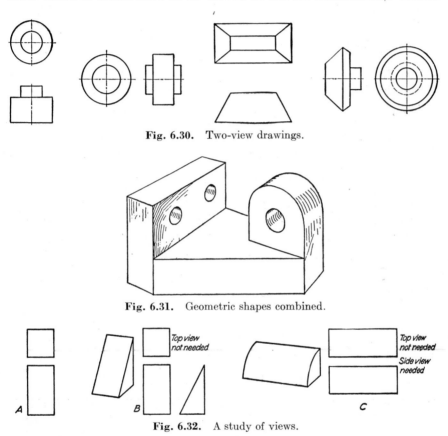

Fig. 6.30. Two-view drawings.

Fig. 6.31. Geometric shapes combined.

Fig. 6.32. A study of views.

shapes of these parts. Figure 6.31, for example, is made up of several prisms and cylinders. If each of these simple shapes is described and their relation to each other is shown, the object will be fully represented. In the majority of cases, the three regular views, top, front, and side, are sufficient to do this.

Sometimes two views are proposed as sufficient for some object, on the assumption that the contour in the third direction would be of the shape that would naturally be expected. For instance *A*, in Fig. 6.32, would be assumed to have a uniform cross section and be a square prism. But the two views *might* be the top and front views of a wedge as shown in three views at B. Two views of an object, as drawn at C, do not describe the piece at all. It might be assumed

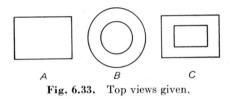

to be square in section, but it could as easily be round, triangular, quarter round, or other shape, which should have been indicated by a required side view. Sketch several different front views for each top view (A, B, and C), Fig. 6.33.

Fig. 6.33. Top views given.

With the object preferably in its functioning position and *with its principal surfaces parallel to the planes of projection*, visualize the object, mentally picturing the orthographic views one at a time to decide on the best combination. In Fig. 6.34, the arrows show the direction of observation for the six principal views of an object, and indicate the mental process of the draftsman. He notes that the front view should show the two horizontal holes, as well as the width and height of the piece; that a top view is needed to show the contour of the vertical cylinder; and that the cutout corner will require a side view to show its shape. He notes further that the

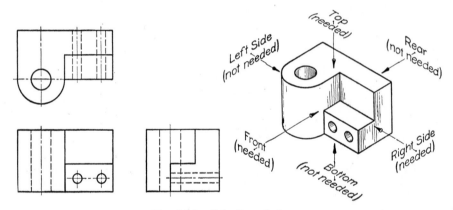

Fig. 6.34. Selection of views.

right-side view would show this cut in full lines, while on the left side it would be hidden. He notes, incidentally, that neither a bottom view nor a rear view would be of any value in describing this object. Thus, he has arrived at the correct choice of front, top, and right-side views for the best description of the piece. As a rule, the side view containing the fewer dotted lines should be preferred. If there is no choice, the right-side view is preferred in standard practice.

In inventive and design work, any simple object should be visualized mentally, and the view selected without a picture sketch. In complicated work a pictorial or orthographic sketch may be used to advantage, but it should not be necessary, in any case, to sketch all possible views in order to make a selection.

Study the drawings in Fig. 6.35 and determine why the views are so chosen.

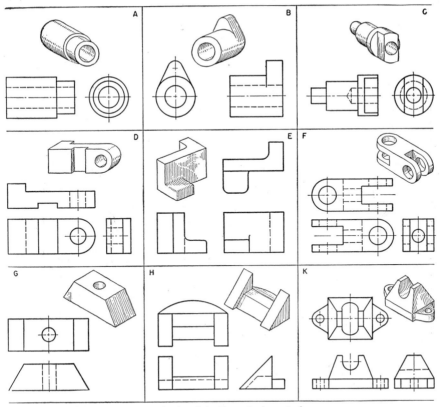

Fig. 6.35. Selection-of-view study.

6.16 Exercises in projection. As can be seen from the foregoing paragraphs of this chapter, the principal problem in learning orthographic projection is first to become thoroughly familiar with the theory and then to practice this theory by translating from a picture of the object to the orthographic views. Figures 6.36 and 6.37 contain a variety of objects shown by a pictorial sketch and the translation into orthographic views. Study the objects in these figures and note (1) how the object is oriented in space, (2) why the orthographic views are chosen, (3) the projection of visible features, (4) the projection of hidden features, and (5) center lines.

6.17 Orthographic representation. The end point of orthographic theory is not simply to understand the theory, but to apply it in the making of drawings. Chapter 8 gives the application for drawings made freehand, and Chap. 9 gives directions for making orthographic instrument drawings.

6.18 First-angle projection. The system of orthographic projection explained in this chapter is known as "third-angle projection." It is the official American Standard universally adopted in the United States and Canada.

If the horizontal and vertical planes of projection should be extended beyond their intersection, four dihedral angles would be formed, which are

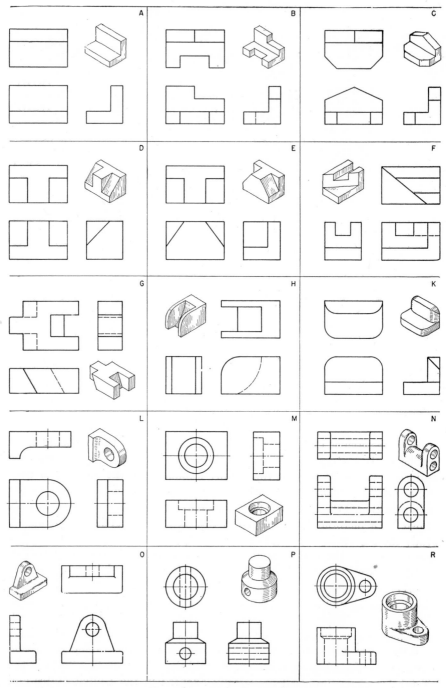

Fig. 6.36. Projection studies.

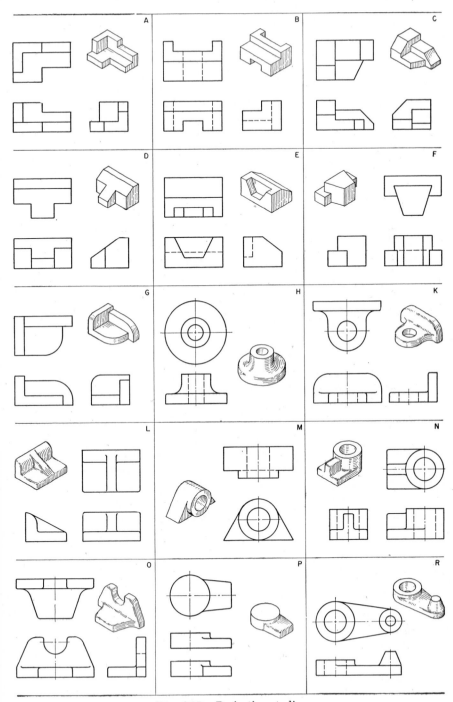

Fig. 6.37. Projection studies.

called, in order, "first," "second," "third," and "fourth angles," numbered as illustrated in Fig. 6.38. Theoretically, the object might be placed in any one of the four angles or quadrants, projected to the planes, and the planes folded about their intersection. Practically, the second and fourth angles would be eliminated, leaving the first and third as possibilities. If the object is placed in the *first angle*, is projected to the planes, and the planes are opened up into one plane, the top view would evidently fall below the front view, and if a profile plane were added, the view of the

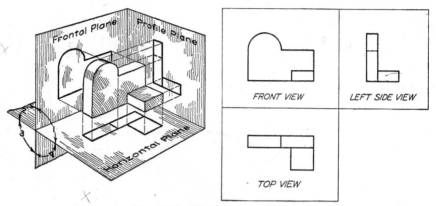

Fig. 6.38.   First-angle projection.

left side of the figure would be to the right of the front view. The system of first-angle projection was formerly in universal use, but was generally abandoned in this country some sixty-five years ago. The student should understand and recognize it, however, as it may be encountered occasionally in old drawings and illustrations, as well as in drawings from some foreign countries. Argument and confusion have arisen and sometimes expensive mistakes have occurred through the misreading of first-angle drawings as made by foreign-trained engineers.

TEXT-FILMS

The following McGraw-Hill Text-Film has been produced for specific correlation with Chaps. 6, 7, 8, and 9:

Orthographic Projection (20-min. sound motion picture).

Demonstrates the theory of orthographic projection; shows how objects, planes, and lines appear from different points of view; gives the methods of projection for separate views; explains concepts of height, width, and depth and their relationship in the projected views; demonstrates the making and reading of a drawing.

This film is accompanied by a coordinated silent filmstrip that reviews and further clarifies the principles of orthographic projection and may be used for oral discussion and examination.

7

Orthographic Reading

7.1 As already stated in Chap. 1, the engineer must be able to *read* and *write* the orthographic language. The necessity of learning to read is absolute, because everyone connected with technical industry must be able to read a drawing without hesitation. Not to have that ability would be an admission of technical illiteracy.

Since reading is a mental process, a drawing is not read aloud. To describe even a simple object with words will be found to be an uncertain and almost impossible task. Reading proficiency develops with experience, for similar conditions and shapes repeat so often that one gradually acquires a background of knowledge that enables him to visualize the shapes shown. Experienced readers will read quickly because they can draw upon their knowledge and easily recognize familiar shapes and combinations without hesitation; but, even so, reading a drawing should be done carefully and deliberately. One cannot expect to read a whole drawing at once any more than he would expect to read a whole page of print at a glance.

7.2 Prerequisites and definition. Before attempting to read a drawing, one should be thoroughly familiar with the principles of orthographic projection as explained in Chap. 6. The arrangement of views and their projection, the space measurements of height, width, and depth, what each line represents, etc., must constantly be kept in mind and used where they apply.

Visualization is the medium through which the shape information on a drawing is translated to give the reader an understanding of the object represented. The *ability to visualize* is often thought to be a "gift" which some people possess and others do not. This, however, is not true. Proof that anyone of reasonable intelligence has a visual memory is had in the fact that they are able to recall and describe scenes at home, actions at sporting events, and even the details of acting and facial expression in a play or motion picture.

The ability to visualize a shape shown on a drawing is almost completely governed by the knowledge of the principles of orthographic projection possessed by the individual. The common adage that "the best way to learn to read a drawing is to learn how to make one" is quite correct, because in learning to make a drawing one is forced to study and apply the principles of orthographic projection.

From the foregoing statements, then, the following definition is derived:

Definition. *"Reading a drawing" is an ability to recognize and apply the principles of orthographic projection to interpret the shape of an object from the orthographic views.*

7.3 Method of reading. A drawing is read by visualizing units or details one at a time from the orthographic projection and mentally orient·· ing and combining these details together finally to interpret the whole object. The form taken in this visualization, however, may not be the same for all readers or for all drawings. Reading is primarily a reversal of the process of making drawings, and inasmuch as drawings are usually first made from a picture of the object, the beginner often attempts to carry the reversal too completely back to the pictorial. The result is that the orthographic views of an object like that shown in Fig. 7.1 are translated to the accompanying picture, thinking of the object as positioned in space or placed on a table or similar surface. Others will need only to recognize in the drawing the geometry of the solids, which in the case of Fig. 7.1 would

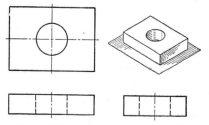

Fig. 7.1. Orthographic views and picture.

be a rectangular prism, so high, so wide, so deep, with a hole passing vertically through the center of the prism. This second reader will have read the views just as completely as the first, but with much less mental effort.

It is, to most, a mental impossibility (and surely an unnecessary requirement) to translate more than just the simplest set of orthographic views into a complete pictorial form that can be pictured in its entirety. Actually the reader will go through a routine pattern of procedure (listed in paragraph 7.4). Much of this will be done subconsciously. For example, consider the object of Fig. 7.2. One observes a visible circle in the top view. From memory of previous projection experience (Chap. 6), this must be either a hole or the end of a cylinder. The eyes rapidly shift back and forth from the top view to the front view, aligning features of the same size ("in projection"), with the mind assuming the several possibilities and finally accepting the fact that, because of the dotted lines and their extent in the front view, the circle represents a hole that extends through the prism. Following a similar pattern of analysis, the reader will find that Fig. 7.3 represents a rectangular prism surmounted by a cylinder. These described steps are done so rapidly that the reader is scarcely aware of the steps and processes involved.

Presumably, the foregoing is the usual method, but how does the beginner develop this ability?

First, as stated in paragraph 7.2, a reasonable knowledge of the principles of orthographic projection is necessary.

Second, as described in paragraphs 7.5 and 7.6, a complete understanding of the meaning of lines, areas, etc., and the mental processes involved must be acquired. To read, one applies these principles. There is very little additional learning required. Careful study of all these items plus practice will develop the ability and confidence needed.

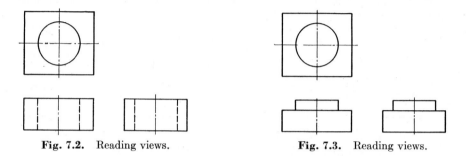

Fig. 7.2. Reading views.   **Fig. 7.3.** Reading views.

7.4 Procedure for reading. The actual steps in reading will not always be identical, because of the wide variety of subject matter (drawings). Nevertheless, the following outline gives the basic procedure and will serve as a guide.

First, orient yourself with the views given.

Second, obtain a general idea of the over-all shape of the object. Think of each view as the object itself, visualizing yourself in front, above, and at the side as the draftsman did in making the views. Study the dominant features and their relation to each other.

Third, start reading the simpler individual features, beginning with the most dominant and progressing to the subordinate. Look for familiar shapes or conditions that your memory retains from previous experience. Read all views of these familiar features to note the extent of holes, thickness of ribs and lugs, etc.

Fourth, read the unfamiliar or complicated features. Remember that every point, line, surface, and solid appears in every view and that you must find the projection of every detail in the given views to learn the shape.

Fifth, as the reading proceeds, note the relationship between the various portions or elements of the object. Such items as the number and spacing of holes, placement of ribs, tangency of surfaces, and the proportions of hubs, etc., should be noted and remembered.

Sixth, reread any detail or relationship not clear at the first reading.

7.5 The meaning of lines. As explained in paragraph 6.13, a line on a drawing indicates (1) the *edge of a surface*, (2) an *intersection of two surfaces*, or (3) a *surface limit*. Because a line on a view may mean any one of these three conditions, the corresponding part of another view must be consulted to determine the meaning. For example, the meaning of line *AB* on the front view of Fig. 7.4 cannot be determined until the side view is consulted. The line is then found to be the edge view of the horizontal surface of the cutout corner.   Similarly, line *CD* on the top view cannot be fully under-stood without consulting the side view where it is identified as the edge view of the vertical surface of the cutout corner.   Line *EF* on the top view and *GH* on the front view are identical in appearance.   However, the side view shows that line *EF* represents the edge view of the rear surface of the triangular block and that line *GH* is the intersection of the front and rear surfaces of the triangular block.

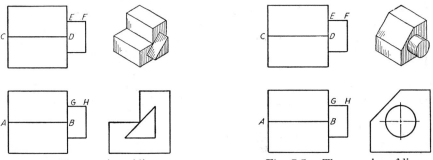

Fig. 7.4.   The meaning of lines.   Fig. 7.5.   The meaning of lines.

The top and front views of the objects shown in Figs. 7.4 and 7.5 are identical.   Nevertheless, lines *AB* and *CD* on Fig. 7.5 do not represent what they did in Fig. 7.4, but are, on Fig. 7.5, the intersection of two surfaces.   Also, lines *EF* and *GH* on Fig. 7.5 are identical in appearance with those on Fig. 7.4, but on Fig. 7.5 they represent the surface limits of the circular boss.

From Figs. 7.4 and 7.5, it is readily seen that one cannot read a drawing by looking at a single view.   Two views will not always describe an object,

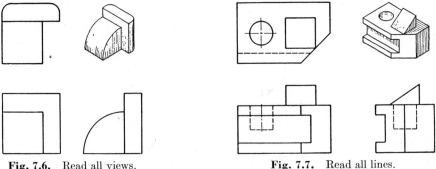

Fig. 7.6.   Read all views.   Fig. 7.7.   Read all lines.

and when three or more views are given all must be consulted to be sure that the shape has been read correctly.   Illustrating with Fig. 7.6, the front and top views show what appears to be a rectangular projection on the front of the object, but the side view shows this projection to be quarter round.   Similarly, the front and side views apparently indicate the rear portion of the object to be a rectangular prism, but the top view shows that the two vertical rear edges are rounded.

One cannot assume a shape from one or two views—*all the views must be read carefully.*

From the foregoing it should be evident that the several *lines,* representing some feature, must be read in all the views. As an exercise in reading the lines on an orthographic drawing, find *all* the lines representing the hole, triangular prism, slot, and cutoff corner of Fig. 7.7.

7.6 The meaning of areas. The term "area" as used here means the contour limits of a surface or combination of tangent surfaces as seen in the different orthographic views. To illustrate, an area of a view as shown in Fig. 7.8 may represent (1) a surface in true shape as at *A,* (2) a foreshort-

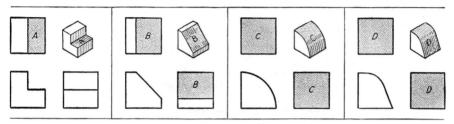

Fig. 7.8. The meaning of areas.

ened surface as at *B,* (3) a curved surface as at *C,* or (4) a combination of tangent surfaces as at *D.*

When a surface is in an oblique position as surface *E* of Fig. 7.9, all principal views of the surface will appear as an area. A study of the surfaces in Figs. 7.8, 7.9, and others will establish with the force of a rule that *a plane surface, whether it be positioned in a horizontal, frontal, profile, or an auxiliary or oblique position, will always appear in a principal orthographic view either as a line or an area.* Principal views of an oblique surface, that

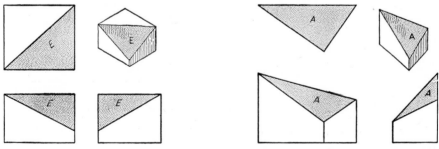

Fig. 7.9. The meaning of areas. **Fig. 7.10.** The meaning of areas.

appear as an area in more than one view, will always have like shapes. As an example, surface *A* of Fig. 7.10 will appear as a triangular area in all the principal views. The length of the edges and the angles between the edges may change, but all views will have the same number of sides. It should be noted that a plane surface bounded by a certain number of sides could never appear to have more or less sides except when the surface appears as an edge. Moreover, the sides in any view will always connect in the same sequence. Illustrating these principles with the block of Fig. 7.11, the front view shows surface B as an edge. The top and side views show the surface as an area having a similar shape, the same number of sides, and with the corners in the same sequence.

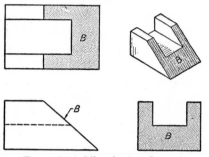

Fig. 7.11. Like shapes of areas.

7.7 Adjacent areas. No two adjacent areas can lie in the same plane. It is simple logic that, if two adjacent areas *did* lie in the same plane, there would be no boundary between the areas, and therefore, orthographically, the two adjacent areas could not exist. In illustration of these statements, note that in Fig. 7.12 areas A, B, C, and D are shown in the front and side views to lie in different planes.

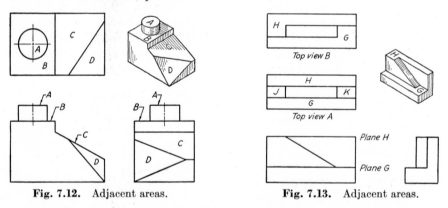

Fig. 7.12. Adjacent areas.   **Fig. 7.13.** Adjacent areas.

Further proof of these principles is given by Fig. 7.13 in which two top views are shown. By analysis of the projection between top and front views, it is seen that areas G and H shown on the top views must lie in planes G and H, respectively, shown on the front view. Also, by projection it is seen that area J of top view A must lie in plane H, and that area K must lie in plane G. Because areas H and J lie in plane H and areas G and K lie in plane G, the correct top view, therefore, is top view B.

Hidden areas may sometimes be confusing to read because the areas may overlap or even correspond with each other. For example, areas A, B, and

C of Fig. 7.14 are not separate areas, because they are all formed by the slot on the rear of the object. The apparent separation into separate areas is caused by the dotted lines from the rectangular hole, which, of course, is not connected with the slot in any way.

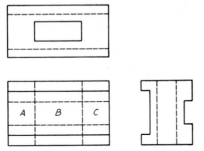

Fig. 7.14. Reading hidden areas.

7.8 Reading lines and areas. The foregoing principles regarding the meaning of lines and areas must be used to analyze any given set of views by correlating a surface appearing as a line or an area with the other views, in which the surface may appear as a line or an area. Illustrating with Fig. 7.15, first orient yourself with the given views. From their arrangement the views evidently are top, front, and right side. An over-all inspection of the views does not reveal familiar geometric shapes, such as a hole or boss, so that an analysis of the surfaces is necessary. Beginning with the trapezoidal area *A* in the top view and then moving to the front

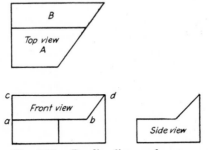

Fig. 7.15. Reading lines and areas.

view, a similar shaped area of the same width is not shown; therefore, the front view of area *A* must appear as an edge, the line *ab*. Next, consider area *B* in the top view. It is seen to be a trapezoidal area (four sides) the full width of the view. Again, going to the front view for a mating area or line, the area *abcd* is of similar shape and has the same number of sides with the corners in projection. Area *abcd*, therefore, satisfies the requirements of orthographic projection and is the front view of area *B*. The side view should be checked along with the other views to see if it agrees. Proceed in like manner to additional areas, correlating them one with another to visualize the shape of the complete object.

Memory and experience will aid materially in reading any given drawing. However, every new set of views must be approached with an open mind, because sometimes a shape that looks like a previously known condition will crowd the correct interpretation from the mind of the reader. For example, area E in Fig. 7.16 is in a vertical position. The front view of

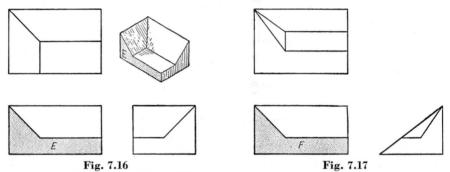

Fig. 7.16   **Fig. 7.17**

Figs. 7.16 and 7.17. Like areas may have different meanings.

Fig. 7.17 is identical with the front view of Fig. 7.16, but in Fig. 7.17 the surface F is inclined to the rear and is not vertical.

7.9 Reading of corners and edges. The corners and edges of areas may be numbered or lettered to identify them for making additional views, or as an aid in reading some complicated shape. If there are no coincident

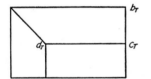

conditions, they are easily named by projection; that is, the top view is directly over the front view, and the side view lies on a horizontal projector to the front view. When coincident conditions are present, it may be necessary to coordinate a point with an adjacent point as shown by Fig. 7.18. Corner c in the front view (C_F) may be in projection with C_T at any one of the three positions marked 1, 2, 3. However, the

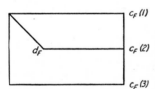

Fig. 7.18. Identification of corners.

point c is one end of an edge dc, and the front view of c must therefore be at position 2. An experienced reader could probably make the above observations without marking the points, but a beginner in many cases can gain much valuable experience by marking corners and edges, especially if the problem is some unusual combination of surfaces.

7.10 Learning to read by sketching. A drawing is interpreted by mentally understanding the shape of the object represented. Proof that the drawing has been read and understood may be shown by making the piece in wood or metal, by modeling it in clay, or by making a pictorial

sketch of it, the latter being the usual method.   Since facility in freehand
sketching is so important to every engineer, its practice
should be started early.   Before attempting to make a
pictorial sketch, a preliminary study of the method of
procedure will be required.   Pictorial sketching may be
based on a skeleton of three axes, one vertical, the other
two at 30 deg,[1] representing three mutually perpendicular
lines, Fig. 7.19.   On these axes are marked the proportionate width, depth, and height of any rectangular
figure.   Circles are drawn in their circumscribing square.

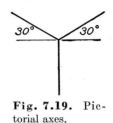

Fig. 7.19. Pictorial axes.

In Fig. 7.20 look at the views given, as described in paragraph 7.4.
Then with a soft pencil (F) and notebook paper make a *very light* pictorial
construction sketch, estimating the height, width, and depth of the object,
and laying the distances off on the axes as at *A*; then sketch the rectangular
box that would enclose the piece, or the block from which it could be cut,
Fig. 7.20*B*.   On the top face of this box sketch very lightly the lines that
occur on the top view of the orthographic drawing, Fig. 7.20*C*.   Note that,

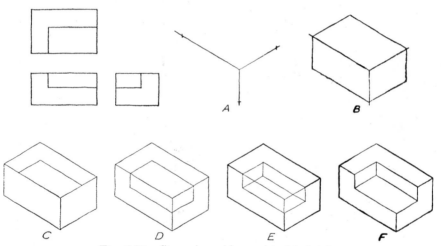

Fig. 7.20.   Stages in making a pictorial sketch.

as will be found later, some of the lines on top views may not be in the top
plane.   Next, sketch lightly the lines of the front view on the front face
of the box or block, and if a side view is given, outline it similarly, Fig. 7.20*D*.
Now, begin to cut the figure from the block, strengthening the visible edges
and adding the lines of intersection where faces of the object meet, as in
Fig. 7.20*E*.   Edges that do not appear as visible lines are omitted unless
necessary to describe the piece.   Finish the sketch, checking back to the
three-view drawing.   The construction lines need not be erased unless they
confuse the sketch.

[1] Isometric position.   Oblique or other pictorial methods may also be used.

7.11   Learning to read by modeling.   An interesting and effective learning method is to model the object in clay or modeling wax, working in much

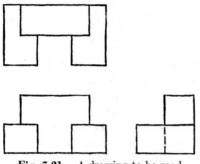

Fig. 7.21.   A drawing to be read.

the same way as when reading by pictorial sketching.   Some shapes may be
modeled by cutting out from the enclosing block; others may be modeled more
easily by first analyzing and dividing
the object into its basic geometric
shapes and then combining these shapes.

Starting with a rectangular block of
clay, perhaps 1 in. square and 2 in. long,
read Fig. 7.21 by cutting the figure from
the solid.   Scribe very lightly, with the
point of the knife or a scriber, the lines
of the three views on the three corresponding faces of the block, Fig. 7.22.
Evidently the first cut could be as shown at *B*, and the second as at *C*.
Successive cuts are indicated at *D* and *E*, and the finished model is indicated
at *F*.

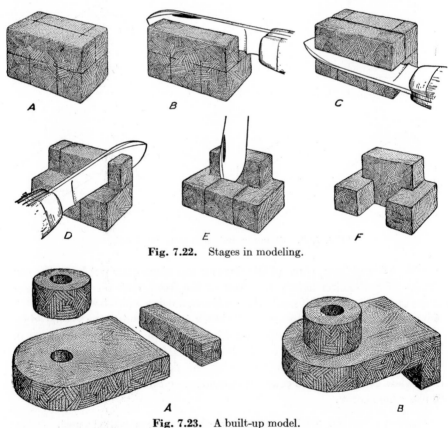

Fig. 7.22.   Stages in modeling.

Fig. 7.23.   A built-up model.

Figure 7.23 illustrates the type of model that can be made by building up the shapes of which the object is composed.

7.12   Calculation of volume as an aid in reading.   In calculating the volume of an object, one is forced to break the part down into its simple geometrical elements, and then carefully to analyze the shape of each element before computation is possible.   Thus, the calculation of volume is primarily an exercise in reading a drawing.   Usually, before the computations are completed, the object has been visualized, but the mathematical record of the volume of each portion and the correct total volume and weight are proof that the drawing has been read and understood.

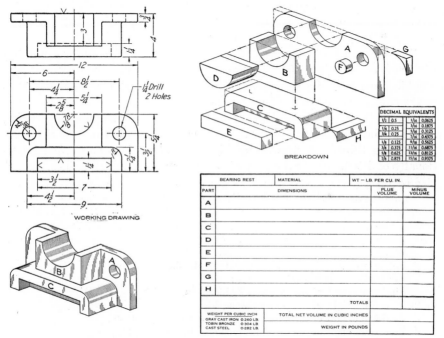

Fig. 7.24.   Shape breakdown for volume and weight calculations.

The procedure closely follows the usual steps in reading a drawing. Figure 7.24 will illustrate the method.

1. Study the orthographic drawing and pick out the principal masses (*A*, *B*, and *C* shown on the breakdown and in the pictorial drawing).   Pay no attention in the beginning to holes, rounds, etc., but study each principal over-all shape and its relation to the other masses of the object.   Record the dimensions of each of these principal portions and indicate plus volume by placing a check mark in the plus-volume column.

2. Examine each principal mass and find the secondary masses (*D* and *E*) that must be either added to or subtracted from the principal portions.   Bosses, lugs, etc., must be added; cutout portions, holes, etc., subtracted.   Record the dimensions of these secondary masses, being careful to indicate plus or minus volume.

3. Further limit the object to its actual shape by locating smaller details, such as holes, fillets, rounds, etc., (parts *F*, *G*, and *H*).   Record the dimensions of these parts.

4. Compute the volume of each portion. This may be done by longhand multiplication or, more conveniently, with a slide rule. Record each volume in the proper column, plus or minus. When all unit volumes are completed, find the net volume by subtracting total minus volume from total plus volume.

5. Multiply net volume by the weight per cubic inch of metal to compute the total weight.

The calculations are simplified if all fractional dimensions are converted to the decimal form. When a slide rule is employed, fractions *must* be converted to decimals. A partial conversion table is given in Fig. 7.24, and a more complete table on page 650.

The complete volume and weight calculation not only gives training in recognition of the fundamental geometrical portions of an object, but also serves to teach neat and concise working methods in the recording of engineering data.

7.13 Exercises in reading. Figures 7.25 and 7.26 contain a number of three-view drawings of block shapes made for exercises in reading orthographic projection and translating into pictorial sketches or models. Proceed as described in the previous paragraphs, making sketches not less than 4 in. over-all. Check each sketch to be sure that all intersections are shown, and that the original three-view drawing could be made from the sketch.

In each three-view drawing of Fig. 7.27, some lines have been intentionally omitted. Read the drawings and supply the missing lines.

7.14 Volume and weight calculations, with slide rule. In calculating the weight of a piece from the drawings, the object should be divided or broken up into the geometric solids (prisms, cylinders, pyramids, cones) of which it is composed. The volume of each of these shapes should be calculated, and these should be added, or sometimes subtracted, to find the total volume which, multiplied by the weight of the material per unit of volume, will give the weight of the object.

A table of weights of materials will be found in the Appendix.

The following problems are suggested:

1. Find the weight of the cast-iron jig block, Fig. 16.42
2. Find the weight of the bearing brass, Fig. 16.51.
3. Find the weight of the wrought-iron guide block, Fig. 16.47.
4. Find the weight of the cast-steel dovetail stop, Fig. 16.48.
5. Find the weight of the malleable-iron bracket, Fig. 16.56.

TEXT-FILMS

The following McGraw-Hill Text-Film has been produced for specific correlation with Chaps. 6, 7, 8, and 9:

Orthographic Projection (20-min. sound motion picture).

Demonstrates the theory of orthographic projection; shows how objects, planes, and lines appear from different points of view; gives the methods of projection for separate views; explains concepts of height, width, and depth and their relationship in the projected views; demonstrates the making and reading of a drawing.

This film is accompanied by a coordinated silent filmstrip that reviews and further clarifies the principles of orthographic projection and may be used for oral discussion and examination.

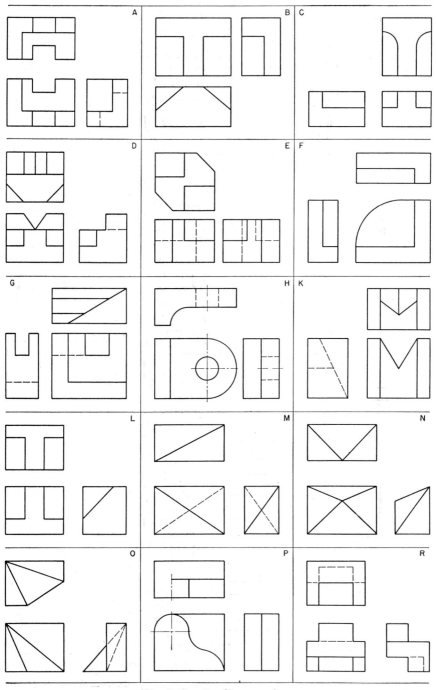

Fig. 7.25. Reading exercises.

Fig. 7.26. Reading exercises.

Fig. 7.27.   Missing line exercises.

8

Orthographic Freehand Drawing

8.1 Facility in making a freehand orthographic drawing is an essential part of the equipment of every engineer, and as sketching requires some mastery of the various skills employed, practice should be started early. Full proficiency in freehand drawing means the mastery of the graphic language and is gained only after much knowledge and skill of drawing with instruments have been acquired. Nevertheless, sketching is an excellent method of learning the fundamentals of orthographic projection and may be employed by the beginner even before much practice with instruments has been had. Time can be saved by working freehand instead of with instruments, thus making it possible to solve more problems in the same amount of time.

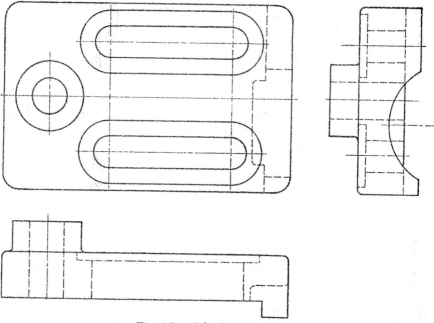

Fig. 8.1. A freehand drawing.

Some experienced teachers advocate the making of freehand sketches before practice in the use of instruments is had. However, some knowledge of the use of instruments and especially of applied geometry is a great help before starting to sketch, because the essentials of line tangents, connections, and intersections, as well as the basic geometry of the part, should be well defined on the freehand drawing. In favor of starting to sketch early, it may be said that freehand drawing is excellent exercise in the accuracy of observation.   Figure 8.1 is an example of a well-made freehand drawing.

8.2 Materials. The only necessary materials for sketching are a pencil (F, HB, or H) sharpened to a long conical point, not too sharp; a pencil eraser to be used sparingly; and paper—notebook, pad, or single sheet clipped on a board.   Coordinate paper ruled with fine lines is often used.

8.3 Technique. The pencil should be held with freedom, and not close to the point.   Vertical lines are drawn downward with a finger movement in a series of overlapping strokes, with the hand somewhat in the position of Fig. 8.2.   Horizontal lines are drawn with the hand shifted to

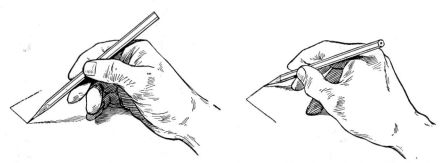

Fig. 8.2. Drawing a freehand vertical line.

Fig. 8.3. Drawing a freehand horizontal line.

the position of Fig. 8.3, using a wrist motion for short lines and a forearm motion for longer ones.   In drawing any straight line between two points, keep the eyes on the point to which the line is to go rather than on the point of the pencil.   Do not try to draw the whole length of a line in a single stroke.   It may be an aid to draw a *very* light line first, then to sketch the finished line, correcting the direction of the light line without rubbing it out. Do not be disturbed by any nervous waviness.   Accuracy of direction is more important than smoothness of line.

It is legitimate in freehand drawing to make long vertical or horizontal lines by using the little finger as a guide along the edge of the pad or clip board.

Steep inclined lines running downward from right to left are drawn easily with the same movement as vertical lines, but those running downward from left to right are much harder to draw (except for left-handed persons).   They may be drawn by turning the paper and drawing them as horizontal lines.   The three important things about a straight line are (1) that it be essentially straight, (2) that it be the right length, and (3) that it go in the right direction.

Circles may be drawn by marking the radius on each side of the center lines or, more accurately, by drawing two diagonals in addition to the center lines, and marking points equidistant from the center of the eight radii. At these points draw short arcs perpendicular to the radii, then complete the circle as shown in Fig. 8.4. A modification is to use a slip of paper as a trammel. Large circles can be done very smoothly, after a little practice, by using the third or fourth finger as a pivot, holding the pencil stationary and rotating the paper under it, or by holding two pencils and using one as a pivot about which to rotate the paper. Another way of drawing a circle is to sketch it in its circumscribing square.

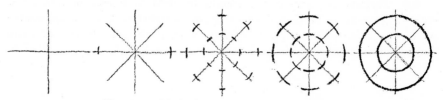

Fig. 8.4.   Method of drawing freehand circles.

8.4 Projection. In making an orthographic sketch, the principles of projection and applied geometry are to be remembered and applied. Sketches are *not* made to scale, but are made to show fair proportions of the object sketched. Note that a scale was not included in the list of materials needed. It is legitimate, however, when coordinate paper is employed, to count the spaces or rulings as a means of proportioning the views and as an aid in making projections. Particular care should be exercised in having the various details of the views in good projection from view to view. An inexcusable mistake is to have a detail sketched to a different size on one view than on another.

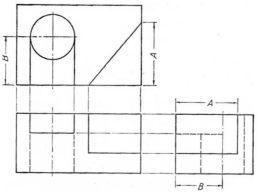

Fig. 8.5.   Freehand projections.

When working on plain paper, projections between the top and front views or between the front and side views are easily made by simply "sighting" between the views, or employing *very* light construction lines as indicated in Fig. 8.5. Projections between the top and side views are laid off by judging the distance by eye, by measuring the distance by holding the finger at the correct distance from the end of the pencil and transferring to the view, or by marking the distance on a small piece of paper and transferring to the view. Note in Fig. 8.5 that distances A, B, and others could be transferred from the top to the side view by the methods just mentioned.

Even though freehand lines are somewhat "wavy" and not so accurate in position as ruled lines, a good freehand drawing should present the same clean workmanlike appearance as a good instrument drawing.

8.5 Method. Practice in orthographic freehand drawing should be started by drawing the three views of a number of simple pieces, developing the technique and the ability to "write" the orthographic language, while

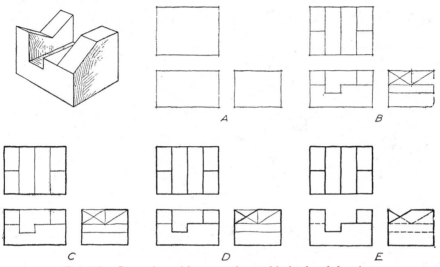

Fig. 8.6. Stages in making an orthographic freehand drawing.

exercising the constructive imagination in visualizing the object by looking at the three projections. Observe the following order of working:

1. Study the pictorial sketch and decide what combination of views will best describe the shape of the piece.
2. Block in the views, as at A, Fig. 8.6, using a very light stroke of a soft pencil (F or No. 2), spacing the views so as to give a well-balanced appearance to the drawing.
3. Build up the detail in each view, carrying the three views along together as at B.
4. Brighten the outline of each view with bold strokes as at C.
5. Brighten the detail with bold strokes, thus completing the full lines of the sketch as at D.
6. Sketch in all dotted lines, using a stroke of medium weight, lighter than the full lines, as at E, thus completing the shape description of the block.
7. Check the drawing carefully, then cover the pictorial sketch and visualize the object from the three views.

After a number of simple pieces have been drawn freehand, the student may "graduate" to more complicated problems such as Figs. 9.34 and 9.53. Faintly ruled cross-section paper may be used if desired.

PROBLEMS

Selections from the following groups of problems are to be made for practice in orthographic freehand drawing. Group I gives practice in drawing the three views of an object, and Group II provides exercises in reading a drawing, as well as practice in freehand drawing. Group III gives experience in drawing from memory.

Group I. Projections from pictorial views. *Figs. 8.7 to 8.21*

These figures contain a number of pictorial sketches of pieces of various shapes. These are to be translated into three-view orthographic freehand drawings. Make them

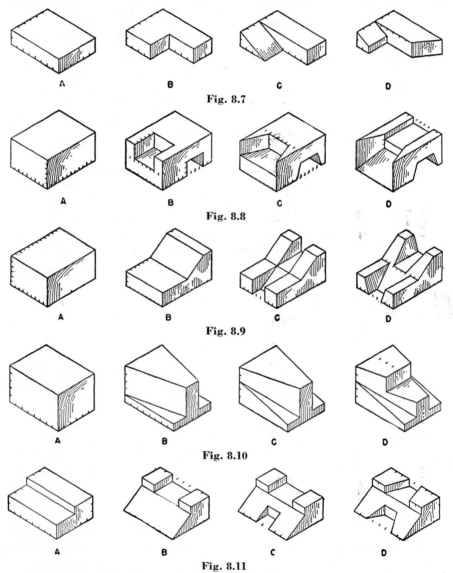

Figs. 8.7 to 8.11. Pieces to be drawn freehand in orthographic projection.

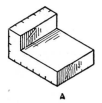 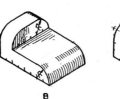 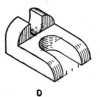

A B C D

Fig. 8.12

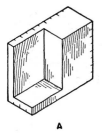 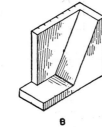 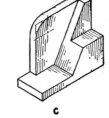 

A B C D

Fig. 8.13

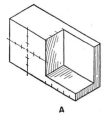 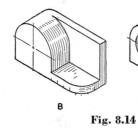 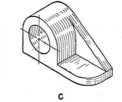 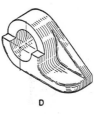

A B C D

Fig. 8.14

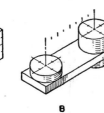 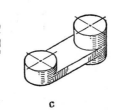

A B C D

Fig. 8.15

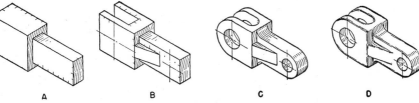

A B C D

Fig. 8.16

Figs. 8.12 to 8.16. Pieces to be drawn freehand in orthographic projection.

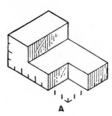
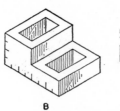
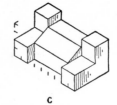
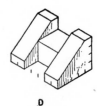

A B C D

Fig. 8.17

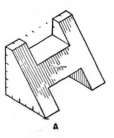
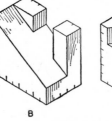
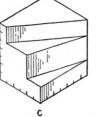
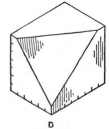

A B C D

Fig. 8.18

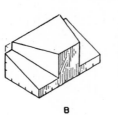
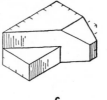
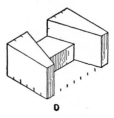

A B C D

Fig. 8.19

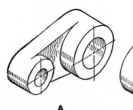
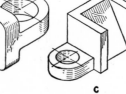
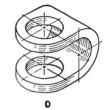

A B C D

Fig. 8.20

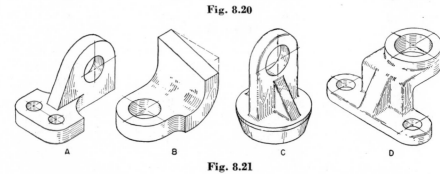

A B C D

Fig. 8.21
Figs. 8.17 to 8.21.   Pieces to be drawn freehand in orthographic projection.

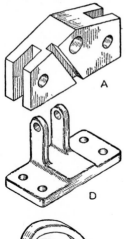
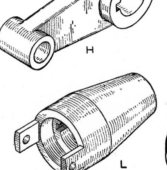
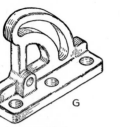
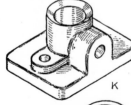
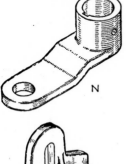
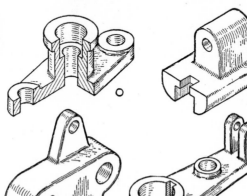

Fig. 8.22.   Pieces to be drawn freehand in orthographic projection.

Fig. 8.23. Views to be supplied, freehand.

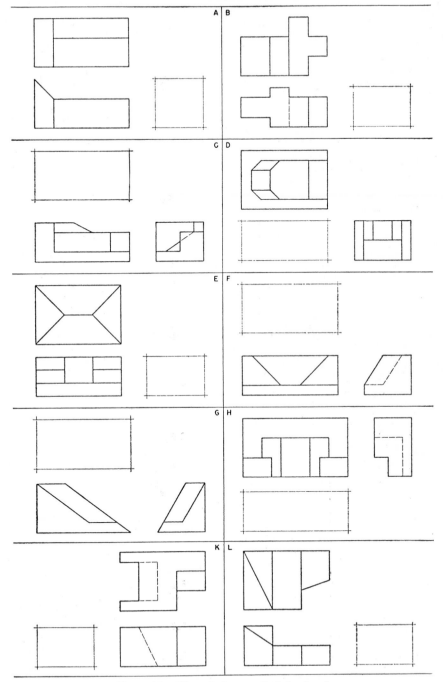

Fig. 8.24. Views to be supplied, freehand.

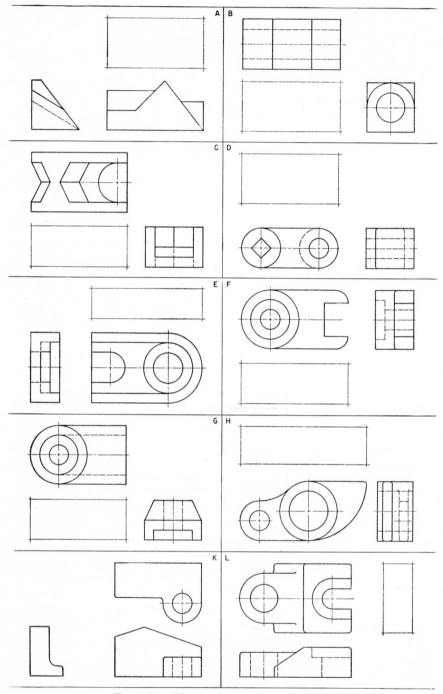

Fig. 8.25. Views to be supplied, freehand.

of fairly large size, the front view, say, 2 to $2\frac{1}{2}$ in. in length, and estimate the proportions of the different parts by eye, or from the proportionate marks shown but without measuring. The problems are graduated in difficulty so that a selection may be made, depending on ability and experience.

Figure 8.22 gives a series of problems that may be used for advanced work in freehand drawing, or later on, by adding dimensions that may be used as dimensioning studies, or freehand working drawing problems.

Group II. Views to be supplied. *Figs. 8.23, 8.24, and 8.25*

These figures contain a number of objects of which two views have been drawn, and the third view is to be supplied. This exercise, as well as developing the ability to draw freehand, will also give valuable practice in reading. These problems may be worked directly in the book, or the views given may be copied to larger size on plain or coordinate paper and then solved.

Group III. Drawing from memory.

One of the valuable assets of an engineer is a trained memory for form and proportion. The graphic memory may be developed to a surprising degree in accuracy and power by systematic exercises in drawing from memory. This training may be commenced as soon as a knowledge of orthographic projection has been acquired.

Select an object not previously used, such as one from Figs. 8.7 to 8.21 or Figs. 9.16 to 9.56; look at it with concentration for a certain time (5 sec to $\frac{1}{2}$ min or more); close the book and make an accurate orthographic sketch. Check with the original, and correct any mistakes or omissions. Follow with several different figures. The next day allow a 2-sec view of one of the objects and repeat the orthographic views of the previous day.

TEXT-FILMS

The following McGraw-Hill Text-Film has been produced for specific correlation with Chaps. 6, 7, 8, and 9:

Orthographic Projection (20-min. sound motion picture).

Demonstrates the theory of orthographic projection; shows how objects, planes, and lines appear from different points of view; gives the methods of projection for separate views; explains concepts of height, width, and depth and their relationship in the projected views; demonstrates the making and reading of a drawing.

This film is accompanied by a coordinated silent filmstrip that reviews and further clarifies the principles of orthographic projection and may be used for oral discussion and examination.

9

Orthographic Instrument Drawing

9.1 Orthographic instrument drawing is the major objective in any drawing course, because a very large percentage of all the drawings used in engineering work are made with instruments. Before attempting an orthographic drawing, one must have a knowledge of orthographic projection as explained in Chap. 6 and, preferably, some experience in orthographic freehand drawing, Chap. 8. In addition, instrument drawing demands, for technique, some skill and facility in the use of instruments, Chap. 4, and a knowledge of applied geometry, Chap. 5. Lettering, Chap. 2, should also be studied and practiced. Careful attention should always be paid to accuracy and neatness.

Speed and accuracy are of prime importance, but neither one should be slighted for the benefit of the other. Unnecessary extreme accuracy will waste time, while excessive speed will result in inaccurate, poorly made drawings. Good drawing habits and practices must be acquired. Instruments must be kept clean and in good working order. The drawing board and table should not be "cluttered" with unneeded equipment. Have a definite place for everything so that time is not lost looking for instruments and tools.

9.2 Drawing sizes. Standard sheets based on multiples of $8\frac{1}{2}$ by 11 in. and 9 by 12 in. are specified by the ASA for drawings. Trimmed sizes of drawing paper and cloth, with recommended border and title dimensions, are given on page 490.

9.3 Spacing the views. View spacing is necessary in order that the drawing may be balanced within the space provided. The draftsman, therefore, must do a little preliminary measuring to locate the views. The following example will describe the procedure. Suppose the piece illustrated in Fig. 9.1 is to be drawn full size on an 11- by 17-in. sheet. With an end-title strip, the working space inside the border will be $10\frac{1}{2}$ by 15 in. The front view will require $7\frac{11}{16}$ in. and the side view $2\frac{1}{4}$ in. This leaves $5\frac{1}{16}$ in. to be distributed between the views and at the ends.

This preliminary planning need not be to exact dimensions, that is, small fractional values, such as $\frac{15}{64}$ in. or $\frac{31}{32}$ in., may be adjusted to $\frac{1}{4}$ and 1 in., respectively, to speed up the planning. In this case the $7\frac{11}{16}$-in. dimension may be adjusted to $7\frac{3}{4}$ in.

The draftsman locates the views graphically and very quickly by measuring with his scale along the bottom border line. Starting at the lower right corner, lay off first $2\frac{1}{4}$ in., then $7\frac{3}{4}$ in. The distance between views may now be decided upon. It is chosen arbitrarily to separate the views without crowding, yet sufficiently close to have the drawing read easily (in this case 1½ in.) and the distance measured; half the remaining distance to the left corner is the starting point of the front view. For the vertical location, the front view is 4 in. high and the top view 2¼ in. deep. Starting at the upper left corner, lay off first 2¼ in., then 4 in.; judge the distance between views (in this case 1 in.) and lay it off; then a point marked at less than half the remaining space will locate the front view, allowing more space at the bottom than at the top for appearance sake.

Spaces for the views are blocked out lightly, and the over-all arrangement is studied, because changes can be easily made at this stage. If satisfactory,

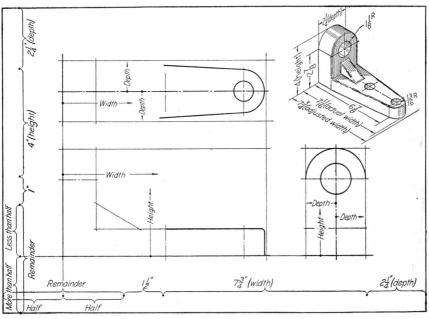

Fig. 9.1. Spacing views.

next select reference lines in each view from which the space measurements of height, width, and depth that appear in the view may be measured. This may be an edge or a center line through some dominant feature as indicated on Fig. 9.1 by the center lines in the top and side views and the medium weight lines in all the views. The directions for height, width, and depth measurements for the views are also shown.

9.4 Projecting the views. After the views have been laid out, the various features of the object may be located and drawn. In accomplishing this, the views should be *carried along together*, that is, *not* attempting to complete one view before proceeding to another. The most characteristic view of a feature should be drawn first and then projected and drawn in the other views before going on to a second feature. As an example, the vertical hole of Fig. 9.2 should be drawn first in the top view, and then the dotted lines representing the limiting elements should be projected and drawn in the front and side views.

In some cases, a view cannot be completed before a feature has been located and drawn in another view. For illustration of this point, study the pictorial drawing of Fig. 9.2 and note from the orthographic views that

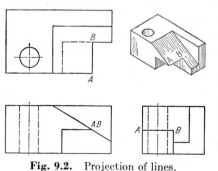

the horizontal slot must be drawn on the front view before the edge AB on the slanting surface can be found in the top view.

Projections (horizontal) between the front and side views are made by employing the T square to draw the required horizontal line (or to locate a required point) as illustrated in Fig. 9.3.

Projections (vertical) between the front and top views are made by using

Fig. 9.2. Projection of lines.

the T square and a triangle as illustrated in Fig. 9.4.

Projections between the top and side views cannot be projected directly, but must be measured and transferred, or found by special construction. In carrying the top and side views along together, the draftsman usually transfers the depth measurement from one to the other either with his

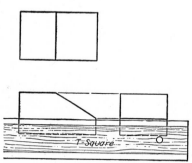

Fig. 9.3. Making a horizontal projection.

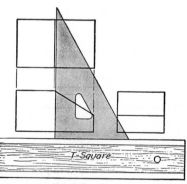

Fig. 9.4. Making a vertical projection.

dividers, as at A, Fig. 9.5, or with his scale, as at B. Sometimes, however, as in the case of an irregular figure, he prefers to "miter" the points around, using a 45° line drawn through the point of intersection of the top and side views of the front face, extended as shown in Fig. 9.6A; or, going back to the method of the glass box, to swing them around with the compasses, as at B. The methods of Fig. 9.6, however, require more time and care to maintain accuracy than do the methods of Fig. 9.5 and are, therefore, *not* recommended.

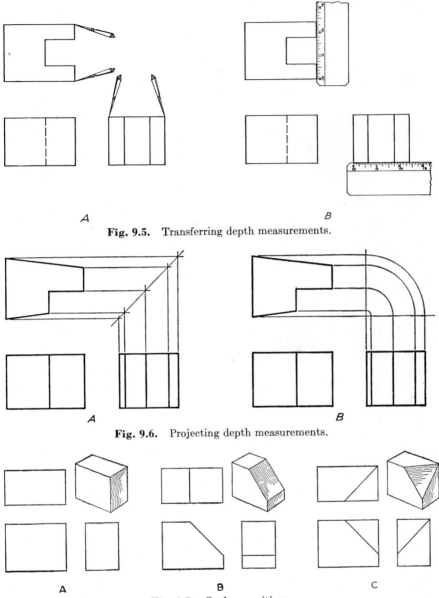

Fig. 9.5.   Transferring depth measurements.

Fig. 9.6.   Projecting depth measurements.

Fig. 9.7.   Surface positions.

9.5   Classification of surfaces and lines.   Any object, depending upon its shape and space position, may or may not have some surfaces parallel or perpendicular to the planes of projection.

Surfaces are classified according to their space relationship with the planes of projection. *Horizontal, frontal,* and *profile* surfaces are illustrated at *A*, Fig. 9.7.   When a surface is inclined to two of the planes of projection (but perpendicular to the third), as at *B*, the surface is said to be *auxiliary*. If the surface is at an angle to all three planes, as at *C*, the term *oblique* is used.

The edges (represented by lines) bounding a surface may, because of object shape or position, also be either in a simple position or inclined to the planes of projection. A line in, or parallel to, a plane of projection receives its name from the plane. Thus, a *horizontal line* is a line in a horizontal plane, a *frontal line* is a line in a frontal plane, and a *profile line* is a line in a profile plane. When a line is parallel to two planes, the line takes the name

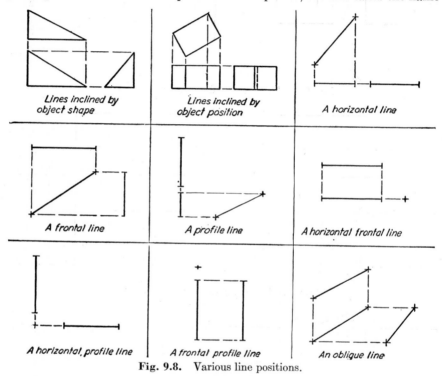

Fig. 9.8. Various line positions.

of both planes, as *horizontal frontal, horizontal profile*, or *frontal profile*. A line not parallel to any plane of projection is called an *oblique line*. Figure 9.8 illustrates various positions of lines.

An edge relative to a plane of projection appears in true length when parallel, as a point when perpendicular, and shorter than true length when inclined. Similarly, a surface relative to a plane of projection appears in its true shape when parallel, as a line when perpendicular, and foreshortened when inclined. As an example, Fig. 9.7 shows at *A* an object with its faces parallel to the planes of projection; top, front, and right-side surfaces are shown in true shape, and the object edges appear either in true length or as points. The inclined surface of the object at *B* does not show in true shape in any of the views, but appears as an edge in the front view. The front and rear edges of the inclined surface are in true length in the front view and foreshortened in the top and side views. The top and bottom edges of the inclined surface appear in true length in top and side views and as points in the front view. The oblique surface of the object at C does not show in true shape in any of the views, but each of the bounding edges shows in true length in one view and is foreshortened in the other two views.

9.6 Projections of surfaces bounded by linear edges. In drawing the projections of inclined surfaces, in some cases the corners of the bounding edges may be used, and in other cases the bounding edges themselves may be projected. In illustration of these methods A, Fig. 9.9, shows a vertical

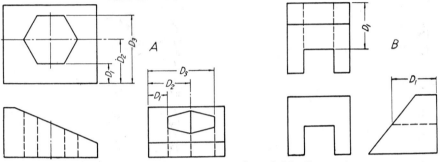

Fig. 9.9. Projections of surfaces bounded by linear edges.

hexagonal hole that may be laid out from specifications in the top view. Then, the front view may be drawn by projecting from the six corners of the hexagon and drawing the four dotted lines to complete the front view. To get the side view, a horizontal projection may be made from each corner on the front view to the side view, thus locating the height of the points needed on the side view. Measurements D_1, D_2, and D_3 then taken from the top view and transferred to the side view will locate all six corners in the side view. Connecting these corners and drawing the three vertical dotted lines completes the view. The object at B, Fig. 9.9, shows a horizontal slot running out on an inclined surface. In the front view, the true width and height of this slot may be laid out from specifications. The projection to the side view is a simple horizontal projection for the dotted line, indicating the top surface of the slot. To get the top view, the width may be projected from the front view and then the position of the runout line measured (distance D_1) and transferred to the top view.

In summary, it may be stated that, if a line will appear at some angle on a view, its two ends must be projected; if a line will appear parallel to its path of projection, the complete line may be projected.

9.7 Projections of an elliptical boundary. The intersection of a cylindrical hole (or cylinder) with a slanting (auxiliary or oblique) surface, as shown in Fig. 9.10, will be an ellipse, and some projections of this elliptical edge will appear as another ellipse. The projection may be made as shown at A, Fig. 9.10, by assuming a number of points on the circular view, projecting them to the edge view and then to an adjacent view. Thus, as an example, points 1 to 4 are located in the top view, projected to the front view, and the projectors are then drawn to the side view. Measurements of depth taken from the top view (as D_1) will locate the points in the side

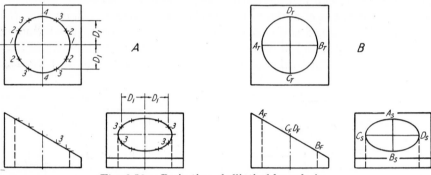

Fig. 9.10.   Projection of elliptical boundaries.

view. A smooth curve is then drawn through the points, employing a french curve for the job.

For an ellipse on an auxiliary surface, the projection may also be made by establishing the major and minor axes of the ellipse, as shown in Fig. 9.10B. A pair of diameters positioned so as to give the largest and smallest extent of the curve will give the required major and minor axes. Thus, in Fig. 9.10B, AB will project to the side view as the smallest or minor axis $A_S B_S$, and CD will project as the largest or major axis $C_S D_S$. The ellipse may then be drawn by one of the methods of Chap. 5, paragraphs 5.45, 5.47, and 5.49.

If the surface intersected by the cylinder is oblique, as shown in Fig. 9.11, a pair of perpendicular diameters located in the circular view will give a pair of conjugate diameters in an adjacent view. Therefore, $A_T B_T$ and $C_T D_T$ projected to the front view will give conjugate axes, which may be employed as explained in Chap. 5, paragraphs 5.46, 5.48, and 5.49, to draw the required ellipse.

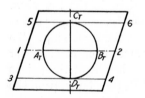
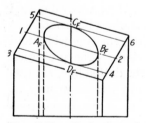

Fig. 9.11.   Projection of an elliptical boundary by employing conjugate axes.

In projecting the axes, they may be extended to the straight line boundary of the oblique surface. Thus the line 1-2 located in the front view and intersected by projection of $A_T B_T$ from the top view locates $A_F B_F$. Similarly, lines 3-4 and 5-6 at the ends of the axis CD locate $C_F D_F$.

9.8 Projections of a curved boundary. Any nongeometrical curve (or a geometrical curve not having established axes) must be projected by locating points on the curve. If the surface is in an auxiliary position, as shown at A, Fig. 9.12, points may be assumed on the curve laid out from data (assumed in this case to be the top view), projected first to the edge view (front) and then to an adjacent (side) view. Measurements, such as 1, 2, etc., from the top view transferred to the side view complete the projection. A smooth curve is then drawn through the points.

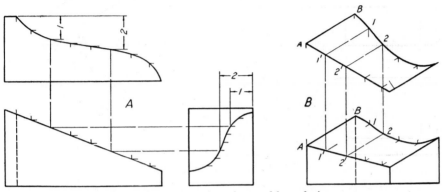

Fig. 9.12. Projection of curved boundaries.

If the surface is oblique, as illustrated in Fig. 9.12B, elements of the oblique surface, such as 1'-1, 2'-2, etc., located in an adjacent view (by drawing the elements parallel to some known line of the oblique surface, such as AB) make it possible to project points on the curve 1, 2, etc., to the adjacent view, as shown.

9.9 Projections by identifying corners. In projecting orthographic views, or in comparing the views with a picture, it will be of much help in some cases to letter or number the corners of the object and, with these identifying marks, to letter, similarly, the corresponding points on each of the views, as in Fig. 9.13. Hidden points directly behind visible points

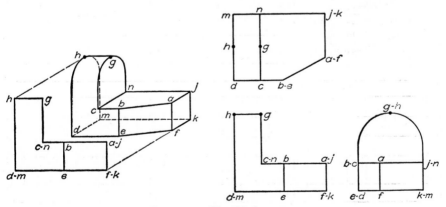

Fig. 9.13. Identified corners.

are lettered to the right of the letter of the visible point, and in this figure, they have been further differentiated by the use of "phantom," or dotted, letters. Study Fig. 9.14 and number, or letter, the corners of the three views to correspond with the pictorial view.

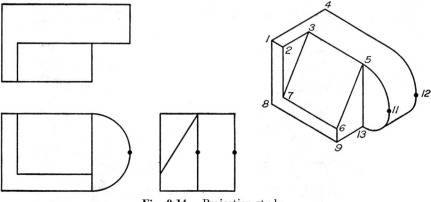

Fig. 9.14. Projection study.

9.10 Order of drawing. The order of working is important, as speed and accuracy depend largely upon the methods employed in laying down lines. Duplications of the same measurement should be avoided, and changing from one instrument to another should be kept at a minimum. Naturally, *all* measurements cannot be made with the scale at one time, or *all* circles and arcs drawn before laying down the compasses, but as much work as possible should be done before shifting to another instrument. An orderly placement of the working tools on the drafting table will save much time when changing from the use of one instrument to another. The usual order of working is illustrated in Fig. 9.15.

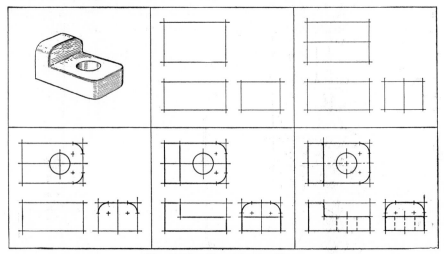

Fig. 9.15. Stages in penciling.

1. **Decide what combination of views will best describe the object.** A freehand sketch will aid in choosing the views and in planning the general arrangement of the sheet.

2. Decide what scale is to be used and, by calculation or measurement, find a suitable standard sheet size, or pick one of the standard drawing sizes, and find a suitable scale.

3. Space the views on the sheet, as described in paragraph 9.3.

4. Lay off the principal dimensions and then "block in" the views with light, sharp, accurate outlines and center lines. Center lines are drawn for the axes of all symmetrical views or parts of views. Thus every cylindrical part should have a center line—the projection of the axis of the piece. Every circle should have two center lines intersecting at its center.

5. Draw in the details of the part, beginning with the dominant characteristic shape and progressing to the minor details, such as fillets and rounds. The different views should be carried along together, projecting a characteristic shape, as shown on one view to the other views, not finishing one view before starting another. Use a minimum of construction and draw the lines to finished weight, if possible, as the views are carried along. *Do not make the drawing lightly and then "heavy" the lines later.*

6. Lay out and letter the title.

7. Check the drawing carefully.

9.11 Order of tracing. If the drawing is to be traced[1] in ink as an exercise in the use of instruments, or for a finished orthographic drawing without dimensions, the order of working is:

1. Place the pencil drawing to be traced on the drawing board, carefully align it with the T square, and put thumbtacks in the two upper corners. Then place the tracing paper or cloth (dull side up) over the drawing. Holding the cloth in position, lift the tacks one at a time and replace them to hold both sheets. Then put tacks in the two lower corners.

2. To remove any oily film, prepare the surface of the cloth or paper by dusting it lightly with prepared pounce or soft white chalk. *Then wipe the surface perfectly clean with a soft cloth.*

3. Carefully set the compasses to the correct line width and ink all full-line circles and circle arcs, beginning with the smallest. Correct line weights are given on page 58.

4. Ink dotted circles and arcs in the same order as full-line circles.

5. Carefully set the ruling pen to draw exactly the same width line as the full-line circles. The best way to match the straight lines to the circles is to draw with the compasses and ruling pen outside the trim line of the sheet, or on another sheet of the same kind, and adjust the ruling pen until the lines match.

6. Ink irregular curved lines.

7. Ink straight full lines in this order: horizontal (top to bottom), vertical (left to right), and inclined (uppermost first).

8. Ink straight dotted lines in the same order. Be careful to match these straight lines with the dotted circles.

9. Ink center lines.

10. Crosshatch all areas representing cut surfaces.

11. Draw pencil guide lines and letter the title.

12. Ink the border.

13. Check the tracing for errors and omissions.

PROBLEMS

Selections from several groups of problems following are to be made for practice in projection drawing. Most of them are intended to be drawn with instruments, but will give valuable training done freehand on either plain or coordinate paper.

[1] A discussion of tracing and reproduction methods will be found in Chap. 28.

The groups are as follows:
   I. Projections from pictorial views.
  II. Views to be supplied.
 III. Views to be changed.
  IV. Drawing from memory.
   V. Volume and weight calculations, with slide rule.

Group I.   Projections from pictorial views. *Problems 1 to 41*

  1. Fig. 9.16. Draw the top, front, and right-side views of the beam support.
  2. Fig. 9.17. Draw the top, front, and right-side views of the vee rest.
  3. Fig. 9.18. Draw three views of the saddle bracket.
  4. Fig. 9.19. Draw three views of the wedge block.
  5. Fig. 9.20. Draw three views of the slotted wedge.

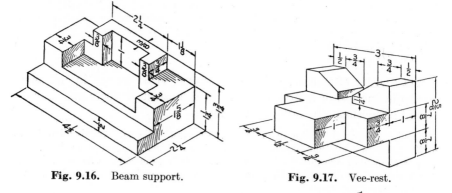

Fig. 9.16.   Beam support.   **Fig. 9.17.**   Vee-rest.

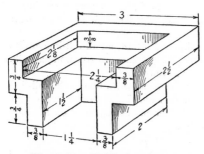
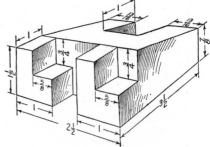

Fig. 9.18.   Saddle bracket.   **Fig. 9.19.**   Wedge block.

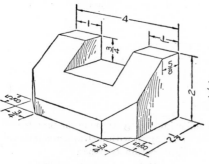
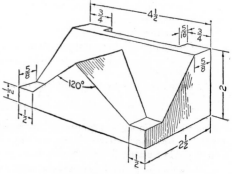

Fig. 9.20.   Slotted wedge.   **Fig. 9.21.**   Pivot block.

6. Fig. 9.21.   Draw three views of the pivot block.
7. Fig. 9.22.   Draw three views of the inclined support.
8. Fig. 9.23.   Draw three views of the corner stop.
9. Fig. 9.24.   Draw three views of the switch base.
10. Fig. 9.25.   Draw three views of the adjusting bracket.
11. Fig. 9.26.   Draw three views of the guide base.
12. Fig. 9.27.   Draw three views of the bearing rest.

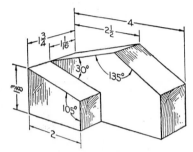

Fig. 9.22.   Inclined support.

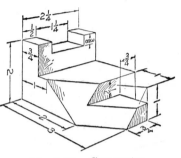

Fig. 9.23.   Corner stop.

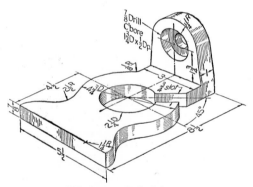

Fig. 9.24.   Switch base.

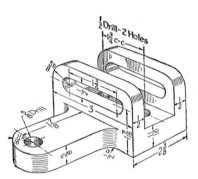

Fig. 9.25.   Adjusting bracket.

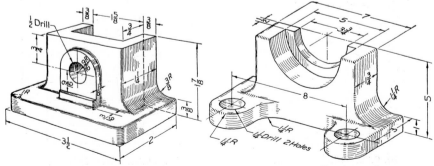

Fig. 9.26.   Guide base.

Fig. 9.27.   Bearing rest.

13. Fig. 9.28.   Draw three views of the swivel yoke.
14. Fig. 9.29.   Draw three views of the truss bearing.
15. Fig. 9.30.   Draw three views of the sliding-pin hanger.
16. Fig. 9.31.   Draw two views of the cover clamp.
17. Fig. 9.32.   Draw two views of the elliptical cam.
18. Fig. 9.33.   Draw two views of the wire thimble.

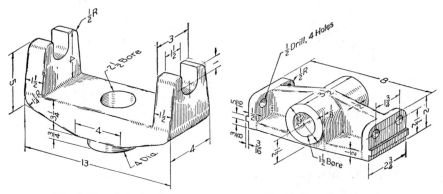

Fig. 9.28.   Swivel yoke.   **Fig. 9.29.**   Truss bearing.

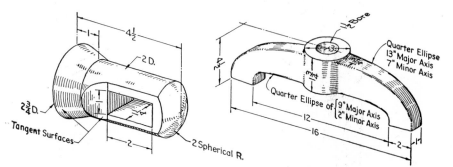

Fig. 9.30.   Sliding-pin hanger.   **Fig. 9.31.**   Cover clamp.

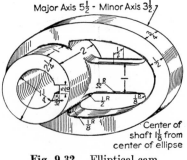

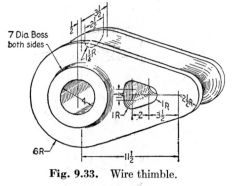

Fig. 9.32.   Elliptical cam.   **Fig. 9.33.**   Wire thimble.

19. Fig. 9.34. Draw three views of the hanger jaw.
20. Fig. 9.35. Draw three views of the adjustable jaw.
21. Fig. 9.36. Draw two views of the shifter fork.
22. Fig. 9.37. Draw three views of the mounting bracket.
23. Fig. 9.38. Draw three views of the hinged bearing.
24. Fig. 9.39. Draw two views of the clamp lever.

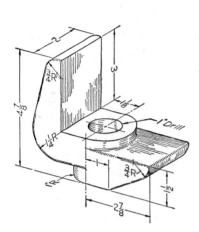

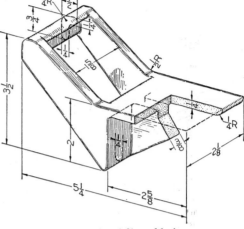

Fig. 9.34. Hanger jaw.   **Fig. 9.35.** Adjustable jaw.

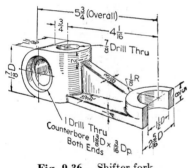

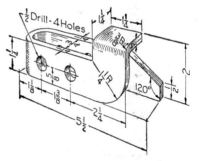

Fig. 9.36. Shifter fork.   **Fig. 9.37.** Mounting bracket.

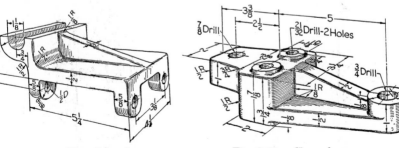

Fig. 9.38. Hinged bearing.   **Fig. 9.39.** Clamp lever.

25. Fig. 9.40.   Draw three views of the bedplate stop.
26. Fig. 9.41.   Draw top, front, and partial side views of the spanner bracket.
27. Fig. 9.42.   Draw two views of the sliding stop.
28. Fig. 9.43.   Draw three views of the clamp bracket.
29. Fig. 9.44.   Draw three views of the tube hanger.
30. Fig. 9.45.   Draw three views of the gage holder.

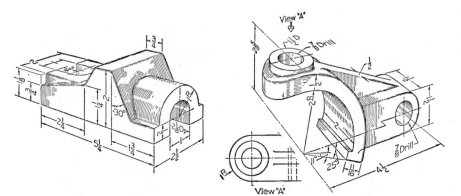

Fig. 9.40.   Bedplate stop.   **Fig. 9.41.**   Spanner bracket.

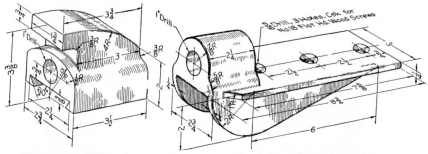

Fig. 9.42.   Sliding stop.   **Fig. 9.43.**   Clamp bracket.

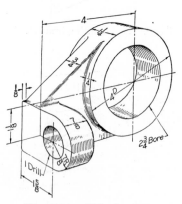 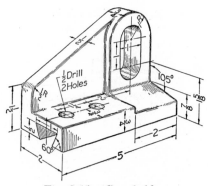

Fig. 9.44.   Tube hanger.   **Fig. 9.45.**   Gage holder.

31. Fig. 9.46.   Draw three views of the shaft guide.
32. Fig. 9.47.   Draw three views of the clamp block.
33. Fig. 9.48.   Draw three views of the offset yoke.
34. Fig. 9.49.   Draw three views of the angle connector.
35. Fig. 9.50.   Draw three views of the buckstay clamp.
36. Fig. 9.51.   Draw three views of the stop base.

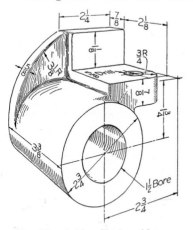

Fig. 9.46.   Shaft guide.

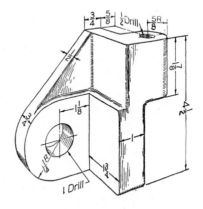

Fig. 9.47.   Clamp block.

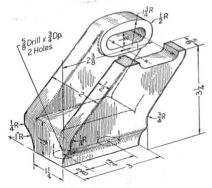

Fig. 9.48.   Offset yoke.

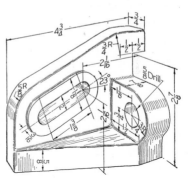

Fig. 9.49.   Angle connector.

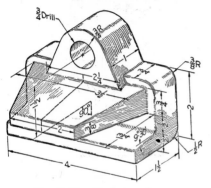

Fig. 9.50.   Buckstay clamp.

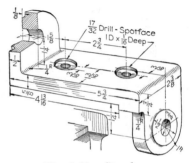

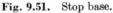

Fig. 9.51.   Stop base.

37. Fig. 9.52. Draw three views of the sliding buttress.
38. Fig. 9.53. Draw two views of the end plate.
39. Fig. 9.54. Draw three views of the plastic switch base.
40. Fig. 9.55. Draw two views of the pawl hook.

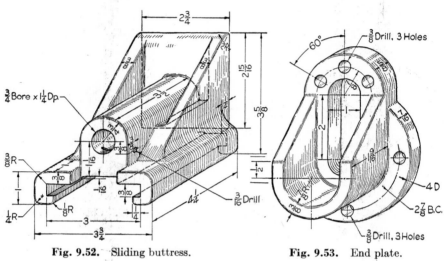

Fig. 9.52. Sliding buttress.   **Fig. 9.53.** End plate.

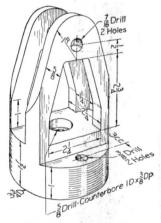

Fig. 9.54. Switch base.

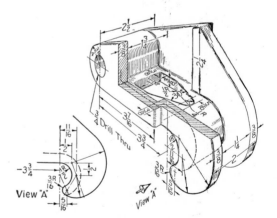

Fig. 9.55. Pawl hook.

41. Fig. 9.56.   Draw three views of the step-pulley frame.

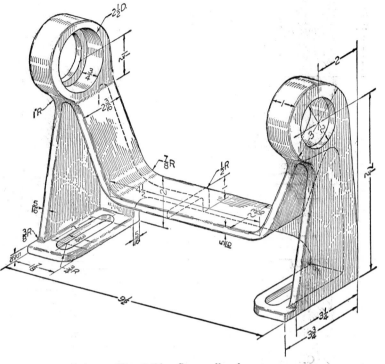

Fig. 9.56.   Step-pulley frame.

Group II.   Views to be supplied.   *Problems 42 to 62*

These problems supply valuable training in reading orthographic views, as well as supplying further practice in the principles of orthographic projection.

In reading the views given, refer to Chap. 7 and apply the principles given there. Pay particular attention to the meaning of lines, paragraph 7.5, the meaning of areas, paragraph 7.6, and the meaning of adjacent areas, paragraph 7.7.   Corners or edges of the object may be numbered or lettered, if preferred, to aid in the reading or, later, to aid in the projection.

A pictorial sketch may be used, if desired, as an aid in reading the views.   This sketch may be made either before the views are drawn and completed or at any time during the making of the drawing.   For some of the simpler objects, a clay model may be of assistance.

After the views given have been read and drawn, project the third view or complete the views as specified in each individual case.

When projecting the views, refer to Chap. 6 and apply the principles given there. Remember that every line representing an edge view of a surface, an intersection of two surfaces, or a surface limit will have a mating projection in the other views.   Be careful to represent all hidden features and pay attention to the precedence of lines, as given in paragraph 6.13.

42. Fig. 9.57.   Draw the views given, completing the top view from information given on the front and side views.   Carry the views along together.

43. Fig. 9.58.   Given top and front views of the block.   Required, top, front, and side views.   See that dotted lines start and stop correctly.

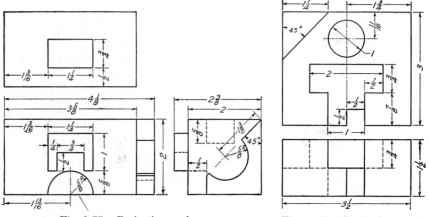

Fig. 9.57.   Projection study.   **Fig. 9.58.**   Projection study.

44. Fig. 9.59.   Given front and right-side views.   Add top view.
45. Fig. 9.60.   Given front and right-side views.   Add top view.
46. Fig. 9.61.   Given front and top views.   Add right-side view.

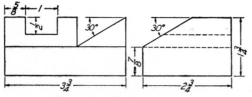

Fig. 9.59.   Projection study.

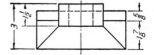

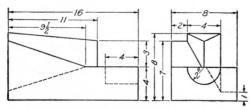

Fig. 9.60.   Bit-point-forming die.

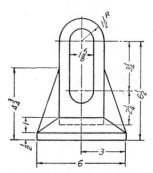

Fig. 9.61.   Rabbeting-plane guide.

47. Fig. 9.62. Given top and front views. Add right-side view.
48. Fig. 9.63. Complete the three views given.

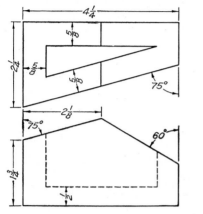

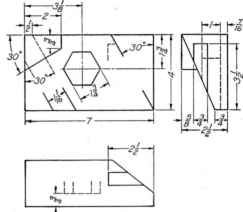

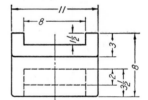

Fig. 9.62. Wedge block.   **Fig. 9.63.** Projection study.

49. Fig. 9.64. Given front and left-side views. Add top view.
50. Fig. 9.65. Given front and right-side views. Add top view.
51. Fig. 9.66. Given front and top views. Add right-side view.

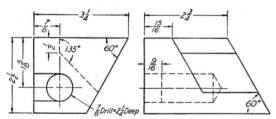

Fig. 9.64. Burner-support key.

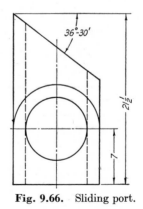

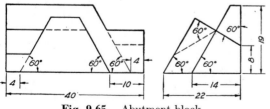

Fig. 9.65. Abutment block.   **Fig. 9.66.** Sliding port.

52. Fig. 9.67.   Assume this part to be right-hand.   Draw three views of left-hand part.

53. Fig. 9.68.   Given front and top views.   Add side view.

54. Fig. 9.69.   Given front and top views.   Add side view.

55. Fig. 9.70.   Given top and front views.   Add left-side view.

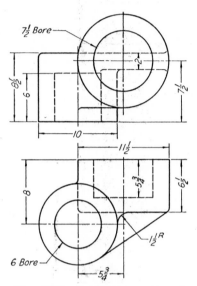

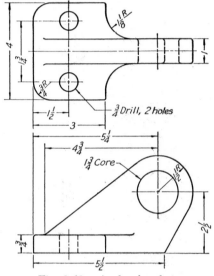

Fig. 9.67.   Bumper support and post cap.

Fig. 9.68.   Anchor bracket.

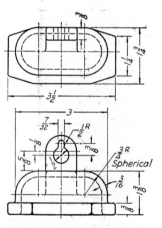

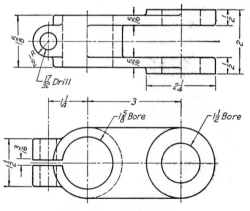

Fig. 9.69.   Entrance head.

Fig. 9.70.   Yoked link.

56. Fig. 9.71.   Given front and top views.   Add side view.
57. Fig. 9.72.   Given front and top views.   Add side view.
58. Fig. 9.73.   Given front and top views.   Add side view.
59. Fig. 9.74.   Given top and front views.   Add side view.

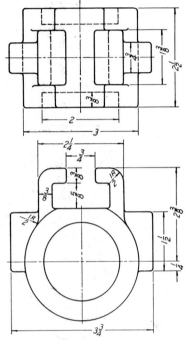

Fig. 9.71.   Rubber-mounting bracket.

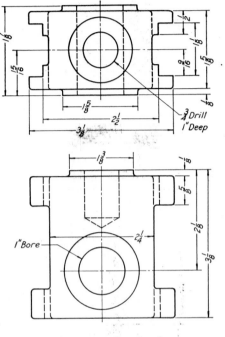

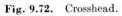

Fig. 9.72.   Crosshead.

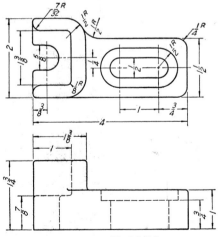

Fig. 9.73.   Tool holder.

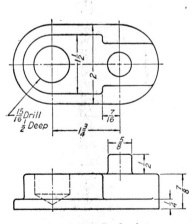

Fig. 9.74.   Lock plate.

60. Fig. 9.75.   Given top and front views.   Add left-side view.
61. Fig. 9.76.   Given top and front views.   Add side view.
62. Fig. 9.77.   Given front and top views.   Add side view.

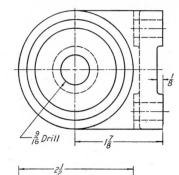

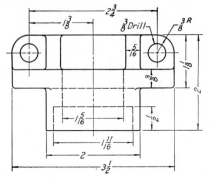

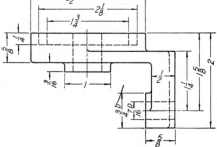

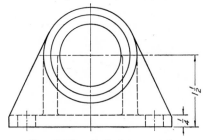

Fig. 9.75.   Bevel-gear mounting.   **Fig. 9.76.**   Cylinder support.

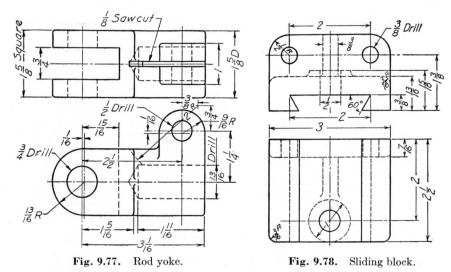

Fig. 9.77.   Rod yoke.   **Fig. 9.78.**   Sliding block.

Group III.   Views to be changed.   *Problems 63 to 68*

These problems are given to develop the ability to visualize the actual piece in space and, from this mental picture, to draw the required views as they would appear if the object were looked at in the directions specified.

In addition to the training that these problems afford in the reading of orthographic views, and also in orthographic projection, they are valuable exercises in developing drawing technique. Note that all the problems given are castings containing the usual features found on such parts, that is, fillets, rounds, runouts, etc., on the unfinished surfaces. Also, sharp corners are formed either by the intersection of an unfinished and finished surface or by two finished surfaces. After finishing one of these problems, check the drawing carefully to make sure that all details of construction have been represented correctly.

63. Fig. 9.78. Given front and top views. Required, new front, top, and side views, turning the block so that the back becomes the front and the top the bottom. The rib contour is straight.

64. Fig. 9.79. Given front, left-side, and bottom views. Draw front, top, and right-side views.

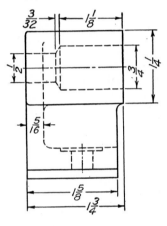

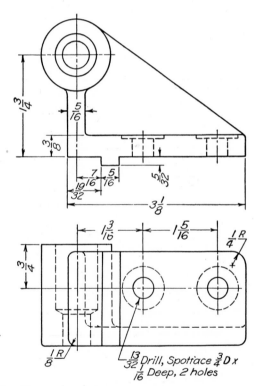

Fig. 9.79. Plunger bracket.

65. Fig. 9.80.   Given front, right-side, and bottom views.   Draw front, top, and left-side views.

66. Fig. 9.81.   Given front, right-side, and bottom views.   Draw new front, top, and right-side views, turning the support so that the back becomes the front.

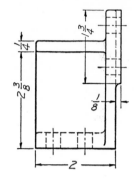

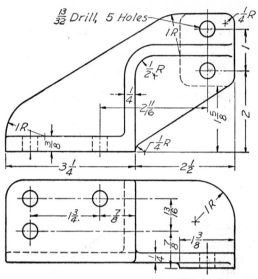

Fig. 9.80.   Offset bracket.

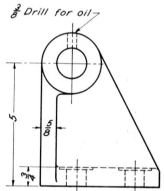

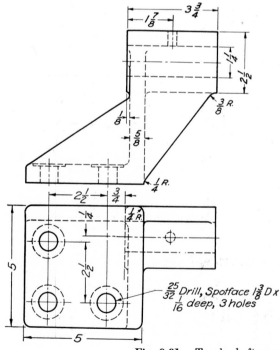

Fig. 9.81.   Toggle-shaft support.

67. Fig. 9.82. Given front and left-side views of the left-hand part. Draw the right-hand part.

68. Fig. 9.83. Given front, left-side, and bottom views. Draw front, top, and right-side views.

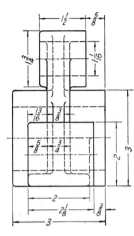
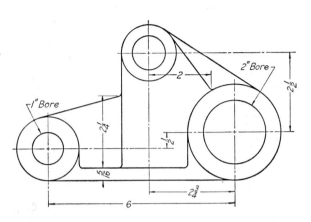

Fig. 9.82. Compound link.

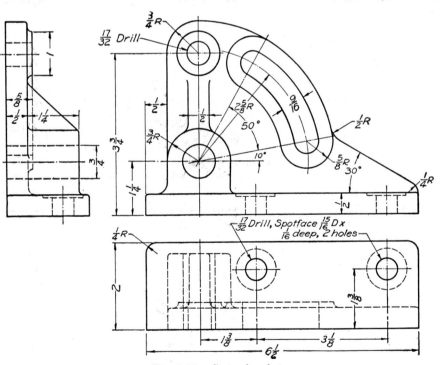

Fig. 9.83. Sector bracket.

Group IV. Drawing from memory

One of the valuable assets of an engineer is a trained memory for form and proportion. The graphic memory may be developed to a surprising degree in accuracy and power by systematic exercises in drawing from memory. This training may be commenced as soon as a knowledge of orthographic projection has been acquired.

Select an object not previously used, such as one from Figs. 9.36 to 9.56, inclusive; look at it with concentration for a certain time (from 5 seconds to $\frac{1}{2}$ minute or more); close the book and make an accurate orthographic sketch. Check with the original, and correct any mistakes or omissions. Follow with several different figures. The next day allow a 2-second view of one of the objects and repeat the orthographic views of the previous day.

Group V. Volume and weight calculations, with slide rule

In calculating the weight of a piece from the drawings, the object should be divided or broken up into the geometric solids (prisms, cylinders, pyramids, cones) of which it is composed. The volume of each of these shapes should be calculated and these added, or sometimes subtracted, to find the total volume which, multiplied by the weight of the material per unit of volume, will give the weight of the object.

A table of weights of materials will be found in the Appendix.

69. Find the weight of the cast-iron anchor bracket, Fig. 9.68.
70. Find the weight of the cast-iron bracket, Fig. 9.71.
71. Find the weight of the wrought-iron tool holder, Fig. 9.73.
72. Find the weight of the cast-steel cylinder support, Fig. 9.76.
73. Find the weight of the malleable-iron sliding block, Fig. 9.78.

TEXT-FILMS

The following McGraw-Hill Text-Film has been produced for specific correlation with Chaps. 6, 7, 8, and 9:

Orthographic Projection (20-min. sound motion picture).

Demonstrates the theory of orthographic projection; shows how objects, planes, and lines appear from different points of view; gives the methods of projection for separate views; explains concepts of height, width, and depth and their relationship in the projected views; demonstrates the making and reading of a drawing.

This film is accompanied by a coordinated silent filmstrip that reviews and further clarifies the principles of orthographic projection and may be used for oral discussion and examination.

10

Auxiliary Views

10.1 Basic concepts. A surface is shown in true shape when projected on a plane parallel to that surface. A line is shown in true length when projected on a plane parallel to the line. Also, a line will appear as a point when projected on a plane perpendicular to the line, and a surface will appear as an edge when projected on a plane perpendicular to the surface. Any view showing the true shape of a surface, or the true length of a line, is known as a *normal view*. A view in which a line appears as a point is known as an *end view*. A view showing the edge of a plane surface is known as an *edge view*.

As the majority of objects are rectangular, they may be placed with their faces parallel to the three principal planes of projection and be fully described by the principal views. In Fig. 10.1, the top, front, and right-

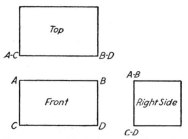

Fig. 10.1. All faces parallel to the principal planes of projection.

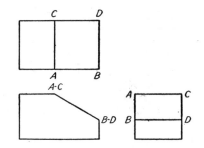

Fig. 10.2. One face inclined to two principal planes of projection.

side views are *normal views*, respectively, of the top, front, and right-side surfaces of the object. Also, the front view shows the *true length* of all the lines in the front face of the object. The top view shows the end view of lines *AC* and *BD*, and the right-side view shows the end view of lines *AB* and *CD*. The top and side views show the front surface (bounded by lines *AB*, *BD*, *DC*, and *CA*) as an edge. Thus, it may be seen that the three principal views will give normal and edge views of the major, or important, surfaces of any rectangular object.

Sometimes, however, the object may have one or more inclined faces whose true shape it is desirable or necessary to show, especially if irregular in outline. Figure 10.2 shows an object with one inclined face *ABDC*. Note that the front view shows the edge view of the inclined surface and also the point view of *AC* and *BD* and the true length of *AB* and *CD*. The side and top views show the true length of *AC* and *BD*. Nevertheless,

169

none of the views shows the *normal view* (true shape) of the inclined surface. In order to show the true shape of the inclined surface, a view known as an *auxiliary* will have to be made, *looking in a direction perpendicular to the slanting surface.*

A practical example is the flanged 45° elbow of Fig. 10.3, a casting having an irregular inclined face which not only cannot be shown in true shape in any of the principal views, but also is difficult to draw in its foreshortened position. An easier and more practical selection of views for this piece is shown in Fig. 10.4, where an auxiliary view looking in a direction perpen-

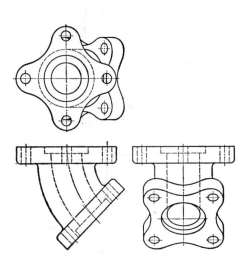

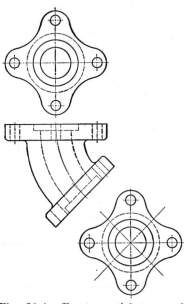

Fig. 10.3. Front, top, and right-side views. **Fig. 10.4.** Front, partial top, and auxiliary views.

dicular to the inclined face shows the true shape of the surface and also allows for simplification of the views.

10.2 Scope. The study of auxiliary views (and also oblique views, Chap. 11) is the basis of engineering geometry,[1] an interesting and valuable subject for engineers, in which the many relationships between points, lines, and planes are studied. The premise of engineering geometry is in the graphical solution to a problem, whereas the purpose here is to treat the representational aspect of drawing. Thus, in this book, the emphasis must be on true shape or *normal views* of solid object surfaces. However, at the end of this chapter, and in Chap. 11, will be found discussions of edge, point, and true-length views as they apply to the representation of solid objects.

---

[1] Also known as descriptive geometry.

10.3 Definition. *An auxiliary view is an orthographic projection on a plane perpendicular to one of the principal planes of projection but inclined to the other two, specifically:*

1. An *elevation auxiliary view*, a projection on a plane perpendicular to the horizontal plane and inclined to the frontal and profile planes.

2. A *right or left auxiliary view*, a projection on a plane perpendicular to the frontal plane and inclined to the horizontal and profile planes.

3. A *front or rear auxiliary view*, a projection on a plane perpendicular to the profile plane and inclined to the horizontal and frontal planes.

10.4 Purposes of auxiliary views. In practical drafting, and according to the scope as given in paragraph 10.2, the chief reason for using an auxiliary view is to show the true shape of a slanting surface. In such cases, the view direction must be perpendicular to the slanting surface, and the auxiliary plane will be parallel to the slanting surface. The edge view of the auxiliary plane, therefore, will be parallel to the edge view of the slanting surface,

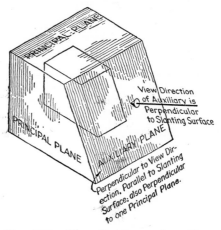

Fig. 10.5. View direction and auxiliary plane relationship.

and both the surface and auxiliary plane will appear as edges on the principal plane to which they are perpendicular. The auxiliary plane is revolved into the plane of the paper by considering it to be hinged to the plane to which it is perpendicular. Figure 10.5 illustrates the principles just mentioned.

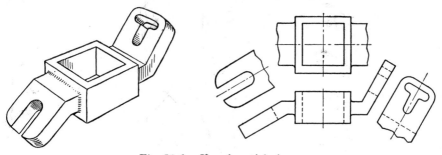

Fig. 10.6. Use of partial views.

In projecting an object on an auxiliary plane, the inclined surface will be shown in its true shape, but the other faces of the object will evidently be foreshortened. In practical work these foreshortened parts are usually omitted as in Fig. 10.6. Views thus drawn are called *partial views*. The exercise of drawing a complete view, however, may aid the student in understanding the subject.

Another important use of an auxiliary view is in the case where a principal view has some part in a foreshortened position, which cannot be drawn without first constructing an auxiliary view in its true shape from which the part can be projected back to the principal view. Figure 10.7 is an illustration of this principle. Note in this figure that the view direction is set up looking along the semihexagonal slot and perpendicular to the face which is at a right angle to the slot. From the auxiliary showing the true semihexagonal shape, the side view and then the front view may be completed.

In most cases the auxiliary view cannot be projected from the principal views, but *must be drawn from dimensional specifications of the surface shape.* The explanations and figures following will illustrate this point.

10.5 Elevation auxiliary views. Elevation auxiliary views are those which would be seen if one walked around the object, starting at the position from which the front view is taken and following a circle with all sight arrows in a horizontal plane, as shown in Fig. 10.8. In this trip the observer

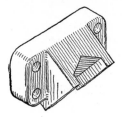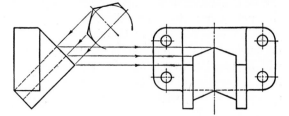

Fig. 10.7. Use of constructional auxiliary.

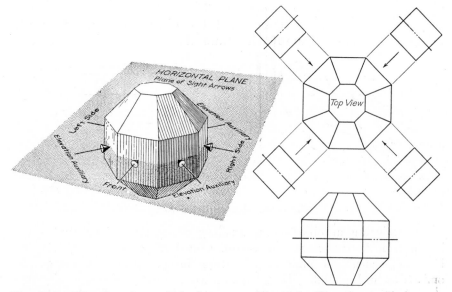

Fig. 10.8. Directions from which elevation auxiliaries are taken.

Fig. 10.9. Elevation auxiliaries.

would successively pass the points from which the right-side view, the rear view, the left-side view, and finally the front view again would be seen. A view from any other point in this plane, as indicated on the figure, would be an elevation auxiliary view. An elevation auxiliary view may thus be taken from the right-front, right-rear, left-rear, or left-front directions. Figure 10.9, an orthographic representation of Fig. 10.8, shows the complete top and front views of the object and indicates the view directions with the partial elevation auxiliary views that show the true shape of the slanting faces. On any drawing, the front, side, and rear views are *elevation* views since they show the *height* of the object. Front, side, rear, and elevation auxiliary views are all made by looking in some particular *horizontal* direction; hence, the height of any point on an elevation auxiliary will be the

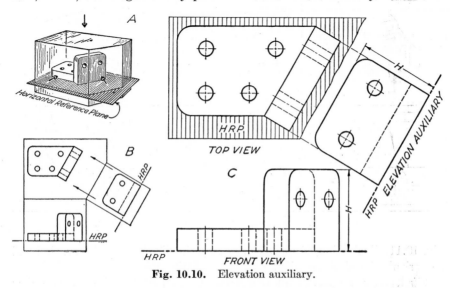

Fig. 10.10.   Elevation auxiliary.

same as the height of the same point in the front and side views. Therefore, all height measurements will be made from some fixed horizontal plane called a "reference plane."

In Fig. 10.10, the right end of the piece is at an angle to the frontal and profile planes, but is perpendicular to the horizontal plane; thus its edge will show in the top view, but its true shape will not appear in either the front or side views. *An elevation auxiliary taken as if looking directly at the surface will show the true shape.* The pictorial drawing A of Fig. 10.10 shows the direction for top, front, and elevation auxiliary views. The auxiliary view direction is perpendicular to the slanting surface to be shown in true shape. Note that the auxiliary projection plane is perpendicular to the view direction and parallel to the slanting surface. The projection planes are shown opened up into one plane (the plane of the drawing paper) at B, directly below the pictorial drawing. In this illustration, note that the rays of projection for the auxiliary will be parallel to the view direction and that the reference plane will be perpendicular to both the view direction and rays of projection.   In this case, the reference plane has been taken at the base of the object.   The larger orthographic illustration C shows the outline of projection planes removed.   Note from both the orthographic views and the pictorial sketch that measurements of height on the auxiliary will be identical with those on the front view.   The auxiliary view of the base is not completed, as it is fully described by the front and top views.

10.6   To draw an elevation auxiliary view.   The first operation in drawing *any* auxiliary is to locate and draw the direction of observation for the view.   This is done by studying the object and locating the principal view, in which the slanting (auxiliary) surface will appear as an edge.   In

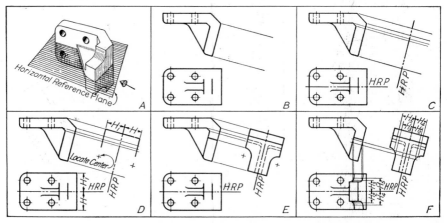

Fig. 10.11.   Stages in drawing an elevation auxiliary.

Fig. 10.11, illustrations A and B show that the direction of observation will be horizontal and perpendicular to the slanting surface.

First, draw the partial top and front views as at B, and locate the view direction by drawing projectors perpendicular to the edge view of the slanting surface, as shown.

Second, locate the reference plane HRP in the front view.   The reference plane may be taken above, below, or through the view, and is chosen for convenience in measuring.   In this case (Fig. 10.11), it is taken through the natural center line of the front view.   The reference plane (HRP) in the auxiliary will be perpendicular to the rays of projection already drawn, and is located at a convenient distance from the top view, as shown at C.

Third, as shown at D, measure the distance (height) from the reference plane of various points needed as, for example, H and H_1, and transfer these measurements with dividers, or scale, to the auxiliary view, measuring from the reference plane in the auxiliary view.

Fourth, complete the auxiliary from specifications of the rounds, etc., as shown at E.   Note that any measurement in the front view, made *toward* the top view, is transferred to the *auxiliary view, toward* the top view. Note also in Fig. 10.11 that the front view could not be completed without using the auxiliary view.

Fifth, to get the front view of the circular portions, the true shape of which shows only on the auxiliary as circle arcs, points are selected on the auxiliary view, projected back to the top view, and then to the front view. On these projectors the heights H_2 and H_3 are transferred from the auxiliary to find the corresponding points in the front view. H_4, H_5, and others will complete the curve in the front view.

10.7 Right and left auxiliary views. The right and left auxiliary views are those which would be seen if one traveled around the object with all sight arrows in a frontal plane, as shown in Fig. 10.12. Right auxiliary

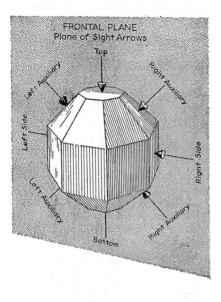

Fig. 10.12. Directions from which right and left auxiliaries are taken.

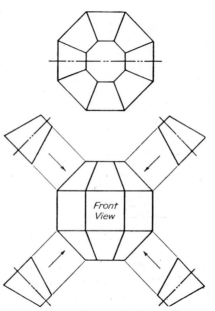

Fig. 10.13. Right and left auxiliaries.

views are those obtained from the right side of the circle, and left auxiliary views are those obtained from the left side of the circle. Thus a right auxiliary view is had by looking in a frontal direction somewhere between the right-side view and either the top or bottom view. Similarly, a left auxiliary view is made by looking in a frontal direction somewhere between the left-side view and either the top or bottom view.

The top, right-side, bottom, left-side, and right and left auxiliary views all have two common features—(1) they are all made by looking in some particular frontal direction, and (2) they all show the depth of the object as a true (not foreshortened) distance. Thus, all depth measurements for right and left auxiliary views will be made from a frontal reference plane (*FRP*), and the distance front to back of any particular point will be identical on top, right-side, bottom, left-side, and right and left auxiliary views. Figure 10.13, an orthographic representation of Fig. 10.12, shows the complete top and front views of the object and indicates the view directions with partial right and left auxiliary views that show the true shape of the slanting faces.

In Fig. 10.14, the right and left surfaces of the object are at an angle to the horizontal and profile planes, but are perpendicular to the frontal plane; thus, the edges of these slanting surfaces will show in the front view, but the true shape will not appear in any principal view. *Right and left auxiliary views taken as if looking directly at the surfaces will show the true shapes.* The pictorial drawing *A* of Fig. 10.14 shows the view directions for top, front, and right and left auxiliary views. The auxiliary view directions are

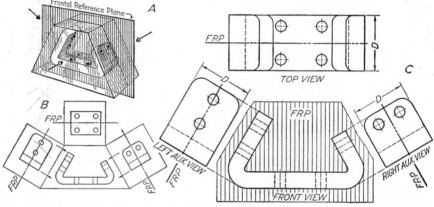

Fig. 10.14. Right and left auxiliaries.

perpendicular to the surfaces to be shown in true shape. In each case, the auxiliary projection plane is perpendicular to the view direction and parallel to the slanting surface. The projection planes are shown opened up into one plane (the plane of the drawing paper) at *B*, directly below the pictorial drawing. Note that the rays of projection for the auxiliary will be parallel to the view direction and that the reference plane will be perpendicular to both the view direction and the rays of projection. In this case the reference plane *FRP* has been taken through the center of the object because of symmetry, front to rear. The larger orthographic illustration *C* shows the outline of projection planes removed. Note from the orthographic views and the pictorial sketch that measurements of depth on the auxiliaries will be identical with those on the top view.

10.8 To draw a right or left auxiliary view. The first step is to visualize the object to be drawn and determine the direction of observation for the auxiliary. This is done by studying the object and locating the principal view in which the slanting (auxiliary) surface will appear as an edge and then imagine a view direction perpendicular to the slanting surface. In Fig. 10.15, illustrations *A* and *B* show that the slanting surface appears as an edge in the front view; therefore, the direction of observation for the auxiliary will be frontal and perpendicular to the slanting surface.

First, draw the partial top and front views, as at *B,* and locate the view direction by drawing projectors perpendicular to the slanting surface, as shown.

Second, locate the reference plane *FRP* in the top view. The reference plane may be taken in front of, through, or to the rear of the view, but is here located at the rear flat surface of the object because of convenience in measuring. The reference plane *FRP* in the auxiliary view will be perpendicular to the rays of projection already drawn and is located at a convenient distance from the front view, as shown at *C.*

Third, as shown at *D,* measure the distance (depths) from the reference plane (of various points needed) and transfer these measurements with dividers or scale to the auxiliary view, measuring from the reference plane

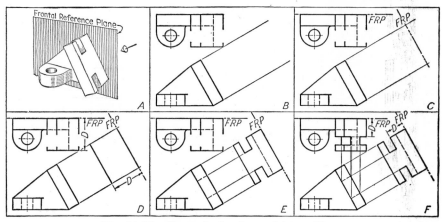

Fig. 10.15. Stages in drawing a right auxiliary.

in the auxiliary view. Note that the points are in front of the reference plane on the top view and, therefore, are measured toward the front on the auxiliary view.

Fourth, from specifications, complete the auxiliary view, as shown at *E.*

Fifth, complete the drawing, as shown at *F.* In this case the top view could have been completed before the auxiliary was drawn. However, it is considered better practice to lay out the true-shape view (auxiliary) before completing the view that will show the surface foreshortened.

The auxiliary view just discussed is a *right auxiliary view,* as explained in paragraph 10.7. Obviously, a left auxiliary view would be used if the object had a slanting face on the left rather than on the right side. The order of drawing would of course be the same.

10.9 Front or rear auxiliary views. The front and rear auxiliary views are those which would be seen if one traveled around the object with all sight arrows in a profile plane, as shown in Fig. 10.16. Front auxiliary views are those obtained from the front half of the circle, and rear auxiliary views are those obtained from the rear half of the circle. Thus, a front auxiliary view is had by looking in a profile direction somewhere between the front view and either the top or bottom view. Similarly, a rear auxiliary view is made by looking in a profile direction somewhere between the rear view and either the top or bottom view.

The front, top, rear, and bottom views and the front and rear auxiliary views all have two common features—(1) they are all made by looking in

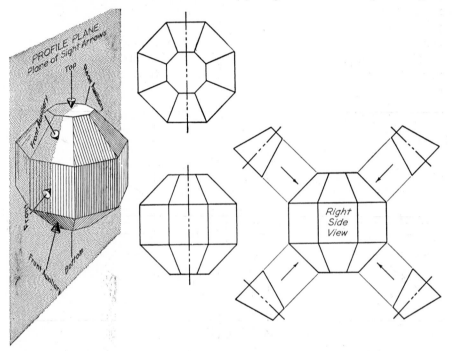

Fig. 10.16. Directions from which front and rear auxiliaries are taken.

Fig. 10.17. Front and rear auxiliaries.

some particular profile direction, and (2) they all show the width of the object as a true (not foreshortened) distance. Thus, all width measurements for front and rear auxiliary views will be made from a profile reference plane *PRP*, and the distance left to right of any particular point will be identical on front, top, rear, bottom, and front and rear auxiliary views. Figure 10.17, an orthographic representation of Fig. 10.16, shows the complete top, front, and side views of the object and indicates the view directions with partial front and rear auxiliary views that show the true shape of the slanting faces.

In Fig. 10.18, the upper portion of the object is at an angle to the horizontal and frontal planes, but is perpendicular to the profile plane; thus, the edge of this slanting surface will show in either side view, but the true shape will not appear in any principal view. *A front auxiliary view, taken as if looking directly at the surface, will show the true shape.* The pictorial drawing *A* of Fig. 10.18 shows the view directions for front, right-side, and front auxiliary views. The auxiliary view direction is perpendicular to the surface to be shown in true shape. Note that the auxiliary projection plane is perpendicular to the view direction and parallel to the slanting surface. The projection planes are shown opened up into one plane (the plane of the drawing paper) at *B*, directly below the pictorial drawing. In this illustra-

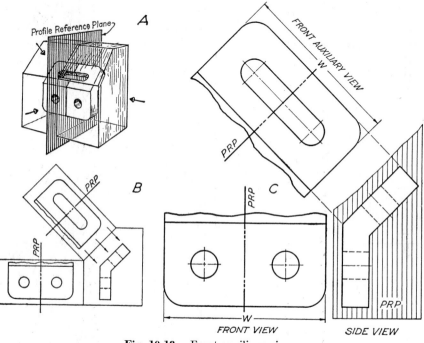

Fig. 10.18.   Front auxiliary view.

tion note that the rays of projection for the auxiliary will be parallel to the view direction and that the reference plane will be perpendicular to both the view direction and the rays of projection. In this case the profile reference plane *PRP* has been taken through the center of the object, because of symmetry, right to left. The larger orthographic illustration *C* shows the outline of projection planes removed. Note from the orthographic views and the pictorial sketch that measurements of width on the auxiliary will be identical with those on the front view.

10.10   To draw a front or rear auxiliary view. The first step is to visualize the object to be drawn and determine the direction of observation for the auxiliary. This is done by locating the principal view in which the slanting (auxiliary) surface will appear as an edge and then imagine a viewing direction perpendicular to the slanting surface. In Fig. 10.19, illustrations *A* and *B* show that the slanting surface appears as an edge in the right-side view; therefore, the direction of observation for the auxiliary will be profile and perpendicular to the slanting surface.

First, draw the partial front, top, and right-side views as at *B* and locate the view direction by drawing projectors perpendicular to the slanting surface, as shown.

Second, locate the profile reference plane *PRP* in the front view. This reference plane is taken at the left side of the object, because both the vertical and slanting portions have a left surface in the same profile plane. The reference plane in the auxiliary view will be perpendicular to the rays

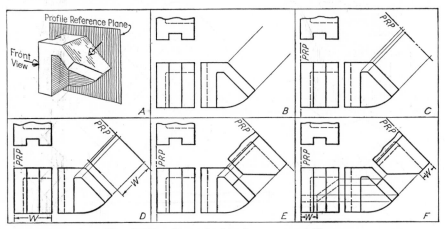

Fig. 10.19.   Stages in drawing a rear auxiliary.

of projection already drawn, and is located at a convenient distance from the right-side view, as shown at *C*.

Third, as shown at *D*, measure the distances (widths) from the reference plane (of various points needed) and transfer these measurements with dividers or scale to the auxiliary view, measuring from the reference plane in the auxiliary view. Note that points to the right of the reference plane on the front view will be measured in a direction *toward* the right-side view on the auxiliary.

Fourth, from specifications of the surface contour, complete the auxiliary, as shown at *E*.

Fifth, complete the right-side and front views by projecting and measuring from the auxiliary view. As an example, one intersection of the cut corner is projected to the right-side view and from there to the front view; the other intersection is measured (distance *W*) from the auxiliary view and then laid off on the front view.

The auxiliary view just discussed is a rear auxiliary view, as explained in paragraph 10.9. Obviously, a front auxiliary view would require that the object have a slanting face on the front rather than on the rear. The general order of drawing would, of course, be the same.

10.11 The edge view of a surface in an auxiliary position. A surface perpendicular to one of the planes of projection, but inclined to the other two, will appear as an edge in the principal view of the plane to which the inclined plane is perpendicular. Thus, for the auxiliary positions the inclined plane appears as an edge in a principal view as follows: (1) a plane perpendicular to the frontal plane appears as an edge in the front view, (2) a plane perpendicular to the horizontal plane appears as an edge in the top view, and (3) a plane perpendicular to the profile plane appears as an edge in either side view.

Study the positions of the inclined planes of Figs. 10.10, 10.14, and 10.18.

10.12 The true length of a line in an auxiliary position. The true length of a line in an auxiliary position will appear in the principal view of the plane to which the line is parallel. Thus, a horizontal line appears in true length in the top view, a frontal line appears in true length in the front view, and a profile line appears in true length in either side view. Study Fig. 10.20.

10.13 The end view of a line in an auxiliary position. The end view of a line in an auxiliary position will appear in an auxiliary view taken in a

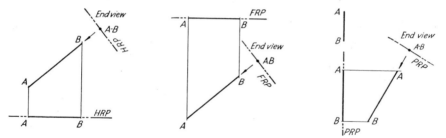

Fig. 10.20. True length and end views of horizontal, frontal, and profile lines.

direction looking along the line. Therefore, if the line is horizontal, an elevation auxiliary will be employed; if frontal, a right or left auxiliary view, and if profile, a front or rear auxiliary view. All three basic positions and the end views are illustrated in Fig. 10.20.

10.14 Summary. The following outline is given as an aid in review and for reference while learning the basic principles and steps in drawing auxiliary views.

I. **General procedure for drawing an auxiliary view.**
   A. Determine the view direction.
   B. Determine the type of auxiliary which will result (elevation auxiliary view, right or left auxiliary view, front or rear auxiliary view).
   C. Lay out partial principal views (top, front, etc.), planning the sheet to leave room for the auxiliary.
   D. Draw projection rays (parallel to the view direction) for the auxiliary.
   E. Locate the reference plane in the proper principal view and also on the auxiliary view (perpendicular to the rays of projection).

    F. Draw the auxiliary view.

        1. By laying out the shape from dimensional specifications.

        2. Or, if distances can be obtained from the principal view, measure them from the reference plane and transfer to the auxiliary (measuring from the reference plane).

        3. Note that, in measuring from the reference plane, a distance *toward* the view projected from will be laid off on the auxiliary *toward* the view projected from.

II. Digest of facts.

    A. Elevation auxiliary view.

        1. Always projected from the top view.

        2. Viewing direction will be horizontal.

        3. Shows true *height.*

        4. Reference plane is horizontal (*HRP*).

        5. Top of object will always be nearest the top view.

    B. Right or left auxiliary views.

        1. Always projected from the front view.

        2. Viewing direction will be frontal.

        3. Shows true *depth.*

        4. Reference plane is frontal (*FRP*).

        5. Front of object will always be nearest the front view.

    C. Front or rear auxiliary views.

        1. Always projected from a side view.

        2. Viewing direction will be profile.

        3. Shows true *width.*

        4. Reference plane is profile (*PRP*).

        5*a.* If auxiliary is projected from a right-side view, right side of object will be nearest the right-side view.

         b. If auxiliary is projected from a left-side view, left side of object will be nearest the left-side view.

PROBLEMS

    1, 2, 3, 4, 5, 6, 7. Figs. 10.21 to 10.27. Draw views given and add auxiliary views, using reference planes indicated.

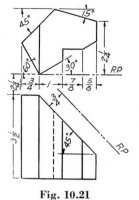
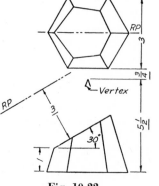
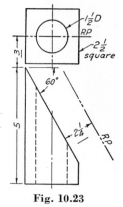

      Fig. 10.21   **Fig. 10.22**   **Fig. 10.23**

          Figs. 10.21 to 10.23. Auxiliary studies.

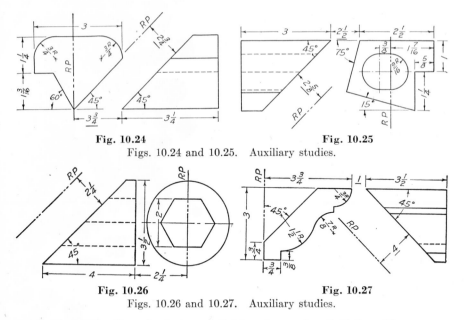

Fig. 10.24   **Fig. 10.25**
Figs. 10.24 and 10.25.   Auxiliary studies.

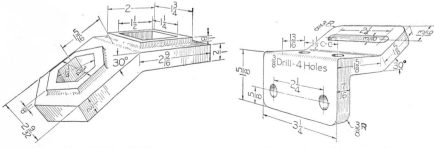

Fig. 10.26   **Fig. 10.27**
Figs. 10.26 and 10.27.   Auxiliary studies.

8. Fig. 10.28.   Draw front view, partial top view, and partial left auxiliary.

9. Fig. 10.29.   Draw partial front view, right-side view, partial top view, and partial front auxiliary.

10. Fig. 10.30.   Draw front view, partial top view, and partial right and left auxiliaries.

11. Fig. 10.31.   Draw top view, partial front view, and partial elevation auxiliaries.

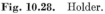

Fig. 10.28.   Holder.   **Fig. 10.29.**   Slotted anchor.

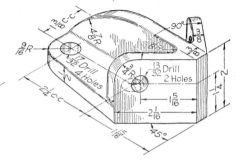

Fig. 10.30.   Connector strip.   **Fig. 10.31.**   Push plate.

12. Fig. 10.32. Draw front view, partial top view, and partial right auxiliary.

13. Fig. 10.33. Draw front view, partial right-side view, and partial right auxiliary. Draw auxiliary before completing the front view.

14. Fig. 10.34. Draw front view, partial top view, and partial right auxiliary.

16. Fig. 10.35. Draw front view, partial top view, and partial right auxiliary.

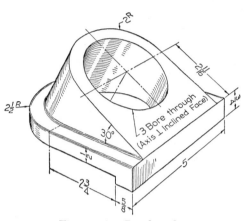

Fig. 10.32. Bevel washer.

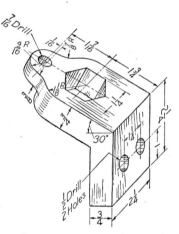

Fig. 10.33. Jig angle.

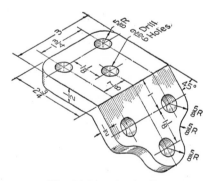

Fig. 10.34. Angle clip.

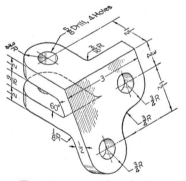
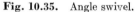

Fig. 10.35. Angle swivel.

16. Fig. 10.36. Draw front view, partial top and right-side views, and partial right auxiliary.

17. Fig. 10.37. Draw front, partial top, and left-side views, and partial right auxiliary.

18, 19. Figs. 10.38 and 10.39. Determine what views and part views will best describe the piece. Submit sketch before starting the drawing.

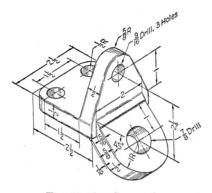

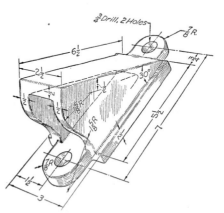

Fig. 10.36. Corner tie.

Fig. 10.37. Channel support.

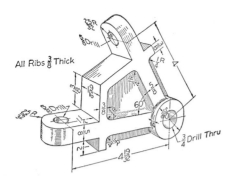

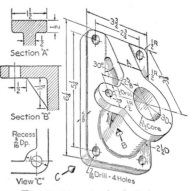

Fig. 10.38. Radial swing block.

Fig. 10.39. Angle-shaft base.

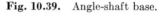

AUXILIARY VIEWS

20. Fig. 10.40. Draw front view, partial bottom view, and partial left auxiliary.

21. Fig. 10.41. Draw front view, partial left-side and bottom views, and partial right auxiliary.

22, 23. Figs. 10.42 and 10.43. Determine what views and part views will best describe the piece.

24. Fig. 10.44. Draw given front view; add necessary views to describe the piece.

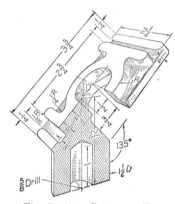

Fig. 10.40. Catenary clip.

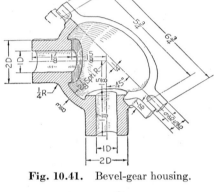

Fig. 10.41. Bevel-gear housing.

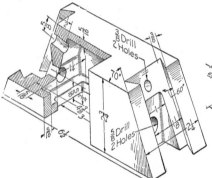

Fig. 10.42. Slide base.

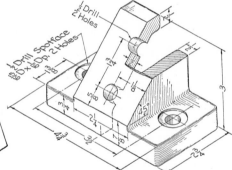

Fig. 10.43. Idler bracket.

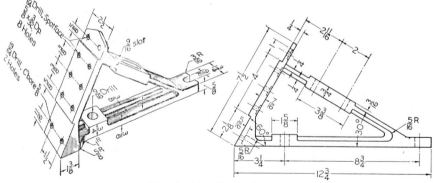
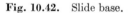

Fig. 10.44. Corner brace.

25. Fig. 10.45. Draw front view, partial left-side view, and partial right auxiliary.

26, 27. Figs. 10.46 and 10.47.   This pair of similar objects has the upper lug in two different positions.   Layouts are for 11- by 17-in. paper.   Draw views and part views as indicated on layouts.

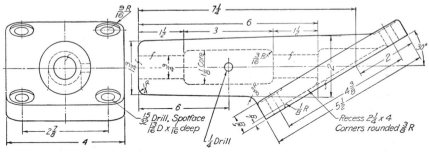

Fig. 10.45. Spindle support.

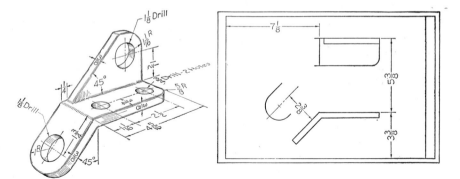

Fig. 10.46. Spar clip, 90°.

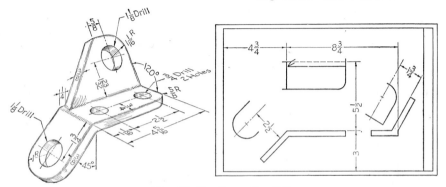

Fig. 10.47. Spar clip, 120°.

An interesting and instructive exercise not only in the drawing of an auxiliary view but also in visualization may be had by turning the object to a new position and then drawing the necessary descriptive views. The following are suggested. Select an object not previously drawn.

28. Fig. 10.28. Turn the object so that the top becomes the front and draw the necessary partial principal views and auxiliary view.

29. Fig. 10.29. Turn the object so that the side becomes the front and draw the necessary partial principal views and auxiliary view.

30. Fig. 10.30. Turn the object so that the top becomes the front and draw the necessary partial principal views and auxiliary views.

31. Fig. 10.33. Turn the object so that the front becomes the side and draw the necessary partial principal views and auxiliary view.

32. Fig. 10.34. Turn the object so that the top becomes the front and draw the necessary partial principal views and auxiliary view.

33. Fig. 10.35. Same instruction as for Prob. 32.

34. Fig. 10.36. Same instruction as for Prob. 32.

35. Fig. 10.43. Same instruction as for Prob. 32.

TEXT-FILMS

The following Text-Film has been designed for direct correlation with Chap. 10:

Auxiliary Views: Single Auxiliaries (20-min. sound motion picture).

Explains and defines auxiliary projection; demonstrates the theory and methods of constructing different types of single auxiliaries; shows that the auxiliary view is sometimes needed for completion of one of the principal views.

The coordinated silent filmstrip may be used to reemphasize the principles of auxiliary projection and for purposes of class review and discussion.

11

Oblique Views

11.1 As explained in Chap. 6, the majority of objects will have their surfaces parallel to the three principal planes of projection and can, therefore, be described by some combination of principal views. Other objects, as described in Chap. 10, may have some faces perpendicular to one of the principal planes, but inclined to the other two, thus requiring an auxiliary view to describe their true shape. A third possibility is that some face of an object may be inclined to *all* the principal planes of projection, in which case the surface is said to be oblique and the view required to show its true shape is known as an *oblique view*.

11.2 Definition. An oblique view is a projection on a plane inclined to all three principal planes of projection.

11.3 Basic concepts. To find the true shape (normal view) of an oblique surface, that is, a surface not perpendicular to any one of the principal planes, as illustrated by the pictorial drawing of Fig. 9.1, two operations are required: *first*, an auxiliary view of the object made in a direction so that the oblique surface appears as an edge; *second*, an auxiliary view made in a direction perpendicular to the edge view. *This second auxiliary is the oblique view.*

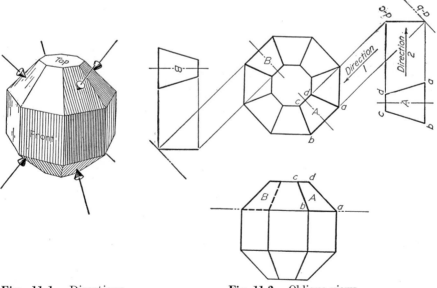

Fig. 11.1. Directions from which oblique views are taken.

Fig. 11.2. Oblique views.

The principle is illustrated by Fig. 11.2, an orthographic representation of Fig. 11.1. Surfaces A and B shown on the figure are oblique surfaces, because they are not parallel or perpendicular to any of the principal planes of projection. If an elevation auxiliary is made looking in direction 1, an edge view of the oblique surface A will be obtained, because, as shown on the figure, the *end views* of the horizontal lines *ab* and *cd* of the surface will be had, *and if one looks along one line of a surface, the surface will appear as an edge*. Next, if a second auxiliary is made looking in direction 2, perpendicular to the edge view, the surface will appear in true shape, because the direction of observation is now perpendicular to the surface.

Thus, we see that two operations (mentioned before) are necessary: *first*, the edge view, and *second*, the oblique view, or normal view of the surface. Also, that the *edge*-view step is necessary so that the second auxiliary may be set up having a direction of observation perpendicular to the oblique surface.

11.4   Edge views. As indicated in paragraph 11.3, the key to determining the direction of observation necessary in order to obtain an edge

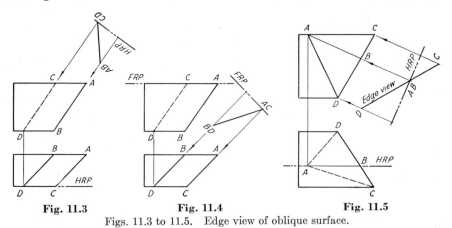

Fig. 11.3   Fig. 11.4   Fig. 11.5

Figs. 11.3 to 11.5.   Edge view of oblique surface.

view is to find a direction that will give an end view of *one line* of the surface. This can be easily done if the surface contains a horizontal, frontal, or profile line as a part of the surface outline. Referring again to Fig. 10.20 and paragraph 10.13, if a line is horizontal, an elevation auxiliary will give the end view; if frontal, a right or left auxiliary view will be used; if profile, a front or rear auxiliary view will be employed. Thus, in Fig. 11.3, lines AB and CD are horizontal and the elevation auxiliary shown having a direction of observation parallel to these lines gives the required end view of the lines and the edge view of surface $ABDC$. In Fig. 11.4, lines AC and BD are frontal. Therefore, a right auxiliary view taken in a direction parallel to these lines will give the required edge view. Study Figs. 11.3 and 11.4 carefully, and note that in each case the auxiliary must be projected from the view showing the true length of a line of the oblique surface. The objects shown in Figs. 11.3 and 11.4 are identical. Edges AB and CD are horizontal. Edges AC and BD are frontal. If no *horizontal, frontal,* or *profile* line is present as a part of the surface outline, one is then laid out on the surface. In Fig. 11.5, the surface outlines AC, CD, and DA are all oblique lines and cannot be used to obtain an edge view in the first auxiliary. However, the horizontal line AB drawn on the front view and then projected to the top view will give the direction for an elevation auxiliary that will show the end view of line AB and, also, the edge view of surface ADC.

11.5 Oblique views. After an edge view of an oblique surface has been obtained, the direction for an oblique view showing the normal view

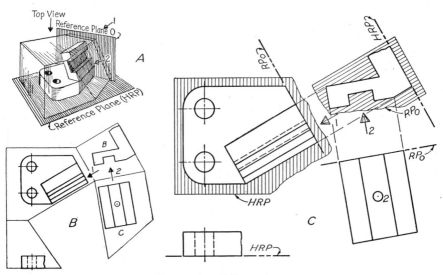

Fig. 11.6. Oblique view.

of the surface may be made. The direction of observation for the oblique view (in order to give a normal view) will be perpendicular to the surface and will, therefore, be perpendicular to the edge view. Figure 11.6 shows at A the pictorial representation of an object with a horizontal base and an oblique notched surface extending upward. The intersection of the oblique surface and the base is a horizontal line, thus giving the direction (1) for an auxiliary showing the edge view of the oblique surface, as described in paragraph 11.4. Perpendicular to the edge view (and perpendicular to the oblique surface) is the direction of observation (2) for the oblique view.

At B is shown the planes of projection opened out into one plane, the paper. Note that the direction of observation (1) is parallel to the lower horizontal edge of the oblique surface, and that the direction (2) for the oblique is perpendicular to the edge view.

Illustration C shows the views enlarged and includes the necessary reference planes. The reference plane for the first auxiliary (edge) view will be horizontal (HRP) and is, for convenience in measuring, taken at the bottom surface of the horizontal base. The reference plane (HRP) in the auxiliary view will be perpendicular to the view direction and to the rays of projection. The reference plane (RP_o) for the oblique view must be (as with any other auxiliary view) *in the oblique view*, perpendicular to the view direction and also the rays of projection. The other view of the reference plane will in this case be placed in the top view perpendicular to the rays between the top view and edge view, *because the distance along the oblique face in the direction of view direction (1) is the measurement that must be made.* A study of pictorial drawing A in connection with orthographic illustration C will show that the oblique reference plane is shown in normal view in the first auxiliary (edge) view. Therefore, the two views that are in projection with the edge view of the oblique surface will show the edge view of the reference plane (RP_o), and both views of the reference plane (RP_o) will be perpendicular to the rays between the edge view and the two views in direct projection with the edge view.

11.6 To draw an oblique view. Figure 11.7 illustrates the progressive steps in drawing an oblique view. The pictorial illustration A shows a

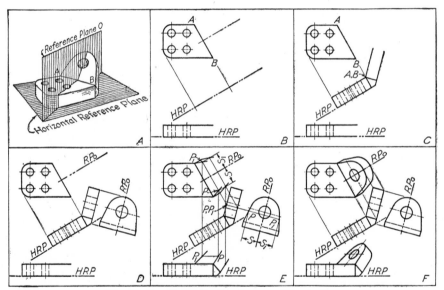

Fig. 11.7. Stages in drawing an oblique view.

typical object having an oblique surface. The line of intersection between the oblique portion and the horizontal base is line AB. In order to get an edge view of the oblique surface, a view may be taken looking in the direction of line AB, thus giving an end view of AB. Because AB is a line of the oblique surface, the edge view will result. The reference plane for this view will be horizontal (HRP), because an elevation auxiliary will be used. The direction of observation for the oblique view will be perpendicular to the oblique surface. The reference plane (RP_o) for the oblique view will be perpendicular to the edge view direction, and thus be perpendicular to edge AB, as shown in illustration A.

B shows partial top and front views.   Also, the projectors and reference plane for the required edge view are shown.

At *C* the edge view has been drawn.   Note that line *AB* appears as a point in the edge view.   The angle that the oblique surface makes with the base is laid out in this view from specifications.

D illustrates the addition of the oblique view.   The projectors for the view are perpendicular to the edge view.   The reference plane is drawn perpendicular to the projectors for the oblique view, and at a convenient distance from the edge view.   The reference plane in the top view is drawn perpendicular to the rays between the top and edge views and is taken midway between points *A* and *B* on the top view, because the oblique surface is symmetrical about this reference plane.   The oblique view is then drawn from specifications of the shape.   The projection back to the edge view may then be made.

The views thus completed at *D* describe the object, but if it is desired for illustrative purposes, or as an exercise in projection, the top and front views may be completed.   *E* and *F* illustrate the method.   Any point, say *P*, may be selected and projected back to the edge view.   From this view a projector is drawn back to the top view.   Then the distance *S* from the oblique view is transferred to the reference plane in the top view.   A number of points so located will complete the top view of the circular portion, and the straight line portion may be projected in similar manner.   The front view is found by drawing projectors to the front view for the points needed, measuring the heights from the reference plane in the edge view and transferring these distances to the front view.   Note that this procedure for completion of the top and front views is the same as for drawing the views originally but in reverse order.

11.7   The true length of an oblique line.   Sometimes it will be necessary to represent the true length of some element of a part or structure, and in other cases the true-length view may be a necessary prelude to the drawing of an end view (described in paragraph 11.8).

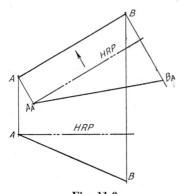

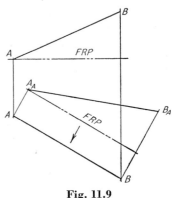

Fig. 11.8   **Fig. 11.9**
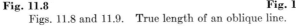
Figs. 11.8 and 11.9.   True length of an oblique line.

If a line is viewed in a direction perpendicular to the line, its true length will be seen. The line can also be assumed to lie in a plane, so that if the normal view of the plane is obtained the true length of the line will also appear. Thus, in Fig. 11.8, the line may be assumed to lie in a vertical plane; then a view direction perpendicular to the top view of the line will show the normal view of the receding plane, and AB as a line in the plane will appear in true length. The elevation auxiliary shown will have a view direction perpendicular to the assumed vertical plane, and the projection is as discussed for an elevation auxiliary in paragraph 10.5. Figure 11.9 illustrates the same principle, but with an assumed frontal receding plane, thus requiring a right auxiliary view.

11.8 The end view of an oblique line. Instead of a normal view of a *surface*, a problem may require the finding of the normal view of a *line* with, in addition, the *end view* of the line. The line may occur as the axis of a hole or boss, usually symmetrical.

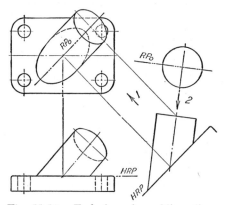

Fig. 11.10.   End view of an oblique line.

First, the true length of the axis must be found, as explained in paragraph 11.7. Then a view made looking in the direction of the axis will give the required end view. Figure 11.10 shows a base on which is mounted a shaft. An auxiliary view, taken in direction (1), perpendicular to the shaft axis gives the true length. A view direction (2), for an oblique view looking along the axis, gives the end view. The oblique reference plane (RP_o) will be drawn perpendicular to the projectors between the auxiliary and oblique views and perpendicular to direction (1) in the top view. Note that the auxiliary and end views of the shaft will be drawn from specifications; then, if desired, projection back to the top and front views may be accomplished.

11.9   Summary

I. **General.**

    A. An oblique view must be projected from an auxiliary view.

    B. An oblique view can show the normal view of an oblique plane, or the end view of an oblique line.

II. **To draw an oblique view.**

    A. Determine direction for auxiliary view (to show edge of plane, or true length of line).

    B. Determine type of auxiliary.

    C. Lay out partial principal views.

    D. Draw projection rays for auxiliary.

    E. Locate reference plane in auxiliary and principal view.

    F. Draw auxiliary view.

G. Determine direction for oblique view.

    1. Perpendicular to edge view for normal view of plane.

    2. Aligned with true length of line for end view.

H. Locate reference plane in oblique and principal views.

    1. Perpendicular to rays between auxiliary view and oblique view.

    2. Perpendicular to rays between auxiliary view and principal view.

I. Draw oblique view.

J. Complete auxiliary and principal views, if required.

PROBLEMS

Group I. Oblique views.

    1. Fig. 11.11. Draw partial front, partial top, partial elevation auxiliary (edge), and oblique views. Edge view is to show the true size of dovetail slot; oblique view is to show the true size of slanting face.

    2. Fig. 11.12. Draw partial front, partial top, elevation auxiliary showing edge view of slanting lug, and oblique view showing true size and shape of slanting lug. Lay out oblique view before completing elevation auxiliary.

    3. Fig. 11.13. Draw the necessary views to describe the adjusting clip, using partial edge and oblique views.

    4. Fig. 11.14. Draw the views given, omitting lugs on top view. Add right auxiliary and oblique view to show true shape of lugs.

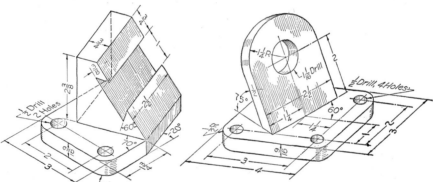

Fig. 11.11. Dovetail clip.   **Fig. 11.12.** Anchor base.

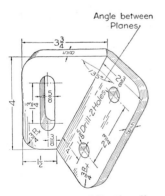
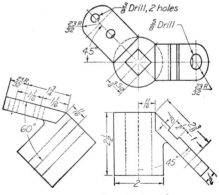

Fig. 11.13. Adjusting clip.   **Fig. 11.14.** Bar-strut anchor.

5. Fig. 11.15.   Draw the views given, using auxiliary and oblique views to obtain shape of lugs.

6. Fig. 11.16.   Draw top, front, and left-side views, using edge and oblique views to obtain shape of socket.

7. Fig. 11.17.   Draw top, front, left-side (alternate position), elevation auxiliary (edge), and oblique views.

8. Fig. 11.18.   Draw top, front, partial elevation auxiliary, and oblique views. The piece is symmetrical about the main axis.

9. Fig. 11.19.   Draw the spar clip using layout for 11- by 17-in. paper as shown. Note that left auxiliary, elevation auxiliary (edge), and oblique views are required.

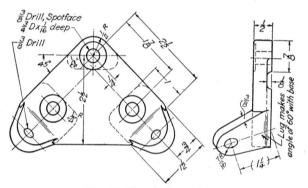

Fig. 11.15.   Cable anchor.

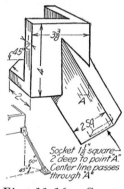

Fig. 11.16.   Corner bracket.

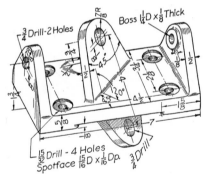

Fig. 11.17.   Transverse connection.

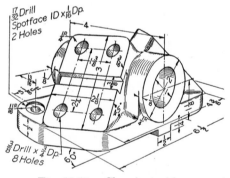

Fig. 11.18.   Chamfer tool base.

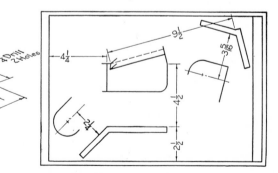

Fig. 11.19.   Spar clip.

10. Fig. 11.20. Draw the layout of the views given and such additional auxiliary and oblique views as are necessary for the description of the piece.

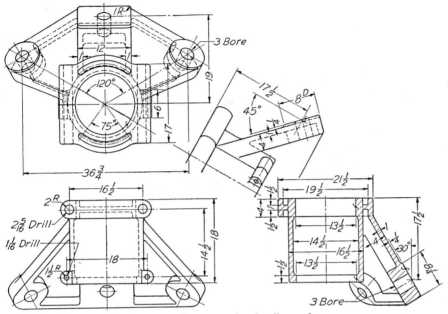

Fig. 11.20. Crane masthead collar and cap.

Group II. True length of lines.

11. Find the true length of the body diagonal of a 2½-in. cube.

12. Find the true length of slanting edges of a right rectangular pyramid. Base, 3 by 1¾ in.; altitude, 3½ in.

13. Draw the two projections of a line 3 in. long making an angle of 30° with F and whose F projection makes 45° with the horizontal, the line sloping downward and backward to the left.

14. Draw a right rectangular pyramid whose slant height is 3½ in. Base is 2 in. square. Find the true length of the slanting edges.

15. Draw a right rectangular pyramid whose base is 2 in. square and whose slanting edges are 3½ in. long. Determine the altitude.

16. Draw a cube having one face frontal whose body diagonal is 2½ in.

17. Draw top and front views of a right rectangular prism, base 1½ by 2¼, whose body diagonal is 3½ in. What is the length of the prism?

TEXT-FILMS

The following Text-Film has been designed for direct correlation with Chap. 11:

Auxiliary Views: Double Auxiliaries (15-min. sound motion picture).

Reviews orthographic projection on three principal planes and on auxiliary planes; shows why a single auxiliary view does not give an accurate picture of an oblique face; describes in detail the theory of the double-auxiliary or oblique view; demonstrates method of drawing an object with an oblique face.

The coordinated silent filmstrip may be used further to illustrate the theory of oblique views and to provide class reviews and discussion.

12

Rotation

12.1   The principal and auxiliary orthographic views, described in the preceding chapters, are secured by the observer assuming a different position for each view, and then recording those views on projection planes perpendicular to their respective lines of sight.   In each instance the object has not been moved; its relationship with the principal planes of projection has remained unchanged.

The same series of views can be obtained by rotating the object about various axes (while the observer remains in a fixed position) and then recording an additional view, for each new position of the object, on one of the projection planes.   It will be obvious that this latter procedure will result in superimposed views; and, while the solutions of many geometric problems are done in this manner, the more frequent solutions that employ rotation procedures combine object rotation with the observer change-of-position routine.

In Fig. 12.1, a comparison of the two methods may be made.   The top and front views of a crank are shown in *A*; in *B* the inclined arm is not drawn

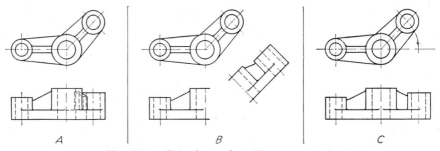

| A | B | C |

Fig. 12.1.   Rotation and auxiliary compared.

in the front view, but is shown in an elevation auxiliary.   The presentation in *B* is preferable to that shown in *A*, since both arms are drawn in their true shape and the distances between the center axis and the end axes are shown in true length in the elevation views.   Comparable to the presentation of *B* is the conventional treatment of *C*.   The front view shows the inclined arm as though it had been rotated into the frontal plane of the other arm; however, the top view shows the actual angular relationship between the arms. This procedure of alignment by rotation is further described in Chap. 13, Sections and Conventions.

Rotation is primarily a means of graphical expression for the designing engineer; however, all personnel of the drafting room should be familiar with its use.   The designer will use rotation to determine such things as (1) clearance between moving and fixed parts, (2) normal views of edges and plane surfaces, and (3) various angular relationships, either existing or designed to meet specific requirements. Draftsmen will constantly be working from design drawings and must, therefore, be able to read the designer's solutions (regardless of the means of such solutions). Both the designer and the draftsman must realize the advantages of rotation procedures in drawing axonometric views and many of the conventional treatments used in the engineering industries.

12.2 Principles of rotation. If an object is rotated about an axis perpendicular to a plane, then (1) *its projection on that plane will change only in*

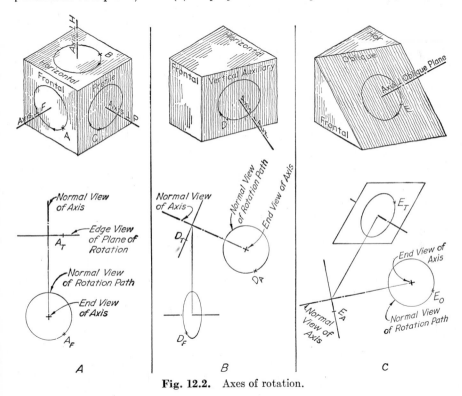

Fig. 12.2. Axes of rotation.

position, not in shape or size, and (2) *the dimensions parallel to the axis will be unchanged.*

Any straight line may be used as an axis of rotation; however, the most expeditious use of rotation is accomplished when both a true length view and an end view of the axis are already drawn. Since the top, front, and side
· views are the ones usually employed for shape description, the axes of rotation customarily used are those perpendicular to the horizontal, frontal, and profile planes of projection, Fig. 12.2*A*. Axes other than the above are occasionally used, but the solution is still accomplished through the use of views that show the normal (true length) and end views of the axis, Fig.

12.2*B* and *C*.   In each illustration, it will be noted, the lettered points rotate about their axes in planes perpendicular to those axes.

The principles of rotation may be further illustrated by the rotation of a rectangular card about an axis perpendicular to the plane of the card.   In a view that shows an end view of the axis, the card will appear in its true shape, regardless of the amount of rotation through which it has been moved.   In

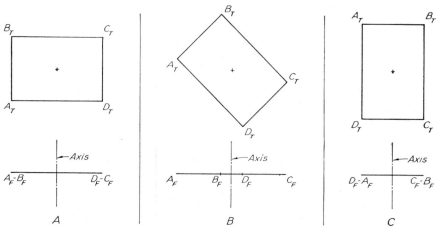

Fig. 12.3.   Rotation about a vertical axis.

the views that show the axis in true length, it will be noted that no movement parallel to the axis occurs during the rotation.   Figure 12.3 shows such a rectangular card in three different positions.

12.3   Rotation of solid objects.   The rotation of solid objects may be divided into three general-purpose classifications: (1) to secure alternate positions of moving parts, (2) to clarify orthographic projection principles, and (3) to secure axonometric views.

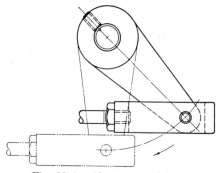

Fig. 12.4.   Alternate position.

An example of the first classification is shown in Fig. 12.4.   The movement of the arm is about the axis of the upper shaft, and the two limiting positions of the arm's movement are drawn.   Such a view will allow for the recognition of clearances that will be required in the final assembly of this unit with the other portions of the completed mechanism.

The second classification (to clarify orthographic projection principles) · is of primary concern early in a beginning course of engineering drawing.   In Fig. 12.5*A*, the top, front, and right-side views of a rectangular prism are drawn.   In *B*, the object has been rotated through an angle of 45°, in a clockwise direction (when viewed from above).   Notice how the principles of rotation apply: the axis of rotation is perpendicular to the horizontal, and the top view, being an end view of the axis, shows the object exactly as it did before, except that the position of that view has been changed. Height, the dimension parallel to the axis, remains the same in position B as it was in position A.

A second rotation of the object is accomplished in Fig. 12.5C, with the axis being perpendicular to the profile plane of projection. Notice can again

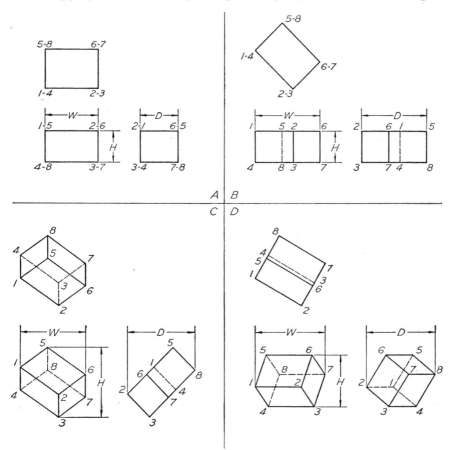

Fig. 12.5. Successive rotations of a solid.

be taken of the strict adherence to the principles of rotation: the side view, in C, is the same as the side view in B, except for its position; width, the dimension parallel to this second axis of rotation, remains the same in C as it was in B.

Rotation of the rectangular prism, from its position as shown in C, is made about an axis perpendicular to the frontal plane of projection. The new top, front, and right-side views of the prism are drawn in D.

In each of the four positions of the prism, a new group of over-all principal dimensions (height, width, and depth) is realized. One dimension, that which is parallel to the axis, is the only one that remains unchanged in successive positions. In A, the dimensions of width, depth, and height are coincidental with the object's dimensions. In B, the dimension of height is the same as it was in A; the width and depth dimensions are, however, considerably at variance with the width and depth in A. Similarly, in C, the dimension of width is the same as it was in B; however, height and depth are changed. In D, depth is repeated from C, while width and height, being dimensions not parallel to the axis of rotation, have changed.

The accomplishment of several successive rotations of a solid, when coupled with a careful study of the above-described dimension conditions, will usually allow the student to realize that height, width, and depth are related to the principal planes of projection, and *not to the object's dimensions*. This realization is absolutely necessary for advanced work in orthographic projection, namely, the study of engineering geometry.

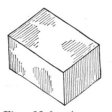

Fig. 12.6. Axonometric resulting from rotation.

Any orthographic view for which the several surfaces of the object being viewed are inclined to the line of sight is an axonometric view of that object. These views are especially useful as pictorial representations. A study of Fig. 12.5 will show that the front view in C and two of the views in D are axonometric views. The front view of C has been repeated in Fig. 12.6, less the hidden detail and with the addition of some shading, to achieve a pictorial effect. Rotation procedures are particularly adaptable in determining such pictorial drawings, and the student is referred to Chap. 16, Pictorial Drawing, for further study in the use of rotation to achieve desired axonometric views.

12.4 Solution of graphical problems by rotation. Rotation, as applied to the solution of engineering geometry problems, is usually restricted to the movement of points, lines, and planes (as contrasted with object rotation) for the purpose of determining normal views of such lines and planes. Since the solution of such problems precedes the making of working drawings for the parts whose designs are based upon the above solutions, a brief résumé of these rotations follows:

12.5 Rotation of a line. Figure 12.7A shows both the top and front views of line RS. A vertical axis RV, arbitrarily positioned through point R, is shown in B. The rotation of line RS about this axis will generate the right-circular cone shown in C; during this rotation it will be seen that point S moves in the plane of the cone's base, a plane perpendicular to the axis. The path of S is the circular contour of the cone's base, shown in true shape in the top view (an end view of the axis). This circular path of rotation appears as a straight line in the front view, for an edge view of the cone's base is secured in that view. It will be further noted that the plane of rotation for S appears perpendicular to the axis, in this normal view of the axis.

An application of the rotation of a line occurs when it is necessary to determine a distance, such as between points R and S, of Fig. 12.7. The frontal element of the cone, RT, is shown in true length in the front view of C. Since all elements of the cone are equal in length, the distance from R to S can be determined by simply measuring the length of element RT, as shown in that front view.

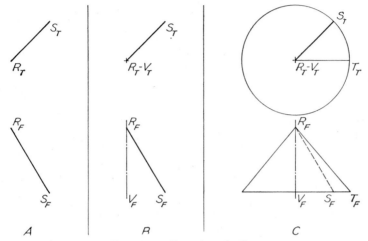

Fig. 12.7. Rotation of a line.

12.6 Rotation of a plane. The determination of the normal view of a plane by rotation is usually accomplished by using a line of the plane as the axis of rotation. In Fig. 12.8A, the presentation shows a triangular surface MNO. PQ, a horizontal line of this plane, is established as the axis of rota-

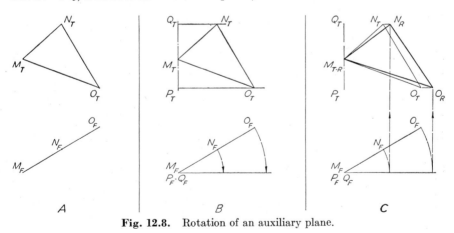

Fig. 12.8. Rotation of an auxiliary plane.

tion. The top view is a normal view of this axis, and the front view is one of its end views. N and O are rotated into the horizontal plane containing the axis, resulting in the top view being a normal view of MNO. In B, the paths of rotation show in their true circle arc shapes in the *front* view, and as

straight lines perpendicular to the axis in the *top* view.   The normal view of
triangle *MNO* is shown superimposed on the original top view, in *C*.   It will
be seen that, since point *M* is on the axis of rotation, the top view of *M*, in
the new position of the surface, remains unchanged from its original position.

If the plane surface is oblique, as *XYZ* of Fig. 12.9, the rotation is most
readily completed by drawing an auxiliary view that will show the end view
of the selected axis of rotation.   Line *ZF*, of plane *XYZ*, is used as the axis
of rotation in the current problem.   This frontal line appears as a point in
the right auxiliary view, where the circular paths of rotation, for points *X*
and *Y*, are shown.   The front view shows those circular paths appearing as

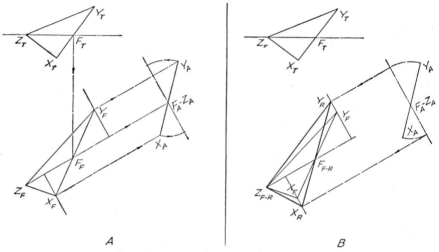

Fig. 12.9.   Rotation of an oblique plane.

straight lines, perpendicular to the axis.   In *B*, the true shape of *XYZ* is
drawn superimposed on the original front view.

12.7   Counterrotation.   In industry, the problem that requires the
determination of a normal view of a plane will usually require that this view
be used as a means to the desired end, rather than as the actual fulfillment of
the requirements.   In such an instance, the problem of Fig. 12.9 might have
been stated as follows: *X*, *Y*, and *Z* are three points on the circumference of
a circle that circumscribes the square *FGHZ*; required: the top and front
views of the square.   In Fig. 12.10*A*, the presentation shows the normal
view of *XYZ*, as determined in Fig. 12.9.   The square *FGHZ* is drawn in
this normal view and then projected to the edge view of the rotated plane.
In *B*, the counterrotation is indicated in the auxiliary view, and the square
is then projected back to the top and front views.   It will be noted that,
since the front view is a normal view of the axis of rotation, the paths of
rotation for points *F*, *G*, and *H* appear as straight lines perpendicular to the
axis in that view.

Various shortcuts in construction are possible, and would be employed by the experienced draftsman; however, the theory of rotation should first be understood before use is made of such shortened constructions.

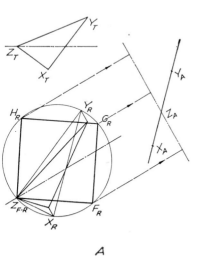 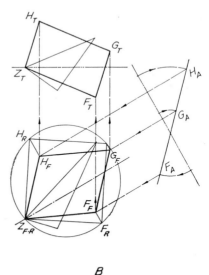

A   *B*

Fig. 12.10. Counterrotation.

12.8 Summary

General

1. A point, rotating in space, always rotates about a straight line as an axis.

2. The axis of rotation is usually established as perpendicular to one of the principal planes of projection (horizontal, frontal, or profile) in order to have normal and end views of the axis available in the views already drawn.

3. A point always rotates in a plane perpendicular to the axis, on a circular path that is centered at the intersection of the axis and the plane of rotation.

4. The circular path of rotation for any point appears in its true shape in an end view of the axis, and as a straight line perpendicular to the axis in all normal views of the axis.

5. Either view showing an end view of the axis will show a rotated object changed in position, but otherwise the same as before the rotation.

6. Any view showing the true length of the axis will show that view of the object changed in shape after rotation, but the dimension parallel to the axis will be unchanged.

7. The rotation of a line is most readily accomplished about an axis that intersects the given line.

8. The rotation of a plane is most readily accomplished about an axis that lies in the plane.

Procedure

1. Determine the axis of rotation and secure both a normal view and an end view of that axis, Fig. 12.11*A*.

2. In the view showing an end view of the axis, draw the rotated view exactly as before, except for its change of position, Fig. 12.11*B*.

3. Determine the dimensions parallel to the axis, in the views showing the axis in true length, and transfer those dimensions to the comparable views of the object in its new position, Fig. 12.11*C*.

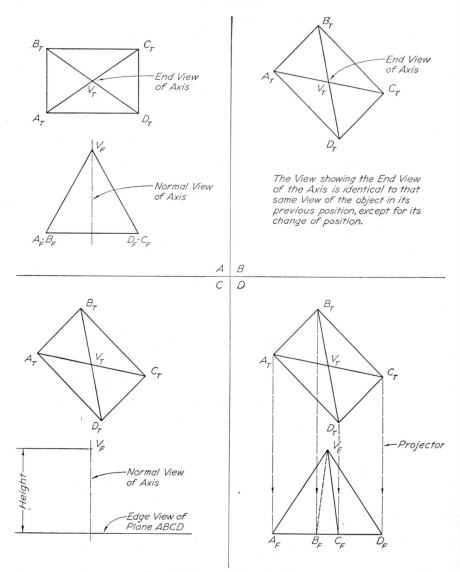

The View showing the End View
of the Axis is identical to that
same View of the object in its
previous position, except for its
change of position.

Fig. 12.11.   Rotation procedure.

4. Project from the view showing the end view of the axis, to the view showing a normal view of the axis, such corners as are needed to complete the views, Fig. 12.11D.

PROBLEMS

Group I.   Rotation of prisms and pyramids.   *Problem 1 (A to J)*

1. Fig. 12.12.   (1) Draw three views of one of the blocks A to J in the position shown.   (2) Rotate from position (1) about an axis perpendicular to H through 15°. (3) Rotate from position (2) about an axis perpendicular to F through 45°.   (4) Rotate from position (1) about an axis perpendicular to P forward through 30°.   (5) Rotate from position (2) about an axis perpendicular to P forward through 30°. (6) Rotate from position (3) about an axis perpendicular to P forward through 30°. (4), (5), and (6) may be placed to advantage under (1), (2), and (3), respectively, so that the widths of front and top views may be projected down directly.

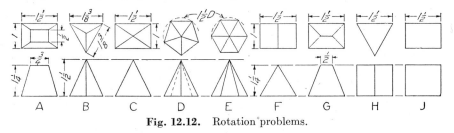

Fig. 12.12. Rotation problems.

Group II. Alternate positions and rotation of lines. *Problems 2 to 6*

2. Fig. 12.13. A rope is secured at point A, threaded in sequence around pulleys B and C, and supports a weight D. The pulley B breaks, allowing the weight D to fall. Show the new position of the weight D and all construction used in finding the new location.

3. Fig. 12.14. The television aerial is braced by three guy wires A, B, and C. A and B are fastened to the roof as shown. C is fastened to a post 8'-0'' above the ground and would make a true angle of 60° if extended to hit the ground. Find the true length of all guy wires, neglecting fastening amounts.

4. Fig. 12.15. The yard hoist boom is 24'-0'' long between points A and B. Point B is 1'-0'' (measured horizontally) from the center of the mast. The boom hoist cable is

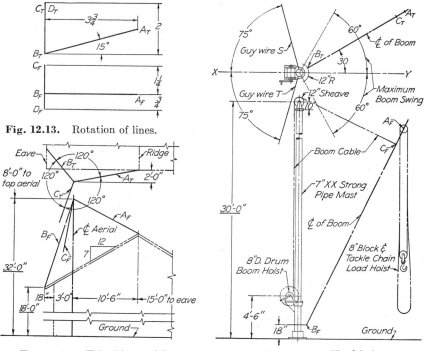

Fig. 12.13. Rotation of lines.

Fig. 12.14. Television aerial.

Fig. 12.15. Yard hoist.

fastened to the boom at point C, 2'-0" from point A. The boom will normally operate between a 30° and 60° angle with the ground and swing to a position 60° each side of center line XY. The guy wires S and T make an angle of 60° with the ground and are fastened to the 10-in.-diameter sheave base. Guy wire S is fastened to the ground, and T is supported 12'-6" from the ground on a shed roof.

    a. Draw the hoist in position shown with the boom making 60° with the ground.

    b. Show the maximum alternate positions of swing of the boom.

    c. Outline the area on the ground which the hoist serves.

    d. What length would be necessary for the boom hoist cable if 3'-0", for fastening and drum make-up, is added to the maximum assembly length?

    e. What is the length of the unwound boom hoist cable for the position shown on your drawing? (Neglect length of the drum and possible build-up of cable on the drum.)

    f. What is the length of guy wires S and T? (Neglect fastening amounts.)

    5. Find the true length of a lateral edge of one of the pyramids of Fig. 12.12B, C, or D.

    6. Find the true length of the body diagonal of a 2½-in. cube.

Group III.   Rotation of planes. *Problems 7 to 11*

    7. Fig. 12.16. Find the true length of AB. Make a detail drawing of the brace.

    8. Fig. 12.16. With the timbers in position shown, draw the brace with the true length of AB, 3'-0".

    9. Make a detail drawing of the brace of Prob. 8.

    10. Fig. 12.17. Draw the complete views of the truncated pyramid. Find the true size of face A by rotation.

    11. Fig. 12.18. Find the true size of surface A by rotation. Show all construction

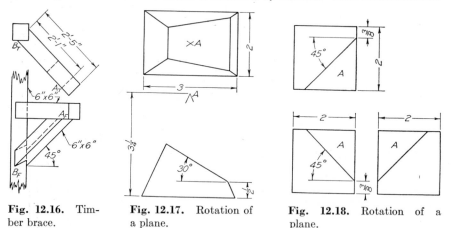

Fig. 12.16. Timber brace.   **Fig. 12.17.** Rotation of a plane.   **Fig. 12.18.** Rotation of a plane.

Group IV.   Rotation and counterrotation. *Problems 12 to 15*

    12. Fig. 12.19. The triangle ABC is the base of a triangular pyramid, altitude 2½ in., whose apex is equidistant from A, B, and C. Rotate until the base is horizontal, counterrotate, and complete the views.

    13. Fig. 12.20. AC is the diagonal of a vertical square $ABCD$. Draw the top, front, and right-side views of the square.

    14. Fig. 12.21. AD is the diagonal of a regular hexagon $ABCDEF$. Point X is on the plane of the hexagon. Draw the top, front, and left-side views of the hexagon.

    15. Fig. 12.22. The triangle ABC is the base of a triangular pyramid, altitude 1¼ in., whose faces make equal angles with the base. Complete the views using rotation and counterrotation.

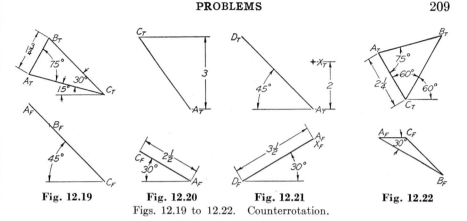

Fig. 12.19   Fig. 12.20   Fig. 12.21   Fig. 12.22

Figs. 12.19 to 12.22.   Counterrotation.

Group V.   Drawing from description.   *Problems 16 to 25*   (Each problem has more than one solution.)

16. Draw three views of a triangular card each edge of which is 2¾ in. long.   One edge is perpendicular to *P*, and the card makes an angle of 30° with *H*.

17. Draw three views of a circular card of 2½ in. diameter, inclined 30° to *H*, and perpendicular to *F*.   (Find eight points on the curve.)

18. Draw three views of a cylinder of 1½ in. diameter, 2 in. long.   Axis of cylinder parallel to *H* and inclined 30° to *F*.

19. Draw top and front views of a rectangular prism, base 1 by 1¾ in., whose body diagonal is 2½ in. long.   The faces of the prism are parallel to the principal planes of projection.

20. Draw the top and front views of a cube whose body diagonal, 2½ in. long, is parallel to both *F* and *H*.

21. Draw top and front views of a hexagonal plinth whose faces are 1 in. square and two of which are parallel to *H*.   The axis makes an angle of 30° with *F*.

22. Draw the two projections of a line 3 in. long making an angle of 30° with *F*, and whose *F* projection makes 45° with a horizontal line, the line sloping downward and backward to the left.

23. Draw three views of a square pyramid whose faces are isosceles triangles 1¾ in. base and 2¼ in. altitude, lying with one face horizontal, and the *H* projection of its axis at an angle of 30° with the frontal plane of projection.

24. Draw the top and front views of a right rectangular pyramid, base 1⅛ by 2 in., altitude 1⅞ in., long edges of base parallel to *F*.   By two rotations, place the pyramid so that the short edges are parallel to *H* and make an angle of 60° with *F* while the apex is in the same horizontal plane as one of the short edges of the base.

25. Draw three views of a triangular pyramid formed of four equilateral triangles whose sides are 2¼ in.   The base makes an angle of 45° with *H*, and one of the edges of the base is perpendicular to *F*.

13

Sections and Conventions

13.1 Sections. Previous chapters have dealt with the method of describing the shape of an object by orthographic views, using dotted lines to indicate hidden parts. If the object is very simple in its interior construction, these hidden lines are not hard to read and understand. Often, however, when the interior is complicated, or when several different pieces are assembled in place, an attempt to show the construction on an exterior view would result in a confusing mass of dotted lines, annoying to draw and difficult if not impossible to read clearly. In such cases one (or more) of the views is made "in section." Even for simple objects where the orthographic views may be read easily, sectional views are often preferred because they give emphasis to the material of which the objects are made and to the void spaces, such as holes, resulting in views which may be read with much less mental effort than exterior views.

Definition: A *section* is an imaginary cut taken through an object so as to reveal the shape or interior construction.

A *sectional view* is either (1) a conventional representation in which a part of an object or machine is imagined to be cut, or broken away and removed, so as to expose the interior; or (2) a conventional representation where a slice of negligible thickness is taken through an object and then revolved, removed, or aligned to show the shape or interior construction.

13.2 Cutting planes. A cutting plane is the imaginary medium used to show the path of cutting an object to make a section. Figure 13.1 pic-

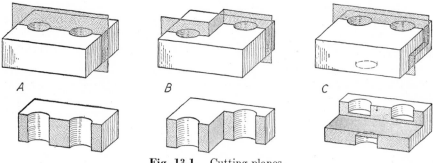

Fig. 13.1. Cutting planes.

tures several objects intersected by cutting planes, giving the *appearance* that the castings have actually been cut through by the plane, and then the front parts removed to expose the interior. The cutting plane may pass directly across the object as at *A*, Fig. 13.1, or it may offset, changing direction forward or backward, so as to pass through features it would otherwise miss, as at B and C.

Figure 13.2 shows several examples of how the cutting plane may pass through a symmetrical object permitting the removal of a portion of the

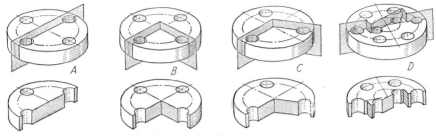

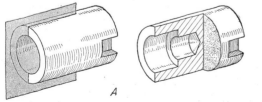
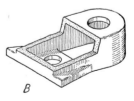

Fig. 13.2. Cutting planes.

object so as better to describe the shape. Note how the cutting planes may change direction so as to pass through the holes.

Figure 13.3A shows the use of more than one plane on the same object. When more than one view is drawn in section, each sectional view should be considered separately without any reference to what has been removed for other views. Thus Fig. 13.3B shows the front half removed for one sec-

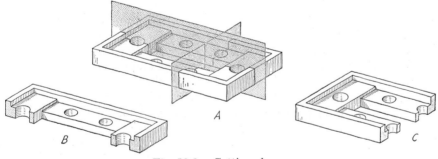

Fig. 13.3. Cutting planes.

tional view, and Fig. 13.3C, a different part removed for another sectional view.

Figure 13.4A shows an object cut part way through and the front portion broken out and removed. The cutting plane in this case cannot be extended through the length of the object, for to do so would remove features that

Fig. 13.4. Cutting planes.

would not then be described. For some objects a portion is broken out and removed to expose the interior as in Fig. 13.4*B*, and even though no cutting plane is used, the principles of sectional drawing will apply in making the orthographic views.

The cutting plane may also be imagined to pass through an object cutting a slice of negligible thickness, which may then be removed, revolved, or aligned to show a shape that otherwise would be difficult to see or describe, see Fig. 13.5.

13.3   The cutting-plane symbol may be shown on the orthographic view where the cutting plane appears as an edge, and may be more completely identified with reference letters along with arrows to show the direction in which the view is taken. See the cutting-plane line symbol in the alphabet of lines, Fig. 4.32, page 58. For an example of its use, see Fig. 13.16.

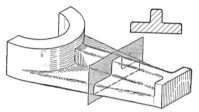

Fig. 13.5.   Cutting plane.

Often when the position of the section is evident, the cutting-plane symbol is omitted, Fig. 13.12. It is not always possible to show the symbol through its entire length; so, in such cases, the beginning and ending of the plane is shown as in section *A-A*, Fig. 28.52. Removed sections usually need the cutting-plane symbol with arrows to show the direction of sight and with letters to name the resulting sectional view, Fig. 13.20.

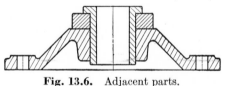

Fig. 13.6.   Adjacent parts.

13.4   Section lining. Wherever material has been cut by the section plane, the cut surface is indicated by section lining, sometimes called "cross-hatching," done with fine lines generally at 45° with the principal lines in the view and spaced uniformly to give an even tint. They are spaced entirely by eye except when some form of mechanical section liner is used. The pitch, or distance between lines, is governed by the size of the surface. For ordinary working drawings, it will not be much less than $\frac{1}{16}$ in. and rarely more than $\frac{1}{8}$ in. *Very* small pieces may require a spacing closer than $\frac{1}{16}$ in. Care should be exercised in setting the pitch by the first two or three lines, and one should glance back at the first lines often in order that the pitch may not gradually increase or decrease.   Nothing mars the appearance of a drawing more than poor section lining.   The "Alphabet of lines," page 58, gives the weight of crosshatch lines.

Two adjacent pieces in an assembly drawing are crosshatched in opposite directions.   If three pieces adjoin, one of them may be sectioned at other

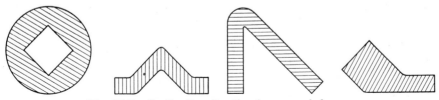

Fig. 13.7.   Section line direction for unusual shapes.

than 45° (usually 30° or 60°, Fig. 13.6), or all pieces may be crosshatched at 45° by using a different pitch for each piece.   If a part is so shaped that 45-deg. sectioning runs parallel, or nearly so, to its principal outlines, another direction should be chosen, Fig. 13.7.

Large surfaces are sometimes sectioned only around the edge, as illustrated by Fig. 13.8.

Very thin sections, as of gaskets, sheet metal, or structural-steel shapes to small scale, may be shown in solid black, with white spaces between the parts where thin pieces are adjacent, Fig. 13.9.

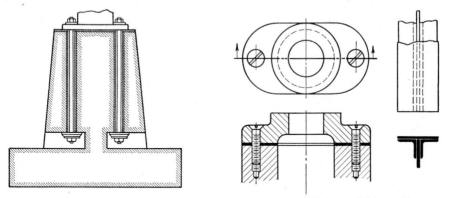

Fig. 13.8.   Outline sectioning.   **Fig. 13.9.**   Thin material in section.

13.5   Code for materials in section.   Symbolical section lining is not commonly used on ordinary working drawings, but sometimes in an assembly section it is desired to show a distinction between materials, and a recognized standard code is of obvious advantage.   The ASA's symbols for indicating different materials will be found in the Appendix, page 688.   Code section lining is used only as an aid in reading the drawing and is not to be taken as the official specification of the materials.   Exact specifications of the material for each piece are always given on the detail drawing.

13.6 Projecting the section. In general, the rules of projection are followed in making sectional views. Figure 13.10 shows the picture of a casting intersected by a cutting plane, giving the appearance that the casting has been cut through by the plane *A-A* and the front part removed, exposing

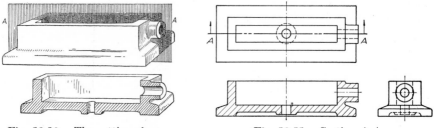

Fig. 13.10. The cutting plane.   Fig. 13.11. Section *A-A*.

the interior. Figure 13.11 shows the drawing of the casting with the front view in section. The edge of the cutting plane is shown on the top view by the cutting-plane symbol, with reference letters and arrows to show the direction in which the view is taken. It must be understood clearly that, in thus removing the nearer portion of the object to make the sectional view, the portion assumed to be removed is not omitted in making other views. Thus, the top and right-side views of the object in Fig. 13.10 are full and complete, and only in the front view has part of the object been represented as removed.

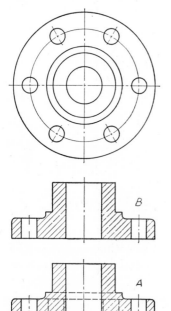

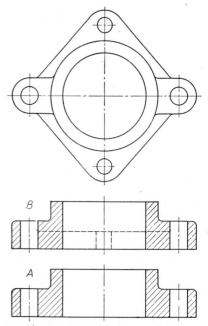

Fig. 13.12. Hidden edges and surfaces not shown.   Fig. 13.13. Hidden edges and surfaces shown.

13.7 Unnecessary hidden detail. Hidden edges and surfaces are not shown unless needed to describe the object. Much confusion may occur if all detail behind the cutting plane is drawn. Figure 13.12A shows a sectional view with all the hidden edges and surfaces shown by dotted lines. These lines complicate the view and do not add any information. View 13.12B is preferred because it is much simpler, is less time-consuming to draw, and is read with less mental effort than the view at A. The holes lie on a circular center line, and where similar details repeat all may be assumed to be alike.

13.8 Necessary hidden detail. Hidden edges and surfaces are shown if necessary for the description of the object. View A, Fig. 13.13, is inadequate since it does not show the thickness of the lugs. The correct treatment is in view B where the lugs are shown by dotted lines.

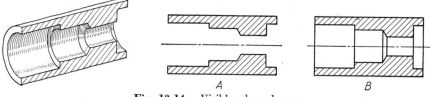

$$A \qquad\qquad\qquad B$$

Fig. 13.14. Visible edges shown.

13.9 Visible detail shown on sectional views. Figure 13.14 shows an object pictorially with the front half removed, thus exposing edges and surfaces behind the cutting plane.

Figure 13.14A shows a sectional view of the cut surface only, with the visible elements omitted. This treatment should never be used. The view should be drawn as at B with the visible edges and surfaces behind the cutting plane included in the sectional view.

13.10 Visible detail not shown on sectional views. Sometimes confusion may occur if all visible detail behind the cutting plane is drawn. Omission of such detail should be carefully considered and may be justified as time saved in drawing. It will apply more often on assembly drawings where the function of the drawing is to show how the pieces fit together rather than to give complete information for making the parts. For an example of omitted detail, see Fig. 13.15.

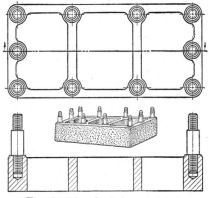

Fig. 13.15. Omission of detail.

13.11 Names of sectional views. The many different types of sectional views have been given names for purposes of identification during discussion and instruction, and for specifying the kind of sectional view desired from a draftsman. Sectional views are not named on the drawings, and workmen do not need the names to use or read the drawings. Different kinds of sectional views may have more than one appropriate name. For example, a revolved, removed, or aligned section may also be a full section. The portion of the object that is assumed to be removed has nothing to do with the name of the section. Names have been assigned in all cases by the amount of the view in section, or the manner in which the view is arranged in relation to the other views of the object.

13.12 **A full section** is one in which the cutting plane cuts entirely across the object showing all the view in section. The path of the cutting plane may go straight along the principal axis or center line as in Fig. 13.10, or it may be offset and change direction as in Fig. 13.16. Observe that the

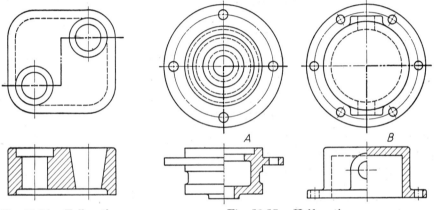

Fig. 13.16. Full section.   **Fig. 13.17.** Half sections.

change in plane direction on the sectional view is not shown, for the cut is purely imaginary and no edge is present on the object at this position.

13.13 **A half section** is a view sometimes used for symmetrical objects, in which one half is drawn in section and the other half as a regular exterior view. The cutting plane is imagined to extend halfway across, stopping at the axis or center line, Fig. 13.17. A half section has the advantage of showing both the exterior and the interior on one view without using dotted lines, but has the disadvantage that inside diameters cannot be dimensioned well. However, the hidden edges may be shown in the exterior portion for clarity and assistance in dimensioning, Fig. 13.17*B*. *Note that a center line separates the exterior and interior portions of the sectional view.*[1]

13.14 **A broken-out section** is a partial section used on an exterior view to show some interior detail without drawing a complete full or half section.

[1] The reason why a center line is used is that theoretically, the cutting of the object is imaginary and, in addition, no edge, edge view of a surface, or surface limit producing a solid line exists at the center of the object. An unfortunate mistake exists in some drafting manuals in which a solid line is also allowed for the line of demarcation between sectioned and exterior portions of a half section. It is certainly hoped that, sometime in the near future, this mistake will be corrected.

Note the irregular break line, which limits the extent of the section, Fig. 13.18.

13.15   A revolved section is made directly on an exterior view and provides a very convenient and useful method of showing the shape of the cross section of some detail of construction,

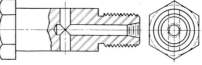

Fig. 13.18. A broken-out section.

such as a rib or the arm of a wheel. The cutting plane is passed perpendicular to the center line or axis of the part to be sectioned and the resulting section revolved or turned up in place, Fig. 13.19. These are used primarily for shape description rather than size description. When lines of the outline interfere with the section, as is sometimes the case, the view may be broken away to make a clear space for the sectional view. Figures 13.34, 13.35, and 13.53 contain some examples of revolved sections.

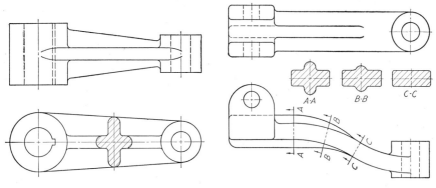

Fig. 13.19.   A revolved section.   **Fig. 13.20.**   Removed sections.

13.16   Removed sections are used for the same purpose as revolved sections, but instead of being drawn on the view they are set off, or shifted, to some adjacent place on the paper, Fig. 13.20. The cutting plane with reference letters should always be indicated unless the place from which the section has been taken is obvious. Removed sections are used whenever restricted space for the section, or the dimensioning of it, prevents the use of an ordinary revolved section. When the shape of a piece changes gradually, or is not uniform, several sections may be required, Fig. 13.21. It is often an advantage to draw them to larger scale than that of the main drawing, in order to show dimensions more clearly. Sometimes sections are removed to a separate drawing sheet. When this practice is employed, the section must be carefully shown on the main drawing with cutting plane and identifying letters. Often these identifying letters are made as a fraction in a circle, with the numerator a letter identifying the section and the denominator a number identifying the sheet. The sectional view is then marked with the same letters and numbers. The American Standard recommends that, whenever possible, a removed section should be drawn in its natural projected position. Note in Fig. 13.21 that this practice is followed.

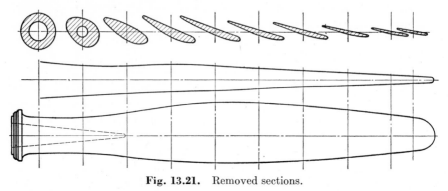

Fig. 13.21. Removed sections.

13.17 An auxiliary section is a sectional view made on an auxiliary plane, and conforms to all the principles of auxiliary views as explained in Chap. 10; thus there may be an elevation auxiliary section, a right or left auxiliary section, a front or rear auxiliary section, or an oblique section. Similarly, half sections, broken-out sections, revolved sections, and removed sections may be used on auxiliary views. Figure 13.22 is an example of an

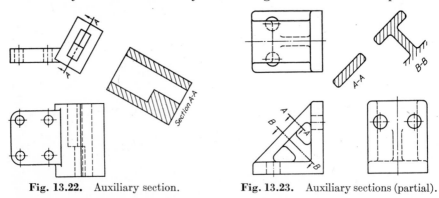

Fig. 13.22. Auxiliary section.   **Fig. 13.23.** Auxiliary sections (partial).

auxiliary in section. Figure 13.23 shows the use of right auxiliary partial sections.

13.18 Assembly sections. As the name implies, an assembly section is one taken through a combination of parts making up a machine or structure. All the previously mentioned types of sections (full, revolved, broken-out, etc.) may be used for increasing the clarity and readability of assembly drawings. Figures 28.41, 28.43, and 28.52 are examples of assembly sections.

The purpose of an assembly section is to reveal the interior of the machine or structure so that the separate parts may be clearly shown and identified, but the separate parts do not need to be completely described. Thus only such hidden details as are necessary for part identification are shown. Also, the small amount of clearance between mating or moving parts is not shown because, if shown, the clearance would have to be greatly exaggerated, thus confusing the drawing. Even the clearance between a bolt and its hole, which may be as much as $\frac{1}{16}$ in., is rarely shown.

Crosshatching practice for assembly sections is explained in paragraph 13.4, and is also shown in Fig. 13.25.

13.19 Five principles in sectioning

1. The cutting plane need not be a continuous single plane, but may be offset or changed in direction so as to show the construction to the best advantage, Fig. 13.24.

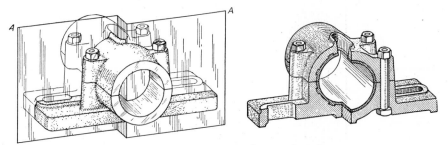

Fig. 13.24. Picture of an offset cutting plane.

2. Section lining, either (a) for the same piece in different views or (b) for the same piece in different parts of the same view, should be identical in spacing and direction.[1]

3. Invisible lines beyond the plane of the section should not be drawn unless necessary for the description or identification of the piece.

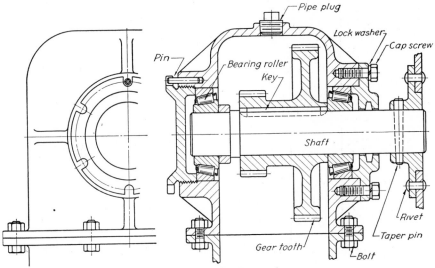

Fig. 13.25. Section study.

4. Adjacent pieces are section-lined in opposite directions and are often brought out more clearly by varying the pitch of the section lines for each piece, using closer spacing for the smaller pieces, Figs. 13.6 and 13.25.

[1] An exception to this rule is made for the crosshatching of an auxiliary view, in order to avoid crosshatch lines either parallel, perpendicular, or nearly so, to the outlines of the view.

5. Shafts, bolts, nuts, rods, rivets, keys, and the like, whose axes occur in the plane of the section, are left in full and not sectioned, Fig. 13.25.

13.20 Conventional sections. All sections are conventions in that they represent an assumed imaginary cut from which, following rather closely the rules of projection, the sectional views are made. However, added clearness will sometimes be obtained by violating the strict rules of projection, resulting in a type of view called a *conventional section*. Some conventions must be used with caution, because they are not always readily understood by the workman. It is impossible to illustrate all the conditions that might occur, but the following discussions and illustrations show the principles that are recognized and accepted as good practice, since they result in added clearness and readability.

13.21 Parts not sectioned. Many machine elements, such as fasteners, pins, and shafts, have no internal construction and, in addition, are more easily recognized by their exterior views. These parts often lie in the path of the section plane, but if they are sectioned (crosshatched) they are more difficult to read because their typical identifying features (boltheads, rivet heads, chamfers on shafts, etc.) are removed. Thus features of this kind should be left in full view and *not sectioned*. To justify this treatment, the assembly is thought of as being sectioned on a particular plane, and then the nonsectioned parts are placed in the half holes remaining after the section is made. Figure 13.24 shows a full section made on an offset cutting plane that passes through a bolt. The treatment shown with the bolt in full view illustrates the above statements. Figure 13.25 shows several nonsectioned parts. It should be evident in this figure that if the shaft, bolts, nuts, rivets, etc., were sectioned the drawing would be confusing and difficult to read.

13.22 Section lines omitted. A basic principle for sectioning circular parts is that any element not continuous (solid) around the axis of the part should be drawn without crosshatching in order to avoid a misleading effect. For example, consider the two pulleys A and B of Fig. 13.26. Pulley A has

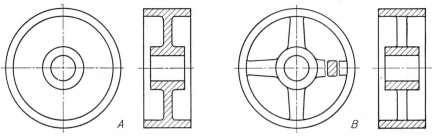

Fig. 13.26. Section lines omitted.

a solid web connecting the hub and rim. Pulley B has four spokes. Even though the cutting plane passes through two of the spokes, the sectional view of B must be made without crosshatching the spokes in order to avoid the appearance of a solid web as in pulley A.

Other machine elements treated in this manner are teeth of gears and sprockets (Fig. 27.5), vanes and supporting ribs of cylindrical parts, equally spaced lugs, and other similar portions.

13.23 Ribs in section. For reasons very similar to those given in paragraph 13.22, when the cutting plane passes longitudinally through the center of a rib or web as in Fig. 13.27A, the crosshatching should be eliminated from the ribs as if the cutting plane were just in front of them, or as if they were temporarily removed and replaced after the section is made. A true sectional view with the ribs crosshatched gives a heavy misleading effect sug-

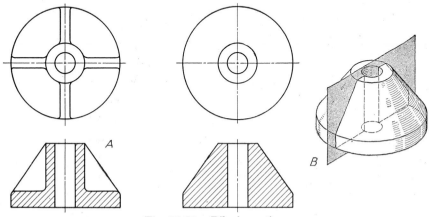

Fig. 13.27. Ribs in section.

gesting a cone shape as shown at B. When the cutting plane cuts a rib transversely, that is, at right angles to its length or axis direction (the direction that shows its thickness), it should always be crosshatched. For an example, see Fig. 13.15.

13.24 Alternate crosshatching. In some cases omitting the crosshatching of ribs or similar parts will give an inadequate and sometimes ambiguous treatment. To illustrate, Fig. 13.28A shows a full section of an idler pulley.

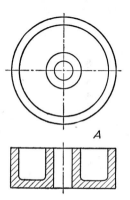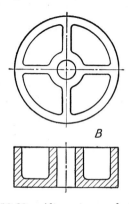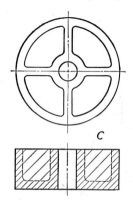

Fig. 13.28. Alternate crosshatching.

At *B* four ribs have been added, and (note) the top surfaces of the ribs are flush with the top of the pulley.   Without crosshatching, the section at *B* is identical with *A* and the ribs of *B* are not identified at all on the sectional view.   A better treatment in this case is to use alternate crosshatching for the ribs as at *C* where half (alternating) the crosshatch lines are carried through the ribs.   Note that the line of demarcation between rib and solid portions is a *dotted* line.

13.25   Lugs in section.   For the same reasons given in paragraphs 13.22 to 13.24, a lug or projecting ear, Fig. 13.29*A*, usually of *rectangular* cross sec-

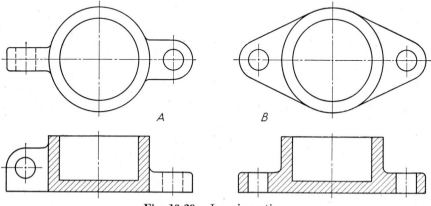

Fig. 13.29.   Lugs in section.

tion, should not be crosshatched.   Note that, in this case, crosshatching either of the lugs would suggest a circular flange.   However, the somewhat similar condition at *B* should have the projecting ears crosshatched as shown, because these ears *are* the base of the part.

13.26   Aligned sections.   Any part having an odd number (3, 5, 7, etc.) of spokes or ribs will give an unsymmetrical and misleading section if the principles of true projection are strictly adhered to, as illustrated by the drawing of a handwheel in Fig. 13.30.   The preferred projection is shown in

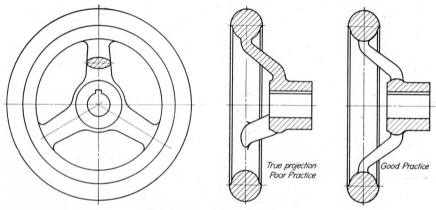

Fig. 13.30.   Aligned section.

the second sectional view where one arm is drawn as if aligned, or in other words, the arm is revolved to the path of the vertical cutting plane and then projected to the side view.   Note that neither arm should be sectioned for reasons given in paragraph 13.22.

This practice of alignment is well justified logically, because a part having an odd number of equally spaced elements is just as symmetrical as a part with some even number and, therefore, should be shown by a symmetrical view.   Moreover, the symmetrical view shows the true *relationship* of the elements, while a true projection does not.

13.27   Aligned ribs, lugs, and holes.   Following the principles given in paragraph 13.26, ribs, lugs, and holes often occur in odd numbers and, therefore, should be aligned to show the true relationship of the elements.   In Fig. 13.31A, true projection of the ribs would show the pair on the right

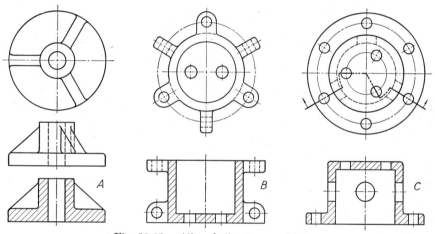

Fig. 13.31.   Aligned ribs, lugs, and holes.

foreshortened, suggesting in the sectional view that they would not extend to the outer edge of the base.   Here, again, the alignment as shown in Fig. 13.31 gives a symmetrical section of a symmetrical part and shows the ribs in their true relationship to the basic part.   To illustrate further, in Figs. 13.31B and C, the lugs and holes are aligned, thus showing the holes at their true radial distance from the axis and, incidentally, eliminating some difficult projections.

In all cases of alignment, one may think of the element as being swung around to a common cutting plane and then projected to the sectional view. Note in Fig. 13.31C that, because an offset cutting plane is used, each hole is brought separately into position on a common cutting plane before projection to the sectional view.

13.28   Conventional practices.   There are violations of the rules of projection in full views, as well as in sectional views, that are desirable because they add to the clearness of the drawing.   One statement can be made with the force of a rule.   *If anything in clearness can be gained by violating a prin-*

ciple of projection, violate it. Permissible violations usually are not readily apparent to the reader. This is true since they describe, in a better and usually simpler form, the actual conditions. Some care and judgment must be used in applying conventional treatments. Draftsmen usually understand their meaning, but workmen often do not. Some unusual conven-

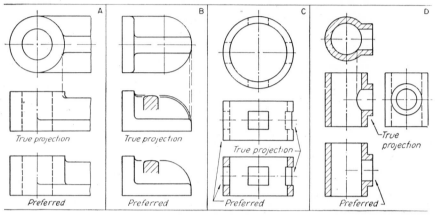

Fig. 13.32. Conventional practices.

tion may be more harmful than helpful, and result in greater ambiguity than true projection.

Some typical examples in which true lines of intersection are of no value as aids in reading and are therefore ignored are shown in Fig. 13.32. In contrast with the above practices, very similar conditions where the proportions differ should show the true line of intersection. Compare the treatment of the similar objects in Figs. 13.32 and 13.33. It would not be good practice to conventionalize the intersections on the objects of Fig. 13.33,

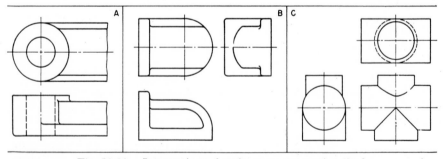

Fig. 13.33. Intersections of surfaces not conventionalized.

because the difference between true projection and the convention is too great.

13.29   Fillets and rounds. In designing a casting, sharp internal angles must never be left, because of the liability to fracture at those points. The radius of the fillet depends on the thickness of the metal and other design conditions. When not dimensioned it is left to the patternmaker. External angles may be rounded for appearance or comfort, with radii ranging from enough merely to remove the sharp edges to an amount nearly equal to the thickness of the piece. An edge made by the intersection of two unfinished surfaces of a casting should always be "broken" by a very small round. A sharp corner on a drawing thus indicates that one or both of the intersecting surfaces are machined. Small fillets, rounds, and "runouts" are best put in

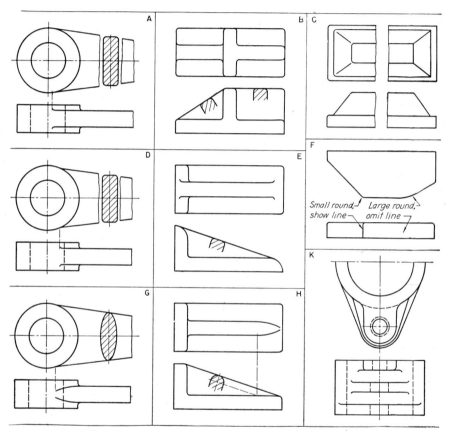

Fig. 13.34. Conventional fillets, rounds, and runouts.

freehand, both in pencil and ink. Runouts, or die-outs as they are sometimes called, are conventional indications of filleted intersections where, theoretically, there would be no line because there is no abrupt change in direction. Figure 13.34 shows some conventional representations of fillets and rounds with runouts of arms and ribs intersecting other surfaces.

13.30 Conventional breaks. In making the detail of a long bar or piece having a uniform shape of cross section, there is rarely any necessity for drawing its whole length. It may be shown to a larger, and thus better, scale by breaking out a piece, moving the ends together, and giving the true length by a dimension as in Fig. 13.35.   The shape of the cross section is indicated either by a revolved section or, more often, by a semipictorial break line as in Fig. 13.36.   This figure also shows some other conventional symbols.

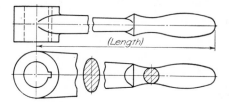

(Length)

Fig. 13.35.   Broken view, with revolved sections.

13.31   Conventional symbols.   Draftsmen use conventional representation for indicating many details, such as screw threads, springs, pipe fittings, electrical apparatus, etc.   These have been standardized by the ASA, whose code for materials in section has already been referred to in paragraph 13.5.

The symbol of two crossed diagonals is used for two distinct purposes: *first*, to indicate on a shaft the position of finish for a bearing, and *second*, to

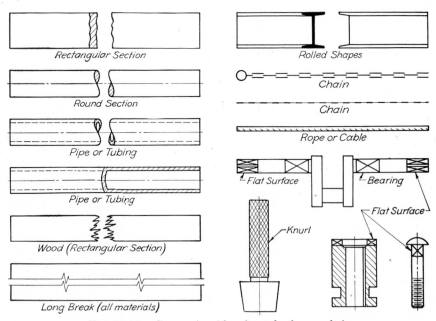

Fig. 13.36.   Conventional breaks and other symbols.

indicate that a certain surface (usually parallel to the picture plane) is flat. These two uses are not apt to be confused, Fig. 13.36.

Because of constant recurrence the representation of screw threads is one of the most important items under conventional symbols.   Up to the time of their official standardization by the ASA, there were a dozen different thread symbols in use.   Now one regular symbol and one simplified one are adopted for American drawings, and both are understood internationally. The symbols for indicating threads on bolts, screws, and tapped holes are given in Chap. 22.   Chapter 24 shows the conventional representation of helical springs.   The conventional methods of representing pipe and fittings are given in Chap. 25.   Welding symbols are shown in Chap. 26.

The conventional symbols mentioned in the previous paragraph are used principally on machine drawings.   Architectural drawing, because of the small scales employed, uses many conventional symbols, and topographic drawing is made up entirely of symbols.

13.32   Aligned and developed views.   There are violations of the rules of true projection in full views, as well as in sectional views, that are recognized as good practice because they add to the clearness of the drawing. For example, if a front view shows a hexagonal bolthead "across corners," the theoretical projection of the side view would be "across flats," but in a working drawing when boltheads occur they should be drawn across corners in both views, to show better the shape and the space needed.

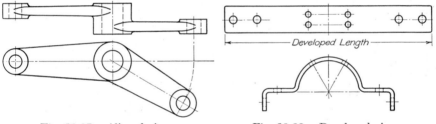

Fig. 13.37.   Aligned view.   Fig. 13.38.   Developed view.

Pieces that have elements at an angle to each other, as the lever of Fig. 13.37, may be shown straightened out, or aligned in one view.   Similarly, bent pieces of the type of Fig. 13.38 should have one view made as a developed view of the *blank* to be punched and formed.   Extra metal must be allowed for bends.

Lugs or parts cast on for holding purposes and to be machined off are shown by phantom lines.   If such parts are in section, the section lines are dotted (see the rail in the rail transport hanger, Fig. 28.49).   Phantom lines are also used for indicating the limiting positions of moving parts and for showing adjacent parts that aid in locating the position or use of a piece.

13.33   Half views.   When space is very limited, it is allowable practice to make the top or the side view of a symmetrical piece as a half view.   If the front is an exterior view, the *front* half of the top or the side view would be used, as in Fig. 13.39; but if the front view is a sectional view, the *rear* half would be used, as in Fig. 13.40.   Figure 13.41 shows another space-saving combination of a half view with a half section. Examples of half views occur in Figs. 28.46, 28.48, and 28.51.

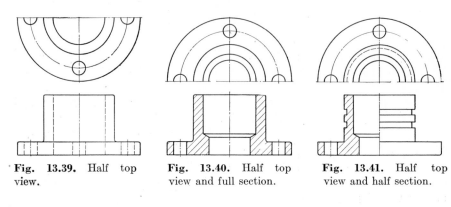

Fig. 13.39. Half top view.

Fig. 13.40. Half top view and full section.

Fig. 13.41. Half top view and half section.

PROBLEMS

Selections from the following problems may be used only for shape description, or as working drawings by adding dimensions.

1. Fig. 13.42. Draw top view and change front and side views to sectional views as indicated.

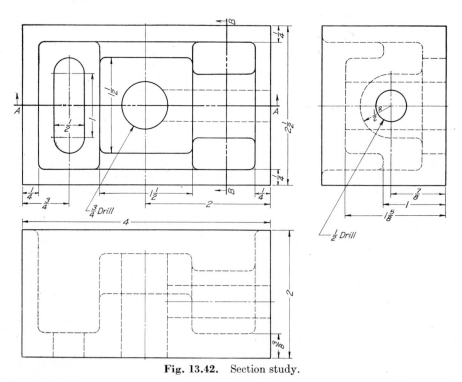

Fig. 13.42. Section study.

2. Fig. 13.43.   Draw top view and make front and two side views in section on cutting planes as indicated.   Scale to suit.

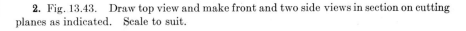

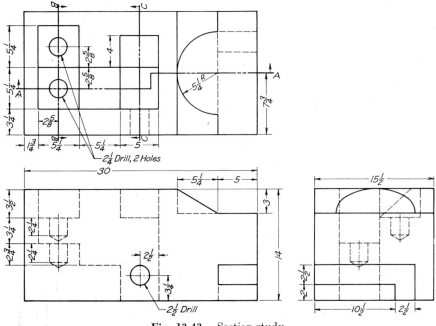

Fig. 13.43.   Section study.

3, 4, 5. Figs. 13.44 to 13.46.   Given side view, draw full front and side view in section. Scale to suit.

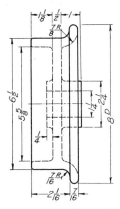

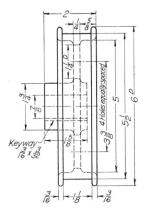

Fig. 13.44.   Flanged wheel.

Fig. 13.45.   Step pulley.

Fig. 13.46.   Flanged pulley.

6, 7. Figs. 13.47 and 13.48.   Change right-side view to a full section.

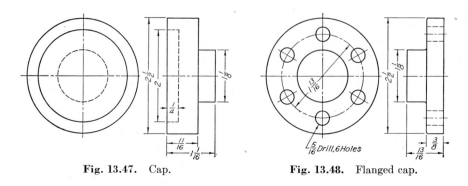

Fig. 13.47.   Cap.   **Fig. 13.48.**   Flanged cap.

8, 9. Figs. 13.49 and 13.50.   Change right-side view to a full section.

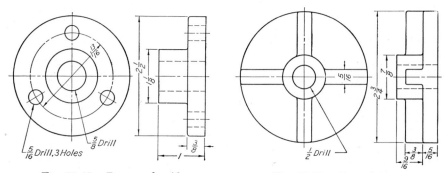

Fig. 13.49.   Pump-rod guide.   **Fig. 13.50.**   Face plate.

10. Fig. 13.51.   Change right-side view to a full section.
11. Fig. 13.52.   Change right-side view to sectional view as indicated.

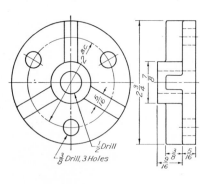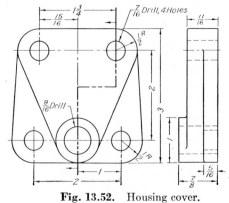

Fig. 13.51.   Ribbed support.   **Fig. 13.52.**   Housing cover.

12, 13. Figs. 13.53 and 13.54.   Change front view to a full section.

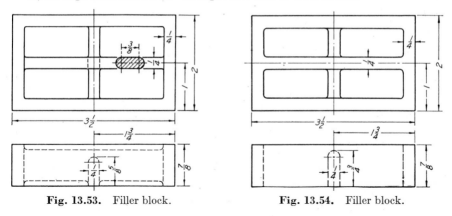

Fig. 13.53.   Filler block.   **Fig. 13.54.**   Filler block.

14, 15. Figs. 13.55 and 13.56.   Select views that will best describe the piece.

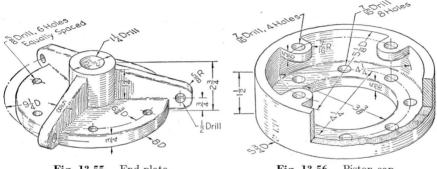

Fig. 13.55.   End plate.   **Fig. 13.56.**   Piston cap.

16. Fig. 13.57.   Draw top view as shown and front view as a full section.
17. Fig. 13.58.   Draw top view as shown and front view in half section on *A-A*.

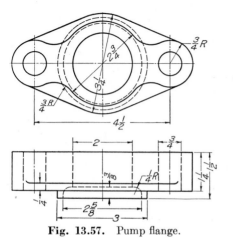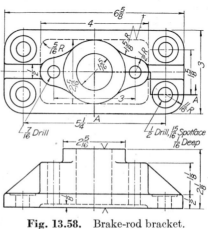

Fig. 13.57.   Pump flange.   **Fig. 13.58.**   Brake-rod bracket.

18. Fig. 13.59.   Draw top view as shown and change front and side views to sections as indicated.

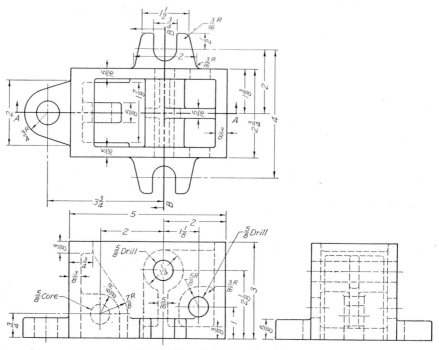

Fig. 13.59.   Bolted anchor-block.

19. Fig. 13.60.   Draw top view and sectional view, or views, to best describe the object.

20. Fig. 13.61.   Draw top view and front view in section.

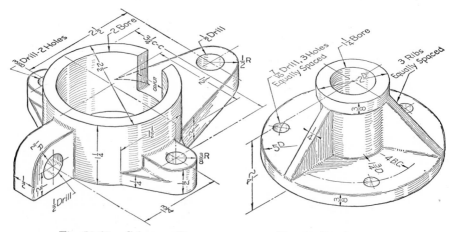

Fig. 13.60.   Column collar.   **Fig. 13.61.**   Stem support.

21. Fig. 13.62. Turn object through 90° and draw given front view as new top view; then make new front view as section *B-B*, and auxiliary section *A-A*. Refer to paragraph 13.17, where instructions for auxiliary sections have been given. Also, paragraphs 10.5 and 10.6 may be referred to for the method of projection for the auxiliary section. Note in this case that the new top view, front view section *B-B*, and auxiliary section *A-A* will completely describe the object. However, if desired, the side view may also be drawn, either as shown or as an aligned view as described in paragraph 13.32.

22. Fig. 13.62. As an alternate for Prob. 22, views may be drawn as follows: with object in position shown, draw front view as shown, draw left-side view as section *B-B*, and draw new top view as an aligned view.

23. Fig. 13.63. Draw three views making side view as a section on *B-B*.

24. Fig. 13.63. Draw three views making top view as a half section on *A-A*.

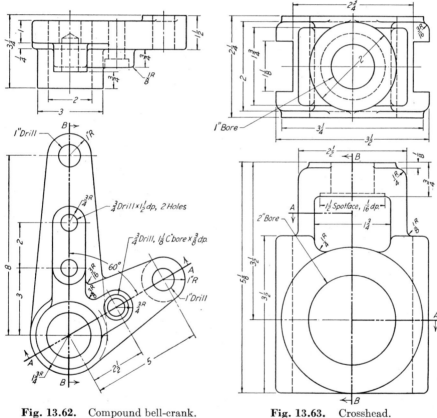

Fig. 13.62. Compound bell-crank.   **Fig. 13.63.** Crosshead.

25. Fig. 13.64. , Draw top view and necessary sectional view or views to best describe the object.

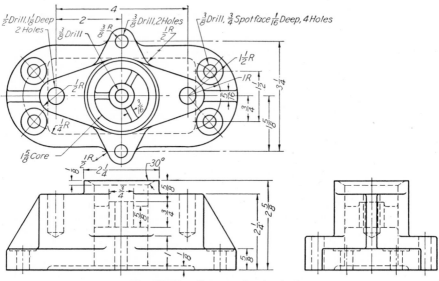

Fig. 13.64. Cover and valve body.

26. Fig. 13.65. Draw top view as shown and new front view in section. Show shape (right section) of link with revolved or removed section. The assembly comprises a cast-steel link, two bronze bushings, steel toggle pin, steel collar, steel taper pin, and part of the cast-steel supporting lug.

27. Fig. 13.66. Select views that will best describe the piece.

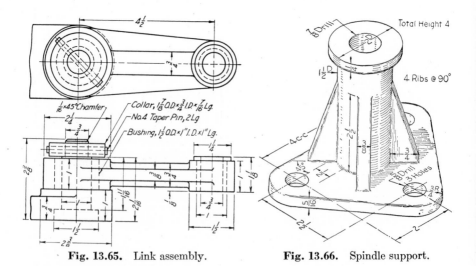

Fig. 13.65. Link assembly.   **Fig. 13.66.** Spindle support.

28. Fig. 13.67. Draw front view and longitudinal section. The assembly comprises a cast-iron base, a bronze bushing, a bronze disk, and two steel dowel pins.

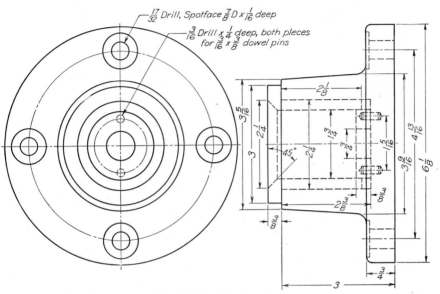

Fig. 13.67. Step bearing.

29. Fig. 13.68. Draw two half-end views and longitudinal section. The assembly consists of cast-iron body, two bronze bushings, steel shaft, cast-iron pulley, and steel taper pin.

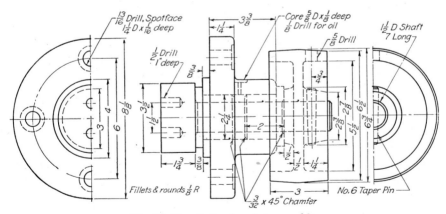

Fig. 13.68. Pulley bracket assembly.

30. Fig. 13.69.   Make an assembly drawing in section.   The bracket is cast iron, the wheel is cast steel, the bushing is bronze, and the pin and taper pin are steel.   Scale: full size.

31. Fig. 13.69.   Make a drawing of the bracket with one view in section.   Material, cast iron.   Scale: full size.

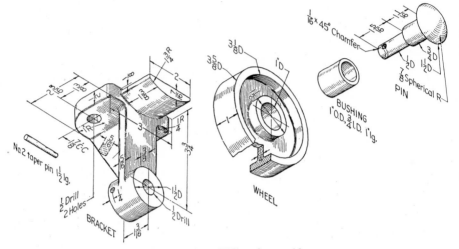

Fig. 13.69.   Sliding-door guide.

32. Fig. 13.69.   Make a drawing of the wheel with one view in section.   Material, cast steel.   Scale: full size.

33. Fig. 13.70.   Make an assembly drawing in section.   The assembly comprises two cast-iron brackets, two bronze bushings, steel shaft, cast-steel roller, and cast-iron base.

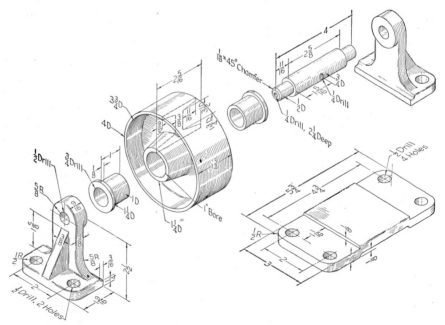

Fig. 13.70.   Bell roller-support.

The bushings are pressed into the roller and the shaft is drilled for lubrication.   Scale: full size.

34. Fig. 13.70.   Make a drawing of the roller and bushing assembly with one view in section.   See Prob. 33 for materials.   Scale: full size.

TEXT-FILMS

The following McGraw-Hill Text-Film was produced for specific use with Chap. 13:

Sections and Conventions (15-min. sound motion picture).

This Text-Film describes the theory and use of sectional views, their various types, and the principles and practices followed in their construction; explains the meaning of symbols used in sectioning; shows other types of conventional practices.

A coordinated silent filmstrip designed as a follow-up to this film summarizes the important facts about sectioning and reemphasizes the key points in the film.

14

Intersections

14.1   In the making of orthographic drawings there is the repeated necessity to represent the *lines of intersection* between the various surfaces of a wide variety of objects.   Nearly every line on a drawing is a line of intersection, generally the intersection of two planes, giving a straight line, or of a cylinder and a plane, giving a circle.   The term "intersection of surfaces" refers, however, to the more complicated lines that occur when geometrical surfaces such as cylinders, cones, and prisms intersect each other.   These lines of intersection may be shown by one of two basic methods: (1) *conventional intersections*, usually used to represent a fillet, round, or runout, as explained in paragraph 13.29 and shown in Fig. 13.34; or (2) *plotted intersections*,[1] employed when an intersection must be located accurately for purposes of dimensioning, or for development of the surfaces.   In sheet-metal combinations the intersections *must* be found before the piece can be developed.   In this chapter we are concerned solely with the method of projecting plotted intersections.

14.2   Basic theory.   When two surfaces intersect, the line of intersection, which is the line common to both, may be thought of as a line in which all the elements of one surface pierce the other.   Any practical problem resolves itself into some combination of the geometrical type forms.   In general, the method of finding the line of intersection of any two surfaces is to pass a series of planes through them in such a way that each plane cuts from each surface the simplest lines.   The intersection of the lines cut from each surface by a plane will give one or more points on the line of intersection.

14.3   Classification of surfaces.   A surface may be considered to be generated by the motion of a line: the generatrix.   Surfaces may thus be divided into two general classes: (1) those which can be generated by a moving *straight* line, and (2) those which can be generated only by a moving *curved* line.   The first are called *ruled surfaces;* the second, *double-curved surfaces.*   Any position of the generatrix is called an *element* of the surface.

Ruled surfaces may be divided into (*a*) *the plane*, (*b*) *single-curved surfaces*, and (*c*) *warped surfaces.*

The plane may be generated by a straight line moving so as to touch two other intersecting or parallel straight lines or a plane curve.

Single-curved surfaces have their elements either parallel or intersecting. In this class are the cylinder and the cone and also a third surface, which we

---

[1] In this book the intersections met with most often and of a practical nature are described and explained.   A full discussion of surfaces, their theory of construction, classification, and properties may be found in any good book on descriptive geometry.

shall not consider, known as the "convolute," in which consecutive elements intersect two and two.

Warped surfaces have no two consecutive elements either parallel or intersecting. There is a great variety of warped surfaces. The surface of a screw thread and that of an airplane wing are two examples.

Double-curved surfaces are generated by a curved line moving according to some law. The commonest forms are *surfaces of revolution*, made by revolving a curve about an axis in the same plane, as the sphere, torus or ring, ellipsoid, paraboloid, hyperboloid, etc. Illustrations of various surfaces may be found in Fig. 5.84.

14.4 Prisms. A prism is a polyhedron whose bases or ends are equal parallel polygons and whose lateral faces are parallelograms. A right prism is one whose lateral faces are rectangles; all others are called oblique prisms. The axis of a prism is a straight line connecting the centers of the bases. A truncated prism is that portion of a prism lying between one of its bases and a plane which cuts all its lateral edges.

14.5 To find the intersection of two prisms. Fig. 14.1. In general, find the line of intersection of a surface on one prism with all surfaces on the

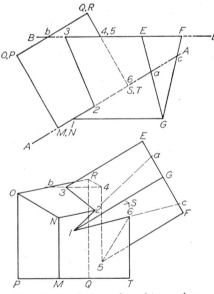

Fig. 14.1.   Intersection of two prisms.

other. Then take a surface adjacent to the first and find its intersection with the other prism. Continue in this manner until the complete line of intersection of the prisms is determined.

The method of locating end points on the line of intersection of two surfaces depends upon the position of the surfaces, as follows:

Both surfaces receding. Their intersection appears as a point in the view in which they recede. Project the intersection to an adjacent view, locating the two ends of the intersection on the edges of one or both intersecting surfaces so that they will lie within the boundaries of the other surface.   The intersection 4-5 of surfaces $QRST$ and $EF3$ was obtained in this manner.

One surface receding, the other oblique.   An edge of the oblique surface may appear to pierce the receding surface in a view in which these conditions exist.   If, in an adjacent view, the piercing point lies on the edge of the oblique surface and within the boundaries of the other surface, then it is an end point on the intersection of the surfaces.   Point 5 lying on edge $F5$ of the oblique surface $FG1$-5 and the surface $QRST$ is located in the top view in this manner.   Point 1 was similarly established.   Point 6 lying on edge ST is found by passing a vertical plane A-A through edge ST.   Plane A-A cuts line $1c$ from plane $GF5$-1 giving point 6 where line $1c$ crosses ST.

Both surfaces oblique.   Find the piercing point of an edge of one surface with the other surface, as follows: Pass a receding plane through an edge of one surface.   Find the line of intersection of the receding plane and the other surface as explained above.   The piercing point of the edge and surface is located where the line of intersection, just found, and the edge intersect.   Repeat this operation to establish the other end of the line of intersection of the surfaces.   Point 3, on the line of intersection 2-3 of the oblique surfaces $NORS$ and $EG1$-3, was found in this manner, by passing the receding plane B-B through edge $E3$; finding the intersection $b4$ of the surfaces, and then locating point 3 at the intersection of $b4$ and $E3$.

14.6   Pyramids.   A pyramid is a polyhedron whose base is a polygonal plane and whose other surfaces are triangular planes meeting at a point called the "vertex."   The axis is a line passing through the vertex and the mid-point of the base.   The altitude is a perpendicular from the vertex to the base.   A pyramid is *right* if the altitude coincides with the axis; it is *oblique* if they do not coincide.   A truncated pyramid is that portion lying between the base and a cutting plane which cuts all the lateral edges.   The frustum of a pyramid is that portion lying between the base and a cutting plane parallel to the base that cuts all the lateral edges.

14.7   To find the intersection of two pyramids.   In general, find where one edge on one pyramid pierces a surface of the other pyramid.   Then find where a second edge pierces, and so on.   To complete the line of intersection the piercing points of the edges of the second pyramid with surfaces of the first will probably also have to be found.   Figure 14.2 illustrates the method. Find where edge AD pierces plane EHG by assuming a vertical cutting plane through edge AD.   This plane cuts line 1-2 from plane EHG, and the piercing point is point P, located first on the front view and then projected to the top view.   Next, find where AD pierces plane EFG by using a vertical cutting plane through AD.   This plane cuts line 3-4 from plane EFG, and the piercing point is point Q.

Having a point P on plane EHG and point Q on plane EFG, the piercing point of edge EG with plane ABD will have to be found in order to draw lines of intersection.   A vertical plane through EG cuts line 5-6 from plane ABD, and the intersection is point R on edge EG. Thus edges of the "first" pyramid pierce surfaces of the "second," and edges of the "second" pierce surfaces of the "first." Continue in this manner until the complete line of intersection $PRQSTV$ has been found.

The use of a vertical cutting plane to obtain the piercing points is perhaps the simplest method and the easiest to visualize. Nevertheless, it should be noted that a plane receding either from the frontal or profile plane could also be used. As an example of the use of a plane receding from the frontal, consider that such a plane has been passed through line CA in the front view. This plane cuts line 7-8 from plane EFG, and the point of intersection is S on line CA. The use of a plane receding from the profile would be basically the same but would, of course, require a side view.

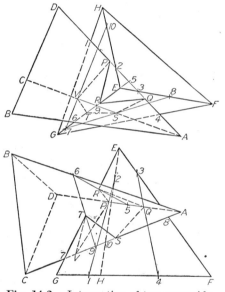

Fig. 14.2.   Intersection of two pyramids.

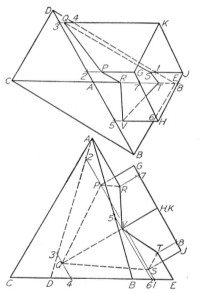

Fig. 14.3.   Intersection of pyramid and prism.

14.8   To find the line of intersection between a prism and a pyramid. Fig. 14.3.   The method, basically, is the same as for two pyramids. Thus, a vertical plane through edge G cuts line 1-2 from surface AED and a vertical plane through edge K cuts line 3-4 from surface AED, giving the two piercing points P and Q on surface AED. A vertical plane through edge AE cuts elements 7 and 8 from the prism and gives piercing points R and T. Continue in this manner until the complete line of intersection $PQSTVR$ is found.

14.9   Cylinders. A cylinder is a single-curved surface generated by the motion of a straight-line generatrix remaining parallel to itself and constantly intersecting a curved directrix. The various positions of the generatrix are elements of the surface. It is a *right* cylinder when the elements are perpendicular to the bases, an *oblique* cylinder when they are not. A truncated cylinder is that portion which lies between one of its bases and a cutting plane, which cuts all the elements. The axis is the line joining the centers of the bases.

14.10   To find the intersection of two cylinders. Fig. 14.4. Cutting planes parallel to the axis of a cylinder will cut straight-line elements from the cylinder. The frontal cutting planes *A*, *B*, *C*, and *D*, *parallel to the axis of each cylinder*, cut elements from each cylinder, the intersections of which are points on the curve. The pictorial sketch shows a slice cut by a plane from the object, which has been treated as a solid in order to illustrate the method more easily.

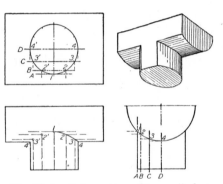

Fig. 14.4.   Intersection of two cylinders.

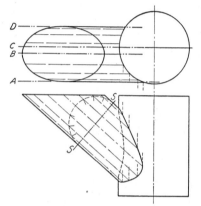

Fig. 14.5.   Intersection of two cylinders, axes not intersecting.

When the axes of the cylinders do not intersect, as in Fig. 14.5, the same method is used. Certain "critical planes" give the limits and turning points of the curve. Such planes should always be taken through the contour elements. For the position shown, planes *A* and *D* give the depth of the curve, the plane *B* the extreme height, and the plane *C* the tangent or turning points on the contour element of the vertical cylinder. After the critical points have been determined, a sufficient number of other cutting planes are used to give an accurate curve.

14.11   Cones. A cone is a single-curved surface generated by the movement, along a curved directrix, of a straight-line generatrix, one point of which is fixed. The directrix is the base, and the fixed point is the vertex of the cone. Each position of the generatrix is an element of the surface. The axis is a line connecting the vertex and the center of the base. The altitude is a perpendicular dropped from the vertex to the base. A cone is *right* if the axis and altitude coincide; it is *oblique* if they do not coincide. A truncated cone is that portion lying between the base and a cutting plane which cuts all the elements. The frustum of a cone is that portion lying between the base and a cutting plane parallel to the base, which cuts all the elements.

14.12   To find the intersection of a prism and a cone.   Fig. 14.6.
Cutting planes should be so selected as to cut either circles or straight lines
from the cone.   In this case cutting planes perpendicular to the coincident
axes have been used.   Thus each plane cuts a circle from the cone and a
hexagon from the prism, whose intersections give points on the curve.   The
curve is limited between the plane A, cutting a circle whose diameter is equal
to the short diameter of the hexagon, and the plane C, cutting a circle whose
diameter is equal to the long diameter.   As the prism is made up of six
vertical planes, the entire line of intersection of cone and prism consists of

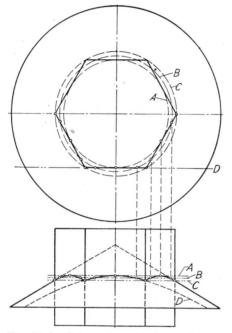

Fig. 14.6.   Intersection of prism and cone.

the ends of six hyperbolas, three of which are visible, one showing its true
shape, as cut by plane D, the two others foreshortened.   This figure illustrates the true curve in a chamfered hexagonal bolthead or nut.   In
practice it is always drawn approximately with three circle arcs.   See
paragraph 23.6.

14.13   To find the intersection of a cylinder and a cone.   Fig. 14.7.
Cutting planes may be taken (1) so as to pass through the vertex of the cone
and parallel to the axis of the cylinder, thus cutting straight-line elements
from both cylinder and cone; or (2) with a right circular cone, when the
cylinder's axis is either parallel or perpendicular to the cone's axis, cutting
planes may be taken parallel to the base so as to cut circles from the cone.
Both systems of planes are illustrated in the figure.   The pictorial sketches
show slices taken by each plane through the objects, which have been treated

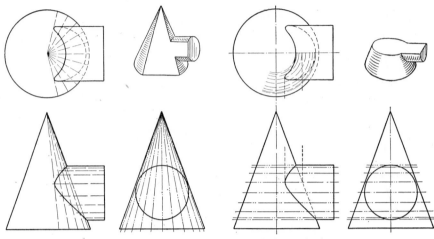

Fig. 14.7.   Intersection of a cylinder and cone.

as solids in order to illustrate the method more easily.   Some judgment is necessary in the selection of both the direction and the number of cutting planes.   More points need to be found at the places of sudden curvature or changes of direction of the projections of the line of intersections.

14.14   To find the intersection of a plane and a surface of revolution. Fig. 14.8.   This problem depends on the principle that planes perpendicular to the axis of any surface of revolution will cut circles (right sections).

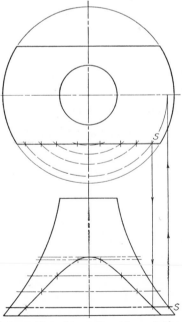

Fig. 14.8.   Intersection of a surface of revolution and a plane.

Thus the line of intersection of a plane and a surface of revolution is found by passing a series of planes perpendicular to the axis of revolution. Each of these planes will cut a straight line from the given plane and a circle from the surface of revolution, the intersection of which will give two points on the curve. In Fig. 14.8 the diameter of the circle cut by the plane S has been projected to the top view and the points at which the circle cuts the "flat" have been projected to the front view to give points on the curve.

PROBLEMS

Selections from the following problems may be made and the figures drawn accurately in pencil on either 8½- by 11-in. or 11- by 17-in. paper. Assume the objects to be thin material with open ends unless otherwise specified.

Group I. Intersections of prisms. *Problems 1 to 6*

1 to 3. Fig. 14.9. Find the line of intersection, considering the prisms as pipes opening into each other. Use particular care in indicating visible and invisible portions of the line of intersection.

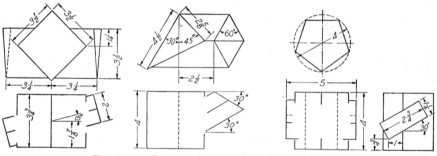

Fig. 14.9. Intersections of prisms (Probs. 1 to 3).

4 to 6. Fig. 14.10. Find the line of intersection, indicating visible and invisible parts, and considering prisms as pipes opening into each other. Note that in Probs. 5 and 6 the vertical pipes must have heads cut out to fit inclined pipe.

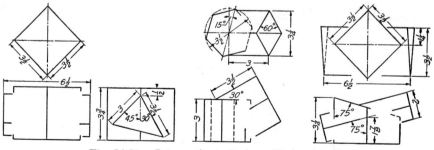

Fig. 14.10. Intersections of prisms (Probs. 4 to 6).

Group II. Intersections of pyramids. *Problems 7 to 11*

7 to 11. Fig. 14.11. Find the lines of intersection.

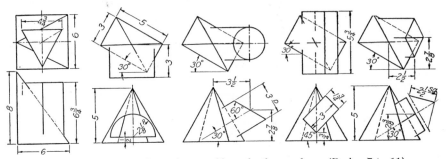

Fig. 14.11. Intersections of pyramids and other surfaces (Probs. 7 to 11).

Group III. Intersections of cylinders. *Problems 12 to 14*

12 to 14. Fig. 14.12. Find the line of intersection, indicating visible and invisible portions and considering cylinders as pipes opening into each other.

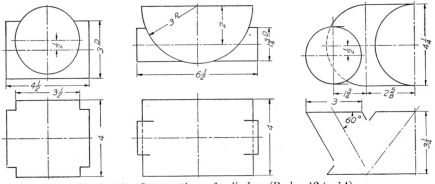

Fig. 14.12. Intersections of cylinders (Probs. 12 to 14).

Group IV. Intersections of cones. *Problems 15 to 25*

15 to 18. Fig. 14.13. Find the lines of intersection.

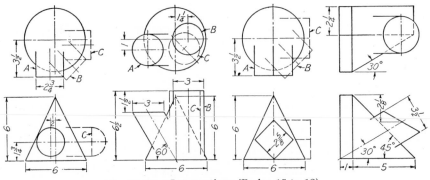

Fig. 14.13. Intersections (Probs. 15 to 18).

19 to 21. Fig. 14.14. Find the lines of intersection.

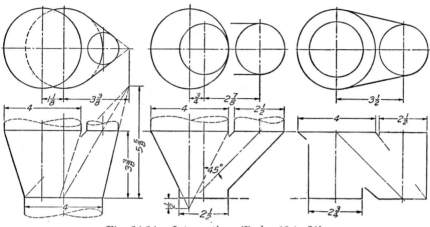

Fig. 14.14. Intersections (Probs. 19 to 21).

22 to 25. Fig. 14.15. Find the lines of intersection.

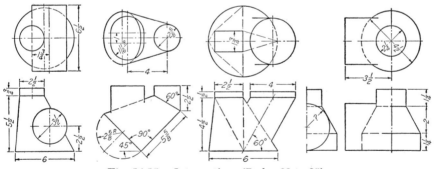

Fig. 14.15. Intersections (Probs. 22 to 25).

The foregoing problems may be used not only for exercises in finding the lines of intersection between various surfaces but after the lines of intersection have been found the individual surfaces may be developed, as described in the next chapter. See Prob. 47 on page 264.

Problems intended for later development should be drawn very accurately, because the accuracy of the development will depend upon the drawing from which it was made. Especially, the line of intersection should be accurately found.

Group V.   Surfaces cut by planes.   *Problems 26 to 30*

26 to 30. Fig. 14.16.   Complete the views, finding the lines of intersection.   Make separate views of sections on the planes indicated.

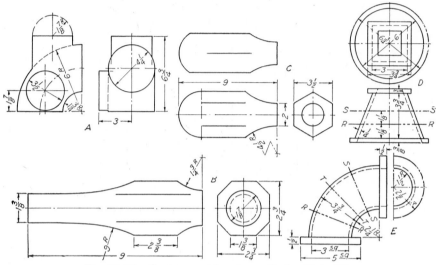

Fig. 14.16.   Surfaces cut by planes (Probs. 26 to 30).

15

Developments

15.1 In many different kinds of construction, full-size patterns of some or all of the faces of an object are required, as, for example, in stonecutting, a template or pattern giving the shape of an irregular face; or in sheet-metal work, a pattern to which a sheet may be cut so that when rolled, folded, or formed it will make the object.

The complete surface laid out in a plane is called the *development* of the surface.

Surfaces about which a thin sheet of flexible material (as paper or tin) can be wrapped smoothly are said to be developable; these include objects made up of planes and single-curved surfaces only. Warped and double-curved surfaces are nondevelopable, and when patterns are required for their construction, they can be made only by methods that are approximate; but, assisted by the ductility or pliability of the material, they give the required form. Thus, while a ball cannot be wrapped smoothly, a two-piece pattern developed approximately and cut from leather may be stretched and sewed on in a smooth cover, or a flat disk of metal may be die-stamped, formed, or spun to a hemispherical or other required shape.

15.2 **Basic considerations.** We have learned the method of finding the true size of a plane surface by projecting it on an auxiliary plane. If the

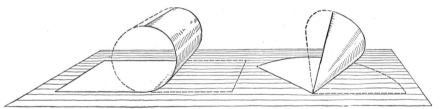

Fig. 15.1. Development of a cylinder and a cone.

true size of all the plane faces of an object are found and joined in order at their common edges so that all faces lie in a common plane, the result will be the developed surface. Usually this may be done to the best advantage by finding the true length of the edges.

The development of a right cylinder is evidently a rectangle whose width is the altitude, and length the rectified circumference, Fig. 15.1; and the development of a right circular cone is a circular sector with a radius equal to the slant height of the cone, and an arc equal in length to the circumference of its base, Fig. 15.1.

As illustrated in Fig. 15.1, developments are drawn with the inside face up. This is primarily the result of working to inside rather than outside dimensions of ducts. This procedure also facilitates the use of fold lines, identified by punch marks at either end, along which the metal is folded in forming the object.

In the laying out of real sheet-metal designs, an allowance must be made for seams and lap and, in heavy sheets, for the thickness and crowding of the metal; there is also the consideration of the commercial sizes of material, as well as the question of economy in cutting, in all of which some practical shop knowledge is necessary. Figure 15.17 and paragraph 15.14 illustrate and explain the usage of some of the more common joints, although the developments in this chapter will be confined to the principles alone.

15.3   To develop a truncated hexagonal prism. Fig. 15.2. First draw two projections of the prism: (1) a normal view of a right section (a section

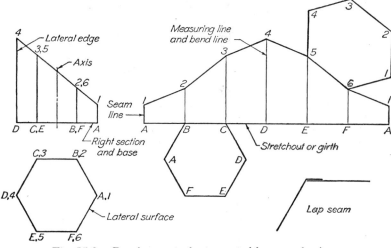

Fig. 15.2.   Development of a truncated hexagonal prism.

or cut obtained by a plane perpendicular to the axis), and (2) a normal view of the lateral edges. The base *ABCDEF* is a right section shown in true size in the bottom view. Lay off on line *AA* of the development the perimeter of the base. This line is called by sheet-metal workers the "stretchout" or "girth" line. At points *A*, *B*, *C*, etc., erect perpendiculars called "measuring lines" or "bend lines," representing the lateral edges along which the pattern is folded to form the prism. Lay off on each of these its length *A1*, *B2*, *C3*, etc., as given on the front view. Connect the points 1, 2, 3, etc., in succession, to complete the development of the lateral surfaces. Note on the pattern that the inside of the lateral faces is toward the observer. For the development of the entire surface in one piece, attach the true sizes of the upper end and the base as shown, finding the true size of the upper end by an auxiliary view as described in paragraph 10.7. For economy of solder or rivets and time, it is customary to make the seam on the shortest edge or surface. In seaming along the intersection of surfaces whose dihedral angle is other than 90°, as in the case here, the lap seam lends itself to convenient assembling.   The flat lock could be used if the seam was made on one of the lateral faces.

15.4   To develop a truncated right pyramid.   Fig. 15.3.   Draw the projections of the pyramid which show (1) a normal view of the base or right section, and (2) a normal view of the axis.   Lay out the pattern for the pyramid and then superimpose the pattern of the truncation.

Since this is a portion of a right regular pyramid, the lateral edges are all of equal length.   The lateral edges OA and OD are parallel to the frontal plane and consequently show in their true length on the front view.   With

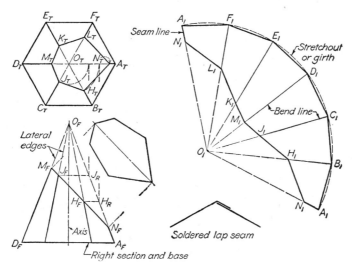

Fig. 15.3.   Development of a truncated right hexagonal pyramid.

center O_1, taken at any convenient place, and a radius O_FA_F, draw an arc which is the stretchout of the pattern.   On it step off the six equal sides of the hexagonal base, obtained from the top view, and connect these points successively with each other and with the vertex O_1, thus forming the pattern for the pyramid.

The intersection of the cutting plane and lateral surfaces is developed by laying off the true length of the intercept of each lateral edge on the corresponding line of the development.   The true length of each of these intercepts, such as OH, OJ, etc., is found by rotating it about the axis of the pyramid until they coincide with O_FA_F, as explained in paragraph 12.5. The path of any point, as H, will be projected on the front view as a horizontal line.   To obtain the development of the entire surface of the truncated pyramid, attach the base; also find the true size of the cut face and attach it on a common line.

The lap seam is suggested for use here for the same reason that was advanced in paragraph 15.3.

The right rectangular pyramid, Fig. 15.4, is developed in a similar way, but as the edge OA is not parallel to the plane of projection it must be rotated to $O_F A_R$ to obtain its true length.

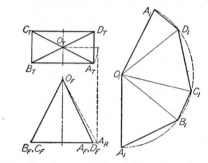

Fig. 15.4. Development of a right rectangular pyramid.

15.5 To develop an oblique pyramid. Fig. 15.5. Since the lateral edges are unequal in length, the true length of each must be found separately by rotating it parallel to the frontal plane, as explained in paragraph 12.5. With O_1 taken at any convenient place, lay off the seam line $O_1 A_1$ equal to $O_F A_R$. With A_1 as center and radius $A_1 B_1$ equal to the true length of AB, describe an arc. With O_1 as center and radius $O_1 B_1$ equal to $O_F B_R$, describe

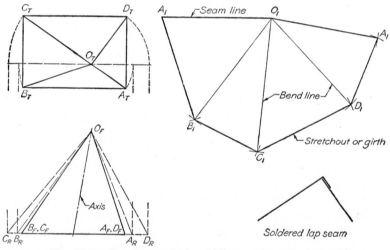

Fig. 15.5. Development of an oblique rectangular pyramid.

a second arc intersecting the first in vertex B_1. Connect the vertices O_1, A_1, B_1, thus forming the pattern for the lateral surface OAB. Similarly, lay out the patterns for the remaining three lateral surfaces, joining them on their common edges. The stretchout is equal to the summation of the base edges. If the complete development is required, attach the base on a common line. The lap seam is suggested as the most suitable for the given conditions.

15.6   To develop a truncated right cylinder.   Fig. 15.6.   The development of a cylinder is similar to the development of a prism.   Draw two projections of the cylinder: (1) a normal view of a right section, and (2) a normal view of the elements.   In rolling the cylinder out on a tangent plane, the base or right section, being perpendicular to the axis, will develop into a straight line.   For convenience in drawing, divide the normal view of the base, here shown in the bottom view, into a number of equal parts by points that represent elements.   These divisions should be spaced so that the chordal distances closely enough approximate the arc to make the stretchout practically equal to the periphery of the base or right section.   Project these elements to the front view.   Draw the stretchout and measuring lines as in

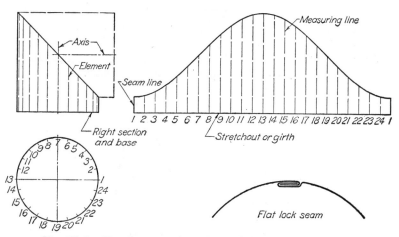

Fig. 15.6.   Development of a truncated right circular cylinder.

Fig. 15.2, the cylinder now being treated as a many-sided prism.   Transfer the lengths of the elements in order, either by projection or with dividers, and join the points thus found by a smooth curve, sketching it in very lightly, freehand, before fitting the french curve to it.   This development might be the pattern of one-half of a two-piece elbow.   Three-piece, four-piece, or five-piece elbows may be drawn similarly, as illustrated in Fig. 15.7.   As the base is symmetrical, only one-half of it need be drawn.   In these cases, the intermediate pieces as B, C, and D are developed on a stretchout line formed by laying off the perimeter of a right section.   If the right section is taken through the middle of the piece, the stretchout line becomes the center line of the development.

Evidently any elbow could be cut from a single sheet without waste if the seams were made alternately on the long and short sides.   The flat lock seam is recommended for Figs. 15.6 and 15.7, although other types could be used.

The octagonal dome, Fig. 15.8, illustrates an application of the development of cylinders.   Each piece is a portion of a cylinder.   The elements are parallel to the base of the dome and show in their true lengths in the top view. The true length of the stretchout line for sections A and A' shows in the front view at $O_F H_F$. By considering $O_T H_T$ as the edge of a plane cutting a right section, the problem is identical with the preceding problem.

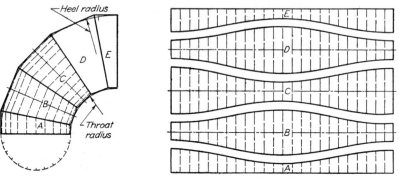

Fig. 15.7. Development of a five-piece elbow.

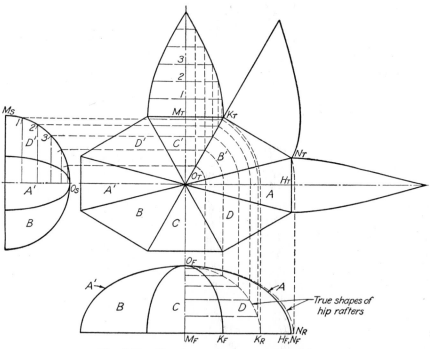

Fig. 15.8. Development of an octagonal dome.

Similarly, the stretchout line for sections B, B', D, and D' shows in true length at $O_F K_R$ in the front view, and for section C and C' at $O_S M_S$ in the side view.

The true shape of hip rafter ON is found by rotating it until it is parallel to the frontal plane, as at $O_F N_R$ in the same manner as in finding the true

length of any line.   A sufficient number of points should be taken to give a
smooth curve.

15.7   To develop a truncated right circular cone.   Fig. 15.9.   Draw the
projections of the cone which will show (1) a normal view of the base or right
section, and (2) a normal view of the axis.   First develop the surface of the
complete cone and then superimpose the pattern for the truncation.

Divide the top view of the base into a sufficient number of equal parts so
that the sum of the resulting chordal distances will closely approximate the
periphery of the base.   Project these points to the front view and draw front
views of the elements through them.   With center A_1 and a radius equal to

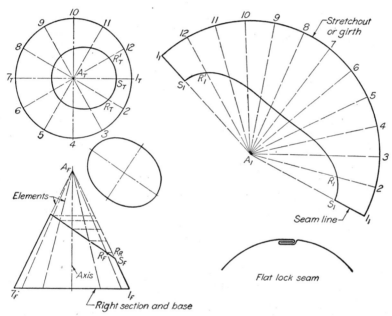

Fig. 15.9.   Development of a truncated right circular cone.

the slant height A_F1_F, which is the true length of all the elements, draw an
arc, which is the stretchout, and lay off on it the chordal divisions of the base,
obtained from the top view.   Connect these points 1_1, 2, 3, etc., with A_1,
thus forming the pattern for the cone.   Find the true length of each element
from vertex to cutting plane by rotating it to coincide with the contour element A_1, and lay off this distance on the corresponding line of the development.   Draw a smooth curve through these points.   The flat lock seam
along element $S1$ is recommended, although other types could be employed.
The pattern for the cut surface is obtained from the auxiliary view.

15.8   Triangulation.   Nondevelopable surfaces are developed approximately by assuming them to be made of narrow sections of developable surfaces.   The commonest and best method for approximate development is
that of triangulation, that is, the surface is assumed to be made up of a large

number of triangular strips or plane triangles with very short bases. This method is used for all warped surfaces and also for oblique cones. Oblique cones are single-curved surfaces and are capable of true theoretical development, but can be developed much more easily and accurately by triangulation.

The principle is extremely simple. It consists merely in dividing the surface into triangles, finding the true lengths of the sides of each, and constructing them one at a time, joining these triangles on their common sides.

15.9   To develop an oblique cone. Fig. 15.10. An oblique cone differs from a cone of revolution in that the elements are all of different lengths. The development of the right circular cone is practically made up of a num-

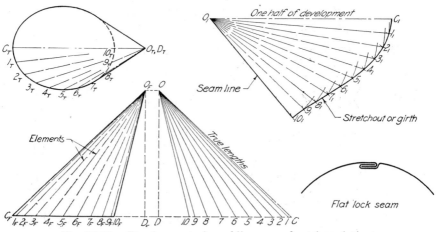

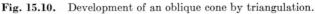

Fig. 15.10.   Development of an oblique cone by triangulation.

ber of equal triangles meeting at the vertex, whose sides are elements and whose bases are the chords of short arcs of the base of the cone. In the oblique cone, each triangle must be found separately.

Draw two views of the cone showing (1) a normal view of the base, and (2) a normal view of the altitude. Divide the true size of the base, here shown in the top view, into a sufficient number of equal parts, so that the sum of the chordal distances will closely approximate the length of the base curve. Project these points to the front view of the base. Through these points and the vertex, draw the elements in each view. Since this cone is symmetrical about a frontal plane through the vertex, the elements are shown only on the front half of it. Also, only one-half of the development is drawn. With the seam on the shortest element, the element OC will be the center line of the development and may be drawn directly at O_1C_1, as its true length is given at O_FC_F. Find the true length of the elements by rotating them until parallel to the frontal plane, or by constructing a "true-length diagram." The true length of any element would be the hypotenuse of a triangle, one leg being the length of the projected element as seen in the top view, the other leg equal to the altitude of the cone. Thus, to make the diagram, draw the leg OD coinciding with or parallel to $O_F D_F$. At D and perpendicular to OD draw the other leg, on which lay off the lengths $D1$, $D2$, etc., equal to $D_T 1_T$, $D_T 2_T$, etc., respectively. Distances from O to points on the base of the diagram are the true lengths of the elements.

Construct the pattern for the front half of the cone as follows: With $O1$ as center and radius $O1$, draw an arc. With C_1 as center and radius $C_T 1_T$, draw a second arc intersecting the first at 1_1; then $O_1 1_1$ will be the developed position of the element $O1$. With 1_1 as center and radius $1_T 2_T$, draw an arc intersecting a second arc with O_1 as center and radius $O2$, thus locating 2_1. Continue this procedure until all the elements have been transferred to the development. Connect the points C_1, 1_1, 2_1, etc., with a smooth curve, the stretchout line, to complete the development. The flat lock seam is recommended for joining the ends of the pattern to form the cone.

15.10   A conical connection between two parallel cylindrical pipes of different diameters is shown in Fig. 15.11. The method used in drawing the

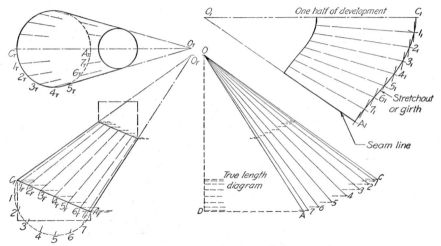

Fig. 15.11.   Development of a conical connection.

pattern is an application of the development of an oblique cone. One-half of the elliptical base is shown in true size in an auxiliary view, here attached to the front view. Find the true size of the base from its major and minor axes; divide it into a number of equal parts so that the sum of these chordal distances closely approximates the periphery of the curve, and project these points to the front and top views. Draw the elements in each view through these points and find the vertex O by extending the contour elements until they intersect. The true length of each element is found by using the vertical distance between its ends as the vertical leg of the diagram and its horizontal projection as the other leg. As each true length from vertex to base is found, project the upper end of the intercept horizontally across from the front view to the true length of the corresponding element to find the true length of the intercept. The development is drawn by laying out each triangle in turn, from vertex to base as in paragraph 15.9, starting on the center line O_1C_1, then measuring on each element its intercept length. Draw smooth curves through these points to complete the pattern. Join the ends of the development with a flat lock seam to form the connection.

15.11 Transition pieces are used to connect pipes or openings of different shapes of cross section. Figure 15.12, showing a transition piece for connecting a round pipe and a rectangular pipe, is typical. These are always developed by triangulation. The piece shown in Fig. 15.12 is, evidently,

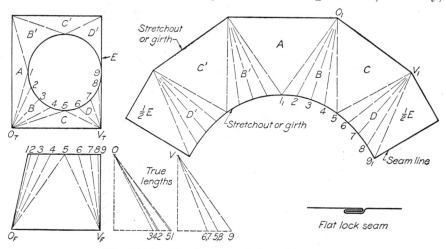

Fig. 15.12. Development of a transition piece.

made up of four triangular planes whose bases are the sides of the rectangle, and four parts of oblique cones whose common bases are arcs of the circle and whose vertices are at the corners of the rectangle. To develop it, make a true-length diagram as in Fig. 15.10. The true length of $O1$ being found, all the sides of triangle A will be known. Attach the development of cones B and B', then those of triangles C and C', and so on.

Figure 15.13 is another transition piece joining a rectangular to a circular pipe whose axes are nonparallel. By using a partial right-side view of the round opening, the divisions of the bases of the oblique cones can be found (as the object is symmetrical, one-half only of the opening need be divided). The true lengths of the elements are obtained as in Fig. 15.11.

With the seam line the center line of the plane E in Figs. 15.12 and 15.13, the flat lock is recommended for joining the ends of the development.

15.12 Triangulation of warped surfaces. The approximate development of a warped surface is made by dividing it into a number of narrow quadrilaterals and then splitting each of these quadrilaterals into two triangles by a diagonal, which is assumed to be a straight line, although really a curve. Figure 15.14 shows a warped transition piece to connect an ovular (upper) pipe with a right circular cylindrical pipe (lower). Find the true size of one-half the elliptical base by rotating it, until horizontal, about an

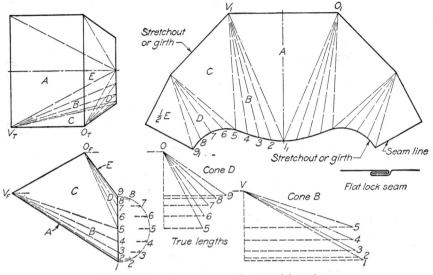

Fig. 15.13.   Development of a transition piece.

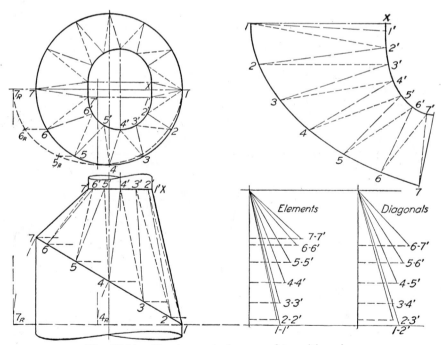

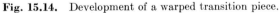

Fig. 15.14.   Development of a warped transition piece.

axis through 1, when its true shape will be seen on the top view. The major axis is 1-7$_R$, and the minor axis through 4$_R$ will be equal to the diameter of the lower pipe. Divide the semiellipse into a sufficient number of equal parts and project these to the top and front views. Divide the top semicircle into the same number of equal parts and connect similar points on each end, thus dividing the surface into approximate quadrilaterals. Cut each into two triangles by a diagonal. On true-length diagrams find the lengths of the elements and the diagonals, and draw the development by constructing the true sizes of the triangles in regular order. The flat-lock seam is recommended for joining the ends of the development.

15.13 To develop a sphere. The sphere may be taken as typical of double-curved surfaces, which can be developed only approximately. It may be cut into a number of equal meridian sections, or lunes, as in Fig. 15.15, and these may be considered to be sections of cylinders. One of these sections, developed as the cylinder in Fig. 15.15, will give a pattern for the others.

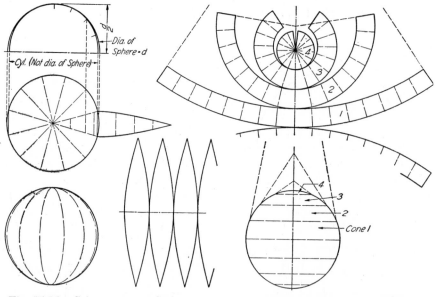

Fig. 15.15. Sphere, gore method.   **Fig. 15.16.** Sphere, zone method.

Another method is to cut the sphere into horizontal sections, or zones, each of which may be taken as the frustum of a cone whose vertex is at the intersection of the extended chords, Fig. 15.16.

15.14 Joints, connectors, and hems. There are numerous joints used in seaming sheet-metal ducts and in connecting one duct to another. Figure 15.17 illustrates some of the more common types, which may be formed by hand on a break or by special seaming machines. No attempt to dimension the various seams and connections has been made here because of the variation in sizes for different gages of metal and in the forming machines of manufacturers.

Hemming is used in finishing the raw edges of the end of the duct. In wire hemming an extra allowance of about $2\frac{1}{2}$ times the diameter of the wire is made for wrapping around the wire. In flat hemming the end of the duct is bent over either once or twice to relieve the sharp edge of the metal.

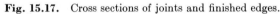

Wired edge   A   B   Flat lock   Soldered   Riveted
Hemmed edges   Lap joints

Pittsburgh   Riveted   Button punched   Elbow   Cup joint
corner lock   Standing seams   slip joint

A   B   C   S-hook slip joint   Cap strip connector
Side outlet joints

Fig. 15.17. Cross sections of joints and finished edges.

PROBLEMS

Selections from the following problems may be made and the figures constructed accurately in pencil without inking. Any practical problem can be resolved into some combination of the "type solids," and the exercises given illustrate the principles involved in the various combinations.

An added interest in developments may be found by working problems on suitable paper, allowing for fastenings and lap, and cutting them out. It is recommended that at least one or two models be constructed in this way.

In sheet-metal shops, development problems, unless very complicated, are usually laid out directly on the metal.

The following problems may be drawn on $8\frac{1}{2}$- by 11-in. or 11- by 17-in. sheets. Assume the objects to be made of thin metal with open ends unless otherwise specified.

Group I. Prisms. *Problems 1 to 6*

1 to 6. Fig. 15.18. Develop lateral surfaces of the prisms.

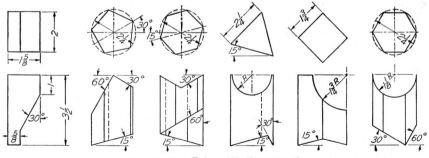

Fig. 15.18. Prisms (Probs. 1 to 6).

Group II. Pyramids. *Problems 7 to 11*

7 to 9. Fig. 15.19. Develop lateral surfaces of the hoppers.
10, 11. Fig. 15.19. Develop lateral surfaces of the pyramids.

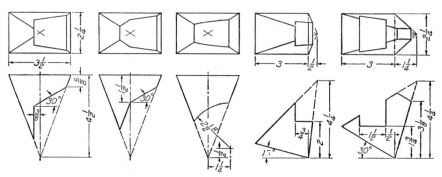

Fig. 15.19. Pyramids (Probs. 7–11).

Group III. Cylinders. *Problems 12 to 18*

12 to 18. Fig. 15.20. Develop lateral surfaces of the cylinders.

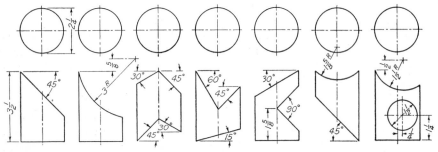

Fig. 15.20. Cylinders (Probs. 12 to 18).

Group IV. Combinations of prisms and cylinders. *Problems 19 to 21*

19 to 21. Fig. 15.21. Develop lateral surfaces.

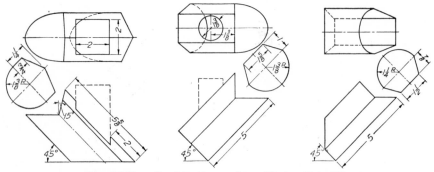

Fig. 15.21. Combination surfaces (Probs. 19 to 21).

Group V. Cones. *Problems 22 to 26*

22 to 26. Fig. 15.22. Develop lateral surfaces.

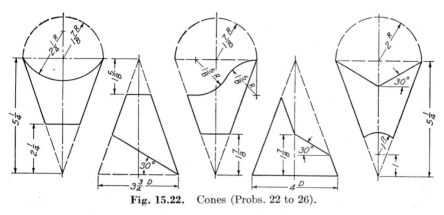

Fig. 15.22. Cones (Probs. 22 to 26).

Group VI. Combinations of surfaces. *Problems 27 to 30*

27 to 30. Fig. 15.23. Develop lateral surfaces of the objects. Note that 28 is a GI gutter, and 29 is a conical hood.

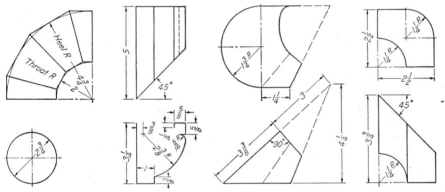

Fig. 15.23. Various surfaces (Probs. 27 to 30).

Group VII. Cones and transition pieces. *Problems 31 to 38*

31 to 34. Fig. 15.24. Develop lateral surfaces of the objects (one-half of Probs. 31, 32, 34).

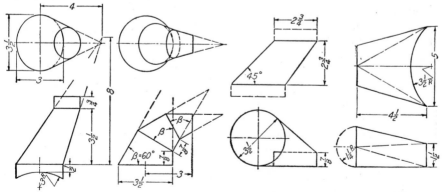

Fig. 15.24. Transition pieces (Probs. 31 to 34).

35 to 37. Fig. 15.25. Develop lateral surfaces of the objects (one-half).

38. Fig. 15.25. Develop surface of one-half of Y connection.

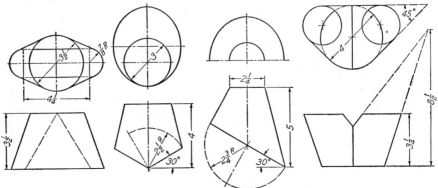

Fig. 15.25. Transition pieces (Probs. 35 to 38).

Group VIII. Furnace-pipe fittings. *Problems 39 to 46*

39 to 46. Fig. 15.26. Develop surfaces and make paper models.

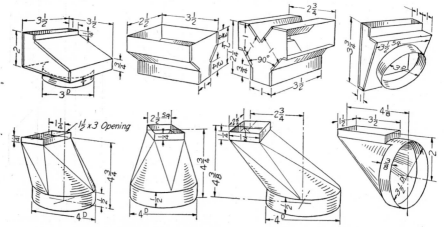

Fig. 15.26. Sheet-metal connections (Probs. 39 to 46).

Group IX. Intersection and development.

47. The problems of Chap. 14 may be used for development of the surfaces after the lines of intersection have been drawn. Select a problem previously drawn from groups I to IV, pages 245 to 247, and develop the surfaces.

TEXT-FILMS

The following McGraw-Hill Text-Film is available for specific correlation with Chap. 15:

Developments (approximately 18-min. sound motion picture).

Explains development of prisms, pyramids, cylinders, cones and transition pieces.

This film is accompanied by a coordinated silent filmstrip that may be used for review and oral discussion.

16

Pictorial Drawing

16.1 In the study of the theory of projection in Chap. 6, it was found that perspective projection shows the object as it appears to the eye but that its lines cannot be measured directly, while orthographic projection, with two or more views, shows it as it really is in form and dimensions but requires a trained imagination to visualize the object from the views. To combine the pictorial effect of perspective drawing with the possibility of measuring the principal lines directly, several forms of one-plane projection or conventional picture methods have been devised, in which the third dimension is taken care of by turning the object in such a way that three of its faces are visible. Along with the advantages of these methods go some disadvantages which limit their usefulness. The distorted effect is often unreal and unpleasant; only certain lines can be measured; the execution occasionally requires more time, particularly if curved lines occur, and it is often difficult to show certain dimensions; but, even with their limitations, a knowledge of these methods is extremely desirable as they can be used to great advantage.

Mechanical or structural details not clear in orthographic projection may be drawn pictorially or illustrated by supplementary pictorial views. Technical illustrations, patent-office drawings, and the like are advantageously made in one-plane projection; layouts and piping plans may be drawn, as in Fig. 25.11; and many other applications will occur to draftsmen who can use these methods with facility. One of the most important reasons for learning them is that they are so useful in making freehand sketches, as already shown in Chap. 7 and explained fully in Chap. 18.

16.2 Pictorial methods. Aside from perspective drawing, explained in Chap. 17, there are two main divisions of pictorial projection: (1) *axonometric*, with its divisions into trimetric, dimetric, and isometric, and (2) *oblique* projection, with several variations. Both methods are illustrated and compared by the drawings of Fig. 16.1. The trimetric form gives the most pleasing effect and allows almost unlimited freedom in orienting the object but is the most difficult to draw. The dimetric method is less pleasing and allows less freedom in orientation but is easier to draw than trimetric. The isometric form is less pleasing than either dimetric or trimetric but is the easiest to draw and, in addition, has the distinct advantage that it is easier to dimension. The oblique method is used principally for objects having circular or curved features only on one face or on parallel faces, and for objects of this type the oblique is very easy to draw and dimension.

The isometric and oblique forms of pictorial projection are the ones most commonly used.

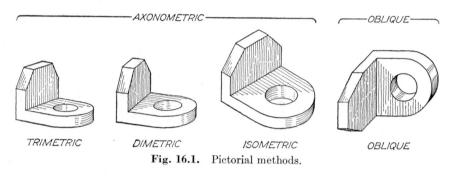

TRIMETRIC   DIMETRIC   ISOMETRIC   OBLIQUE

Fig. 16.1.   Pictorial methods.

16.3   Axonometric projection as shown in the tabular classification on page 2 is, theoretically, simply orthographic projection in which only one plane is used, the object being turned so that three faces show.   Imagine a transparent vertical plane with a cube behind it, one face of the cube being parallel to the plane.   The projection on the plane, that is, the front view of the cube, will be a square, Fig. 16.2.   Rotate the cube about a vertical axis through any angle less than 90°, and the front view will now show two faces, both foreshortened, Fig. 16.3.   From this position tilt the cube forward (rotation axis perpendicular to profile) any amount less than 90°.   Three faces will now be visible on the front view, Fig. 16.4.   Thus there can be an

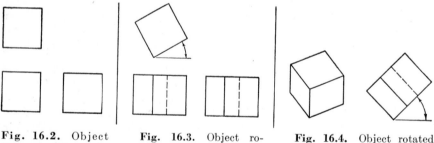

Fig. 16.2. Object faces parallel to picture plane.

Fig. 16.3. Object rotated about a vertical axis.

Fig. 16.4. Object rotated about a profile axis.

infinite number of axonometric positions, only a few of which are ever used for drawing.   The simplest of these is the *isometric* (equal-measure) position, in which the three faces are foreshortened equally.

16.4   Isometric projection.   If a cube in position A, Fig. 16.5, is rotated about a vertical axis through 45° as shown in B, then tilted forward as in C until the edge RU is foreshortened equally with RS and RT, the front view of the cube in this position is said to be an "isometric projection." (The cube has been tilted forward until the body diagonal through R is perpendicular to the front plane.   This makes the top face slope approximately

35°16'.[1])   The projections of the three mutually perpendicular edges RS, RT, and RU meeting at the front corner R make equal angles, 120°, with each other and are called *isometric axes*.   Since the projections of parallel lines are parallel, the projections of the other edges of the cube will be, respectively, parallel to these axes.   Any line parallel to an edge of the cube, whose projection is thus parallel to an isometric axis, is called an *isometric line*.   The planes of the faces of the cube and all planes parallel to them are called *isometric planes*.

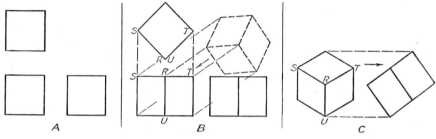

Fig. 16.5.   The isometric cube.

The isometric axes RS, RT, and RU are all foreshortened equally because they are at the same angle to the picture plane.

   16.5   Isometric drawing.   In nearly all practical use of the isometric system this foreshortening of the lines is disregarded, and *their full lengths are laid off on the axes*, as explained in paragraph 16.6.   This gives a figure of exactly the same shape but larger in the proportion of 1.23 to 1, linear, or in optical effect 1.23³ to 1.00³, Fig. 16.6.   Except when drawn beside the same

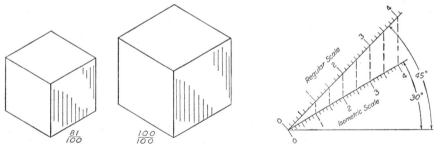

Fig. 16.6.   Isometric projection and isometric drawing compared.

Fig. 16.7.   Isometric scale.

piece in orthographic projection, the effect of increased size is usually of no consequence, and as the advantage of measuring the lines directly is of such great convenience, isometric drawing is used almost exclusively instead of isometric projection.

   [1] In paragraph 12.1 the statement is made that the only difference between rotation and auxiliary projection is that in the former the object is moved and in the latter the plane is moved.   Thus an auxiliary view on a plane perpendicular to a body diagonal of the cube in position B would be an isometric projection, as illustrated by the dotted view.

In isometric projection the isometric lines have been foreshortened to approximately 81/100 of their length, and an isometric scale to this proportion can be made graphically as shown in Fig. 16.7 if it becomes necessary to make an isometric projection by the method of isometric drawing.

16.6   To make an isometric drawing.   If the object is rectangular, start with a point representing a front corner and draw from it the three isometric axes 120° apart, one vertical, the other two with the 30° triangle, Fig. 16.8.

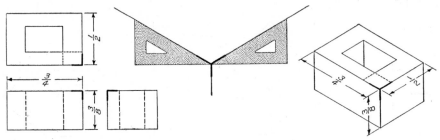

Fig. 16.8.   Isometric axes, first position.

On these three lines measure the height, width, and depth of the object, as indicated; through the points so determined draw lines parallel to the axes, completing the figure.   To draw intelligently in isometric, it is necessary to remember the direction of the three principal isometric planes.   Hidden lines are omitted except when needed for the description of the piece.

It is often more convenient to build up an isometric drawing from the lower front corner, as illustrated in Fig. 16.9, starting from axes in what may be called the "second position."

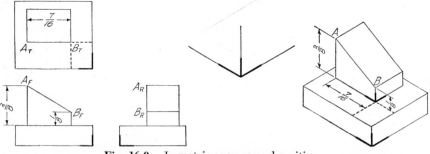

Fig. 16.9.   Isometric axes, second position.

16.7   Nonisometric lines.   Edges whose projections or drawings are not parallel to one of the isometric axes are called "nonisometric lines."   The one important rule is, *measurements can be made only on the drawings of isometric lines;* and, conversely, measurements *cannot* be made on the drawings of *nonisometric* lines.   For example, the diagonals of the face of a cube are nonisometric lines, and although equal in length, their isometric drawings will not be at all of equal length on the isometric drawing of the cube.   Since a nonisometric line does not appear in the isometric drawing in its true length, the isometric view of each end of the line must be located and the isometric view of the line found by joining these two points. In Fig. 16.9, AB is a nonisometric line whose true length could not be measured on the isometric drawing.

In locating edge AB the vertical distances above the base to points A and B are parallel to the vertical isometric axis and can, therefore, be laid off as shown in Fig. 16.9.

16.8 Nonisometric lines—boxing method. When the object contains many nonisometric lines, it is drawn either by the "boxing method" or the

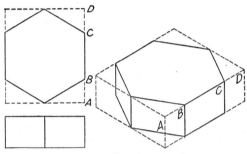

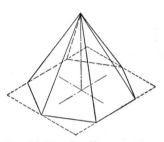

Fig. 16.10. Box construction.

Fig. 16.11. Semibox construction.

"offset method." In the first method, the object is enclosed in a rectangular box, which is drawn around it in orthographic projection. The box is then drawn in isometric and the object located in it by its points of contact, as in Figs. 16.10 and 16.12. It should be noted that the isometric views of lines which are parallel on the object are parallel. Knowledge of this may often be used to save a large amount of construction, as well as to test for accuracy. Figure 16.10 might be drawn by putting the top face into isometric and drawing vertical lines equal in length to the edges downward from each corner. It is not always necessary actually to enclose the whole object in a rectangular "crate." The pyramid, Fig. 16.11, would have its base enclosed in a rectangle and the apex located by erecting a vertical axis from the center.

The object shown in Fig. 16.12 is composed almost entirely of noniso-

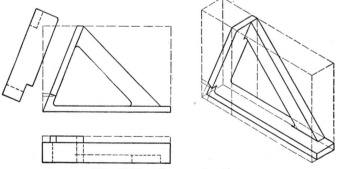

Fig. 16.12. Box construction.

metric lines. In such cases the isometric cannot be drawn without first making the orthographic views necessary for boxing. In general, the boxing method is adapted to objects which have the nonisometric lines in isometric planes.

16.9 Nonisometric lines—offset method. When the object is made up of planes at a number of different angles, it is better to locate the ends of the edges by the offset method. In this method, perpendiculars are dropped from each point to an isometric reference plane. These perpendiculars,

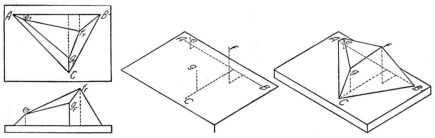

Fig. 16.13.   Offset construction.

which are isometric lines, are located on the drawing by isometric coordinates, the dimensions being taken from the orthographic views. In Fig. 16.13, line AB is used as a base line and measurements are made from it as shown. Figure 16.14 is another example of offset construction, using a vertical plane as a reference plane.

16.10 Angles in isometric. The three isometric axes, referred back to the isometric cube, are mutually perpendicular but in the isometric drawing

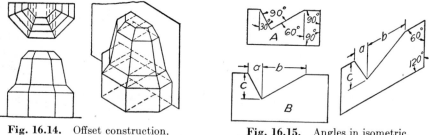

Fig. 16.14.   Offset construction.   Fig. 16.15.   Angles in isometric.

appear at 120° to each other. For this reason angles, specified in degrees, do not appear in their true size on the isometric drawing and must, therefore, be laid off by coordinates which will be parallel to the isometric axes. Thus, if an orthographic drawing has edges specified by angular dimensions as at A, Fig. 16.15, *a view to the same scale as the isometric drawing* is made as at B, from which the coordinate dimensions a, b, and c can be transferred with dividers or scale to the isometric drawing.

16.11 Curves in isometric. For the same reasons given in paragraphs 16.7 and 16.10, a circle or any other curve will not show in its true shape when drawn in isometric. A circle on any isometric plane will be an ellipse, and a curve will be shown as the isometric projection of the true curve.

Any curve may be drawn by plotting points on it from isometric reference lines (coordinates) which are parallel to the isometric axes as shown in Fig. 16.16. A circle plotted in this way is shown in Fig. 16.17. Note in both these figures that coordinates *a* and *b* are parallel to the isometric axes and that the coordinate distances must be obtained from an orthographic view drawn to the same scale as the isometric.

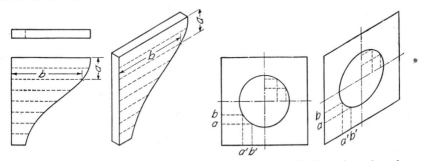

Fig. 16.16.   Curves in isometric.   Fig. 16.17.   Circle, points plotted.

16.12 Isometric circle arcs occur so frequently that they are usually drawn by a four-centered approximation, which is sufficiently accurate for all ordinary work. Geometrically, the center for any arc tangent to a straight line lies on a perpendicular from the point of tangency, Fig. 16.18*A*. In isometric, if perpendiculars are drawn from the middle point of each side

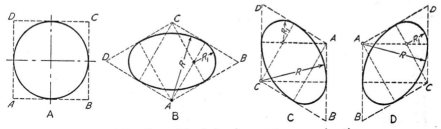

Fig. 16.18.   Isometric circles, four-center approximation.

of the circumscribing square, the intersections of these perpendiculars will be centers for arcs tangent to two sides, Fig. 16.18*B*. Two of these intersections will evidently fall at the corners *A* and *C* of the isometric square, as the perpendiculars are altitudes of equilateral triangles. The construction of Fig. 16.18*B*, *C*, and *D* may thus be made by simply drawing 60° lines from the corners *A* and *C*, and then drawing arcs with radii *R* and R_1, as shown.

Figure 16.19 shows the method of locating and laying out a hole in isometric from the given orthographic views. First locate and then draw the center lines for the hole by laying out the distances *X* and *Y* as shown. Construct an isometric square on these lines with sides equal to the diameter of the hole, by laying out the radius *R* in each direction from the intersection of these center lines. The four-center method is then used as shown in Fig. 16.18. Should the piece be thin enough, a portion of the back side of the hole will be visible. To determine this, drop the thickness T back on an isometric line and swing the large radius R_1 of the isometric circle with this point as a center. If the arc thus drawn comes within the boundary of the

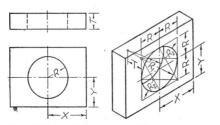

Fig. 16.19. Locating and laying out a hole in isometric.

isometric circle, that portion of the back would be visible. In extra thin pieces, portions of the small arcs R_2 might be visible. These would be determined in a similar manner.

If a true ellipse is plotted by the method of paragraph 16.11, in the same square as this four-center approximation, it will be a little longer and narrower and of much more pleasing shape but, in the great majority of drawings, the difference is not sufficient to warrant the extra expenditure of time required in execution.

The isometric drawing of a *sphere* is a circle with its diameter equal to the long axis of the ellipse inscribed in the isometric square of a great circle of the sphere. It would thus be 1.23/1.00 of the actual diameter (the isometric *projection* of a sphere would be a circle of the actual diameter of the sphere).

16.13 Isometric arcs. To draw any circle arc, the isometric square of its diameter should be drawn in the plane of its face, with as much of the four-center construction as is necessary to find centers for the part of the circle needed, as illustrated at A, B, and C, Fig. 16.20. The arc occurring

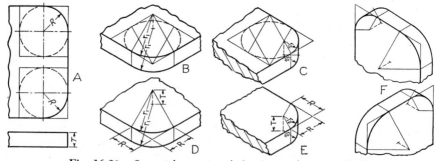

Fig. 16.20. Isometric quarter-circles (approximate method).

most frequently is the quarter circle. Note that in illustrations D and E only two construction lines are needed to find the center of a quarter circle in an isometric plane. Measure the true radius R of the circle from the corner on the two isometric lines as shown, and draw *actual* perpendiculars from these points. Their intersection will be the required center for radius R_1 or R_2 of the isometric quadrant. F illustrates the construction for the two vertical isometric planes.

16.14 Reversed isometric. It is often desirable to show the lower face of an object by tilting it *back* instead of *forward*, thus reversing the usual position so as to show the underside. The construction is just the same, but the directions of the principal isometric planes must be kept clearly in mind. Figure 16.21 shows the reference cube and the position of the axes, as well as

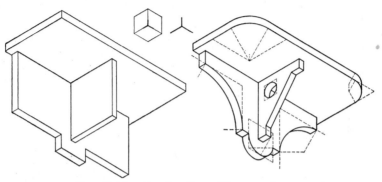

Fig. 16.21. Construction with reversed axes.

the application of reversed-isometric construction to circle arcs. A practical use of this construction is in the representation of such architectural features as are naturally viewed from below. Figure 16.22 is an example.

Sometimes a piece may be shown to better advantage with the main axis horizontal, as in Fig. 16.23.

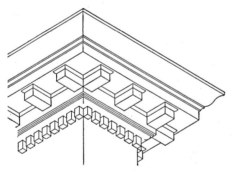

Fig. 16.22. An architectural detail on reversed axes.

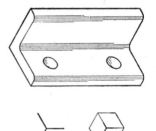

Fig. 16.23. Isometric with main axis horizontal.

16.15 Isometric sections. Isometric drawings are, from their pictorial nature, usually outside views, but sometimes a sectional view may be employed to good advantage to show a detail of shape or interior construction. The cutting planes are taken as isometric planes, and the section lining is done in a direction to give the best effect which is, in almost all cases, in the direction of the long diagonal of a square drawn on the surface. As a general rule, a half section would be made by outlining the figure in full, then cutting out the front quarter as in Fig. 16.24. For a full section, the cut face would be drawn first and the part of the object behind it added afterward, Fig. 16.25.

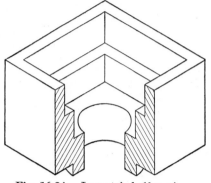 

Fig. 16.24. Isometric half section.　　　　Fig. 16.25. Isometric full section.

16.16　Dimetric projection.　The reference cube can be rotated into any number of positions in which two edges will be equally foreshortened, and the direction of axes and ratio of foreshortening for any one of these positions might be taken as a basis for a system of dimetric drawing. A simple dimetric position is one with the ratios 1 to 1 to $\frac{1}{2}$. In this position the tangents of the angles are $\frac{1}{8}$ and $\frac{7}{8}$, making the angles approximately 7° and

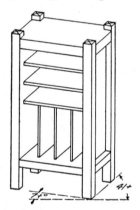

Fig. 16.26. Dimetric drawing.

41°. Figure 16.26 shows a drawing in this system. Dimetric is seldom used because of the difficulty of drawing circles.

16.17　Trimetric projection.　Any position with three unequal axes would be called "trimetric." Although with some of these positions the effect of distortion might be lessened, the added time required makes trimetric drawing impractical, except when drawn by projection as explained in paragraph 16.26.

16.18　Oblique projection.　When the projectors make an angle other than 90° with the picture plane, the resulting projection is called "oblique projection." Refer to paragraph 1.2 with tabular classification. The name *cavalier projection* is given to that special and most-used case of *oblique projection* in which the projectors make an angle of 45° with the plane of projection. It is often called by the general name *oblique projection*, or *oblique drawing*. The principle of it is as follows: Imagine a vertical plane with a rectangular block behind it, having its long edges parallel to the plane. Assume a system of parallel projecting lines in any direction making an angle of 45° with the picture plane (they could be parallel to any one of the elements of a 45° cone with its base in the picture plane). Then that face of the block which is parallel to the plane is projected in its true size, and the

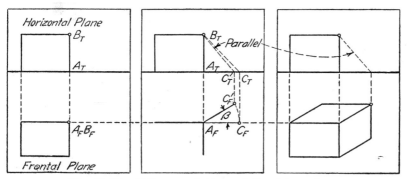

Fig. 16.27. Oblique projection and the picture plane.

edges perpendicular to the plane are projected in their true length. Figure 16.27 illustrates this principle. The first panel shows the regular orthographic projection of a rectangular block with its front face in the frontal plane. An oblique projector from the back corner B is the hypotenuse of a 45° right triangle of which AB is one side and the projection of AB on the plane is the other side. When this triangle is horizontal, the projection on the plane will be AC. If the triangle is rotated about AB through any angle β, C will revolve to C' and $A_F C_F'$ will be the oblique projection of AB.

16.19 To make an oblique drawing. Oblique drawing is similar to isometric drawing in having three axes representing three mutually per-

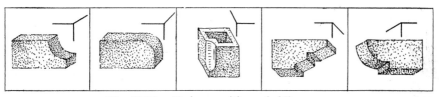

Fig. 16.28. Various positions of oblique axes.

pendicular edges, upon which measurements can be made. Two of the axes are always at right angles to each other, being in a plane parallel to the picture plane. The third or cross axis may be at any angle to the horizontal, 30° or 45° being generally used, Fig. 16.28. It is thus more flexible than isometric drawing. For a rectangular object, Fig. 16.29, start with a point representing a front corner (A) and draw from it the three oblique axes, one vertical, one horizontal, and one at an angle. On these three axes measure the height, width, and depth of the object. In this case, the width is made up of the 2½-in. distance and the 1⁵⁄₁₆-in. radius. Locate the center of the arc and draw it as shown. When the hole in the figure is drawn, the center for the arc will be at the same point as the center for the outside arc on the

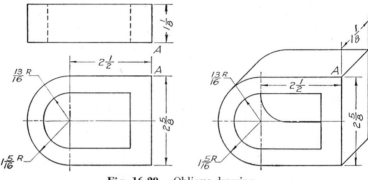

Fig. 16.29. Oblique drawing.

front face. The center for the rear arc of the hole will be 1⅛-in. rearward on a depth axis line through the front center.

16.20 Object orientation for oblique. Any face parallel to the picture plane will evidently be projected without distortion, an advantage over isometric of particular value in the representation of objects with circular or irregular outline.

The **first rule** for oblique projection is, *place the object with the irregular outline or contour parallel to the picture plane.* Note in Fig. 16.30 the distortion of B and C over that of A.

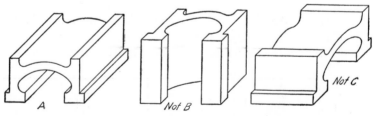

Fig. 16.30. Illustration of first rule.

One of the greatest disadvantages in the use of either isometric or oblique drawing is the effect of distortion produced by the lack of convergence in the receding lines—the violation of perspective. In some cases, particularly with large objects, this becomes so painful as practically to preclude the use of these methods. It is perhaps even more noticeable in oblique than in isometric and, of course, increases with the length of the cross axis.

Hence the **second rule** : *preferably, the longest dimension should be parallel to the picture plane.*   In Fig. 16.31, A is preferable to B.

In case of conflict between these two rules, the first should always have precedence, as the advantage of having the irregular face without distortion

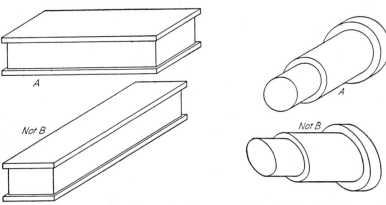

Fig. 16.31.   Illustration of second rule.

Fig. 16.32.   Precedence of first rule.

is greater than that gained by the second rule, as illustrated in Fig. 16.32. The first rule should be given precedence even with shapes that are not irregular if, in the draftsman's judgment, the distortion can be lessened, as in the example of Fig. 16.33, where B is perhaps preferable to A.

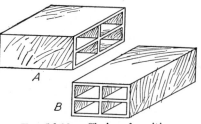

Fig. 16.33.   Choice of position.

16.21   Starting plane.   It will be noted that, so long as the front of the object is in one plane parallel to the plane of projection, the front face of the oblique projection is exactly the same as the orthographic.   When the front is made up of more than one plane, particular care must be exercised in preserving the relationship by selecting one of these planes as the starting plane and working from it.   In such a piece as the link, Fig. 16.34, the front bosses may be imagined as cut off on the plane A-A, and the front view, that is, the section on A-A, drawn as the front of the oblique projection.   On cross axes through the centers C and D, the distances, CE behind and CF in front of the plane A-A, may be laid off.

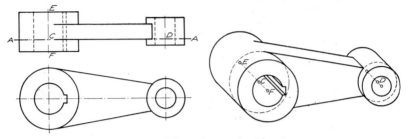

Fig. 16.34.   Offsets from reference plane.

When an object has no face perpendicular to its base, it may be drawn in a similar way by cutting a right section and measuring offsets from it, as in Fig. 16.35. This offset method, previously illustrated in the isometric drawings of Figs. 16.13, 16.14, and 16.16, will be found to be a most rapid and convenient way for drawing almost any figure, and it should be studied carefully.

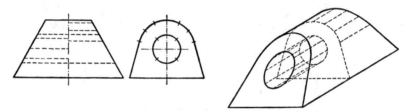

Fig. 16.35.   Offsets from right section.

16.22   Circles in oblique.   When it is necessary to draw circles that lie on oblique faces, they may be either plotted and drawn with the french curve or approximated, with circle arcs drawn with the compasses on the same principle as the four-center isometric approximation shown in Fig. 16.18. In isometric it happens that *two of the four intersections of the perpendiculars from the middle points* of the containing square fall at the corner of the square,

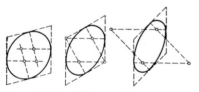

Fig. 16.36.   Oblique circle construction.

and advantage is taken of the fact. In oblique, the position of the corresponding points depends on the angle of the cross axis. Figure 16.36 shows three squares in oblique positions at different angles and the construction of their inscribed circles.

16.23   Arcs in oblique.   Circle arcs representing rounded corners, etc., are drawn in oblique by the same method given for isometric arcs in paragraph 16.13. The only difference will be that the angle of the sides tangent to the arc will vary according to the angle of depth axis chosen.

16.24   Cabinet drawing is that case of oblique projection in which the parallel projectors make with the picture plane an angle of such a value that distances measured parallel to the cross axis are reduced one-half that of cavalier projection. The appearance of excessive thickness that is so disagreeable in cavalier projection is entirely overcome in cabinet projection. The cross axis may be at any angle with the horizontal but is usually taken at either 30° or 45°. The comparative appearances of cavalier and cabinet drawing are illustrated in Fig. 16.37.

16.25 Other forms. Cabinet drawing, explained above, is popular because of the easy ratio, but the effect is often too thin. Other oblique drawing ratios, such as 2 to 3 or 3 to 4, may be used with pleasing effect.

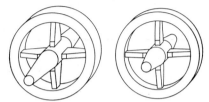

Fig. 16.37. Oblique and cabinet drawing compared.

16.26 Axonometric projection from orthographic views. In making pictorial drawings of complicated parts, especially whenever curves must be plotted, projection from orthographic views may give an advantage in speed and ease of drawing. Any position, isometric, dimetric, or trimetric, may be used.

The three axes of an axonometric drawing are *three mutually perpendicular edges* in space.   If the angle of rotation and the angle of tilt of the object are known or decided upon, the three axes for the pictorial drawing and the location of the orthographic views for projection to the pictorial may easily be found.   Figure 16.38 will illustrate the procedure.   At G is shown the three orthographic views of a cube.   The three mutually perpendicular edges OA, OB, and OC will be foreshortened differently when the cube is rotated in space for some axonometric position, but the ends of the axes A, B, and C will always lie on the surface of a sphere whose radius is $OA = OB = OC$, as illustrated by G'.   At any particular angle of tilt of the cube, the axis ends A and B will describe an ellipse, as shown, if the cube is rotated about the axis OC.   The axis OC will appear foreshortened at oc'.   Thus, for any particular position of the cube in space, representing some desired axonometric position, the axes may be located and their relative amounts of foreshortening found.

Moreover, if a face of the cube is rotated about a *frontal axis perpendicular to the axis which is at right angles to the face*, an orthographic view of the face, in projection with the axonometric view, will result.   Thus, the top and right-side views may be located as at J and projected as at K to give the axonometric drawing.

The drawings at H, J, and K will illustrate the practical use of the theory of rotation just described.   The actual size of the sphere is unimportant, as it is used only to establish the direction of the axes.   First, the desired angle of rotation R and the angle of tilt T are decided upon and laid out as shown at H.   The minor axis for the ellipse upon which A and B will lie is found by projecting vertically from c and drawing the circle as shown. A and B on the major-axis circle of the ellipse will be at a and b; on the minor-axis circle they will be at a_m and b_m; and they are found in the axonometric position by projecting as in the concentric-circle ellipse method to a' and b'. The foreshortened position of C is found by projecting horizontally across from c to c'.

The top orthographic view of the cube (or object) will be parallel to oa and ob, and projection from the orthographic view to the axonometric will be vertical (parallel to aa' and bb').

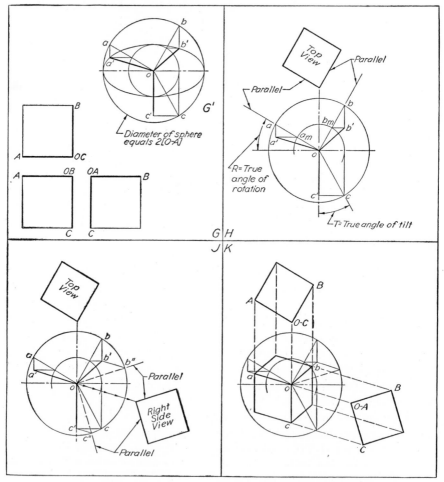

Fig. 16.38. Axonometric projection from orthographic views.

Projection from an orthographic right-side view would be as shown at J. The right side of the cube, containing axes OC and OB, is found by projecting from b' and c', parallel to oa', to locate b'' and c'' on the circle representing the sphere. The sides of the cube (or object) are parallel to ob'' and oc'', as shown at J. Projection from the right-side view to the axonometric view is in the direction of oa', as indicated.

The axonometric drawing is shown projected at K. The dashed lines

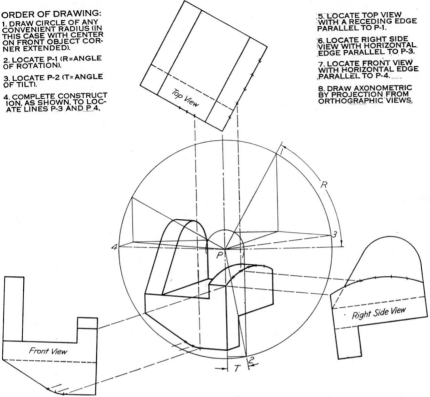

ORDER OF DRAWING:
1. DRAW CIRCLE OF ANY CONVENIENT RADIUS (IN THIS CASE WITH CENTER ON FRONT OBJECT CORNER EXTENDED).

2. LOCATE P-1 (R = ANGLE OF ROTATION).

3. LOCATE P-2 (T = ANGLE OF TILT).

4. COMPLETE CONSTRUCTION, AS SHOWN, TO LOCATE LINES P-3 AND P-4.

5. LOCATE TOP VIEW WITH A RECEDING EDGE PARALLEL TO P-1.

6. LOCATE RIGHT SIDE VIEW WITH HORIZONTAL EDGE PARALLEL TO P-3.

7. LOCATE FRONT VIEW WITH HORIZONTAL EDGE PARALLEL TO P-4.

8. DRAW AXONOMETRIC BY PROJECTION FROM ORTHOGRAPHIC VIEWS.

Fig. 16.39. An axonometric drawing by projection.

indicate the actual projectors, and the light solid lines and circles show the necessary construction just described.

One advantage of this method is that the angle of rotation and tilt can be decided upon so that the object may be shown in the best position. Figure 16.39 is an example of an axonometric drawing made by projection. The curved faces are plotted by projecting points as shown.

16.27 Isometric projection from orthographic views. Isometric is, of course, a special case of axonometric projection in which all three axes are foreshortened equally. The work of finding the axes for isometric projection from orthographic views is reduced if the views are located by angle, as illustrated in Fig. 16.40.

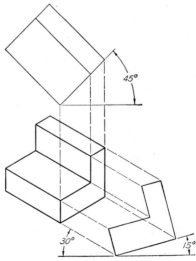

Fig. 16.40. Isometric by projection.

16.28   Oblique projection from orthographic views.   In oblique projection the projectors make some oblique angle with the picture plane.   The actual angle of the projectors (with horizontal and frontal planes) is not critical, and a variety of angles may be used.   The making of an oblique drawing by projection from the views is very simple, as illustrated by Fig. 16.41.   The picture plane is located, and one face of the object is made coincident with the picture plane.   The front view is located at a convenient

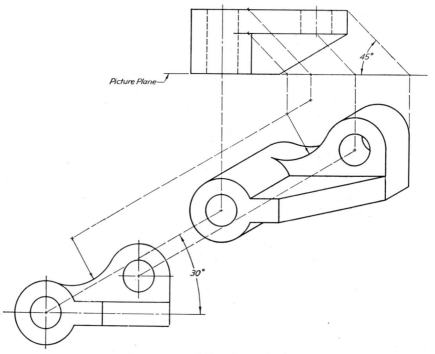

Fig. 16.41.   Oblique by projection.

place on the paper, as shown.   The angle of the projectors in the top view may be assumed (in this case 45°) and projections made to the picture plane as shown.   The angle of the projectors in the front view may be then assumed (in this case 30°).   Projection from the front view at the assumed angle, and vertically from the picture plane, as shown, will locate the necessary lines and points for the oblique view.

Reversed axes may be obtained by projecting downward from the front view.   An axis to the left may be had by changing the direction of the projectors in the top view.   Any desired oblique axes may be had by altering the angles (top and front) for the projectors.

PROBLEMS

The following problems are intended to serve two purposes: (1) furnish practice in the various methods of pictorial representation, and (2) furnish practice in reading and translating orthographic projection

In reading a drawing remember that a line on any view always means an edge or change in direction of the surface of the object, and that one must always look at another view to interpret the meaning of the line.

Group I.   Isometric drawings.   *Problems 1 to 24.   Figs. 16.42 to 16.65*

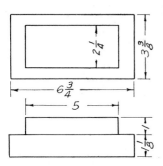

Fig. **16.42.**   Jig block.

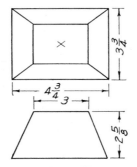

Fig. **16.43.**   Frustum of pyramid.

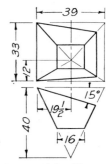

Fig.   **16.44.** Hopper.

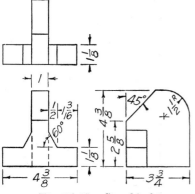

Fig. **16.45.**   Stop block.

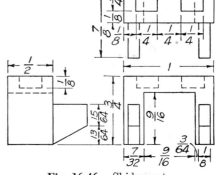

Fig. **16.46.**   Skidmount.

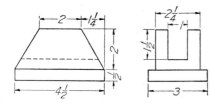

Fig. **16.47.**   Guide block.

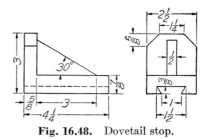

Fig. **16.48.**   Dovetail stop.

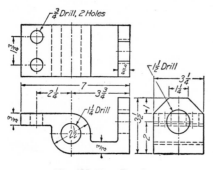

Fig. 16.49.   Bracket.

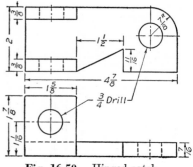

Fig. 16.50.   Hinged catch.

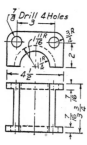

Fig. 16.51.
Bearing.

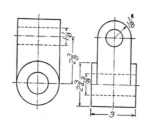

Fig. 16.52.   Cross link.

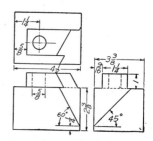

Fig. 16.53.   Wedge block.

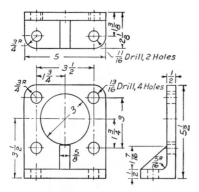

Fig. 16.54.   Head attachment.

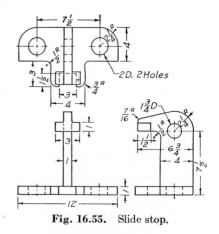

Fig. 16.55.   Slide stop.

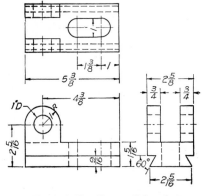

Fig. 16.56. Dovetail bracket.

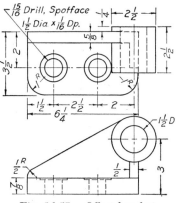

Fig. 16.57. Offset bracket.

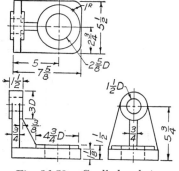

Fig. 16.58. Cradle bracket.

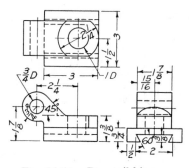

Fig. 16.59. Dovetail hinge.

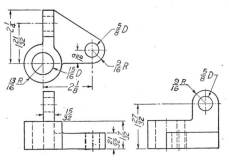

Fig. 16.60. Cable clip.

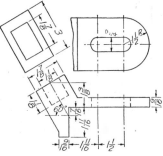

Fig. 16.61. Strut anchor.

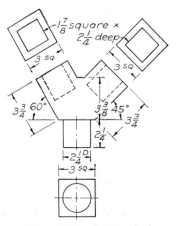

Fig. 16.62. Strut swivel.

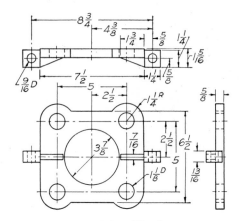
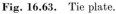

Fig. 16.63. Tie plate.

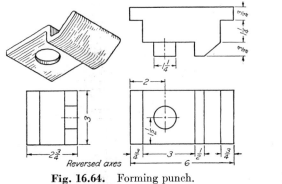

Fig. 16.64. Forming punch.

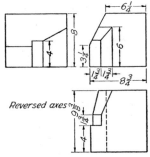

Fig. 16.65. Springing stone.

Group II. Isometric sections. *Problems 25 to 36. Figs. 16.66 to 16.77*

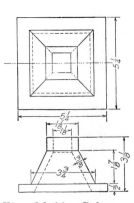

Fig. 16.66. Column base.

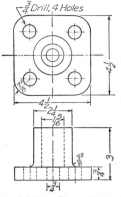

Fig. 16.67. Base plate.

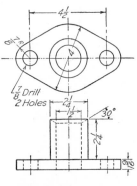
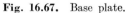

Fig. 16.68. Gland.

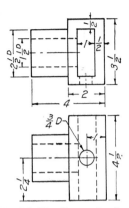

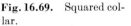

Fig. 16.69. Squared collar.

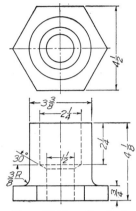

Fig. 16.70. Blank for gland.

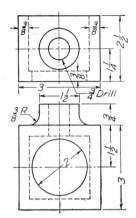

Fig. 16.71. Sliding cover.

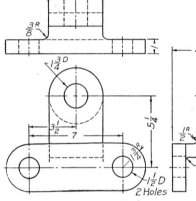

Fig. 16.72. Rod support.

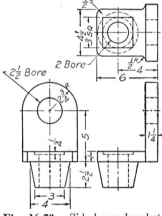

Fig. 16.73. Side-beam bracket.

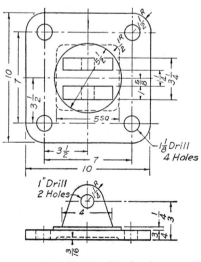

Fig. 16.74. Head yoke.

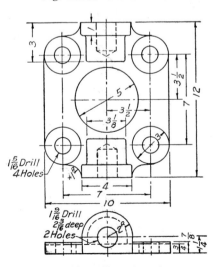

Fig. 16.75. Trunnion plate.

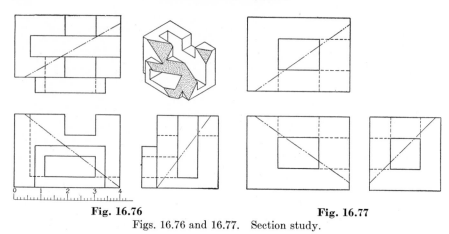

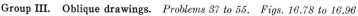

Fig. 16.76   **Fig. 16.77**

Figs. 16.76 and 16.77.   Section study.

Group III.   Oblique drawings.   *Problems 37 to 55.   Figs. 16.78 to 16.96*

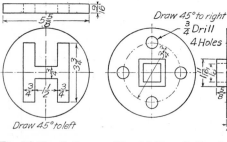

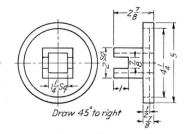

Fig. 16.78.   Letter
die.

Fig. 16.79.   Guide plate.

Fig. 16.80.   Brace base.

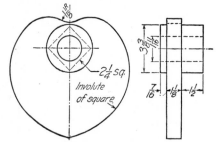

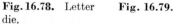

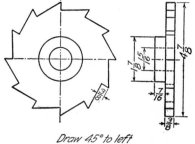

Draw half size and 30° to right

Fig. 16.81.   Heart cam.

Draw 45° to left

Fig. 16.82.   Ratchet wheel.

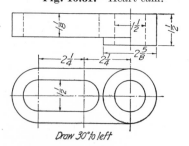

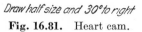

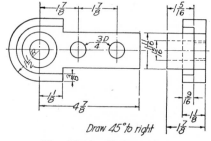

Draw 30° to left

Fig. 16.83.   Slotted link.

Draw 45° to right

Fig. 16.84.   Swivel plate.

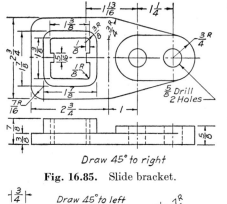

Fig. 16.85. Slide bracket.

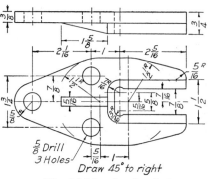

Fig. 16.86. Jaw bracket.

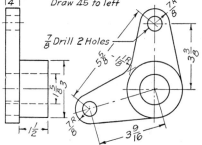

Fig. 16.87. Bell crank.

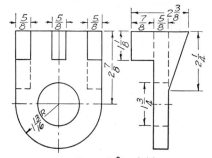

Fig. 16.88. Stop plate.

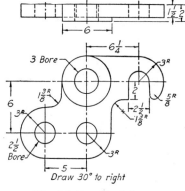

Fig. 16.89. Hook brace.

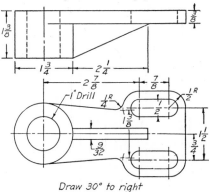

Fig. 16.90. Adjusting rod support.

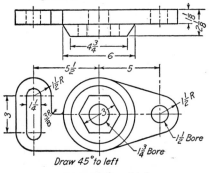

Fig. 16.91. Link

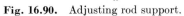
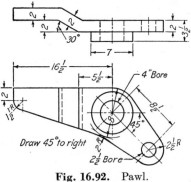

Fig. 16.92. Pawl.

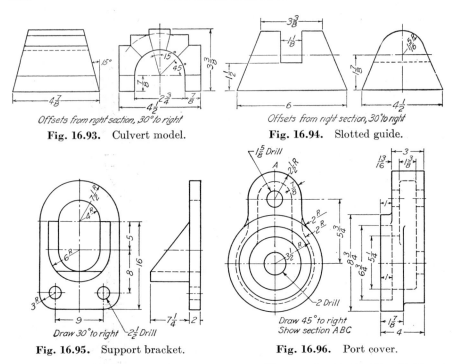

Offsets from right section, 30° to right

Fig. 16.93.   Culvert model.

Offsets from right section, 30° to right

Fig. 16.94.   Slotted guide.

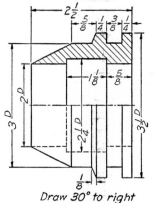

Draw 30° to right   —$2\frac{1}{2}$ *Drill*

Fig. 16.95.   Support bracket.

Draw 45° to right
Show section A B C

Fig. 16.96.   Port cover.

Group IV.   Oblique sections.   *Problems 56 to 65.   Figs. 16.97 to 16.100; Figs. 16.67 and 16.68*

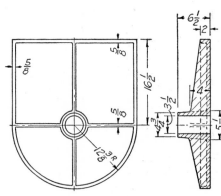

Draw 30° to right

Fig. 16.97.   Sliding cone.

Draw 30° to right

Fig. 16.98.   Conveyor trough end.

56. Fig. 16.97.   Oblique full section of sliding cone.
57. Fig. 16.97.   Oblique half section of sliding cone.
58. Fig. 16.98.   Oblique full section of conveyor trough end.
59. Fig. 16.98.   Oblique half section of conveyor trough end.
60. Fig. 16.99.   Oblique full section of ceiling flange.
61. Fig. 16.99.   Oblique half section of ceiling flange.
62. Fig. 16.100.   Oblique full section of hanger flange.
63. Fig. 16.100.   Oblique half section of hanger flange.
64. Fig. 16.67.   Oblique half section of base plate.
65. Fig. 16.68.   Oblique half section of gland.

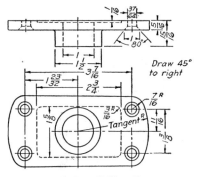

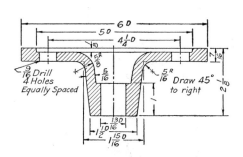

Fig. 16.99.   Ceiling flange.   Fig. 16.100.   Hanger flange.

Group V.   Dimetric and cabinet drawing.   *Problems 66 to 69*

66. Fig. 16.42.   Make a dimetric drawing of the jig block.
67. Fig. 16.47.   Make a dimetric drawing of the guide block.
68. Fig. 16.68.   Make a cabinet drawing of the gland.
69. Fig. 16.99.   Make a cabinet drawing of the ceiling flange.

Group VI.   Axonometric and oblique projection from orthographic views

Any of the problems given in this chapter (Figs. 16.42 to 16.100) may be used for making axonometric or oblique projections from the orthographic views by first drawing the orthographic views to suitable scale and then employing these views as described in paragraphs 16.26 to 16.28 to obtain the pictorial projection.

Group VII.   Pictorial drawings from machine parts

Machine parts, either rough castings and forgings or finished parts, offer valuable practice in making pictorial drawings.   Choose pieces to give practice in isometric and oblique drawing.   Use the most appropriate form of representation, and employ sections and half-section treatments where necessary to give clearer description.

Group VIII.   Pictorial working drawings.   *Problems 70 to 77*

Any of the problems in this chapter offer practice in making complete pictorial working drawings.   Follow the principles of dimensioning in Chap. 20.   The form and placement of the dimension figures are given on page 357.

70. Fig. 16.48.   Pictorial working drawing of dovetail stop.
71. Fig. 16.50.   Pictorial working drawing of hinged catch.
72. Fig. 16.63.   Pictorial working drawing of tie plate.
73. Fig. 16.74.   Pictorial working drawing of head yoke.
74. Fig. 16.86.   Pictorial working drawing of jaw bracket.
75. Fig. 16.90.   Pictorial working drawing of adjusting rod support.
76. Fig. 16.96.   Pictorial working drawing of port cover.
77. Fig. 16.99.   Pictorial working drawing of ceiling flange.

Group IX.   Reading exercises.   *Figs. 16.101, 16.102, 16.103*

These figures are to be sketched freehand in one of the pictorial systems, as a test of the ability to read orthographic projections.   They may also be used as reading problems by requiring other orthographic views, particularly the figures with two views given. All surfaces are plane or cylindrical surfaces, and several of the two-view problems may have two or more possible solutions.

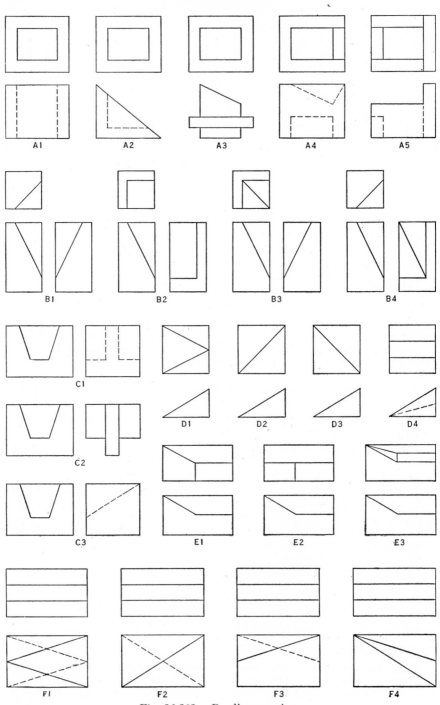

Fig. 16.101. Reading exercises.

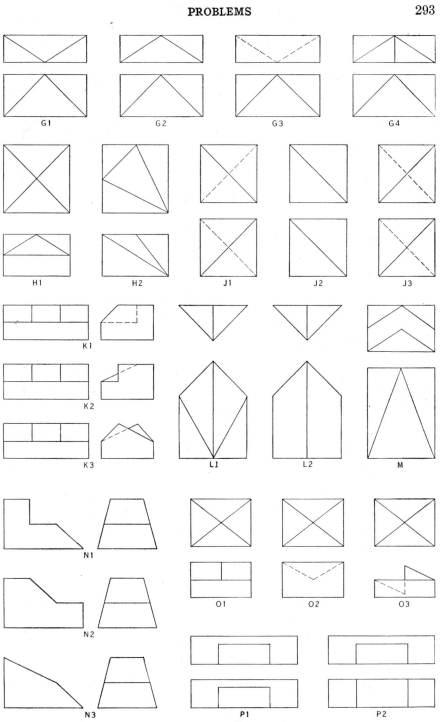

Fig. 16.102. Reading exercises.

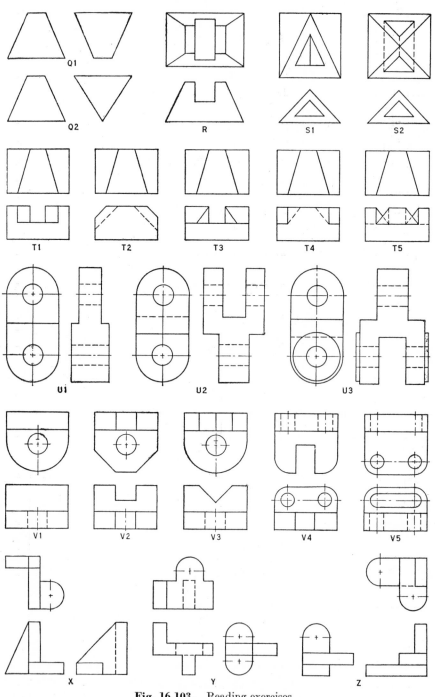

Fig. 16.103. Reading exercises.

17

Perspective Drawing

17.1   Perspective drawing is the representation of an object as it appears to an observer stationed at a particular position relative to the object. Geometrically it is the figure resulting when visual rays from the eye to the object are cut by a picture plane.   There is a difference between "artists' perspective" and "geometrical perspective" in that the artist draws the object as he sees it before him, or as he visualizes it through his creative imagination, while geometrical perspective is projected mechanically on a plane from views or measurements of the object represented.   Projected geometrical perspective is, theoretically, very similar to the optical system in photography.

In a technical way, perspective is used more in architecture and in illustration than in other branches, but every engineer will find it of advantage to know the principles of the subject.

17.2   Fundamental concepts.   Let one imagine himself standing on the sidewalk of a city street, as in Fig. 17.1, with the picture plane erected

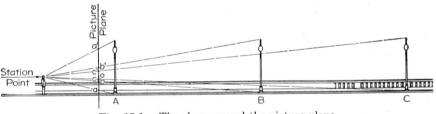

Fig. 17.1.   The observer and the picture plane.

between him and the street scene ahead.   Visual rays from the observer's eye to the ends of the lamppost A intercept a distance aa' on the picture plane.   Similarly, rays from post B intercept bb', a lesser distance than aa'. This apparent diminution in the size of like objects as the distance from the objects to the eye increases agrees with our everyday experience, and is the keynote of perspective drawing.   It is evident from the figure that succeeding lampposts will intercept shorter distances on the picture plane than the preceding ones, and that a post at infinity would show only as a point o at the level of the observer's eye.

In Fig. 17.2, the plane of the paper is the picture plane, and the intercepts aa', bb', etc., show as the heights of their respective lampposts as they diminish in their projected size and finally disappear on the horizon.   In a similar way the curbings and balustrade appear to converge at the same point O.   Thus a system of parallel horizontal lines will vanish at a single point on the horizon, and all horizontal planes will vanish on the horizon.

295

Verticals such as the lampposts and the edges of the buildings, being parallel to the picture plane, pierce the picture plane at an infinite distance and therefore show as vertical lines in the picture.

Fig. 17.2.   The perspective.

17.3   Definitions and nomenclature.   Figure 17.3 illustrates perspective theory and names the points, lines, and planes used.   An observer in viewing an object selects his *station point* and thereby determines the *horizon plane*

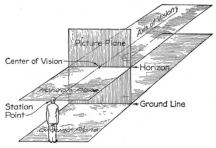

Fig. 17.3.   Perspective nomenclature.

as the horizontal plane at eye level. This horizon plane is normally above the horizontal *ground plane* upon which the object is assumed to rest.   The *picture plane* is usually located between the station point and the object being viewed and is ordinarily a vertical plane perpendicular to the horizontal projection of the line of sight to the object's center of interest.   The *horizon line* is the intersection of the horizon plane and picture plane, and the *ground line* is the intersection of the ground plane and picture plane.   The *axis of vision* is the line through the station point that is perpendicular to the picture plane.   The piercing point of the axis of vision with the picture plane is the *center of vision*.

17.4   Selection of the station point.   Care must be exercised in selecting the station point, for an indiscriminate choice may result in a distorted drawing.   If the station point is placed to one side of the drawing, the same effect is had as when a theater screen is viewed from a position close to the front and well off to one side; heights are seen properly but not horizontal distances.   Therefore, the *center of vision should be somewhere near the picture's center of interest.*

Wide angles of view will result in a violent convergence of horizontal lines and so should be avoided.   The angle of view is the included angle θ between the widest visual rays, Fig. 17.4.   Figure 17.5 shows the difference in perspective foreshortening for different lateral angles of view. In general, an angle of about 20° will give the most natural picture.

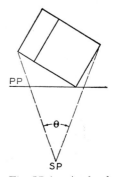

Fig. 17.4.   Angle of view, lateral.

The station point should be located where the object will be seen to best advantage, and for this reason, on large objects such as buildings, etc., the station point is usually taken at a normal standing height of about 5 ft above the ground plane. For small objects, however, the best representation demands that the top, as well as the lateral surfaces, be seen, and the station point must be elevated accordingly. Figure 17.6 shows the angle of elevation Ω between the horizon plane and the extreme visual ray. By contrasting several different angles of elevation (Ω),

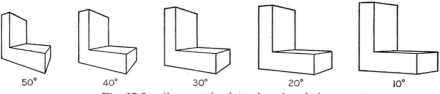

50°   40°   30°   20°   10°

Fig. 17.5.   Comparative lateral angles of view.

Fig. 17.7 shows the effect of elevation of the station point. In general, the best picturization is had at an angle of about 20° to 30°.

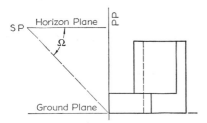

Fig. 17.6.   Angle of view, elevation.

It may be established, therefore, that *the visual rays to the object should be kept within a right circular cone whose elements make an angle of not more than 15° with the cone axis.*

In choosing the station point, its position should always be offset to one side and also offset vertically from the exact middle of the object, or a rather stiff and awkward perspective will be had. Similarly, in locating the object with reference to the picture plane, the faces should not make identical angles with the picture plane or the same stiffness will appear.

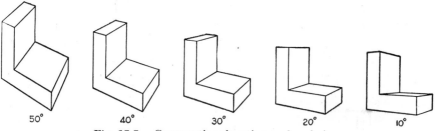

50°   40°   30°   20°   10°

Fig. 17.7.   Comparative elevation angles of view.

17.5 To draw a perspective. Perspective projection is based on the theory that visual rays from the object to the eye pierce the picture plane,

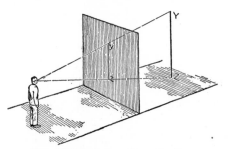

and form an image of the object on the plane. Thus in Fig. 17.8, the image of line YZ is formed by the piercing points y and z of the rays. Several projective methods may be used. The simplest method, basically, but the most laborious to draw, is illustrated by the purely orthographic method of Fig. 17.9, in which the top and side views are drawn in orthographic. The

Fig. 17.8. Perspective of a line.

picture plane (edge view) and the station point are located in each view. Assuming that the line YZ of Fig. 17.8 is one edge of the L-shaped block of Fig. 17.9, visual rays from Y and Z will intersect the picture plane in the top

view, thus locating the perspective of the points laterally. Similarly, the intersections of the rays in the side view give the perspective heights of Y and Z. Projection from the top and side views of the picture plane gives the perspective of YZ, and a repetition of the process for the other lines will complete the drawing.

17.6 The use of vanishing points and measuring lines will facilitate the projections. Let it be required to make a perspective of the sliding block of Fig. 17.10. The edge view of the picture plane (plan view) is drawn, Fig. 17.11, and behind it the top view of the object is located and drawn. In this

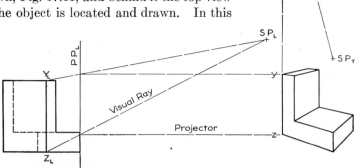

Fig. 17.9. Perspective drawing, orthographic method.

case, one side of the object is oriented at 30° to the picture plane in order to emphasize the L shape more than the end of the block. The station point is located a little to the left of center and far enough in front of the picture

plane to give a good angle of view.   The ground line is then drawn, and on
it is placed the front view of the block
from Fig. 17.10. The height of the
station point is then decided—in this
case well above the block so that the
top surfaces will be seen—and the horizon
line drawn at the station-point height.

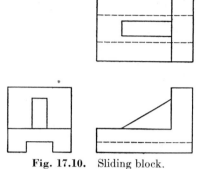

To avoid the labor of redrawing the
top and front views in the positions just
described, the views may be cut from the
orthographic drawing, oriented in position, and fastened with tacks or tape.

The vanishing point for any horizontal

Fig. 17.10.   Sliding block.

line may be found by drawing a visual
ray from the station point *parallel* to the horizontal line, and finding

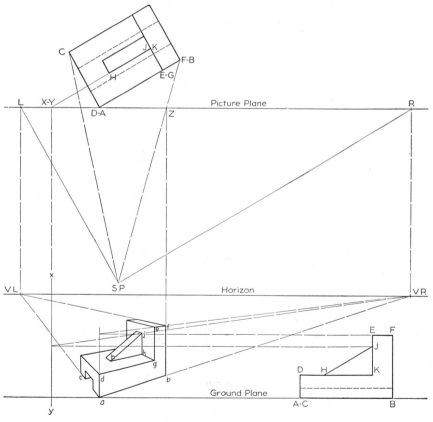

Fig. 17.11.   Use of vanishing points and measuring lines.

the piercing point of this visual ray with the picture plane.   Thus, in Fig.
17.11, the line *SP* to *R* is parallel to the edge *AB* of the object, and *R* is the

piercing point. Point R is then projected to the horizon line, locating VR, the vanishing point for AB and all edges parallel to AB. The vanishing point VL for AC and edges parallel to AC is found similarly, as shown.

In visualizing the location of a vanishing point, imagine that the edge, as for example AB, is moved to the right along the ground, still making the same angle with the picture plane; the intercept of AB will become less and less until, when A is in coincidence with R, the intercept will be zero. R then must be the top view of the vanishing point for all lines parallel to AB.

Point A lies in both the picture plane and the ground plane and will therefore be shown in the perspective at a, on the ground line, and in direct projection with the top view. The perspective of AB is determined by drawing a line from a to VR (the perspective *direction* of AB) and then projecting the intercept Z (of the visual ray SP to B) to the line, thus locating b.

All lines behind the picture plane are foreshortened in the picture, and only those lying in the picture plane will appear in their true length. For this reason, *all measurements must be made in the picture plane.* Since AD is in the picture plane, it will show in its actual height as ad.

A *measuring line* will be needed for any verticals such as BF that do not lie in the picture plane. If a vertical is brought forward to the picture plane along some established line, the true height can be measured in the picture plane. If, in Fig. 17.11, BF is imagined as moved forward along ab until b is in coincidence with a, the true height can be measured vertically from a. This vertical line at a is then the measuring line for all heights in the vertical plane containing a and b. The height of f is measured from a and, from this height point, a vanishing line is drawn to VR; then from Z (the piercing point in the picture plane of the visual ray to F) f may be projected to the perspective.

The measuring line may also be thought of as the intersection of the picture plane with a vertical plane that contains the distance to be found. Thus ad, extended, is the measuring line for all heights in surface $ABFEGD$. The triangular rib of Fig. 17.11 is located by continuing surface HJK until it intersects the picture plane at XY, thereby establishing xy as the measuring line for all heights in HJK. In the figure, the height of J is measured on the measuring line xy, and j is found as described for f.

Note that heights can either be measured with a scale on the measuring line or they can be projected from the front view as indicated in Fig. 17.11.

Summary

1. Draw the top view (edge of the picture plane).
2. Orient the object relative to the picture plane so that the object will appear to advantage, and draw the top view of the object.
3. Select a station point that will best show the shape of the object.
4. Draw the horizon and ground line.
5. Find the top view of the vanishing points for the principal horizontal edges by drawing lines parallel to the edges, through the station point, and to the picture plane.

6. Project from the top views of the vanishing points to the horizon line, thus locating the vanishing points for the perspective.

7. Draw the visual rays from the station point to the corners of the object in the top view, locating the piercing point of each ray with the picture plane.

8. Start the picture, building from the ground up, and from the nearest corner to the more distant ones.

17.7 Planes parallel to the picture plane. Objects having circles or other curves in a vertical plane may be oriented with their curved faces parallel to the picture plane. The curves will then appear in true shape.

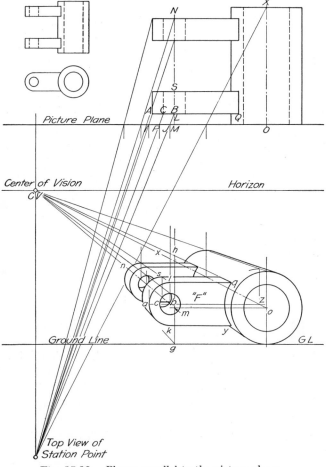

Fig. 17.12.   Planes parallel to the picture plane.

This method, often called "parallel perspective," is also suitable for interiors and for street vistas and similar scenes where considerable depth is to be represented.

The object of Fig. 17.12 has been placed so that the planes containing the circular contours are parallel to the picture plane. The horizontal edges parallel to the picture plane will appear horizontal in the picture and will have no vanishing point. Horizontals perpendicular to the picture plane are parallel to the axis of vision and will vanish at the center of vision CV. Except for architectural interiors, the station point is usually located above the object and either to the right or left, yet not so far in any direction as to cause unpleasant distortion. For convenience, one face of the object is usually placed in the picture plane and is therefore not reduced in size in the perspective.

In Fig. 17.12, the end of the hub is in the picture plane; thus the center o is projected from O in the top view, and the circular edges are drawn in their true size. The center line ox is vanished from o to CV. To find the perspective of center line MN, a vertical plane is passed through MN intersecting the picture plane in measuring line gh. A horizontal line from o intersecting gh locates m, and m vanished to CV is the required line.

By using the two center lines from o and m as a framework, the remaining construction is simplified. A ray from the station point to B pierces the picture plane at J, which, projected to mn, locates b. The horizontal line bz is the center line of the front face of the nearer arm, and the intercept IJ gives the perspective radius ab. The circular hole having a radius CB has an intercept PJ, giving cb as the perspective radius. The arc qy has its center on ox at z. On drawing the tangents lq and ky, the face "F" is completed.

The remaining construction for the arms is exactly the same as that for face "F." The centers are moved back on the center lines, and the radii are found from their corresponding intercepts on the picture plane.

17.8   Circles in perspective.   The perspective of a circle is a circle only when its plane is parallel to the picture plane; the circle appears as a straight line when its plane is receding from the station point. In all other positions the circle projects as an ellipse whose axes are not readily determinable. The major axis of the ellipse will be at some odd angle except when a vertical circle has its center on the horizon plane; then the major axis will be vertical. Also, when a horizontal circle has its center directly above, below, or on the center of vision, the major axis will be horizontal. It should be noted that in all cases the center of the circle is not coincident with the center of the ellipse representing the circle, and that concentric circles are not represented by concentric ellipses. The major and minor axes of the ellipses for concentric circles are not even parallel except in special cases.

The perspective of a circle may be plotted point by point, but the most rapid solution is had by enclosing the circle in a square, as shown in Fig. 17.13, and plotting points at the tangent points and at the intersections of the diagonals. The eight points thus determined are usually sufficient to

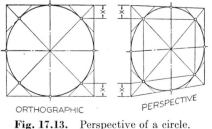

ORTHOGRAPHIC   PERSPECTIVE

Fig. 17.13.   Perspective of a circle.

give an accurate curve. The square, with its diagonals, is first drawn in the perspective. From the intersection of the diagonals, the vertical and horizontal center lines of the circle are established; where these center lines cross the sides of the square are four points on the curve. In the orthographic view, the measurement X is made, then laid out *in the picture plane* and vanished, crossing the diagonals at four additional points.

It must be realized that the curve is tangent to the lines enclosing it, and that the *direction* of the curve is established by these tangent lines; if the lines completing the circumscribing octagon are projected and drawn, the direction of the curve is established at eight points.

17.9 Craticulation. The perspectives of irregular curves may be had by projecting a sufficient number of points to establish the curve, but, if the curve is complicated, the method of craticulation may be used to advantage. A square grid is overlaid on the orthographic view as shown in Fig. 17.14;

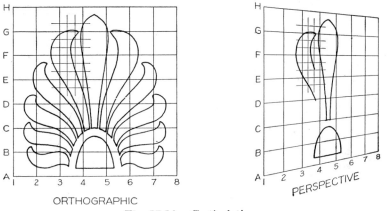

Fig. 17.14. Craticulation.

then the grid is drawn in perspective, and the outlines of the curve transferred by inspection from the orthographic view.

17.10 Measuring points. It has been shown that all lines lying in the picture plane will be their own perspectives and may be scaled directly on the perspective drawing. The adaptation of this principle has an advantage in laying off a series of measurements, such as a row of pilasters, because it avoids a confusion of intercepts on the picture plane and the inaccuracies due to long projection lines.

In the measuring-points method, a surface, such as the wall between A and B of Fig. 17.15, is rotated into the picture plane for the purpose of making measurements, as shown at AB'. While in the picture plane, the entire surface can be laid out directly to the same scale as the top view; therefore, ab' and other horizontal dimensions of the surface are established along the ground line as shown. The counterrotation of the wall to its actual position on the building and the necessary projections in the perspective are based on the principle that the rotation has been made about a vertical axis, and that any point has traveled in a horizontal plane. By drawing, as usual, a line parallel to BB', from the station point to the picture plane, and then projecting to the horizon, the vanishing point MR is found. This vanishing point is termed a *measuring point* and may be defined as the vanishing point for lines joining corresponding points of the actual and rotated positions of the face considered. The divisions on ab' are therefore vanished to MR; where this construction intersects ab (the perspective of AB), the lateral position of the pilasters, in the perspective, is determined.

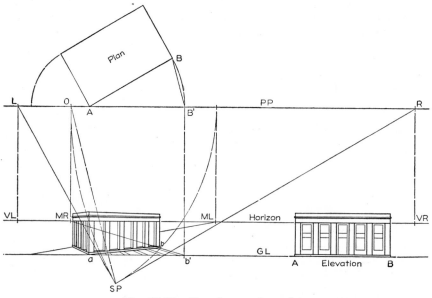

Fig. 17.15.   Use of measuring points.

Heights are scaled on the vertical edge through a, as this edge lies in the picture plane. The perspective of the wall between A and B is completed by the regular methods previously described. For work on the end of the building, the end wall is rotated as indicated, measuring point ML is found, and the projections are continued as described for the front wall.

Measuring points may be more readily located if the draftsman will recognize that the triangles ABB' and $R\ O\ SP$ are similar. Therefore, a measuring point is as far from its corresponding vanishing point as the station point is from the picture plane, measuring the latter parallel to the face concerned. MR can then be found by measuring the distance from the station point to R and laying off RO equal to the measurement, or by swinging an arc, with R as center, from the station point to O, as shown. The measuring point MR is then projected from O.

17.11   Inclined lines. Any line neither parallel nor perpendicular to either the picture plane or the horizon plane is termed an inclined line. Any line may have a vertical plane passed through it, and if the vanishing line of the plane is found, a line in the plane will vanish at some point on the vanishing line of the plane. Vertical planes will vanish on vertical lines, just as horizontal planes vanish on a horizontal line, the horizon. In Fig. 17.16, the points *a*, *b*, *c*, *d*, and *e* have all been found by regular methods previously described. The vanishing point of the horizontal *ab* is *VR*. A vertical line through *VR* is the vanishing line of the plane of *abc* and all planes *parallel* to *abc*. This vanishing line is intersected by the extension of *de* at *UR*, thereby determining the vanishing point for *de* and all edges *parallel* to *de*.

The vanishing point for inclined lines may also be located on the theory that the vanishing point for any line may be determined by moving the line

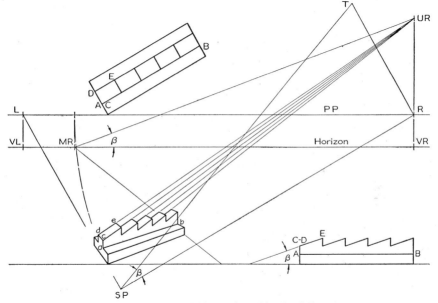

Fig. 17.16. Vanishing point of inclined lines.

until it appears as a point, while still retaining its original angle with the picture plane. The vanishing point of *de* may therefore be located by drawing a line through the station point parallel to *DE* and finding its piercing point with the picture plane. This is done by laying out *SP T* at the angle β to *SP R* and erecting *RT* perpendicular to *SP R*. Then *RT* is the height of the vanishing point *UR* above *VR*.

If measuring points are used for the initial work on the perspective, it will be an advantage to recognize which one of the measuring points was used for determining horizontal measurements in the parallel vertical planes containing the inclined lines; at that measuring point the angle β is laid out, either above or below the horizon depending upon whether the lines slope up or down as they go into the distance. Where this construction intersects the vanishing line for the vertical planes containing the inclined lines, the vanishing point is located.

17.12   Inclined planes.   An inclined plane is any plane neither parallel nor perpendicular to either the picture plane or the horizon plane.   The vanishing line for an inclined plane may be found by locating the vanishing points for any two systems of parallel lines in the inclined plane.   For determining the vanishing line of plane *ABCD* of Fig. 17.17, the vanishing point *VL* of the horizontal edges *AD* and *BC* is one point, and the vanishing

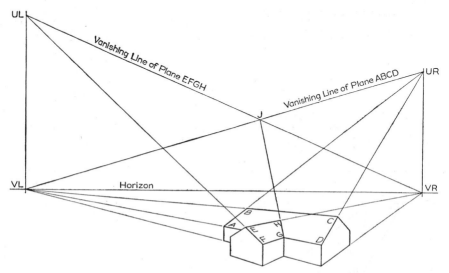

Fig. 17.17.   Vanishing lines of inclined planes; vanishing point for intersection of two inclined planes.

point *UR* for the inclined edges *AB* and *DC* gives a second point on the vanishing line *VL UR* for plane *ABCD*.

It is often necessary to draw the line of intersection of two inclined planes. The intersection will vanish at the point of intersection of the vanishing lines of both planes.   The intersection *J* of the two vanishing lines of the roof planes of Fig. 17.17 is the vanishing point of the line of intersection of the two planes.

PROBLEMS

The following give a variety of different objects to be drawn in perspective.   A further selection may be made from the orthographic drawings in other chapters.

1. Fig. 17.18. Double wedge block.
2. Fig. 17.19. Notched holder.

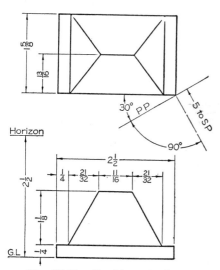

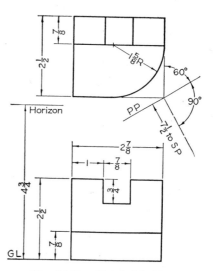

Fig. 17.18. Double-wedge block.

Fig. 17.19. Notched holder.

3. Fig. 17.20. Crank.
4. Fig. 17.21. Corner lug.

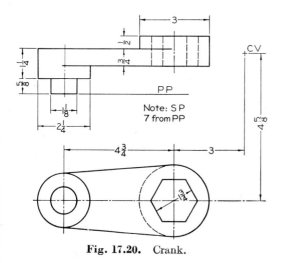

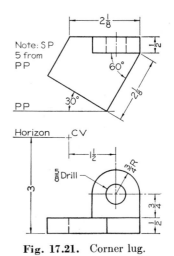

Fig. 17.20. Crank.

Fig. 17.21. Corner lug.

5. Fig. 17.22.   House.
6. Fig. 17.23.   Church.

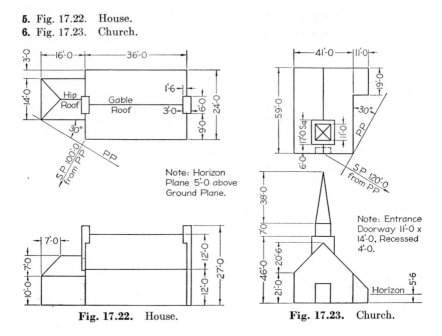

Note: Horizon
Plane 5'-0 *above*
Ground Plane.

Note: Entrance
Doorway 11'-0 x
14'-0, Recessed
4'-0.

Fig. 17.22.   House.   **Fig. 17.23.**   Church.

18

Pictorial Sketching

18.1   The necessity that the engineer be trained in freehand sketching was emphasized in Chap. 8.   What was said there, however, referred particularly to sketching in orthographic projection; now let it be remarked that, before the engineer can be said to be adequately equipped to use the graphic language, he must possess the ability to sketch *pictorially* with skill and facility.

In designing and inventing, the first ideas come into the mind in pictorial form, and preliminary sketches made in this form preserve the ideas as visualized.   From this record the preliminary orthographic design sketches are made.   A pictorial sketch of an object or of some detail of construction can often be used to explain it when the orthographic projection cannot be read intelligently by a client or a workman.   If a working drawing is difficult to understand, one of the best ways of reading it is to start a pictorial sketch of it.   Usually before the sketch is finished, the orthographic drawing is perfectly clear.   Often again, a pictorial sketch may be made more quickly and may serve as a better record than would orthographic views of the same piece.   The young engineer should not be deterred by any fancied lack of "artistic ability."   An engineer's sketch is a record of information, not a work of art.   The one requirement for both is *good proportion.*

18.2   Methods.   Although not an accurate classification, there may be said to be three pictorial methods: axonometric, oblique, and perspective. The mechanical construction of the first two has been explained in detail in Chap. 16, and the third in Chap. 17.

18.3   Prerequisites.   At the outset, it should be clearly understood that pictorial sketching means the making of a pictorial drawing *freehand.*   The same construction for locating points and lines and for drawing circles and arcs with instruments will be used in pictorial sketching.   From this standpoint, a knowledge of the constructions given in earlier chapters is necessary before pictorial sketching is attempted.   Note in Fig. 18.1 that the ellipses

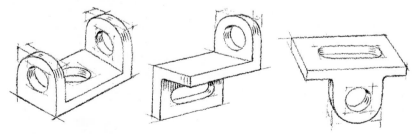

Fig. 18.1.   Choice of axes and basic construction.

representing holes and rounded contours have been "boxed in" first with construction lines representing the enclosing square in exactly the same manner as for an instrument drawing.

18.4 Materials and technique. The same materials, pencil grades, etc., as used for orthographic freehand drawing, described in Chap. 8, are employed for pictorial sketching. Also, the directions given there for drawing straight lines, circles, and arcs will apply.

18.5 Axonometric sketching—choice and direction of axes. After a clear visualization, the first step in the procedure is to select the best position from which to view the object and thus determine the direction of the axes. It will be remembered that there are an infinite number of positions for the three axes that represent three mutually perpendicular lines, and that the simplest is the isometric position. Sketches may be made on isometric axes, but unless it is important to show some feature on the top, a much better effect is gained and the distortion greatly lessened by drawing the cross axes at a much smaller angle with the horizontal, Fig. 18.1. Since measurements are not made on sketches, the axes may be foreshortened until the proportion is satisfactory to the eye; moreover the effect of distortion may be overcome still further by slightly converging the receding lines. Objects of rectangular outline are best adapted to sketching in axonometric projection. Figures 18.1, 18.4, and 18.6 show examples of pictorial sketches.

18.6 Ellipse method of establishing axes. A successful method of establishing the direction of the two horizontal axes for cylindrical objects (but adaptable for other shapes) is to sketch first a horizontal ellipse (with a little practice this can be done with a free sweep of the arm), Fig. 18.2.

Fig. 18.2. Ellipse method of establishing axes.

At some point, as A, draw a tangent. Through A and the center of the ellipse draw one of a pair of conjugate diameters of the ellipse, and at the other end of this diameter draw a second tangent parallel to the first. Complete the axonometric square by drawing the other two sides parallel to the diameter. Then add the vertical axis and necessary edges parallel to it, as in Fig. 18.2.

18.7 Axonometric circles. A circle in pictorial drawing is always an ellipse whose major axis is at right angles to the shaft or rotation axis of the circle. Thus its minor axis coincides on the drawing with the picture of the shaft axis, Fig. 18.3.

Note particularly that by the above rule *all* circles on horizontal planes are drawn as ellipses *with the major axis horizontal*, Fig. 18.4.

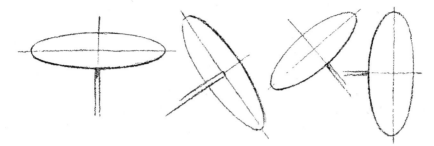

Fig. 18.3. Relation of ellipse axes to axis of rotation.

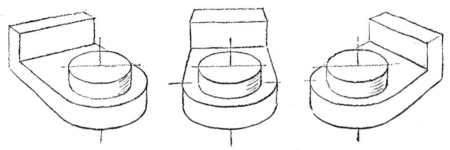

Fig. 18.4. Horizontal circles in axonometric.

In almost every case it is best to draw the enclosing square for the ellipse as indicated in Fig. 18.5. By this method the size of the ellipse and the thickness of the cylindrical portion represented are easily judged. Note in Fig. 18.5 that the center lines or "rotation axes" of the cylindrical features

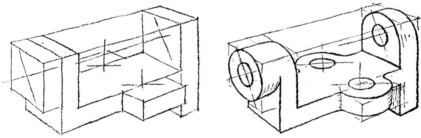

Fig. 18.5. Blocking in a sketch.   **Fig. 18.6.** Completing a sketch.

and the directions for the major axes of the ellipses are drawn as an aid in sketching the curves. Figure 18.6 shows the ellipses and the sketch completed.

18.8 Oblique sketching. The advantage of oblique projection in preserving one face without distortion is of particular value in sketching, as illustrated by Fig. 18.7. The painful effect of distortion in oblique

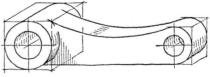

Fig. 18.7. An oblique sketch.

drawing done mechanically may be greatly lessened in sketching, by foreshortening the cross axis to a pleasing proportion. By converging the lines parallel to the cross axis, the effect of perspective is obtained. This converging in either axonometric or oblique is sometimes called "fake perspective."

18.9 Perspective sketching. A sketch made in perspective gives a better effect than either axonometric or oblique. For constructing a perspective drawing of a proposed structure from its plans and elevations, a knowledge of the principles of perspective drawing is required, but for making a perspective sketch from the object, one may get along by observing the ordinary phenomena of perspective which affect everything we see: the fact that objects appear smaller in proportion as their distance from the eye increases, that parallel lines appear to converge as they recede, that horizontal lines and planes appear to "vanish" on the horizon.

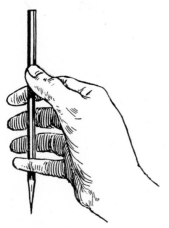

Fig. 18.8. Estimating proportion.

In perspective sketching from the model, the drawing is made simply by observation, the directions and proportionate lengths of lines being estimated by sighting and measuring on the pencil held at arm's length, one's knowledge of perspective phenomena being used as a check. With the drawing board or sketch pad held in a comfortable drawing position perpendicular to the line of sight from the eye to the object, the direction of a line is tested by holding the pencil at arm's length parallel to the board and rotating the arm until the pencil appears to coincide with the line on the model, then moving it parallel to this position back to the board. The apparent lengths of lines are estimated in the same way; holding the pencil in a plane perpendicular to the line of sight, one marks with the thumb the length of pencil which covers the line of the model, rotates the arm with the thumb held in position until the pencil coincides with another line, and then estimates the proportion of this measurement to the second line, Fig. 18.8.

The sketch should be made lightly, with free sketchy lines, and no lines should be erased until the whole sketch has been blocked in. *Do not make the mistake of getting the sketch too small.*

In starting a sketch from the object, set it in a position to give the most advantageous view, and sketch the directions of the principal lines, running them past the limits of the figure toward their vanishing points. Block in the enclosing squares for all circles and circle arcs and proceed with the figure, drawing the main outlines first and adding details later; then brighten the sketch with heavier lines. A good draftsman often adds a few touches of surface shading, but the beginner should be cautious in attempting it.

Figure 18.9 shows the general appearance of a "one-point" perspective sketch before the construction lines have been erased. Figure 18.10 is an example showing the object turned at an angle to the picture plane.

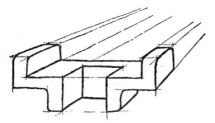

Fig. 18.9. A perspective sketch (one plane parallel to the picture plane.)

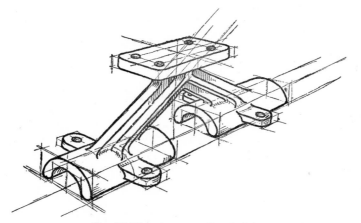

Fig. 18.10. A perspective sketch.

18.10 Order of sketching. Because of the variety of objects that will, require representation, the order of procedure will not always be the same. The following, however, will serve as a guide:

1. Visualize the object's shape and proportions from the orthographic views, a model or other source.

2. Mentally picture the object in space and decide the pictorial position that will best describe its shape.

3. Decide on what type of pictorial to use (axonometric, oblique, or perspective).

4. Pick a suitable paper size.

5. Sketch suitable axes for the type of pictorial to be used and block in, lightly, the enclosing "box" or "boxes" for the part.

6. Sketch in the construction for details, as illustrated by Figs. 18.1, 18.5, 18.7, and 18.10, starting with the most dominant and progressing to the subordinate, being careful the while to preserve the proportions and relationships of the various features. Draw the enclosing parallelogram for ellipses, representing cylindrical features and use other construction as needed.

7. Complete the details, as in Fig. 18.6, by sketching them directly to the final weight desired. Complicated features, however, may be sketched lightly and, when satisfactory to the eye, then heavied.   Do not use any hidden lines unless necessary for the description of the piece.

8. Check the sketch for errors of shape or proportion and correct if necessary.

9. Remove any construction that may be objectionable or that may confuse the representation.

PROBLEMS

The problems following are to be used to develop not only an ability in pictorial sketching, but also the ability to read orthographic drawings.   Make the sketches to suitable size on 8½- by 11-in. paper, choosing the most appropriate form of representation, axonometric, oblique, or perspective with partial, full, or half sections as needed. Small fillets and rounds may be ignored and shown as sharp corners.

Group I.   *Figs. 18.11 and 18.12*

Make pictorial sketches of the objects shown.

Group II.   *Figs. 16.42 to 16.77*

Select an object not previously drawn with instruments and make an axonometric sketch.

Groups III.   *Figs. 16.78 to 16.100*

Select an object not previously drawn with instruments and make an oblique sketch.

Group IV.   *Figs. 17.18 to 17.23*

Select an object not previously drawn with instruments and make a perspective sketch.

TEXT-FILMS

The following McGraw-Hill Text-Film is available for specific correlation with Chap. 18:

Pictorial Sketching (approximately 12-min. sound motion picture).

Demonstrates types of pictorial sketches and explains position of object, choice of axes, use of construction lines, methods of sketching circles, etc.

This film is accompanied by a coordinated silent filmstrip that may be used for review and oral discussion.

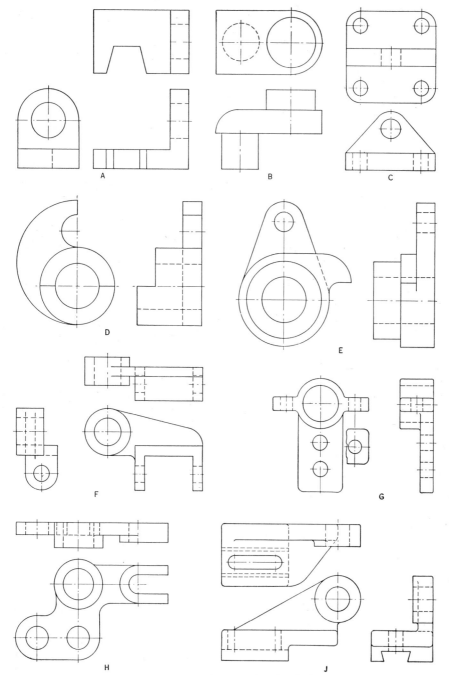

Fig. 18.11. Objects to be sketched.

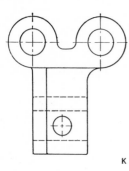
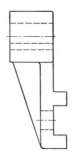
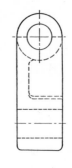
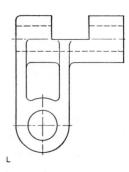

K

L

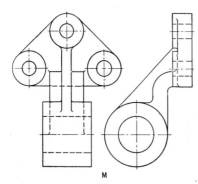
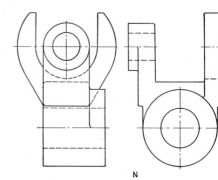

M

N

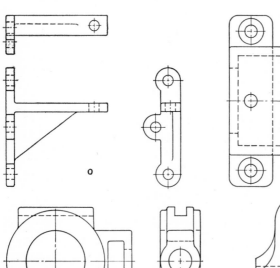
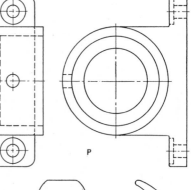

O

P

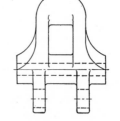

Q

R

Fig. 18.12. Objects to be sketched.

19

The Drawings and the Shop

19.1   The test of any working drawing for legibility, completeness, and accuracy is the production of the object or assembly by the shop without further information than that given on the drawing.   The draftsman's knowledge of shop methods will, to a great extent, govern the effectiveness and completeness of the dimensioning and notes; the proper specification of machining operations, heat-treatment, and finish; the accuracy to be main-

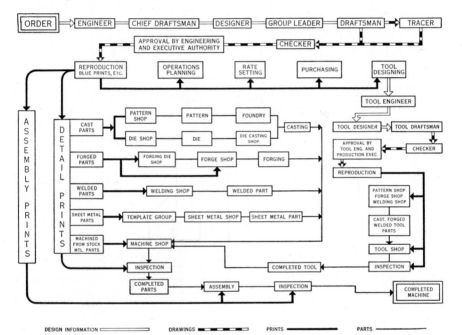

Fig. 19.1.   Development and distribution of drawings.

tained on mating parts; and, in some cases, the order of machining.   The young draftsman, whenever opportunity permits, should follow operations through the shops, get acquainted with shopmen, and enlarge his knowledge by reading and discussion.   The glossary of shop terms, page 691, should be studied, in connection with the dimensioning and notes on the various working drawings in this book, to gain an acquaintance with the terms and the form of designation in the notes.   This chapter is thus given as an introduction to those following on dimensioning and working drawings.

The relation of drawings, and the prints made from them, to the operations of production is illustrated in the graphical chart, Fig. 19.1.   This chart shows in diagrammatic form the different steps in the development of the drawings and their distribution and use in connection with the shop operations, from the time the order is received until the finished machine is delivered to the shipping room.

19.2   Effect of the basic manufacturing method on the drawing.   In the drawing of any machine part, a first consideration is the manufacturing process to be used, as on this depends the representation of the detailed features of the part and, to some extent, the choice of dimensions.   Special or unusual methods may occasionally be used, but most machine parts are

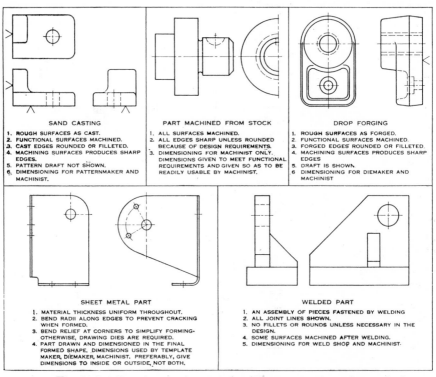

SAND CASTING

1. ROUGH SURFACES AS CAST.
2. FUNCTIONAL SURFACES MACHINED.
3. CAST EDGES ROUNDED OR FILLETED.
4. MACHINING SURFACES PRODUCES SHARP EDGES.
5. PATTERN DRAFT NOT SHOWN.
6. DIMENSIONING FOR PATTERNMAKER AND MACHINIST.

PART MACHINED FROM STOCK

1. ALL SURFACES MACHINED.
2. ALL EDGES SHARP UNLESS ROUNDED BECAUSE OF DESIGN REQUIREMENTS.
3. DIMENSIONING FOR MACHINIST ONLY. DIMENSIONS GIVEN TO MEET FUNCTIONAL REQUIREMENTS AND GIVEN SO AS TO BE READILY USABLE BY MACHINIST.

DROP FORGING

1. ROUGH SURFACES AS FORGED.
2. FUNCTIONAL SURFACES MACHINED.
3. FORGED EDGES ROUNDED OR FILLETED.
4. MACHINING SURFACES PRODUCES SHARP EDGES
5. DRAFT IS SHOWN.
6. DIMENSIONING FOR DIEMAKER AND MACHINIST

SHEET METAL PART

1. MATERIAL THICKNESS UNIFORM THROUGHOUT.
2. BEND RADII ALONG EDGES TO PREVENT CRACKING WHEN FORMED.
3. BEND RELIEF AT CORNERS TO SIMPLIFY FORMING- OTHERWISE, DRAWING DIES ARE REQUIRED.
4. PART DRAWN AND DIMENSIONED IN THE FINAL FORMED SHAPE, DIMENSIONS USED BY TEMPLATE MAKER, DIEMAKER, MACHINIST. PREFERABLY, GIVE DIMENSIONS TO INSIDE OR OUTSIDE, NOT BOTH.

WELDED PART

1. AN ASSEMBLY OF PIECES FASTENED BY WELDING
2. ALL JOINT LINES SHOWN.
3. NO FILLETS OR ROUNDS UNLESS NECESSARY IN THE DESIGN.
4. SOME SURFACES MACHINED AFTER WELDING.
5. DIMENSIONING FOR WELD SHOP AND MACHINIST.

Fig. 19.2.   Drawing requirements for different manufacturing methods.

produced by (1) casting, (2) forging, (3) machining from standard stock, (4) welding, or (5) forming from sheet stock.

Each of the different methods will produce a characteristic detailed shape and appearance of the parts, and these features must be shown on the drawing.   Figure 19.2 shows and lists typical features of each method and indicates the differences in drawing practice.

19.3   The drawings.   For the production of any part, a detail working drawing is necessary, complete with shape and size description, and giving, where needed, the operations that are to be performed by the shop. Machined surfaces must be clearly indicated, with dimensions chosen and placed so as to be useful to the various shops without the necessity of adding or subtracting dimensions or scaling the drawing.

Two general practices may be followed: (1) the "single-drawing" system, in which only one drawing, showing the finished part, is made to be used by all the shops involved in producing the part; and (2) the "multiple-drawing" system, in which different drawings are prepared, one for each shop, giving only the information required by the shop for which the drawing is made.

The second practice is recommended, as the drawings are much easier to dimension without ambiguity, are somewhat simpler and more direct, and

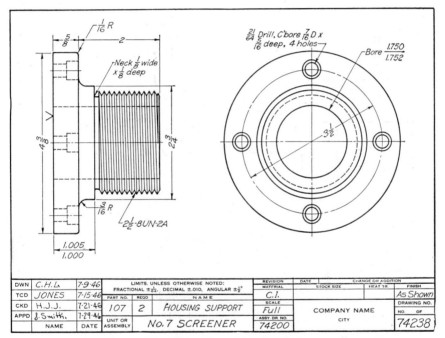

Fig. 19.3.   A working drawing.

are therefore easier for the shop to use.   Figure 19.3 is a "single drawing," to be used by both the pattern shop and the machine shop.   Figures 21.3 and 21.4 are "multiple" drawings, Fig. 21.3 for the patternmaker, and Fig. 21.4 for the machine shop.

19.4   Sand castings.   The drawing, Fig. 19.3, shows (in the title strip) that the material to be used is cast iron (C.I.), indicating that the part will be formed by pouring molten iron into a mold, in this case a "sand mold," resulting in a sand casting.   Before the part can be cast, however, the shape of the part must be produced in the sand mold.

19.5   The pattern shop.   The drawing is first used by the patternmaker who will make a pattern, or "model," of the part in wood.   From this, if a large quantity of castings is required, a metal pattern, often of aluminum, is made.   The patternmaker provides for the shrinkage of the casting by making the pattern oversize, using a "shrink rule" for his measurements. He also provides additional metal (machining allowance) for the machined surfaces, indicated on the drawing (1) by finish marks, (2) by dimensions indicating a degree of precision attainable only by machining, or (3) by notes giving machining operations.   The patternmaker also provides the "draft" or slight taper, not shown on the drawing, so that the pattern can be withdrawn easily from the sand.   A "core box," for the making of sand cores for the hollow parts of the casting, is also made in the pattern shop. A knowledge of patternmaking is of great aid in dimensioning, as almost all the dimensions are used by the patternmaker while only the dimensions for finished features will be used by the machine shop.

19.6   Drawings of castings.   Casting drawings are usually made as a single drawing of the machined casting, having dimensions for both the

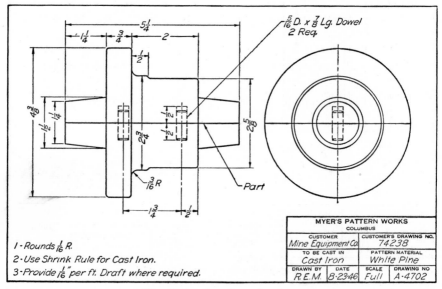

Fig. 19.4.   A pattern drawing.

patternmaker and machinist, Fig. 19.3.   If the "multiple" drawing system is followed, a drawing of the unmachined casting, with allowances for machining accounted for and having no finish marks or finish dimensions, will be made for the patternmaker; then a second drawing for the machinist shows the finished shape and gives machining dimensions.

For complicated or difficult castings, a special "pattern drawing" may be made, Fig. 19.4, showing every detail of the pattern, including the amount of draft, the parting line, "core prints" for supporting the cores in the mold, and the pattern material.   Similar detail drawings may also be made for the core boxes.

19.7 The foundry. The pattern and core box, or boxes, are sent to the foundry, and sand molds made so that molten metal may be poured into the molds and allowed to cool, forming the completed rough casting. Figure 19.5 shows a cross section of a two-part mold, showing the space left by the

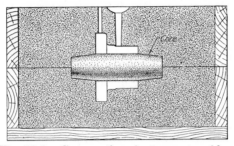

Fig. 19.5. Cross section of a two-part mold.

pattern, and the core in place. Only in occasional instances does the foundryman call for assistance from the drawing, as his job is simply to reproduce the pattern in metal.

Permanent molds, made of cast iron coated on the molding surfaces with a refractory material, are sometimes an advantage in that the mold may be used over and over again, thus saving the time to make an individual sand mold for each casting. This method is usually limited to small castings.

Die castings are made by forcing molten metal under pressure into a steel die mounted in a special die-casting machine. Alloys with a low melting point are used in order to avoid damaging the die. Because of the accuracy possible in making the die, a fine finish and accurate dimensions of the part may be obtained; thus machining may be unnecessary.

19.8 Forgings. Forgings are made by heating metal to make it plastic and then forming the metal to shape on a power hammer with or without the aid of special steel dies. Large parts are often hammered with dies of generalized all-purpose shape.

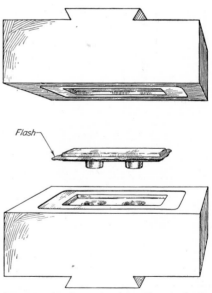

Fig. 19.6. Drop-forging dies and the forged part.

Smaller parts in quantity may warrant the expense of making special dies. Some small forgings are made with the metal cold.

Drop forgings are the most common and are made in dies of the kind shown in Fig. 19.6. The lower die is held on the bed of the drop hammer, and the upper die is raised by the hammer mechanism. The hot metal is placed between the dies and the upper die dropped several times, causing the metal to flow into the cavity of the dies. The slight excess of material will form a thin fin or "flash" surrounding the forging at the parting plane of the dies, Fig. 19.6. This flash is then removed in a "trimming" die made for the purpose. Considerable draft must be provided for release of the forging from the dies.

19.9 Drawings of forgings. Forging drawings either are prepared according to the multiple system, one drawing for the diemaker and one for the machinist, Fig. 21.6, or are made as a single drawing for both, Fig.

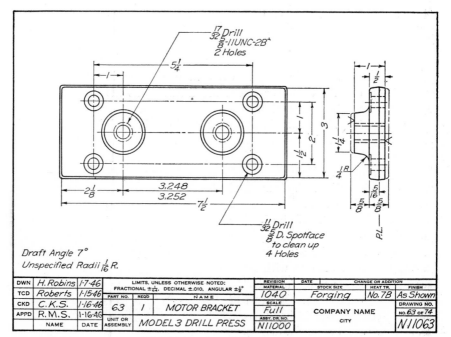

Fig. 19.7. A working drawing.

19.7. In either case, the parting line and draft should be shown, and the amount of draft specified. On the single drawing, the shape of the finished forging is shown in full outline and the machining allowance is indicated by "alternate position" lines, thus completing the shape of the rough forging. This single drawing, therefore, combines two drawings into one, with complete dimensions for both diemaker and machinist.

19.10 The machine shop. The machine shop produces parts machined from stock material, and also finishes castings, forgings, etc., requiring machined surfaces. Cylindrical and conical surfaces are machined on a lathe. Flat or plane surfaces are machined on a planer, shaper, milling machine, broaching machine, or in some cases (facing), on a lathe. Holes are drilled, reamed, counterbored, and countersunk on a drill press or lathe; holes are bored on a boring mill or lathe. For exact work, grinding machines with wheels of abrasive material are used. Grinders are also coming into greatly increased use for operations formerly made with cutting tools. In quantity production, many special machine tools and automatic machines are in use. The special tools, jigs, and fixtures made for the machine parts are held in the toolroom ready for the machine shop.

19.11 Fundamentals of machining. All machining operations remove metal, either to make a smoother and more accurate surface, as by planing, facing, milling, etc., or to produce a surface not previously existing, as by drilling, punching, etc. The metal is removed by a hardened steel, carbide, or diamond cutting tool (machining), or an abrasive wheel (grinding); the product, or "work piece," as well as the tool or wheel, being held and guided by the machine. When steel cutting tools are used, the product must remain relatively soft until after all machining has been performed upon it, but if diamond-tipped tools are used, or if grinding wheels are employed, the product may be hardened by heat-treatment before finishing.

All machining methods may be classified according to the operating principle of the machine performing the work.

1. The surface may be *generated* by moving the work with respect to a cutting tool, or the tool with respect to the work, following the geometric laws for producing the surface.

2. The surface may be *formed* with a specially shaped cutting tool, moving either work or tool while the other is stationary.

The forming method is, in general, less accurate than the generating method, as any irregularities in the cutter are reproduced on the work. In some cases a combination of the two methods is used.

19.12 The lathe. Called the "king of machine tools," the lathe is said to be capable of producing all other machine tools. Its primary function is for machining cylindrical, conical, and other surfaces of revolution, but with special attachments a great variety of operations can be performed. Figure 19.8 shows the casting made from the drawing of Fig. 19.3 held in the lathe chuck. As the work revolves, the cutting tool is moved

Fig. 19.8. Facing.

across perpendicular to the axis of revolution, removing metal from the base and producing a plane surface by generation. This operation is called *facing*. After being faced, the casting is turned around and the finished base is aligned against the face of the chuck, bringing the cylindrical surface into position for *turning* to the diameter indicated in the thread note on the drawing.   The neck shown at the intersection of the base with the body is turned first, running the tool into the casting to a depth slightly greater than the depth of the thread.   The cylindrical surface is then turned (generated) by moving the tool parallel to the axis of revolution, Fig. 19.9.   Figure 19.10

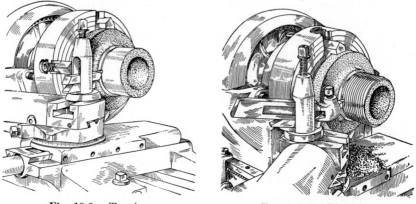

Fig. 19.9.   Turning.   **Fig. 19.10.**   Threading.

shows the thread being cut on the finished cylinder.   The tool is ground to the profile of the thread space, carefully lined up to the work, and moved parallel to the axis of revolution by the lead screw of the lathe.   This operation is a combination of the fundamental processes, the thread profile being formed while the helix is generated.

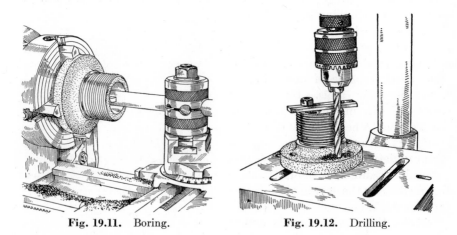

Fig. 19.11.   Boring.   **Fig. 19.12.**   Drilling.

The hole through the center of the casting, originally cored, is now finished by *boring*, as the cutting of an interior surface is called, Fig. 19.11. The tool is held in a boring bar and moved parallel to the axis of revolution, thus generating an internal cylinder.

Note that in these operations the dimensions used by the machinist have been (1) the finish mark on the base and thickness of the base, (2) the thread note and outside diameter of the thread, (3) the dimensions of the neck, (4) the distance from the base to the shoulder, and (5) the diameter of the bored hole.

Long cylindrical pieces to be turned in the lathe are supported by conical centers, one at each end.   Figure 19.19 illustrates the principle.

19.13   The drill press.   The partially finished piece of Fig. 19.3 is now taken to the drill press for drilling and counterboring the holes in the base according to the dimensions on the drawing.   These dimensions give the diameter of the drill, the diameter and depth of the counterbore, and the location of the holes.   The casting is clamped to the drill-press table, Fig.

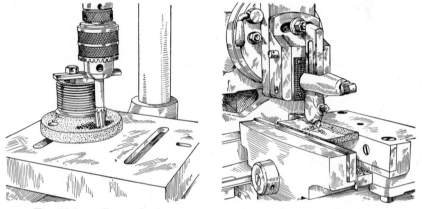

Fig. 19.13.   Counterboring.   **Fig. 19.14.**   Shaping.

19.12, and the rotating drill brought into the work by a lever operating a rack and pinion in the head of the machine.   The cutting is done by two ground lips on the end of the drill, Fig. 19.21A.   Drilling can be done in a lathe, the work revolving while the drill is held in, and moved by, the tail-stock.   In Fig. 19.13 the drill has been replaced by a counterboring tool, Fig. 19.21C, whose diameter is the size specified on the drawing, and which has a cylindrical pilot on the end to fit into the drilled hole, thus ensuring concentricity.   This tool is fed in to the depth shown on the drawing.

Study the drawing of Fig. 19.3 with the illustrations of the operations and check, first, the dimensions that would be used by the patternmaker, and, second, those required by the machinist.

19.14   The shaper and the planer.   The drop forging of Fig. 19.7 requires machining on the base and boss surfaces.

Flat surfaces of this type may be machined on a shaper or a planer.   In this case the shaper, Fig. 19.14, is used because of the relatively small size of the part.   The tool is held in a ram which moves back and forth across the work, taking a cut at each pass forward.   Between the cuts the table moves laterally, so that closely spaced parallel cuts are made until the surface is completely machined.

The planer differs from the shaper in that its bed, carrying the work, moves back and forth under a stationary tool. It is generally used for a larger and heavier type of work than that done on a shaper.

19.15 Parts machined from standard stock. The shape of a part will often lend itself to machining directly from standard stock, such as bars, rods, tubing, plates, and blocks; or from extrusions and rolled shapes, such as angles and channels. Hot-rolled (HR) and cold-rolled (CR) steel are common materials.

Parts produced from stock are usually finished on all surfaces, and a general note "Finish all over" on the drawing eliminates the use of finish marks. Figure 19.15 is the drawing of a part to be made from bar stock. Note the specification of material, stock size, etc., in the title.

19.16 The turret lathe. The *quill* of Fig. 19.15, produced in quantity, may be made on a turret lathe, except for the rack teeth and the outside

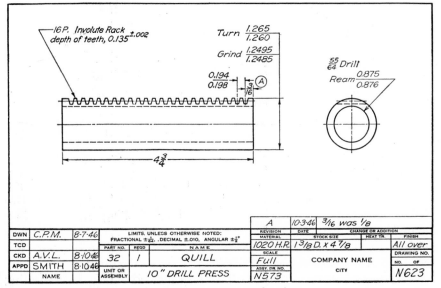

Fig. 19.15. A working drawing.

diameter grinding. The stock is held in the collet chuck of the lathe. First the end surface is faced, and then the cylindrical surface (OD) is turned. The work piece is then ready for drilling and reaming. The turret holds the various tools and swings them around into position as needed. A center drill starts a small hole to align the larger drill, and then the drill and reamer are brought successively into position. The drill provides a hole slightly undersize, and then the reamer, cutting with its fluted sides, cleans out the hole and gives a smooth surface finished to a size within the dimensional limits on the drawing. Figure 19.16 shows the turret indexed so that the drill is out of the way and the reamer is in position. At the right is seen the cutoff tool ready to cut the piece to the length shown on the drawing.

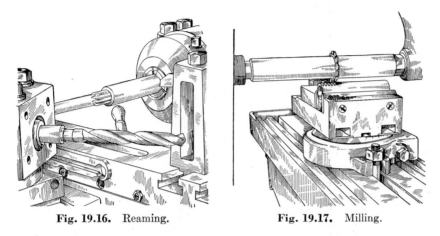

Fig. 19.16. Reaming.   **Fig. 19.17.** Milling.

19.17 The milling machine. The dimensions of the rack teeth, Fig. 19.15, give the depth and spacing of the cuts, and also the specifications for the cutter to be used. This type of work may be done on a milling machine. The work piece is held in a vise and moved horizontally into the rotating milling cutter, which, in profile, is the shape of the space between the teeth, Fig. 19.17. The cuts are spaced by moving the table of the machine to correspond with the distance shown on the drawing. Note that this operation is a forming process, as the shape depends upon the contour of the cutter. With several cutters mounted together (gang milling), a number of teeth can be cut at the same time.

There are many types of milling cutters made to cut on their periphery, their sides, or their ends, for forming flat, curved, or special surfaces. Three milling cutters are shown in Fig. 19.18.

19.18 The grinder. The general purpose of grinding is to make a smoother and more accurate surface than can be obtained by turning, planing, milling, etc. In many cases,

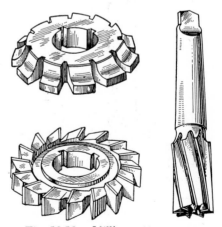

Fig. 19.18. Milling cutters.

pieces hardened by heat-treatment will warp slightly, and as ordinary machining methods are impractical with hardened materials, such parts are finish-ground after hardening.

The limit dimensions for the outside diameter of the quill, Fig. 19.15, indicate a grinding operation on a cylindrical grinder, Fig. 19.19. The abrasive wheel rotates at high speed, while the work piece, mounted on a mandrel between conical centers, rotates slowly in the opposite direction.

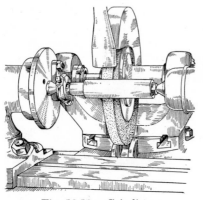

The wheel usually moves laterally to cover the surface of the work piece. The work piece is gaged carefully during the operation to bring the size within the dimensional limits shown on the drawing and to check for a cylindrical surface without taper. The machine for flat surfaces, called a "surface grinder," holds the work piece on a flat table moving back and forth under the abrasive wheel. The table "indexes" laterally after each pass under the work.

Fig. 19.19. Grinding.

19.19 Lapping, honing, and superfinishing are methods of producing smooth, accurate, mirrorlike surfaces after grinding. All three methods use very fine abrasives, (1) powdered and carried in oil on a piece of formed soft metal (lapping), or (2) in the form of fine-grained compact stones (honing and superfinishing) to rub against the surface to be finished and reduce scratches and waviness.

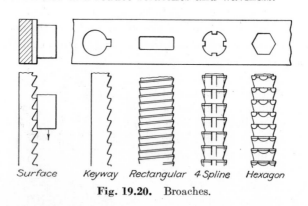

Surface   Keyway   Rectangular   4 Spline   Hexagon

Fig. 19.20. Broaches.

19.20 The broaching machine. A broach is a long tapered bar having a series of cutting edges (teeth), each successively removing a small amount of material until the last edge forms the shape desired. For flat or irregular external surfaces, the broach and work piece are held by the broaching machine and the broach is passed across the surface of the work piece. For internal surfaces, the broach is either pulled or pushed through a hole to give the finished size and shape.

Some machined shapes can be more economically produced by broaching than by any other method. Figure 19.20 shows several forms of broaches and the shapes they produce.

19.21 Small tools. The shop uses a variety of small tools, both in powered machines and as hand tools. Figure 19.21 shows, at *A*, a *twist drill*, available in a variety of sizes (numbered, lettered, fractional, and metric) for producing holes in almost any material; at *B*, a *reamer*, used to enlarge and smooth a previously existing hole and to give greater accuracy than is possible by drilling alone; at *C*, a *counterbore;* and at *D*, a *countersink*, both used to enlarge and alter the end of a hole (usually for screwheads). A *spot-facing tool* is similar to a counterbore. *Taper, plug,* and *bottoming taps* for cutting the thread of a tapped hole are shown at *E, F,* and *G*. A die for threading a rod or shaft is shown at *H*.

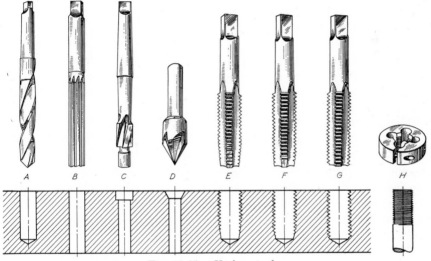

Fig. 19.21. Various tools.

19.22 Welded parts. Simple shapes cut from standard rod, bar, or plate stock may be combined by welding to form a finished part. Some machining after welding is frequently necessary. Chapter 26 discusses welding drawings.

19.23 Parts from standard sheet. A relatively thin sheet or strip of standard thickness may first be cut to size "in the flat," then bent, formed, punched, etc., to form the final required part. The drawing should be made so as to give information for the "template maker," and also the information required for bending and forming the sheet. Sometimes separate developments (Chap. 15) are made. The thickness of sheet stock is specified by giving (1) the gage (see table, page 669) and the equivalent thickness in decimals of an inch, or (2) only the decimal thickness (the practice followed in specifying aluminum sheet). Figure 21.7 is a working drawing of a sheet-metal part.

19.24 Plastics. Plastics are available either in standard bar, rod, tubing, sheet, etc., from which parts can be made by machining, or in granular form to be used in "molding," a process similar to die-casting in which the material is heated to a plastic state and compressed by a die (compression molding) or injected under pressure into a die (injection molding). Metal inserts for threads, wear bushings, etc., are sometimes cast into the part. Consideration should be given the diemaker when dimensioning the drawing.

19.25 Heat-treatment is a general term applied to the processing of metals by heat and chemicals to change the physical properties of the material.

The glossary of shop terms, page 691, gives definitions of such heat-treatment processes as annealing, carburizing, casehardening, hardening, normalizing, and tempering.

The specification of heat-treatment may be given on the drawing in several ways: (1) by a general note listing the steps, temperatures, and baths to be used; (2) by a standard heat-treatment number (SAE, or company standard) in the space provided in the title block; (3) by giving the Brinell or Rockwell hardness number to be attained; or (4) by giving the tensile strength, in pounds per square inch, to be attained through heat-treatment.

Figures 19.7, 21.1, 21.2, and 21.6 illustrate these methods.

19.26 Tools for mass production. Many special machine tools, either semiautomatic or fully automatic, are used in modern factories. These machines are basically the same as ordinary lathes, grinders, etc., but contain mechanisms to control the movements of cutting tools and produce identical parts with little attention from the operator, once the machine is "tooled up." Automatic screw machines and centerless grinders are examples.

19.27 Jigs and fixtures. Jigs for holding the work and guiding the tool, or fixtures for holding the work, greatly extend the production rate for general-purpose machine tools. Chapter 29 describes their use.

19.28 Inspection. Careful inspection is an important feature of modern production. Good practice requires inspection after each operation. For production in quantity, special gages are usually employed, but in small quantity production, the usual measuring instruments, calipers and scale, micrometers, dial gages, etc., are used. For greater precision in gaging, electrical, air, or optical gages are often employed.

19.29 Assembly. The finished separate pieces come to the assembly department to be put together according to the assembly drawings. Sometimes it is desirable or necessary to perform some small machining operation during assembly, often drilling, reaming, or hand finishing. In such cases the assembly drawing should carry a note explaining the required operation, and give dimensions for the alignment or location of the pieces. If some parts are to be combined before final assembly, either a subassembly drawing or the detail drawings of each piece will give the required information. "$\frac{1}{8}$ drill in assembly with piece No. 107" is a typical note form for an assembly machining operation.

TEXT-FILMS

The following McGraw-Hill Text-Film has been designed for direct correlation with Chap. 19:

The Drawings and the Shop (15-min. sound motion picture).

Portrays the relationship between the drawing and the various production operations in shop and factory; demonstrates the working of basic machines and the organization of modern production methods; shows the importance of the drawing in giving the basic information for production processes.

The accompanying coordinated silent filmstrip reviews the material in the film and presents questions for discussion and examination.

20

Dimensions and Notes

20.1   After the shape of an object has been described by orthographic. (or pictorial) views, the value of the drawing for the construction of the object depends upon the dimensions and notes to give the description of *size*.   In general, the description of shape and size together gives complete information for producing the object represented.

The dimensions put on the drawing are *not necessarily* those used in making the drawing but are those required for the proper functioning of the part after assembly, selected so as to be readily usable by the workers who are to make the piece.   The draftsman must thus first study the machine and understand its functional requirements and then put himself in the place of the patternmaker, diemaker, machinist, etc., and mentally construct the object to discover which dimensions would best give the information.

20.2   Method.   Three basic steps are involved in the study of dimensioning practice:

(1) *Fundamentals and technique.*   One must first have a thorough knowledge of the lines and symbols used for dimensions and notes, and the weight and spacing of the lines on the drawing.   These lines, symbols, and techniques are the "tools" for clear, concise representation of size.   See paragraphs 20.3 to 20.13, inclusive.

(2) *Selection of distances to be given.*   The most important consideration from the standpoint of ultimate operation of a machine and the proper working of the individual parts is the selection of distances to be given.   From the functional requirements, the "breakdown" of the part into its geometrical elements, and the requirements of the shop for production, this selection is made.   See paragraphs 20.14 to 20.19, inclusive.

(3) *Placement.*   After the distances to be given have been decided upon, the next step is the actual placement of the dimensions showing these distances on the drawing.   The dimensions should be placed in an orderly arrangement clear and easy to read and in positions where they may be readily found without undue search by persons reading the drawing.   See paragraphs 20.20 to 20.40, inclusive.

20.3   Dimension forms.   Two basic methods are used to give a distance on the drawing, a *dimension*, Fig. 20.1, or a *note*, Fig. 20.2.   A dimension is used to give the distance between two points, lines, or planes or some combination of points, lines, and planes.   The numerical value gives the actual distance, the dimension line indicates the direction in which the value applies, and the arrowheads indicate the points between which the value applies.   Extension lines refer the dimension to the view when the dimen-

sion is placed outside the view. A note provides a means of giving explanatory information along with a size. The leader and arrowhead refer the
word statement of the note to the proper place on the drawing. Notes
applying to the object as a whole are given without a leader in some convenient place on the drawing.

The lines and symbols used in dimensioning are: dimension lines, arrowheads, extension lines, leaders, numerical values, notes, finish marks, etc.

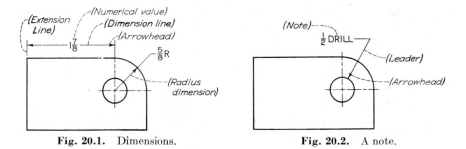

Fig. 20.1.   Dimensions.   Fig. 20.2.   A note.

20.4 Line weights. Dimension lines, extension lines, and leaders are
made with fine full lines the same width as the center lines, so as to contrast with the heavier outlines of the views. Note the line widths given
in the alphabet of lines, page 58.

20.5 Arrowheads are carefully drawn freehand, making the sides either
in one stroke, or in two strokes toward the point, as shown in enlarged form
in Fig. 20.3. The general preference is for the solid head, Fig. 20.4. The

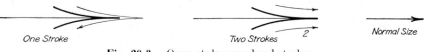

Fig. 20.3.   Open-style arrowhead strokes.

solid head is usually made thinner and slightly longer than the open head
and has practically no curvature to the sides. It is made in one stroke and
then filled, if necessary, without lifting the pen or pencil; a rather blunt
pencil or pen is required with this style head. The bases of arrowheads

Fig. 20.4.   Solid-style arrowhead strokes.

should not be made wider than one-third the length. All arrowheads on
the same drawing should be the same type, either open or solid, and the
same size, except in restricted spaces. Arrowhead lengths will vary somewhat depending upon the drawing size. One-eighth inch is a good general
length for small drawings and $\frac{3}{16}$ in. for larger drawings.

Poor arrowheads ruin the appearance of an otherwise carefully made drawing. Avoid the incorrect shapes and placements shown in Fig. 20.5.

Fig. 20.5. Incorrect arrowheads.

20.6 **Extension lines** extend from the view to a dimension placed outside the view. They should not touch the outline of the view, but should start about $\frac{1}{16}$ in. from it and extend about $\frac{1}{8}$ in. beyond the last dimension line, Fig. 20.6*A*. This example is printed approximately one-half size.

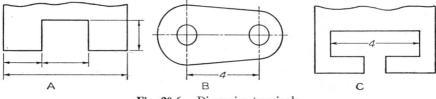

Fig. 20.6. Dimension terminals.

Dimensions are preferably kept outside the views, but occasionally may be placed to better advantage inside. Thus dimensions may terminate at *center lines* or visible *outlines of the view, B* and *C*, Fig. 20.6. Where a measurement between centers is to be shown as at *B*, the center lines are continued to serve as extension lines, extending about $\frac{1}{8}$ in. beyond the last dimension line. Usually the outline of the view becomes the terminal for arrowheads, as at *C*, when a dimension must be placed inside the view. This might occur because of limited space, when extension lines in crossing parts of the view would cause confusion, or when very long extension lines would make the dimension difficult to read.

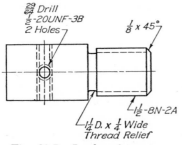

Fig. 20.7. Leaders for notes.

20.7 **Leaders** are *straight* (not curved) lines leading from a dimension value or an explanatory note to the feature on the drawing to which the note applies, Fig. 20.7. An arrowhead is used on the pointing end of the leader, but never on the note end. The note end of the leader should terminate with a short horizontal bar at the mid-height of the lettering, and should run either to the beginning or the end of the note, never to the middle.

Leaders should be drawn at an angle to contrast with the principal lines of the drawing which are mainly horizontal and vertical. Thus leaders are usually drawn at 30°, 45°, or 60° to the horizontal; 60° looks best. When several leaders are used, the appearance of the drawing is improved if the leaders can be kept parallel.

20.8 Figures for dimension values must be carefully lettered in either vertical or inclined style.   In an effort for neatness the beginner often gets them too small.   One-eighth inch for small drawings and $\frac{5}{32}$ in. for larger drawings are good general heights.

The general practice is to leave a space in the dimension line for the dimension value, Fig. 20.8.   It is universal in structural practice and common in architectural practice to place the values above a continuous dimension line, Fig. 20.8.

General Practice   Structural Practice

Fig. 20.8.   Placing dimension values.

20.9 Common fractions should be made with the fraction bar parallel to the guide lines of the figure, and with the numerator and denominator each somewhat smaller than the height of the whole number, so that the total fraction height is twice that of the integer, Fig. 20.9.   Avoid the incorrect forms shown.   The figures should not touch the fraction bar.

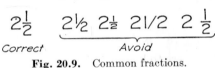

Correct   Avoid

Fig. 20.9.   Common fractions.

20.10 Feet and inches are indicated thus: 9'-6".   When there are no inches, it should be so indicated, as 9'-0", 9'-0½".   When dimensions are all in inches, the inch mark is preferably omitted from all the dimensions and notes, unless there is some possibility of misunderstanding; thus "1 bore" is clearer as, and should be, "1" bore."

In some machine industries all dimensions are given in inches.   In others, where feet and inches are used, the ASA recommends that dimensions up to and including 72 in. be given in inches, and greater lengths in feet and inches.

In structural drawing, length dimensions should be given in feet and inches.   Plate widths, beam sizes, etc., are given in inches.   Inch marks are omitted, even though the dimension is in feet and inches, Fig. 20.8.

In the United States if no foot or inch marks appear on the drawing, the dimension values indicate inches unless a different unit of measurement is indicated by general note.   Drawings made in foreign countries employing the metric system are commonly dimensioned in millimeters.

20.11 The reading direction of figures is arranged according to either the aligned system or the unidirectional system.

The aligned system is the older of the two methods.   The figures are oriented to be readable from a position *perpendicular* to the dimension line; thus the guide lines for the figures will be parallel to the dimension line, and the fraction bar in line with the dimension line, Fig. 20.10.   The figures should be arranged so as to be readable from the *bottom* or *right side* of the drawing.   Avoid running dimensions in the directions included in the shaded area; if this is unavoidable, they should read downward with the line.

The unidirectional system originated in the automotive and aircraft industries. Sometimes called the "horizontal system," all figures are oriented to read from the bottom of the drawing. Thus the guide lines and fraction bars are horizontal regardless of the direction of the dimension, Fig. 20.11. The "avoid" zone of Fig. 20.10 has no significance with this system.

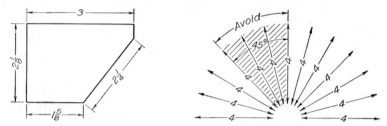

Fig. 20.10.   Reading direction, aligned system.

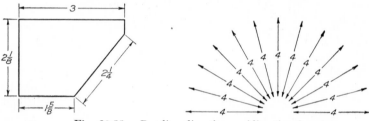

Fig. 20.11.   Reading direction, unidirectional system.

Notes must be lettered horizontally and read from the bottom of the drawing in either system.

20.12   Finish marks are used to indicate that certain surfaces of metal parts are to be machined, and that allowance must therefore be provided for finish. Finish marks need not be used for parts made by machining from rolled stock, as the surfaces are necessarily machined. Neither are they necessary on drilled, reamed, or counterbored holes nor on similar machined features when the machining operation is specified by note.

Fig. 20.12.   ASA finish mark.

The standard mark recommended by the ASA is a 60° **V** with its point touching the line representing the edge view of the surface to be machined. The **V** is placed on the "air side" of the surface. Figure 20.12 shows the normal size of the **V** and its position for lines in various directions as applied on a drawing.

The symbol which has been in use for many years is an italic *f* with its cross mark intersecting the line representing the surface to be finished, Fig. 20.13.

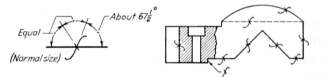

Fig. 20.13. "Italic *f*" finish mark.

Finish marks should be placed on all views in which the surface to be machined appears as a line, including dotted lines. If the part is to be machined on all surfaces, the note "Finish all over," or "FAO," is used, and the marks on the views are omitted.

In addition to the finish mark indicating a machined surface, it may be necessary in some cases to indicate the degree of smoothness of the surface. The ASA gives a set of symbols to indicate various conditions of *surface quality.* These symbols are explained and illustrated in the following chapter, paragraph 21.30.

20.13 Systems of writing dimension values. Dimension values may be given either as common fractions, $\frac{1}{4}$, $\frac{3}{8}$, etc., or as decimal fractions, 0.26, 0.375, etc.; and from these, three systems are evolved.

The common-fraction system, used in general drawing practice including architectural and structural work, has all dimension values written as units and common fractions as $3\frac{1}{2}$, $1\frac{1}{4}$, $\frac{3}{8}$, $\frac{1}{16}$, $\frac{3}{32}$, $\frac{1}{64}$. Values thus written can be laid out with a steel tape or scale graduated in sixty-fourths of an inch.

The common-fraction, decimal-fraction system is used principally in machine drawing whenever the degree of precision calls for fractions of an inch smaller than those on the ordinary steel scale. To continue the use of common fractions below $\frac{1}{64}$, such as $\frac{1}{128}$ or $\frac{1}{256}$, is considered impractical. The method followed is to give values (1) in units and common fractions for distances not requiring an accuracy closer than $\frac{1}{64}$ in.; and (2) in units and decimal fractions, as 2.375, 1.250, 0.1875 etc., for distances requiring greater precision. The decimal fractions are given to as many decimal places as the degree of precision requires.

The complete decimal system uses decimal fractions exclusively for all dimension values. This system has the advantages of the metric system, but uses the inch as its basis, thus making it possible to use present measuring equipment.

The ASA complete decimal system[1] uses a two-place decimal for all values where common fractions would ordinarily be used. The digits after the decimal point are preferably written to even fiftieths, .02, .10, .36, etc., so that when halved as for radii, etc., two-place decimals will result. Writ-

[1] Z14.1, 1946.

ing the values in even fiftieths allows the use of scales divided in fiftieths, Fig. 20.14, which are much easier to read than scales divided in hundredths.

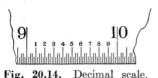

Fig. 20.14. Decimal scale.

Dimension values for distances requiring greater precision than that expressed by the two-place decimal are written to three, four, or more decimal places as the degree of precision may require.

Figure 20.15 is a detail drawing dimensioned according to the ASA decimal system. The advantage of this system in calculating, adding, and checking, and in doing away with all conversion tables, as well as in lessening chances for error, is apparent.

Designers and draftsmen working in the complete decimal system will find it necessary to think in terms of tenths and hundredths of inches instead of thinking in common fractions. New designs must be made in decimal

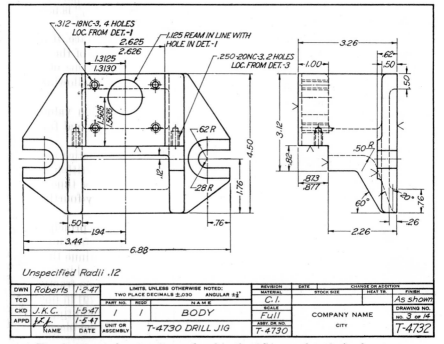

Fig. 20.15. A drawing dimensioned in the ASA complete decimal system.

sizes without reference to common fractional sizes. However, until standard-stock materials, tools, and commercial parts are available in decimal sizes, some dimensions will have to be given as the decimal equivalent of a common fraction. Thus, for example, a standard ⅜-16UNC-2A thread would be given as 0.375-16UNC-2A.

Decimal equivalents of some common fractions come out a greater number of decimal places (significant digits) than is necessary or desirable for use as a dimension value, and in such cases, the decimal should be adjusted or

"rounded off" to a lesser number of decimal places. The following procedure from the American Standards[1] is recommended.

When the figure beyond the last figure to be retained is less than 5, the last figure
retained should not be changed. *Example:* 3.46325, if cut off to three places should be
3.463.

When the figures beyond the last place to be retained amount to more than 5, the last
figure retained should be increased by 1. *Example:* 8.37652, if cut off to three places, •
should be 8.377.

When the figure beyond the last place to be retained is exactly 5 with only zeros
following, the preceding number, if even, should be unchanged; if odd, it should be
increased by 1. *Example:* 4.365 becomes 4.36 when cut off to two places. Also 4.355
becomes 4.36 when cut off to two places.

20.14 Theory of dimensioning. Any object can be "broken down"
into a combination of basic geometrical shapes, principally prisms and cylinders. Occasionally, however, there will be parts of pyramids and cones,
now and then a double-curved surface, and very rarely, except for surfaces
of screw threads, a warped surface. Any of the basic shapes may be either
positive or negative, taken in the sense that a hole is a negative cylinder.
Figure 7.24 illustrates a machine part broken down into its fundamental
shapes.

If the *size* of each of these elemental shapes is dimensioned and the relative location of each is given, measuring from center-to-center, from base
lines, or from the surfaces of each other, the dimensioning of any piece can
be done systematically. Dimensions may thus be classified as *size dimensions* and *location dimensions.*

20.15 Size dimensions. As every solid has three dimensions, each of
the geometrical shapes making up the object must have its height, width,
and depth indicated in the dimensioning.

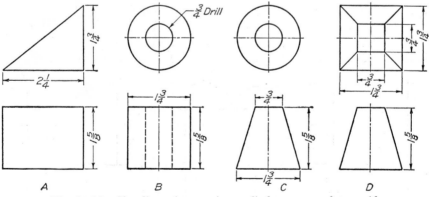

Fig. 20.16. Size dimensions—prism, cylinder, cone, and pyramid.

The *prism,* often in plinth or flat form, is the most common shape and
requires three dimensions for square, rectangular, or triangular, Fig. 20.16*A*.

[1] Z25.1, 1940.

For regular hexagonal or octagonal types, usually only two dimensions are given, either the distance "across corners" and the length or "across flats" and the length.

The *cylinder,* found on nearly all mechanical pieces as a shaft or a boss or a hole, is the second most common shape. A cylinder obviously requires only two dimensions, diameter and length, Fig. 20.16*B*. Partial cylinders, such as fillets and rounds, are dimensioned by radius instead of diameter. A good general rule is to dimension complete circles with a diameter, and circle arcs (partial circles) with a radius.

Right cones may be dimensioned with the altitude and the diameter of the base. They usually occur as frustums, however, and require the diameters of the ends and the length, Fig. 20.16*C*. Sometimes it is desirable to dimension cone frustums as *tapers,* or with an angular dimension, as described in paragraph 20.29.

Right pyramids are dimensioned by giving the dimensions of the base and the altitude. These also are often frustums, requiring dimensions of both bases, Fig. 20.16*D*.

Oblique cones and pyramids are dimensioned in the same way as right cones and pyramids, but with an additional dimension parallel to the base to give the offset of the vertex.

Spheres are dimensioned by giving the diameter, other surfaces of revolution by dimensioning the generating curve.

Warped surfaces are dimensioned according to their method of generation, and as their representation requires numerous sections, each of these must be fully dimensioned by ordinate and abscissa dimensions.

20.16 Location dimensions. After the basic geometric shapes have been dimensioned for size, the location of each relative to the others must be given. *Location must be established in height, width, and depth directions.* Rectangular shapes are located with reference to their faces, cylindrical and conical shapes to their center lines and their ends.

A basic shape will often coincide or align with another on one or more of its faces. In such cases, the alignment serves partially to locate the parts

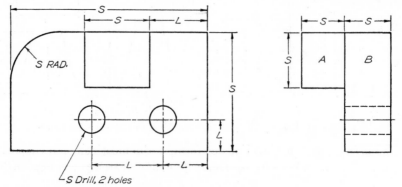

Fig. 20.17. Size and location dimensions.

and eliminates the need of a location dimension in a direction perpendicular to the line of coincidence. Thus in Fig. 20.17, prism A requires only one dimension for complete location with respect to prism B, as two surfaces are in alignment and two in contact.

Coincident center lines often eliminate the need of location dimensions. In the cylinder, Fig. 20.16B, the center lines of the hole and cylinder coincide and no location dimensions are needed. The two holes of Fig. 20.17 are on the same center line, and the dimension perpendicular to the coincident center line locates both holes in that direction.

20.17 The selection of dimensions. The dimensions arrived at by reducing the part to its basic geometry will, in general, fulfill the requirements of practical dimensioning. These dimensions, however, sometimes require alteration to ensure satisfactory functioning of the part and also to give the information in the best way from the standpoint of production. The draftsman must therefore *correlate the dimensions on drawings of mating parts to ensure satisfactory functioning and, at the same time, select dimensions convenient for the workmen to use.*

Here our study of drawing as a language must be supplemented by a knowledge of shop methods. To be successful, the machine draftsman must have an intimate knowledge of patternmaking, foundry practice, forging, and machine-shop practice; as well as, in some cases, sheetmetal working, metal and plastic die casting, welding, and structural-steel fabrication.

The beginning student without this knowledge should not depend upon his instructor alone, but as recommended in the previous chapter, should set about to inform himself by observing work going through the shops and reading books and periodicals on methods used in modern production work.

The selection of size dimensions arrived at by "shape breakdown" will usually meet the requirements of the shop since the basic shapes result from the fundamental shop operations. However, size dimensions are often preferred in note form instead of a regular dimension whenever a shop process is involved, such as drilling, reaming, counterboring, punching, etc.

The selection of location dimensions ordinarily requires more consideration than for size dimensions because there are, usually, several ways in which a location might be given. In general, location dimensions will be given between finished surfaces, center lines, or a combination thereof, Fig. 20.20. Remember that rough castings or forgings will vary in size, and do not locate machined surfaces from unfinished surfaces. The only exception is when an initial or *starting dimension* is given to locate the first surface to be machined from which, in turn, the other machined surfaces are located. *Coinciding center lines of unfinished and finished surfaces often take the place of a starting dimension.*

The location of a point or center by offset dimensions from two center lines or surfaces, Fig. 20.18, is preferred over angular dimensions, Fig. 20.19, unless the angular dimension is more practical from the standpoint of construction.

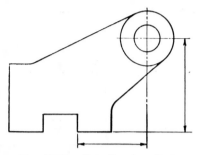

Fig. 20.18. Location by offsets.

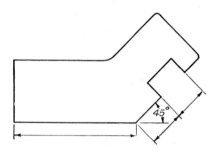

Fig. 20.19. Location by angle.

20.18 The correlation of dimensions. Mating parts must have their dimensions correlated so that the two parts will fit and function as intended. Figure 20.20 will illustrate this principle. Note that the tongue of the bracket is to fit the groove in the body and also note that the drilled holes in both pieces must align. Study the dimensioning of both pieces and observe that the location dimensions are correlated so that the intended alignment and fitting of the parts will be accomplished.

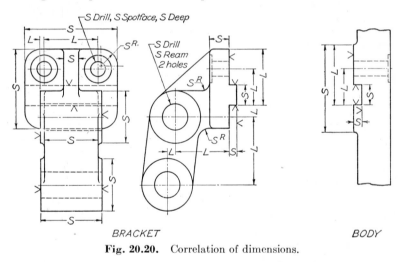

Fig. 20.20. Correlation of dimensions.

Dimensions must not only be correlated with the dimensions of the mating part, but the accuracy to which these distances are produced must meet certain requirements or the parts still may not fit and function properly. Distances between the surfaces or center lines of finished features of an object must usually be more accurately made than unfinished features. In Fig. 20.21, note that the location dimensions between center lines or surfaces of finished features are given as three-place decimals, as dimension A. Location dimensions for unfinished features are given as common fractions, as dimension B. The decimal dimensions call for greater precision in manufacture than do the common fractions. Dimension B is in this case used by the patternmaker to locate cylinder C from the right end of the piece.   The machinist will first locate the finished hole in this cylinder, making it concentric with the cylinder; then all other machined surfaces are located from this hole, as, for example, the spline location by dimension A.   The four spot-faced holes are located with reference to each other with fractional dimensions, since the holes are oversize for the fastenings used, allowing enough shifting of the fastenings in the holes so that great accuracy in location is not necessary.   The mating part, with its holes to receive the screws, would be similarly dimensioned.

Study Fig. 20.21 and note the classification, size, or location, of each dimension.

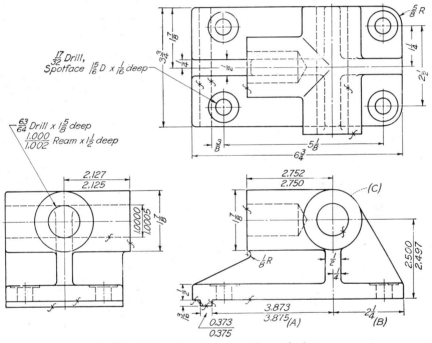

Fig. 20.21.   An example of dimensioning.

20.19   Superfluous dimensions.   *Duplicate* or *unnecessary* dimensions are to be avoided because of the confusion and delay they may cause.   When a drawing is changed or revised, a duplicate dimension may not be noticed and changed along with its counterpart; hence the distance will have two different values, one incorrect.   An unnecessary dimension is any dimension, other than a duplicate, that is not essential in making the piece.   Because of the allowable variation permitted the manufacturer on each dimension, difficulties will be encountered if unnecessary dimensions occur when parts are to be interchangeable.   Actually, under these circumstances, it should only be possible to establish a point on the object in any given direction with but one dimension. Unnecessary dimensions will always occur when all the individual dimensions are given, in addition to the over-all dimension, Fig. 20.22. One dimension of the series must be omitted if the over-all is used, thus allowing only one possible location from each dimension, Fig. 20.23. Occasionally it is desirable, for reference or checking purposes, to

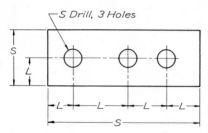

Fig. 20.22. One dimension unnecessary.

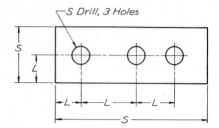

Fig. 20.23. Unnecessary dimension omitted.

give all dimensions in a series and also give the over-all dimension. In such cases, one dimension not to be used in manufacturing is marked with the abbreviation "Ref.," as indicated in Fig. 20.24.

In architectural and structural work, where the interchangeability of parts usually has no consideration, unnecessary dimensions cause no difficulty and all dimensions are given as in Fig. 20.22.

Although as pointed out, it is important not to "overdimension" a part, it is equally important that sufficient dimensions be given to locate every point, line, or surface of the object. The workman should never be required to scale a dimension from the drawing. All necessary distances must be given.

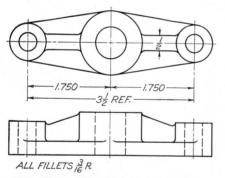

Fig. 20.24. One reference dimension.

However, dimensions for similar features, such as the thickness of several ribs, obviously of the same size, need not be repeated, Fig. 20.24. Also, such details as the size of fillets and rounds can be provided for with a general note. If the draftsman will mentally go through the manufacture or even the drawing of the part, checking each dimension as he needs it, he will easily discover any superfluous or omitted dimensions.

20.20 The placement of dimensions. After the distances have been selected as outlined in paragraph 20.2, it is then possible to decide (1) the *view* on which the distance will be indicated, (2) the particular *place* on that view, and (3) the *form* of the dimension itself. Numerous principles, some with the force of a rule, can be given, but in any case the important consideration is *clarity*.

20.21   Views—the contour principle.   One of the views of an object will usually describe the shape of some detailed feature better than will the other view or views, and the feature is then said to be "characteristic" in that particular view.   In reading a drawing, it is natural to look for the dimensions of a given feature wherever that feature appears most characteristic, and it certainly follows that an advantage in clarity and in ease of reading will be had by following this principle in dimensioning the drawing.   In Fig. 20.25, the rounded corner, the drilled hole, and the lower notched corner are all characteristic in, and dimensioned on, the front view.   The projecting shape on the front of the object is more characteristic in the top view and is dimensioned there.

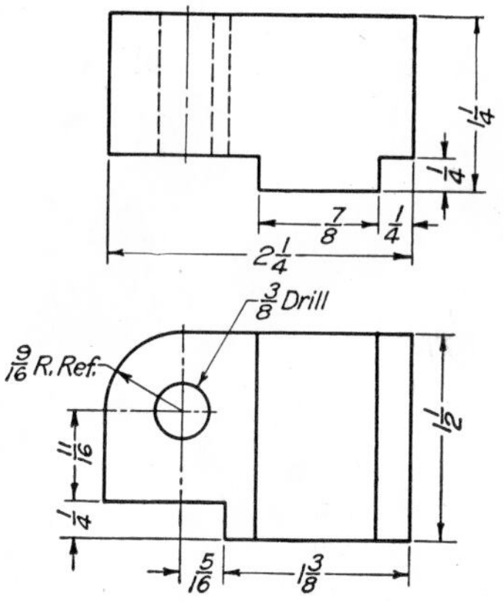

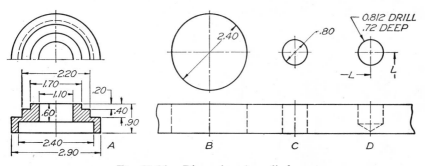

Fig. 20.25.   The contour principle applied.

Dimensions for prisms should be placed so that two of the three dimensions are on the view showing the contour shape and the third on one of the other views, Figs. 20.16 and 20.25.

Dimensions for cylinders, the diameter and length, are usually best placed on the noncircular view, Fig. 20.26A.   This practice keeps the dimensions

Fig. 20.26.   Dimensions for cylinders.

on one view, a convenience for the workman.   Occasionally a cylindrical hole may be dimensioned with the diameter at an angle on the circular view, as indicated at *B*.   This practice should never be used unless there is a clear space for the dimension value.   In some cases, however, the value can be carried outside the view as in *C*.   When a round hole is specified by a note, as at *D*, the leader should point to the circular view if possible.   The note has an advantage in that the diameter, operation, and depth may all be given together.   Giving the diameter on the circular view as at *B*, *C*, or *D* may make for ease of reading, as the location dimensions will likely be given there also, as indicated at *D*.   When it is not obvious from the drawing, a dimension may be indicated as a diameter by following the value with the letter *D*, as shown in Fig. 20.27.

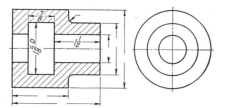

Fig. 20.27. Dimensions inside the view.

PRINCIPLES FOR THE PLACEMENT OF DIMENSIONS

1. Dimensions outside the view are preferred, unless added clearness, simplicity, and ease of reading will result from placing some of them inside. For appearance's sake they should be kept off the cut surfaces of sections. When it is necessary that they be placed there, the section lining is omitted around the numbers, Fig. 20.27.

2. Dimensions between the views are preferred unless there is some reason for placing them elsewhere, as there was in Fig. 20.25, where the dimension for the lower notched corner and the location of the hole must come at the bottom of the front view.

3. Dimensions should be applied to one view only; that is, with dimensions between views, the extension lines should be drawn from one view, not from both views, Fig. 20.28.

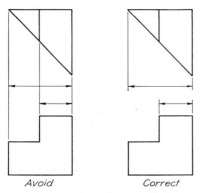

Avoid　　　　*Correct*

Fig. 20.28. Dimensions applied to one view only.

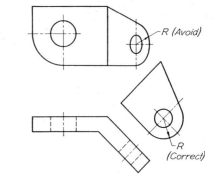

Fig. 20.29. Dimensioned distance normal.

4. Dimensions should be placed on the view that shows the distance in its true length (not foreshortened), Fig. 20.29.

5. Dimension lines should be spaced, in general, ½ in. away from the outlines of the view. This applies to a single dimension or the first dimension of several in a series.

6. Parallel dimension lines should be spaced uniformly with at least ⅜ in. between lines.

7. Values should be midway between the arrowheads, except when a center line interferes, Fig. 20.30, or when the values of several parallel dimensions are staggered, Fig. 20.31.

8. Continuous or staggered dimension lines may be used, depending upon convenience and readability. Continuous dimension lines are preferred where possible, Figs. 20.32 and 20.33.

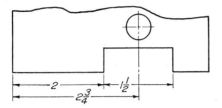

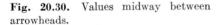

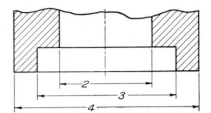

Fig. 20.30. Values midway between arrowheads.

Fig. 20.31. "Staggered" values.

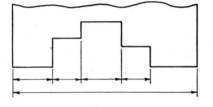

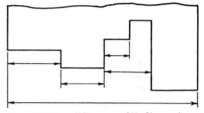

Fig. 20.32. Continuous dimensions.

Fig. 20.33. "Staggered" dimensions.

9. Always place the longer dimension outside the shorter ones to avoid crossing dimension lines with the extension lines of other dimensions. Thus, an over-all dimension (maximum size of piece in a given direction) will be outside of all other dimensions.

10. Dimensions should never be crowded. If the space is small, follow one of the methods of paragraph 20.22, Dimensioning in Limited Space.

11. Center lines are used to indicate the symmetry of shapes and as such frequently eliminate the need of a location dimension. They should be considered as part of the dimensioning and drawn in finished form at the time of dimensioning. They should extend about ⅛ in. beyond the shape for which they indicate symmetry unless they are carried farther to serve as extension lines. Center lines should not be continued between views.

12. All notes must read horizontally (from the bottom of the drawing).

Practices to Avoid

1. Never use a center line, a line of a view, or an extension line as a dimension line.

2. Never place a dimension line on a center line or place a dimension line where a center line should properly be.

3. Never allow a line of any kind to pass through a dimension figure.

4. Avoid the crossing of two dimension lines or the crossing of an extension line and a dimension line.

5. Avoid dimensioning to dotted lines if possible.

20.22 Dimensioning in limited space. Dimensions should never be crowded into a space too small to contain them. One of the methods of Fig. 20.34 may be used to avoid the difficulty. Sometimes a note may be appropriate. If the space is very small and crowded, an enlarged removed section or part view may be used, Fig. 20.35.

20.23 Arcs and curves. Arcs should be dimensioned by giving the radius on the view that shows the true shape of the curve. The dimension line for a radius should always be drawn as a radial line at an angle, Fig.

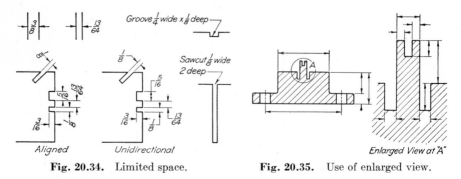

Aligned   Unidirectional   Enlarged View at 'A'

Fig. 20.34. Limited space.   **Fig. 20.35.** Use of enlarged view.

20.36, never horizontal or vertical, and only one arrowhead is used. There is no arrowhead at the arc's center. The numerical value should be followed by the letter R. Depending upon the size of the radius and the available space for the value, the dimension line and value are either both inside, or the line inside and the value outside, or, for small arcs, both outside as shown in the illustration.

When the center of an arc lies outside the limits of the drawing, the center is moved closer along a center line of the arc and the dimension line is jogged

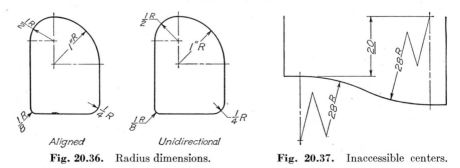

Aligned   Unidirectional

Fig. 20.36. Radius dimensions.   **Fig. 20.37.** Inaccessible centers.

to meet the new center, Fig. 20.37. The portion of the dimension line adjacent to the arc is a radial line of the true center.

A curved line made up of circle arcs is dimensioned by radii with the centers located, as in Fig. 20.38. Irregular curves are usually dimensioned by offsets as in Fig. 20.39, or by ordinate and abscissa dimensions.

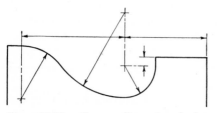

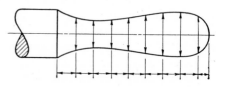

Fig. 20.38. Curve dimensioned by radii.   **Fig. 20.39.** Curve dimensioned by offsets.

20.24   Angles.   The dimension line for an angle is a circle arc with its center at the intersection of the sides of the angle, Fig. 20.40.   The value is placed to read horizontally with the exception that, in the aligned system, large arcs only have the value aligned with the dimension arc.   Angular values should be written in the form 35°7′ with no dash between the degrees and minutes.

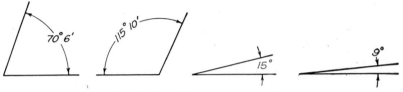

Fig. 20.40.   Dimensions for angles.

20.25   Notes.   Notes are word statements giving information that cannot be given by the views and dimensions.   They may be classified as either *general* or *specific*.   A general note applies to the entire part, and a specific note applies to an individual feature.   Occasionally a note will save making an additional view, or even, for example, with a note used to indicate right- and left-hand parts, save making an entire drawing.

Do not be afraid to put notes on drawings.   Supplement the graphic language by the English language whenever added information can be conveyed, but be careful to word it so clearly that the meaning cannot possibly be misunderstood.

General notes do not require the use of a leader and should be grouped together above the title block.   Examples are, "Finish all over," "Fillets ¼R, rounds ⅛R, unless otherwise specified," "All draft angles 7°," "Remove burs," etc.

Much of the information provided in the title strip of a machine drawing is a grouping of general notes.   Stock size, material, heat-treatment, etc., are general notes in the title of the drawing of Fig. 21.1.

Specific notes almost always require a leader and, therefore, should be placed fairly close to the feature to which they apply.   Most common are notes giving an operation with a size as "½ Drill, 4 holes."

Recommended forms for the wording of notes occurring more or less frequently are given in Fig. 20.41.

When lower-case lettering is used, capitalization of words in notes depends largely on company policy.   One common practice is to capitalize all important words.   However, for long notes as on civil or architectural drawings, the grammatical rules for capitalization usually prevail.

20.26   Dimensions and specifications for holes.   Drilled, reamed, bored, punched, or cored holes are usually specified by note giving the diameter, operation, and depth if required.   If there is more than one hole of the same kind, the leader needs to point to but one hole, and the number of holes

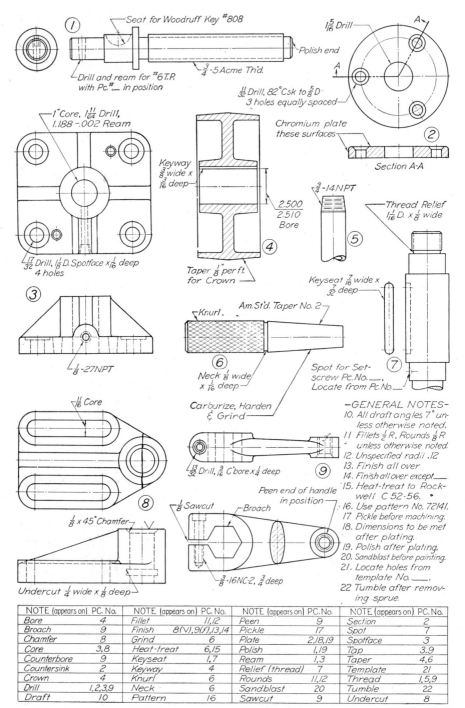

NOTE (appears on)	PC. No.	NOTE (appears on)	PC. No.	NOTE (appears on)	PC. No.	NOTE (appears on)	PC. No.
Bore	4	Fillet	11,12	Peen	9	Section	2
Broach	9	Finish	8(V),9(f),13,14	Pickle	17	Spot	7
Chamfer	8	Grind	6	Plate	2,18,19	Spotface	3
Core	3,8	Heat-treat	6,15	Polish	1,19	Tap	3,9
Counterbore	9	Keyseat	1,7	Ream	1,3	Taper	4,6
Countersink	2	Keyway	4	Relief (thread)	7	Template	21
Crown	4	Knurl	6	Rounds	11,12	Thread	1,5,9
Drill	1,2,3,9	Neck	6	Sandblast	20	Tumble	22
Draft	10	Pattern	16	Sawcut	9	Undercut	8

Fig. 20.41. Approved wording for notes on drawings.

stated in the note, Fig. 20.42. Several operations involving one hole may be grouped in a common note. Figures 20.42 to 20.45 show typical dimen-

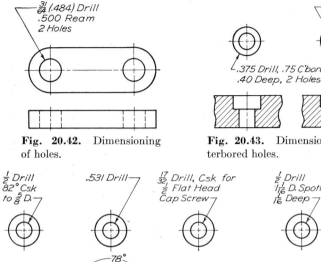

Fig. 20.42. Dimensioning of holes.

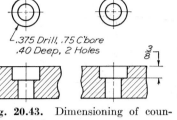

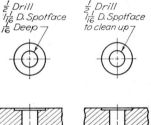

Fig. 20.43. Dimensioning of counterbored holes.

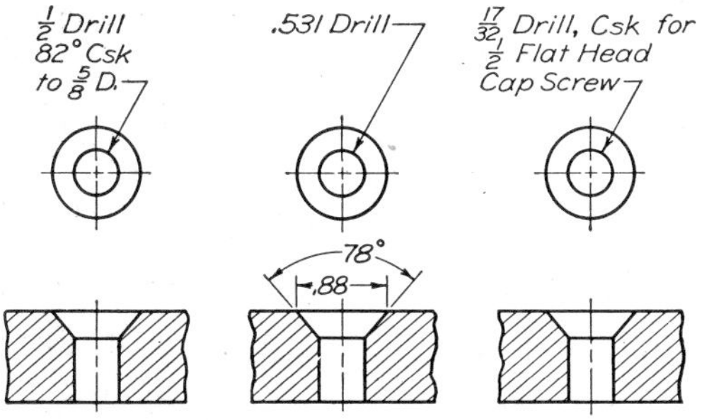

Fig. 20.44. Dimensioning of countersunk holes.

Fig. 20.45. Dimensioning of spot-faced holes.

sioning practice for drilled and reamed, counterbored, countersunk, and spot-faced holes.

The ASA specifies that standard drill sizes be given as decimal fractions, such as 0.250, 0.375, 0.750, 1.500. If the size is given as a common fraction, the decimal equivalent should be added.

The leader to a hole should point to the circular view if possible. With concentric circles, the arrowhead should touch the inner circle (usually the first operation) unless an outer circle would pass through the arrowhead. In such a case, the arrow should be drawn to touch the outer circle.

Holes made up of several diameters and involving several stages of manufacture may be dimensioned as shown in Fig. 20.46. This method of dimensioning combines notes with the regular dimensions.

Threaded holes are dimensioned and specified as described in Chap. 22.

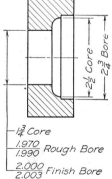

Fig. 20.46. Specifying several operations on large holes.

20.27 Location of holes. Mating parts held together by bolts, screws, rivets, etc., must have their holes for fastenings located from common datum surfaces or lines, in order to assure matching of the holes. When two or more holes are on an established center line, the holes will require location in one direction only, Fig. 20.47. If the holes are not on a common center line, they will require location in two directions, as in Fig. 20.48. The method

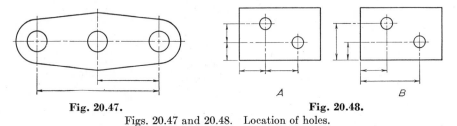

Fig. 20.47.   Fig. 20.48.

Figs. 20.47 and 20.48.   Location of holes.

at *B*, where the locations are referred to a common base line, is preferred for precision work.

Hole circles are circular center lines often called "bolt circles" on which the centers of a number of holes are located.

One practice is to give the diameter of the hole circle and a note specifying the size of the holes, the number required, and the spacing, as in Fig. 20.49*A*. If one or more holes are not in the regular equally spaced position, their location may be given by an offset dimension, as shown at *B*. An angular

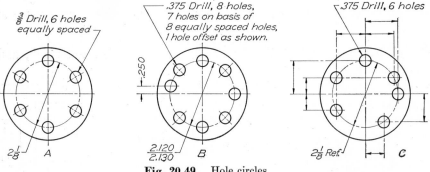

Fig. 20.49.   Hole circles.

dimension is sometimes used for this purpose but, in general, should be avoided in more precise work.

The coordinate method for locating holes, Fig. 20.49*C*, is preferred in precision work. The hole circle is often drawn and its diameter given for reference purposes, as indicated on the figure. The diameter of a hole circle is invariably given on the circular view.

20.28   Chamfers. Chamfers may be dimensioned by note, as in Fig. 20.50*A*, if the angle is 45°. The linear size is understood to be the short side of the chamfer triangle in conformity with the dimensioning without a note as shown at *B*. If the chamfer angle is other than 45°, it should be dimensioned as at *C*.

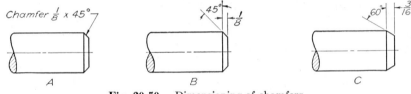

Fig. 20.50.   Dimensioning of chamfers.

20.29   Tapers.   The term "taper" as used in machine work usually means the surface of a cone frustum.   The dimensioning will depend on the method of manufacture and the accuracy required.   If a standardized taper (see Appendix, page 668) is used, the specification should be accompanied by one diameter and the length, Fig. 20.51*A*.   At *B* is illustrated the general

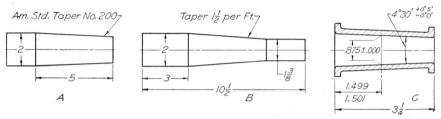

Fig. 20.51.   Dimensioning of tapers.

method of giving the diameters of both ends and the taper per foot.   An alternate method is to give one diameter, the length, and the taper per foot. Taper per foot is defined as the difference in diameter in inches for 1 ft of length.   *C* illustrates the method of dimensioning for precision work where a close fit between the parts, as well as a control of entry distance, is required. Because of the inaccuracy resulting from measuring at one of the ends, a gage line is established where the diameter is to be measured.   The entry distance is controlled through the allowable variation in the location of the gage line, and the fit of the taper is controlled by the accuracy called for in the specification of the angle.

20.30   Batters, slopes, grades. *Batter* is a deviation from the vertical, such as is found on the sides of retaining walls, piers, etc., and *slope* is a deviation from the horizontal. Both are expressed as a ratio with

Fig. 20.52.   Dimensioning of batters and slopes.

one factor equal to unity, as illustrated in Fig. 20.52.   *Grade* is identical to slope but is expressed in percentage, the inclination in feet per hundred feet. In structural work, angular measurements are shown by giving the ratio of run to rise with the larger side 12 in., Fig. 30.2.

20.31   Shapes with rounded ends should be dimensioned according to their method of manufacture.   Figure 20.53 shows several similar contours and the typical dimensioning for each.   The link *A*, to be cut from thin

material, has the radius of the ends and the center distance given as it would
be laid out.   At B is shown a cast pad dimensioned similar to A, with
dimensions most usable for the patternmaker.   The drawing at C shows a
slot machined from solid stock with an end-milling cutter.   The dimensions
give the diameter of the cutter and the travel of the milling-machine table.
The slot at D is similar to C but is dimensioned for quantity production
where, instead of the table travel, the over-all length is wanted for gaging
purposes.   Pratt and Whitney keys and key seats are dimensioned by this
method.

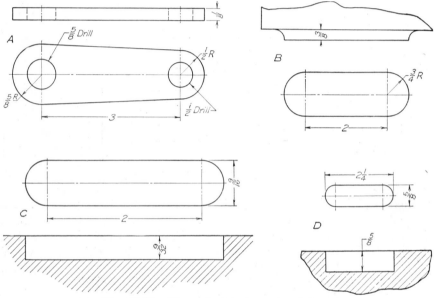

Fig. 20.53.   Dimensioning of round-end shapes.

20.32   The order of dimensioning.   A systematic order of working is a
great help in placing dimensions.   Figure 20.54 will illustrate the procedure.
At A the shape description is complete. B shows the extension lines placed
and center lines extended where necessary, thus planning for the positions
of both size and location dimensions.   Here the placement of each dimension
can be studied and alterations made if desirable or necessary.   At C the
dimension lines have been added.   Next, arrowheads and leaders for notes
are drawn as at D.   Values are then added and notes lettered as at E and F.

It is desirable to add the notes *after* the dimensions have been placed.
If the notes are placed first, they may occupy a space desired for a dimension.
Because of the freedom allowed in the use of leaders, notes may be given in
almost any available space.

20.33   Revision of dimensions.   As a project is being developed, changes
in design, engineering methods, etc., may make it necessary to change some
drawings either before or after they have been released to the shop.   If the

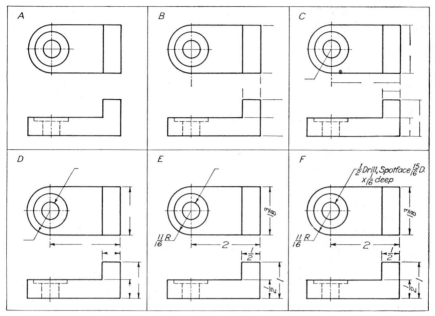

Fig. 20.54. Order of dimensioning.

change is a major one, the drawing may have to be remade, but if the change is minor, in many cases the dimension values may be altered and the shape description left unchanged. In this case the out-of-scale dimensions should be indicated by one of the methods of Fig. 20.55. Drawing changes should be listed in tabular form either in connection with the title block or in the upper right corner, with reference letters and the date, as explained in paragraph 28.19.

Fig. 20.55. Out-of-scale dimensions.

20.34 The dimensioning of auxiliary views. In placing dimensions on an auxiliary view all the principles of dimensioning will apply as for any other drawing, but with special attention paid to the contour principle, described in paragraph 20.21. An auxiliary view is made for the purpose of showing the true contour and *size* of some slanting face, and for this reason the dimensioning of the face should be placed where it is easiest to read, *which will be on the auxiliary view.* Note in Fig. 20.56 that the spacing and size of holes, as well as the size of the inclined face, are dimensioned on the auxiliary view. Note further that the angle and location dimension tying the inclined face to the rest of the object could not be placed on the auxiliary view.

20.35 The dimensioning of sectional views. Dimensions that must be placed on sectional views may, in most cases, be placed outside the view so as not to be crowded within crosshatched areas. However, sometimes a dimension *must* be placed across a crosshatched area, and when this is necessary the crosshatching is left out around the dimension figures as illustrated in Fig. 20.27. Examples showing dimensioning practice on sectional views are given in Figs. 28.36, 28.38, and 28.41.

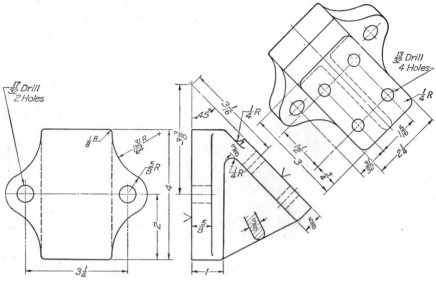

Fig. 20.56. Dimensioning on an auxiliary view.

20.36 Dimensioning a half section. In general, the half section is difficult to dimension clearly without some possibility of giving misleading, ambiguous, or crowded information. Generous use of notes and careful placement of the dimension lines, leaders, and figures will in most cases make the dimensioning clear; but, if a half section cannot be clearly dimensioned, an extra view or part view should be added on which to describe the size.

Inside diameters should be followed by the letter *D*, and the dimension line carried over the center line, as in Fig. 20.57, to prevent the possibility of reading the dimension as a radius. Sometimes the view and the dimensioning may both be clarified by showing the dotted lines on the unsectioned side. Dimensions of internal parts, if placed inside the view, will prevent the confusion between extension lines and the outline of external portions.

20.37 The dimensioning of pictorial drawings. Pictorial drawings are often more difficult to dimension than orthographic drawings because there is only one view instead of several and the dimensioning may become crowded unless the placement is carefully planned. In general, the princi-

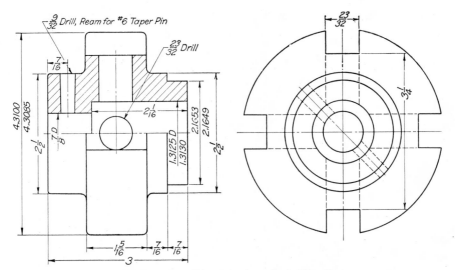

Fig. 20.57. Dimensioning of a half section.

ples of dimensioning for orthographic drawings should be followed whenever possible. The following rules should be observed.

1. Dimension and extension lines should be placed so as to lie either *in* or *perpendicular* to the face on which the dimension applies. See Figs. 9.36 and 9.37.

2. Dimension numerals should be placed so as to lie in the plane in which the dimension and extension lines lie. See Figs. 9.39 and 9.55.

3. Leaders for notes and the lettered note should be placed so as to lie in a plane either parallel or perpendicular to the face on which the note applies. See Figs. 10.29 and 10.46.

4. Finish may be indicated by the standard finish (**V**) symbol. The symbol is applied *perpendicular* to the face with its point touching a short line lying in the surface. The symbol and line should be parallel to one of the principal axes. If the symbol cannot be applied in the above manner, the finish symbol may be attached to a leader pointing to the face. See Figs. 28.20 and 28.33.

5. Lettering of dimension values and of notes should be made so that the lettering appears to lie in or parallel to one of the principal faces of the pictorial drawing. To do this the lettering must be the *pictorial representation* of *vertical* figures. Note the place-ment and lettering of the dimension values and the notes of Figs. 28.56 and 28.59.

The American Standard, Y14, also allows the use of the unidirectional system with either vertical or slant lettering for pictorial drawings. This is done principally to make possible the use of mechanical lettering devices. If this system is employed, the following should be observed:

1. Dimension values may be lettered to read from the bottom of the sheet.

2. Notes may be lettered so that they lie *in the picture plane*, to read from the bottom of the sheet. Notes should be kept off the view, if possible.

20.38 The metric system. Knowledge of the metric system will be an advantage, as it will be found on all drawings from countries where this sys-tem is standard and with increasing frequency on drawings made in the

United States. The first instance of international standardization of a mechanical device is that of ball bearings, which have been standardized in the metric system.

Scale drawings in the metric system are not made to English or American scales, but are based on divisions of 10, as full size, then 1 to 2, 1 to 2½, 1 to 5, 1 to 10, 1 to 20, 1 to 50, and 1 to 100. The unit of measurement is the millimeter (mm), and the figures are all understood to be millimeters, without any indicating marks. Figure 20.58 is an example of metric dimensioning. A table of metric equivalents is given in the Appendix.

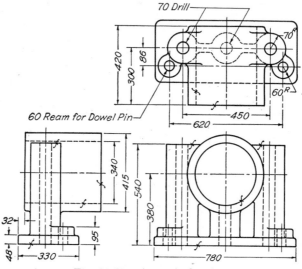

Fig. 20.58. A metric drawing.

20.39 Standard sizes, parts, and tools. In the dimensioning of any machine part, there is often the necessity of specifying some standard thickness or diameter, or the size produced by some standard tool. The American Standard, prevailing company standard, or manufacturer's standard should be consulted in order to assure giving correct information.

Wire and sheet-metal gages are given by number and are followed by the equivalent thickness or diameter in decimal form.

Bolts and screws are supplied in fractional and numbered sizes.

Keys are available in manufacturer's numbered sizes or, for square and flat keys, in fractional sizes.

Rivets, depending upon the variety, are to be had in fractional or numbered sizes.

Drills are available in numbered, lettered, fractional, and metric sizes.

Reamers, milling cutters, and other standard tools are available in a variety of standard sizes.

The Appendix gives tables of standard wire and metal gages, bolt and screw sizes, key sizes, etc. ASA or manufacturer's standards will give further information required.

20.40 Dimensioning practice by industry. As already indicated to some extent, special dimensioning practices may prevail in the several branches of engineering and in architecture. These practices are discussed in the chapters on architectural drawing, structural drawing, jigs and fixtures, welding drawings, etc., and also in the chapter on working drawings.

PROBLEMS

The problems following are given as studies in dimensioning in which to apply the principles of this chapter. Attention should be given to the methods of manufacture as described in Chap. 19. A function for the part should be assumed in order to fix the location of finished surfaces and to limit the possibilities in the selection of dimensions.

Group I. Dimensioned drawings from pictorial views

The problems presented in pictorial form in Chaps. 9 to 13 may be used as dimensioning problems, either dimensioning one already drawn as an exercise in shape description, or, for variety, one not previously made. Because of the difference in method of representation, the dimensions on a pictorial drawing and those on an orthographic drawing of the same object will not necessarily correspond; therefore, pay no attention to the placement of dimensions on the pictorial drawings except for obtaining sizes needed. A selection of 12 problems, graded in order of difficulty, is given below.

1. Fig. 9.16. Beam support. No finished surfaces.
2. Fig. 9.20. Slotted wedge. Slot and base finished.
3. Fig. 9.23. Corner stop. Slot at top, cut corner, and base finished.
4. Fig. 9.26. Guide base. Vertical slot, boss on front, and base finished.
5. Fig. 9.36. Shifter fork. Holes and fork surfaces finished.
6. Fig. 9.36. Shifter fork. All contact surfaces finished.
7. Fig. 9.46. Shaft guide. L-shaped pad and end of hub finished.
8. Fig. 10.33. Jig angle. Finished all over.
9. Fig. 10.39. Angle shaft base. Base and slanting surface finished.
10. Fig. 10.38. Radial swing block. All contact surfaces finished.
11. Fig. 11.17. Transverse connection. Base pads finished.
12. Fig. 11.18. Chamfer tool base. Contact surfaces finished.

Group II. Dimensioned drawings from models

An excellent exercise in dimensioning is to make a detail drawing from a pattern, casting, or forging, or from a model made for the purpose. Old or obsolete patterns can often be obtained from companies manufacturing a variety of small parts, and "throwout" castings or forgings are occasionally available. In taking measurements from a pattern, a shrink rule should always be used, and allowance must be made for finished surfaces.

Group III. Pieces to be drawn and dimensioned

The illustrations are printed to scale, as indicated in each problem. Transfer distances with dividers or by scaling, and draw the objects to a convenient scale on a paper size to suit. For proper placement of dimensions, more space should be provided between views than is shown in the illustrations.

Use the aligned or horizontal dimensioning systems as desired. It is suggested that some problems be dimensioned in the complete decimal system.

13. Fig. 20.59.   Stud shaft, shown half size.   Machined from steel bar stock.

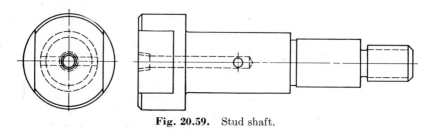

Fig. 20.59.   Stud shaft.

14. Fig. 20.60.   Shaft bracket, shown half size.   Malleable iron.   Hole in base is drilled and counterbored for a socket-head cap screw.   Base slot and front surface of hub are finished.   Hole in hub is bored and reamed.   The function of this part is to support a shaft at a fixed distance from a machine bed, as indicated by the small pictorial view.

15. Fig. 20.61.   Idler bracket, shown half size.   Cast iron.   Hole is bored and reamed.   Slot is milled.

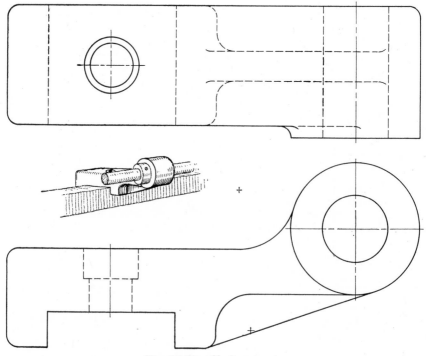

Fig. 20.60.   Shaft support.

16. Fig. 20.61. See Prob. 15. Draw and dimension the righthand part.

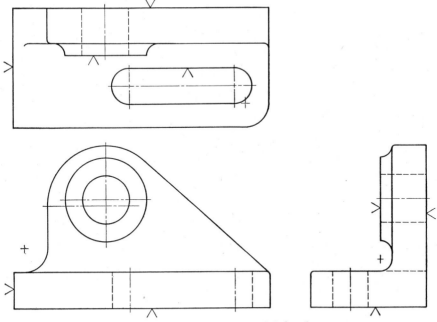

Fig. 20.61. Idler bracket, left hand.

17. Fig. 20.62. Filter flange, shown half size. Cast aluminum. The small holes are drilled. Add spot faces.

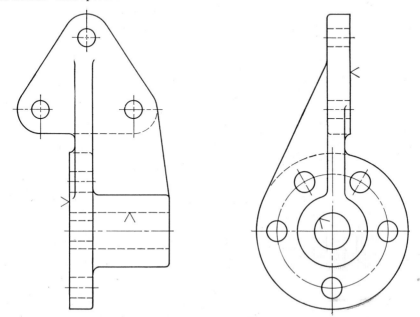

Fig. 20.62. Filter flange.

TEXT-FILMS

The following McGraw-Hill Text-Films have been correlated directly with Chaps. 20 and 21:

Dimensioning Techniques (silent filmstrip).

Stresses techniques, choice, and placement in standard dimensioning practice; illustrates and explains the various dimensioning symbols; demonstrates proper techniques of applying these symbols to various drawings.

Selection of Dimensions (20-min. sound motion picture).

Introduces the principles that govern the choice of dimensions; shows that these principles are based on (*a*) the functional characteristics of the object and (*b*) the manufacturing methods used in making the object.

21

Precision and Limit Dimensioning

21.1 Modern production methods are based on the principle that the engineering department is responsible for the correctness and completeness of the drawings and that manufacturing then proceeds in the various shops to produce exactly what is called for by the drawings. This procedure clearly defines the responsibility of the designing and manufacturing groups, minimizes confusion in the drafting room and in the shop, ensures the interchangeability of parts, and guarantees, in so far as is possible, proper functioning of a completed machine. Thus working drawings must be clearly and completely dimensioned from the standpoint of the *functioning of the part*, the *method of production*, and the *manufacturing process to be used* so that nothing is left to the discretion of the shop.

21.2 Precision and tolerance. In the manufacture of any machine or structure, quality is a primary consideration. The manufacturing care put into the product determines the relative quality and, in part, the accompanying relative cost and selling price.

Precision is the degree of accuracy necessary to ensure functioning as intended. As an example, a cast part will usually have on it two types of surfaces: (1) mating surfaces and (2) nonmating surfaces. The mating surfaces will be machined to the proper smoothness and at the correct distance from each other. The nonmating surfaces, exposed to the air and having no important relationship to other parts or surfaces, will be left in the original rough-cast form. Thus the mating surfaces ordinarily require much greater manufacturing precision than do the nonmating surfaces. The dimensions on the drawing must indicate which surfaces are to be finished and the precision required in finishing. However, because of the impossibility of producing any distance to an absolute size, some variation must be allowed in manufacture.

Tolerance is the allowable variation for any given size and provides a practical means of achieving the precision required. The tolerance on any given dimension varies according to the degree of precision necessary for that particular dimension. For nonmating surfaces, the tolerance may vary from 0.01 in. for small parts to as much as 1 in. on very large parts. For mating surfaces, tolerances as small as a few millionths of an inch are sometimes necessary (for extremely close-fitting surfaces), but usually surfaces are finished to an accuracy of 0.001 to 0.010, depending upon the function of the part. Figure 21.1 shows variously toleranced dimensions on a machine drawing.

In some cases particularly in structural and architectural work, tolerances are not stated on the drawing but are given in a set of specifications or are understood to be of an order standard for the industry.

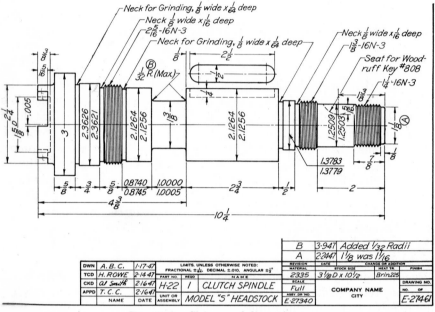

Fig. 21.1. Toleranced dimensions.

21.3 Production methods and dimensioning practice. Production methods may be classified as (1) *unit production*, the term applied when one or only a few devices or structures are to be built, and (2) *quantity* or *mass production*, indicating that a large number of practically identical machines or devices are to be made with the parts interchangeable from one machine to another.

Unit-production methods almost always apply to large machines and structures, especially if custom made. The large size to some extent eliminates the need for great accuracy. Each individual part is produced to fit, or is fitted to the adjacent parts, frequently on the job, by experienced workmen in accordance with common fractional dimensions and directions given on the drawings. Since interchangeability of parts is no object, tolerances are not ordinarily used.

Similar methods are employed for unit production of smaller machines and mechanical devices. The drawings may have common fractional dimensions exclusively on the assumption that the parts will be individually fitted in the shop. Thus, in this case, the manufacturing group accepts the responsibility for the proper functioning of the machine and, in some cases, even the design of some of the parts. Skilled workmen are employed for this work. Usually each machine is completed before another is started, and the parts will not be interchangeable.

Quantity-production methods will be employed whenever a great number of identical products are to be made. After a part has been detailed, the operations-planning group of the engineering department will plan the shop operations step by step. Then special tools are designed by the tool-design group so that, in production, semiskilled workmen may perform operations that would otherwise require skilled workmen. These tools, built by the highly skilled toolmaker, simplify and greatly increase the rate of production.

One workman performs a single operation on the part, after which it is passed to a second workman who performs another operation, and so on until the completed part results. The specially designed tools and equipment make it possible to produce parts of high quality at low cost; moreover, it is relatively simple to produce parts with dimensional exactness consistent with the requirements for interchangeability. The assembly may also be made by semiskilled workers using special assembly fixtures and tools.

With this system, nothing can be left to the judgment of the workman. In preparing drawings intended for quantity production, it is necessary for the engineering department to assume full responsibility for the success of the resulting machine by making the drawings so exact and complete that, if followed to the letter, the resulting parts cannot fail to be satisfactory. The engineering department alone is in a position to correlate corresponding dimensions of mating parts, establish dimensional tolerances, and give complete directions for the entire manufacturing job.

It is sometimes expedient for concerns doing unit or small production work to follow the methods of the quantity-production system. The advantage is interchangeable parts, which may be produced without reference or fitting to each other.

21.4 Principles for the selection of dimensions. Systematic selection of dimensions demands attention to the *use* or *function* of the part and the *manufacturing process* to be used in producing the part.

The *functional principle* recognizes that it is essential to dimension between points or surfaces associated through their functional relationship with points or surfaces of mating parts. This is accomplished by correlating the dimensions on a drawing of one part with the mating dimensions on the drawing of a mating part and arranging the tolerances of these dimensions to ensure interchangeability and proper functioning.

The *process principle* or "workman's rule," as it is sometimes called, recognizes that the work of manufacture may be made easier by giving directly the dimensions the shop will find most convenient to "work to" in producing the part. Here a knowledge of manufacturing processes and procedure is necessary, as explained in Chaps. 19 and 20.

In some cases there may be a conflict between these two principles, and whenever this occurs the functional principle must take precedence; any attempt to satisfy both principles in this case would result in overdimensioning, as described in paragraph 20.19, causing confusion for the workman and possible malfunctioning of the part. With few exceptions, however, dimensions can be chosen to satisfy both principles.

21.5 Procedure for the selection of dimensions. A systematic procedure is, of course, desirable. The following steps will illustrate and serve as a guide:

1. The part should be carefully studied along with the mating part or parts. Pay particular attention to the mating and controlling surfaces. Dimensions meeting functional requirements are planned before any dimensions are placed on the drawing so that the correlation with dimensions of mating parts may be made.

2. Study the part to determine whether or not the manufacturing processes may be simplified by some alteration of any of the functional dimensions. Changes should not be made if the functioning of the part would be impaired in any way.

3. Select the nonfunctional dimensions, being guided by the process principle, so that the dimensions are readily usable by the workmen. Avoid overdimensioning and duplication.

In general, dimensions for mating surfaces are governed by the functional and process principles, and the dimensions for nonmating surfaces are governed by the process principle only.

Occasionally the manufacturing process will not be known at the time of dimensioning. This may happen either when there are optional methods of manufacture, all equally good, or when the details of the manufacturing equipment of a contracting firm are unknown. In such cases, the dimensions should be selected and toleranced in a logical manner so that the part, regardless of how produced, cannot fail to be satisfactory. The size and location dimensions arrived at by the shape-breakdown system described in Chap. 20 will apply here to a great extent, since these dimensions will fulfill most production requirements. Contracting firms will often redraw incoming part drawings, dimensioning them to result in the most economical production with their own shop equipment.

21.6 Methods of part production. In following the process principle, the basic method of part production, casting, forging, etc., as described in Chap. 19, must be known. The manufacturing procedures followed with the particular type of part involved are then considered in selecting the dimensions. The only workman to be considered in dimensioning a part cut from solid stock is the machinist. For parts produced by casting, the workmen to be considered are the patternmaker (for sand castings) or the diemaker (for die castings) and, for finishing, the machinist. Forged parts subject to quantity production will be dimensioned for the diemaker and machinist. For parts produced from sheet stock, the template maker, the diemaker, and the machinist must be considered; information for making the template and for forming the blank is obtained from a detail drawing showing the part as it should be when completed. In any case, one drawing, appropriately dimensioned, must show the finished part.

The several paragraphs following give examples of the dimensioning of machine parts for quantity production.

21.7   Dimensioning a part machined from stock.   Figure 21.2 is a detail drawing of the stud from the rail-transport hanger, Fig. 28.49.   This assembly drawing should be studied to determine the function of the stud.   The stud is produced by machining on a lathe.   Cold-rolled steel stock, $1\frac{1}{4}$ in. in diameter, is used.   The stock diameter is the same as the large end of the stud, thus eliminating one machining operation.

Shape breakdown of the part results in a series of cylinders each requiring two dimensions, diameter and length.   The important functional dimensions

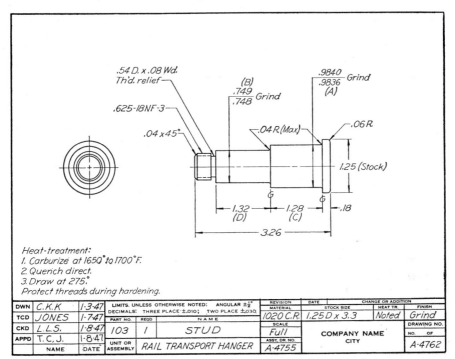

Fig. 21.2.   Dimensioning of a part machined from stock.

have been marked (on Fig. 21.2) with the letters A, B, C, and D.   Diameter A is given to correlate with the bore of the bearings; a four-place decimal limit provides for the desired fit.   Dimension B is a three-place decimal limit to correlate with a similar dimension for the hole in the hanger. Dimension C is made 0.03 in. larger than the combined width of the two bearings in order to allow the inner races of the bearings to "creep."   Dimension C, a two-place decimal, can vary by ± 0.010 in., but clearance for the bearings is assured under all conditions.   Dimension D is made approximately 0.05 in. less than the length of the hanger hub to ensure that the nut will bear against the hanger rather than on the shoulder of the stud.

Functional dimensions need not always be extremely accurate dimensions.   Note that dimensions C and D, with the relatively broad tolerance of two-place decimals, will allow the part to function as intended.

The thread specification may be considered as a functional dimension wherein the tolerance is provided through the thread class.

The remainder of the dimensions have been selected to best suit shop requirements.   Note that the thread length and over-all dimension cannot both be given, or the part would be overdimensioned.

21.8   Dimensioning a casting.   The dimensions required for sand castings may be classified as those used by the patternmaker, those used by the machinist, and those used by the patternmaker and machinist.   Since a

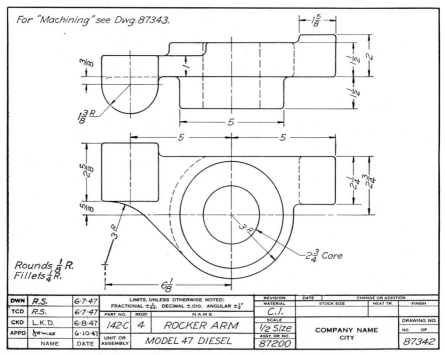

Fig. 21.3.   Dimensioning of an unmachined casting.

cast part has two distinct phases in its manufacture, the drawings, in this case, have been made according to the multiple system explained in Chap. 19, one for the patternmaker, Fig. 21.3, and one for the machinist, Fig. 21.4.

The *casting drawing* gives the shape of the unmachined casting and carries dimensions for the patternmaker only.   Shape breakdown will show that each geometric shape has been dimensioned for size and then located, resulting in dimensions easily usable by the workman.   Some of the dimensions might be altered, depending upon how the pattern is made; the most logical and easily usable combination should be used.   Note that the main central shape is dimensioned as it would be laid out on a board.   Note also that several of the dimensions have been selected to agree with required functional dimensions of the machined part, although the dimensions employed have been selected so as to be directly usable by the patternmaker; they also achieve the *main objective*, which is to state *the sizes that the unmachined casting must fulfill when produced.*

The *machining drawing* shows only the dimensions required by the machinist. These are almost all functional dimensions and have been selected to correlate with mating parts. It is important to note that a starting point must be established in each of the three principal directions for machining the casting. In this case, a starting point is provided by (1)

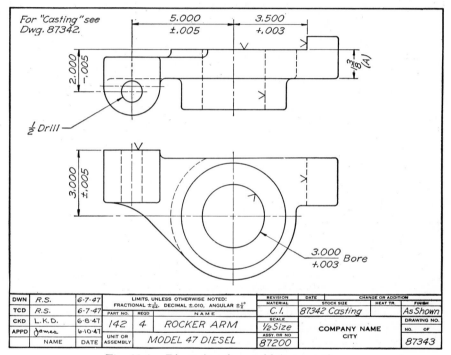

Fig. 21.4. Dimensions for machining a casting.

the coincidence of the center lines of the large hole and cylinder (location in two directions), and (2) dimension *A* to locate the machined surface on the back, from which is located the drilled hole. Dimension *A* is a common fraction carrying the broad tolerance of $\pm \frac{1}{64}$ in., as there is no functional reason for working to greater precision.

Figure 21.5 is a drawing for the same part used in Figs. 21.3 and 21.4, but with the casting drawing dispensed with and the patternmaker's dimensions incorporated in the drawing of the finished part. In combining the two drawings, some dimensions are eliminated, as the inclusion of all the dimensions of both drawings would result in overdimensioning; thus the patternmaker must make use of certain machining dimensions in his work. In working from the drawing of Fig. 21.5, the patternmaker provides for machining allowance, being guided by the finish marks. If the drawing of Fig. 21.3 is used, the engineering department provides for the machining allowance by showing and dimensioning the rough casting oversize where necessary for machining, and no finish marks are used.

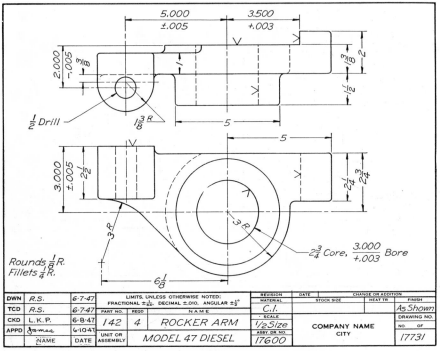

Fig. 21.5. All dimensions for a casting.

21.9   Dimensioning a drop forging.   Figure 21.6 is a drawing of a drop forging showing, at the left, the unmachined forging and, at the right, the machined forging. The drawing of the unmachined forging carries the dimensions it must fulfill when produced; these dimensions have been selected so as to be most useful to the diemaker for producing the forging dies. As the draft on drop forgings is considerable, it is shown on the drawing and dimensioned, usually, by a note. If the draft varies for different portions of the part, the angles may be given on the views. The dimensions parallel to the horizontal surfaces of the die are usually given so as to specify the size at the *bottom of the die cavity.* Thus, in dimensioning, one may visualize the draft as stripped off; then its apparent complication will no longer be a difficulty.

The machining drawing shows the dimensions for finishing. These dimensions are all functional, selected from the required function of the part. Study the illustration carefully.

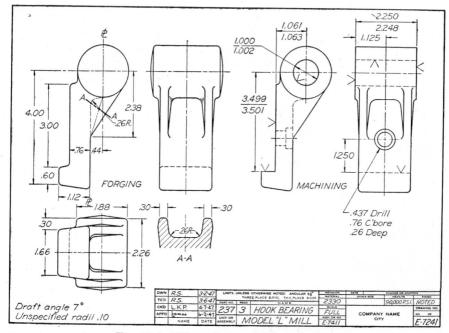

Fig. 21.6. Dimensioning of a drop forging.

21.10 Dimensioning a sheet-metal part. Parts to be made of thin materials are usually drawn showing the part in its finished form, as in Fig. 21.7. The template maker first uses this drawing to lay out a flat pattern of the part. If only a few parts are to be made, this template will serve as a pattern for cutting the blanks. Then the part is formed and completed by hand. If a large number of parts are to be made, the diemaker will use the template and drawing in making up the necessary dies for blanking, punching, and forming. The work of both template maker and diemaker is simplified by giving the dimensions to the same side of the material (either inside or outside, whichever is more important from the functional standpoint), as shown in Fig. 21.7. Dimensions to rounded edges (bends) are given to the theoretical sharp edges, which are called *mold lines*. The thickness of the material is given in the "stock" block of the title strip. Note that, in the figure, the holes are located in groups (because of functional requirements) and that important functional dimensions are three-place decimals.

21.11 Fits of mating parts. The working parts of any machine will have some definite relationship to their mating parts in order to achieve a particular function, as free rotation, free longitudinal movement, clamping action, permanent fixed position, etc. In accomplishing these, the old practice was to mark the drawings of both parts with the same fractional dimension and add a note such as "running fit" or "drive fit," leaving the

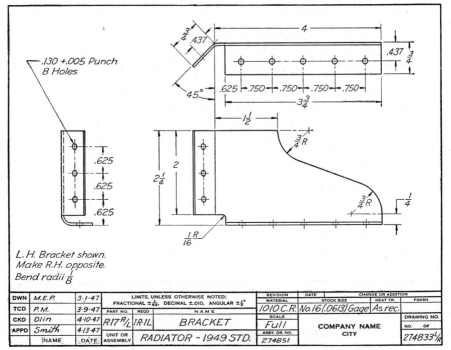

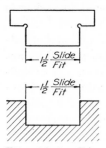

Fig. 21.7. Dimensioning of a sheet-metal part.

difference in size required (allowance) to the experience and judgment of the machinist.

The tongue of Fig. 21.8 is to slide longitudinally in the slot. Thus, if the slot is machined first and measures 1.499 in., and the machinist, from his experience, assumes an allowance of 0.004 in., he then carefully machines the tongue to 1.495 in., and the parts will fit and function as desired. In making up a second machine, if the slot measures, say, 1.504 in. after machining, the tongue is made 1.500 in. and an identical fit obtained; but the tongue of the first machine would be much too loose in the slot of the second machine, and the tongue of the second would not enter the slot of the first. The parts are, therefore, not interchangeable.

Fig. 21.8. Dimensioning a fit, old practice.

Since it is not possible to work to absolute sizes, it is necessary where interchangeable assembly is required, to give the dimensions of mating parts with "limits," that is, the maximum and minimum sizes within which the actual measurements must fall in order for the part to be accepted. The dimensions for each piece are given to three- or four-place decimals, the engineering department taking all the responsibility for the correctness of fit required.

Figure 21.9 shows the same tongue and slot of Fig. 21.8, but dimensioned for interchangeability of parts. In this case, for satisfactory functioning, it is decided that the tongue must be at least 0.002 in. smaller than the slot, but not more than 0.006 in. smaller. This would provide an average fit similar to that used in the previous example. The maximum and minimum sizes acceptable for each part can then be figured.

The value 1.500 in. has been assigned as the size of the minimum acceptable slot. This value minus the minimum clearance 0.002 in. gives a size for the maximum tongue of 1.498. The maximum allowable clearance 0.006 minus the minimum allowable clearance 0.002 gives the amount 0.004 available as the total manufacturing tolerance for both parts. This has been evenly divided and applied as 0.002 to the slot and 0.002 to the tongue. Thus the size of the maximum slot will be the size of the minimum slot *plus* the slot tolerance, or 1.500 + 0.002 = 1.502. The size of the minimum tongue will be the size of the maximum tongue *minus* the tongue tolerance, or 1.498 − 0.002 = 1.496.

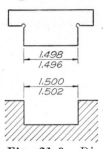

Fig. 21.9. Dimensioning a fit with limits.

A study of Fig. 21.9 will show that, made in any quantity, the two parts will allow interchangeable assembly and that any pair will fit approximately the same as any other pair, as planned. This system is essential in modern quantity production manufacture.

21.12 Nomenclature. The terms used in limit dimensioning are so interconnected that their meaning should be clearly understood before a detailed study of the method is attempted.

The ASA gives the following definitions:

Nominal size. A designation given to the subdivision of the unit of length having no specified limits of accuracy but indicating a close approximation to a standard size.

Basic size. The exact theoretical size from which all limiting variations are made.

Allowance (neutral zone). An intentional difference in the dimensions of mating parts, that is, the minimum clearance space (or maximum interference) which is intended between mating parts. It represents the condition of the tightest permissible fit, or the largest internal member mated with the smallest external member. It is to provide for different classes of fit.

Tolerance. The amount of variation permitted in a size of a part.

Limits. The extreme permissible dimensions of a part.

In illustration of these terms, a pair of mating parts are dimensioned in Fig. 21.10. In this example the *nominal size* is 1½ in. The *basic size* is 1.500. The *allowance* is 0.004. The *tolerance* on the tongue is 0.002, and on the slot it is 0.001. The *limits* are, for the tongue, 1.496 (max) and 1.494 (min) and for the slot, 1.501 (max) and 1.500 (min).

Sometimes a somewhat broader definition is used for *basic size,* in which both parts are considered to be basic in their most desirable size. Following this conception, the basic tongue of Fig. 21.10 would be 1.496 and the basic slot would be 1.500.

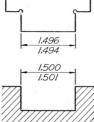

21.13   General fit classes.   The fits established on machine parts may be classified as follows:

A *clearance fit* is the condition when the internal part is smaller than the external part, as illustrated by the dimensioning of Fig. 21.11.   In this case, the largest shaft is 1.495 in. and the smallest hole 1.500 in., leaving a clearance of 0.005 for the tightest possible fit.

An *interference fit* is the opposite of a clearance fit, having a definite interference of metal for all possible conditions.   The parts must be assembled by pressure or by heat expansion of the external member.   Figure 21.12 is an illustration where the shaft is 0.001 in. larger than the hole for the loosest possible fit.   The allowance in this case is 0.003 in. interference.

Fig. 21.10. An example of limit dimensioning.

A *transition fit* is the condition when either a clearance fit or an interference fit may be had; a minimum shaft in a maximum hole will give clearance, and a maximum shaft in a minimum hole will give interference.   Figure 21.13

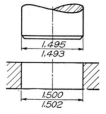

Fig. 21.11. A clearance fit.

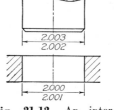

Fig. 21.12. An interference fit.

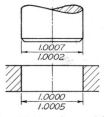

Fig. 21.13. A transition fit.

illustrates a transition fit where the smallest shaft in the largest hole results in 0.0003 in. clearance, and the largest shaft in the smallest hole results in 0.0007 in. interference.

21.14   Selective assembly.   Sometimes the fit desired may be so close and the tolerances so small that the cost of producing interchangeable parts is prohibitive.   In this case, tolerances as small as practical are established, then the parts are gaged and graded as, say, *small, medium,* and *large.*   A small shaft in a small hole, medium in medium, or large in large, will produce approximately the same fit allowance.   Transition and interference fits often require a selection of parts in order to get the amount of clearance or interference desired.   Antifriction bearings are usually assembled selectively.

21.15   Basic-hole and basic-shaft systems.   Production economy depends to some extent upon which mating part is taken as a standard size. In the *basic-hole system,* the hole can often be made with a standard tool, and the minimum size of the hole is taken as a base from which all variations are made.

Where a number of different fits of the same nominal size are required on one shaft, as for example, when bearings are fitted to line shafting, the *basic-shaft system* is employed in which the maximum shaft size is taken as the basic size.

21.16 Unilateral and bilateral tolerances. A unilateral tolerance is one in which the total allowable variation is in *one* direction, either plus or minus (not both) from the basic value. A bilateral tolerance is one in which the tolerance is divided, with part plus and the remainder minus from the basic value.

In general, mating surfaces should be toleranced unilaterally and non-mating surfaces toleranced bilaterally. One important exception is in the location of holes that *mate* with other holes or pins, as shown in Fig. 21.30. In this case, the basic size is the same for both parts, and the tolerances are bilateral as the variation is equally dangerous in either direction. The sizes of the pins and holes, however, are dimensioned with unilateral tolerances.

21.17 Methods of expressing tolerances. Tolerances may be either *specific*, given with the dimension value, or they may be *general*, as a note in the title block. The general tolerances apply to all dimensions not carrying a specific tolerance. The general tolerance should be allowed to apply whenever possible, using specific tolerances only when necessary. If no tolerances are specified, the value usually assumed for fractional dimensions is $\pm \frac{1}{64}$ in., for angular dimensions $\pm \frac{1}{2}°$, and for decimal dimensions $\pm$ the nearest significant figure, as for example, ± 0.01 in. for a two-place decimal and ± 0.001 in. for a three-place decimal.

There are several methods for expressing tolerances. The method preferred in quantity-production work, where gages are extensively employed,

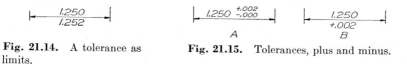

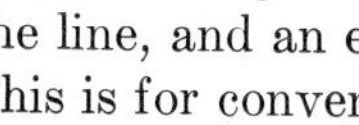

Fig. 21.14. A tolerance as limits.

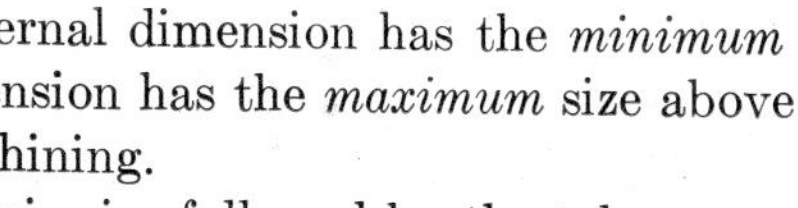

Fig. 21.15. Tolerances, plus and minus.

is to write the two limits representing the maximum and minimum acceptable sizes, as in Fig. 21.14. An internal dimension has the *minimum* size above the line, and an external dimension has the *maximum* size above the line. This is for convenience is machining.

Another method is to give the basic size followed by the tolerance, plus and minus (with the plus above the minus), Fig. 21.15*A*. If only one tolerance value is given, as at *B*, the other value is assumed to be zero.

Unilateral tolerances may be expressed by giving the two limits, as in Fig. 21.14, or by giving one limiting size and the tolerance, as 2.750 $+0.005$ or 2.750 $^{+0.005}_{-0.000}$; for fractional dimensions, $\frac{1}{2} -\frac{1}{32}$ or $\frac{1}{2} ^{+0}_{-\frac{1}{32}}$; for angular dimensions, $64°15'30'' + 0°45'0''$ or $64°15'30'' ^{+0°45'0''}_{-0° \ 0'0''}$.

Bilateral tolerances are expressed by giving the basic value followed by the divided tolerance, both plus and minus (commonly equal in amount), as $1.500 \; {}^{+0.002}_{-0.002}$ or $1.500 \; \pm 0.002$; for fractional dimensions, $1\frac{1}{2} \; {}^{+\frac{1}{64}}_{-\frac{1}{64}}$ or $1\frac{1}{2} \; \pm\frac{1}{64}$; for angular dimensions, $30°0' \; {}^{+0°10'}_{-0°10'}$ or $30°0' \; \pm 0°10'$.

21.18 Decimal places of a dimension value should be carried to the same number of places as the tolerance. For example, with a tolerance of 0.0005 on a nominal dimension of $1\frac{1}{2}$ in., the basic value should be written 1.5000. Tolerances for common fractional values should be given as common fractions, as $\frac{7}{8} \; \pm\frac{1}{64}$. Tolerances for decimal values should be given as decimal fractions, as $0.750 \; \pm 0.010$.

21.19 Fundamentals for tolerance selection. Experience in manufacturing is needed as well as a study of the particular mechanism involved before the engineer can decide on the precision necessary and specify the proper fits and tolerances. The following quotation from the ASA Standard is pertinent:

In choosing the class of fit for manufacture, the engineer should keep in mind that cost usually increases proportionately to the accuracy required, and no finer class of fit should be chosen than the functional requirements actually demand. It is axiomatic that the closer the fit the smaller the manufacturing tolerance, and usually the greater the cost. The length of engagement of the fit also plays an important part in the selection of the class of fit for a piece of work. It is obvious that a long engagement will tolerate more looseness than a short one, and due regard should be paid to this feature.

A table of fits, such as the ASA table of cylindrical fits explained in paragraph 21.22, may be taken as a guide for ordinary work.

In many cases practical experience is necessary in determining the fit conditions guaranteeing proper performance; often it is difficult to determine the definite size at which performance fails, and critical tolerances are sometimes determined through exhaustive testing of experimental models.

It is essential to know the precision attainable with various machine tools and machining methods. As an example, holes to be produced by drilling must not be specified to a smaller tolerance than can be attained by drilling. Attainable manufacturing precision is discussed in paragraph 21.20. A knowledge of the kind and type of equipment is needed to assure that the tolerances specified can be attained.

21.20 Manufacturing precision. The different manufacturing processes all have inherent minimum possible accuracies, depending upon the size of the work, the condition of the equipment, and, to some extent, the skill of the workmen. The following *minimum* tolerances are given as a guide and are based on the assumption that the work is to be done on a quantity-production basis with equipment in good condition. Greater precision may be attained by highly skilled workmen on a unit-production basis.

In general, the following are recommended as tolerances for dimensions having *no effect on the function of the part:* for sizes of 0 to 6 in., $\pm \frac{1}{64}$; 6 to 18 in., $\pm \frac{1}{32}$; 18 in. and larger, $\pm \frac{1}{16}$ (or more).

Sand castings. For the unmachined surfaces, a tolerance of $\pm \frac{1}{32}$ is recommended for small castings and a tolerance of $\pm \frac{1}{16}$ for medium-size castings. On larger castings, the tolerance should be increased to suit the size. Small and medium-size castings will rarely be below the nominal size, since the pattern is "rapped" for easy removal from the sand, thus tending to increase the size.

Die castings and plastic molding. A tolerance of $\pm \frac{1}{64}$ or less can easily be held with small and medium-size parts; for large parts the tolerance should be increased slightly. Hole-center distances can be maintained within 0.005 to 0.010, depending on the distance of separation. Certain alloys may be die-cast to tolerances of 0.001 or less.

Forgings. The rough surfaces of drop forgings weighing 1 lb or less can be held to $\pm \frac{1}{32}$; for weights up to 10 lb, $\pm \frac{1}{16}$; for weights up to 60 lb, $\pm \frac{1}{8}$. Because of die wear, drop forgings tend to increase in size as production from the die increases.

Drilling. For drills from No. 60 to No. 30, $+0.002 - 0.000$; No. 29 to No. 1, $+0.004 - 0.000$; from $\frac{1}{4}$ to $\frac{1}{2}$ in., $+0.005 - 0.000$; from $\frac{1}{2}$ to $\frac{3}{4}$ in., $+0.008 - 0.000$; from $\frac{3}{4}$ to 1 in., $+0.010 - 0.000$; from 1 to 2 in., $+0.015 - 0.000$.

Reaming. In general, a tolerance of $+0.0005 - 0.0000$ can be held with diameters up to $\frac{1}{2}$ in. For diameters from $\frac{1}{2}$ to 1 in., $+0.001 - 0.000$, and from 1 in. and larger, $+0.0015 - 0.0000$.

Lathe turning. Rough work: For diameters of $\frac{1}{4}$ to $\frac{1}{2}$ in., a total tolerance of 0.005; for diameters of $\frac{1}{2}$ to 1 in., 0.007; for diameters of 1 to 2 in., 0.010; for diameters of 2 in. and larger, 0.015.

Finish turning. For diameters of $\frac{1}{4}$ to $\frac{1}{2}$ in., a total tolerance of 0.002; for diameters of $\frac{1}{2}$ to 1 in., 0.003; for diameters of 1 to 2 in., 0.005; for diameters of 2 in. and larger, 0.007.

Milling. When single surfaces are to be milled, tolerances of 0.002 to 0.003 can be maintained. With two or more surfaces to be milled, the most important may be toleranced to 0.002 and the remainder as 0.005. In general, 0.005 is a good value to use with most milling work.

Planing and shaping. These operations are not commonly used with small parts in quantity production work. For larger parts, tolerances of 0.005 to 0.010 may be maintained.

Broaching. Diameters up to 1 in. may be held within 0.001; diameters of 1 to 2 in. 0.002; diameters of 2 to 4 in., 0.003. Surfaces up to 1 in. apart may be held within 0.002; 1 to 4 in. apart, 0.003; 4 in. apart and over, 0.004.

Threads. Tolerances for ASA threads are provided on the pitch diameter through the thread class given with the specification. For a given class, the tolerances increase as the size of the thread increases. These tolerances may be found in ASA B1.1-1949.

Grinding. For both cylindrical and surface grinding, a tolerance of 0.0005 can be maintained.

21.21 Selection of tolerances. A common method of determining and applying tolerances is to determine at the outset how much clearance or interference there can be between the mating parts and *still allow the parts to function properly.* The difference between the tightest and loosest conditions will be the *sum* of the tolerances of both parts. This value may be halved, then, to obtain tolerances for the individual parts; or if it is believed desirable because of easier machining on one part, slightly less tolerance may be used on that part, with a proportionately larger tolerance on the part more difficult to machine. The following example will illustrate the procedure.

Assume that a running fit is to be arranged between a 2-in. shaft and bearing, and in order to provide clearance for a film of oil it is determined that the parts cannot fit closer than 0.002 in. Also, in order to prevent excessive looseness and radial movement of the shaft, it is determined that the parts cannot be looser than 0.007 in. Then we have the following calculations:

Loosest fit.............. 0.007, max clearance
Tightest fit............. 0.002, min clearance (allowance)
Difference.............. 0.005, sum of tolerances
½ of difference......... 0.0025, possible value for each tolerance

Assuming that the shaft will be ground and the bearing reamed, 0.002 may be used for the shaft tolerance and 0.003 for the bearing tolerance, since these values conform better to the precision attainable by these methods of production.

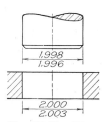

Figure 21.16 illustrates the completed dimensions. Note that the minimum hole is taken as the basic size of 2.000 and the tolerance of 0.003 applied. Then the largest shaft size will be the basic size minus the value for the tightest fit (allowance); the shaft tolerance then subtracted from the maximum shaft size gives the minimum shaft size. From the figure, the 2.003 bearing minus the 1.996 shaft gives 0.007, the loosest fit; the 2.000 bearing minus the 1.998 shaft gives 0.002, the tightest fit.

Fig. 21.16. Limits calculated from maximum and minimum clearance.

21.22 ASA cylindrical fits. The ASA has made a classification of eight kinds of fits and has compiled tables of limits for external and internal members, for different sizes in each class. These limits are tabulated in the Appendix, page 670.

ASA CLASSIFICATION OF FITS

Loose fit (class 1)—large allowance. This fit provides for considerable freedom and embraces certain fits where accuracy is not essential.

Examples: Machined fits of agricultural and mining machinery; controlling apparatus for marine work; textile, rubber, candy, and bread machinery; general machinery of a similar grade; some ordnance material.

Free fit (class 2)—liberal allowance. For running fits with speeds of 600 rpm or over and journal pressures of 600 lb per sq in. or over.

Examples: Dynamos, engines, many machine-tool parts, and some automotive parts.

Medium fit (class 3)—medium allowance. For running fits under 600 rpm and with journal pressures less than 600 lb per sq in.; also for sliding fits and the more accurate machine-tool and automotive parts.

Snug fit (class 4)—zero allowance. This is the closest fit that can be assembled by hand and necessitates work of considerable precision. It should be used where no perceptible shake is permissible and where moving parts are not intended to move freely under a load.

Wringing fit (class 5)—zero to negative allowance. This is also known as a "tunking fit," and it is practically metal-to-metal. Assembly is usually selective and not interchangeable.

Tight fit (class 6)—slight negative allowance. Light pressure is required to assemble these fits, and the parts are more or less permanently assembled, such as the fixed ends of studs for gears, pulleys, rocker arms, etc.   These fits are used for drive fits in thin sections or extremely long fits in other sections and also for shrink fits on very light sections. Used in automotive, ordnance, and general machine manufacturing.

Medium force fit (class 7)—negative allowance.   Considerable pressure is required to assemble these fits, and the parts are considered permanently assembled.   These fits are used in fastening locomotive wheels, car wheels, armatures of dynamos and motors, and crank disks to their axles or shafts.   They are also used for shrink fits on medium sections or for long fits.   These fits are the tightest which are recommended for cast-iron holes or external members as they stress cast iron to its elastic limit.

Heavy force and shrink fit (class 8)—considerable negative allowance.   These fits are used for steel holes where the metal can be highly stressed without exceeding its elastic limit.   These fits cause excessive stress for cast-iron holes. Shrink fits are used where heavy force fits are impractical, as on locomotive wheel tires, heavy crank disks of large engines, etc.

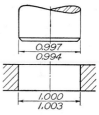

Example of limit dimensioning and use of the ASA tables. Suppose a 1-in. shaft is designed to run with a class 1 fit, basic-hole system.   The *nominal size* is then 1 in. and the *basic size* is 1.000 in.   The ASA table, page 670, shows that the hole may vary from 0.000 to +0.003, which is the *tolerance on the hole.*   The tolerance applied to the basic size of 1.000 would give 1.000 as the minimum size of the hole and 1.003 as the maximum, Fig. 21.17.

Fig. 21.17. An ASA clearance fit.

The table shows that the shaft may vary from −0.003 to −0.006.   The *actual tolerance on the shaft* is the difference between these two minus values, or 0.003 in.   The two minus values applied to the basic size of 1.000 would give 0.997 as the maximum size of the shaft and 0.994 as the minimum. From the definition of allowance, the difference between maximum shaft (0.997) and minimum hole (1.000) would be 0.003 clearance.

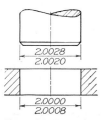

Fig. 21.18. An ASA interference fit.

The foregoing example is a clearance fit.   The first four classes of the ASA fits will all result in clearance fits. Number 5 is a transition fit.   The last three classes will give interference fits except in the smaller sizes, where transition fits will result unless selective assembly is used.

In the following example, the shaft is to be permanently assembled in a hole (hub) with an interference fit, Fig. 21.18.

Nominal size 2 in.   Class 8 fit.   Basic size 2.000.   From the ASA table, page 67⠄.
         Hole or External Member   Shaft or Internal Member
              +0.0008 and 0.0000   +0.0028 and +0.0020
These values applied to the basic size give the limit dimensioning, Fig. 21.18.
         Tolerance on hole: 2.0008 − 2.0000 = 0.0008
         Tolerance on shaft: 2.0028 − 2.0020 = 0.0008
         Allowance: 2.0000 − 2.0028 = 0.0028, interference

21.23   Base-line dimensioning.   Dimensions may be given either (1) in *successive* form, having each dimension from the one immediately preceding, Fig. 21.19; or (2) in *coordinate* or "base-line" form, having all dimensions referred to a common datum or reference, Fig. 21.20. To save space, base-line dimensions are sometimes arranged along a single line in *progressive* fashion, as indicated by the horizontal dimensions of Fig. 21.21. This method should be used only in limited space and when many dimensions are needed. The position of a point dimensioned by the base-line system is not dependent upon the cumulative tolerances of preceding dimensions.

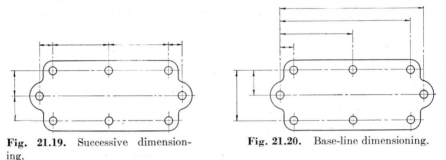

Fig. 21.19. Successive dimensioning.   **Fig. 21.20.** Base-line dimensioning.

21.24 Cumulative tolerances. Tolerances are said to be cumulative when a position in a given direction is controlled by more than one tolerance. Thus in Fig. 21.22, the position of surface Y with respect to surface W is controlled by the additive tolerances on dimensions A and B. If it is important, functionally, to hold surface Y with respect to surface X, the dimensioning used is good. If, however, it is more important to hold surface Y

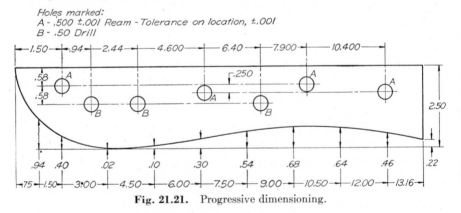

Fig. 21.21. Progressive dimensioning.

with respect to surface W, the harmful effect of cumulative tolerances can be avoided by dimensioning as in Fig. 21.23. Cumulative tolerance, however, is always present; thus in Fig. 21.23, the position of surface Y with respect to surface X is now subject to the cumulative tolerances of dimensions A and C.

In machine drawing, confusion in the shop may result from cumulative tolerances when the drawing is overdimensioned. This is illustrated in

Fig. 21.24, where one of the surfaces will be positioned by two dimensions, both of which are subject to a tolerance. Thus surface Z may be positioned with respect to surface W by means of dimensions A, B, and D and be within ± 0.003 in. of the basic position; this variation is inconsistent with the tolerance on dimension E. The situation may be clarified by assigning smaller tolerances to dimensions A, B, and D so that, cumulatively, they will be equal to ± 0.001 or less. This is poor practice, however, since it will probably increase the production cost. Another solution is to increase the tolerance on dimension E to ± 0.003 if the function of the part will permit. The best solution, however, is to eliminate one of the four dimensions, since one

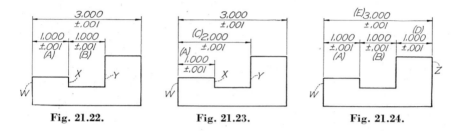

Fig. 21.22.   Fig. 21.23.   Fig. 21.24.

dimension is superfluous. If all four dimensions are given, one should be marked "Ref.," and its tolerance thus eliminated.

21.25 Tolerance for symmetry. Older practice in dimensioning symmetrical pieces frequently took advantage of the symmetry to avoid giving certain location dimensions. Following this practice, the part illustrated in Fig. 21.25, which is symmetrical about the vertical center line, has no hori-

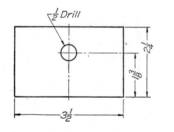

Fig. 21.25. Symmetry assumed.

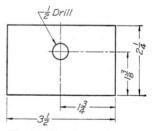

Fig. 21.26. Symmetry controlled.

zontal dimension to locate the hole. The assumption is that the shop will center the hole in the part.

The above practice is to be avoided on drawings intended for quantity production, however, since with no locating dimension there is no tolerance to indicate how much the hole can be out of symmetry with the rest of the part and still function satisfactorily. Modern practice is to give a center-line locating dimension with a value of one-half the total size; the tolerance on this dimension controls the symmetry of the piece, Fig. 21.26.

21.26   Coinciding center lines and dimensions.   In many cases there will be a coincidence of the center lines for two different features of a part. Often one center line is for an unfinished feature and the other (and coincident) center line for a finished feature.   Figure 21.27 shows at A the drawing of a link dimensioned for the patternmaker.   If holes are to be machined

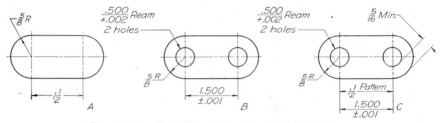

Fig. 21.27.   Coinciding center lines and dimensions.

in this link, the drawing would be as at B; the patternmaker would not use the dimension between centers, as shown, but would assume the nominal dimension of $1\frac{1}{2}$ in. with the usual pattern tolerance of $\pm\frac{1}{32}$ in.   The clearest dimensioning in this case would be as at C.

In any case where there is a coincidence of centers, it may be difficult to indicate the limits within which the coincidence must be maintained.   In example C of Fig. 21.27, there are actually two horizontal center lines, one

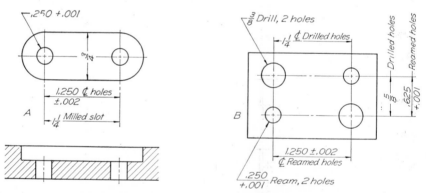

Fig. 21.28.   Coinciding center lines and dimensions.

for the cast link and another for hole centers.   One method of controlling the deviation from coincidence is to give the wall thickness as a minimum, which is understood to apply in all radial directions.

In cases where the coincident center lines are both for finished features with differing tolerances, there may be a serious ambiguity on the drawing unless the dimensioning is specially arranged.   Figure 21.28 shows at A a milled slot with nominal dimensions and, on the coincident center lines, two accurate holes with a closely toleranced center distance.   Unless the dimensioning is cleared by two separate dimensions as shown, the machinist would not know the difference in tolerance. A somewhat more difficult case is shown at *B* where pairing holes are diagonally opposite. Unless all the holes are to be toleranced the same on their center distance, the dimensioning must be made clear with notes as shown.

The Army Ordnance method of dimensioning and tolerancing, described in paragraph 21.31, provides a simple and direct means of handling the above and similar problems.

21.27 Tolerance of concentricity. Tolerance of concentricity is a special case of tolerance for symmetry in which there is a coincidence of centers. In most cases, concentric cylinders, cones, etc., generated about com-

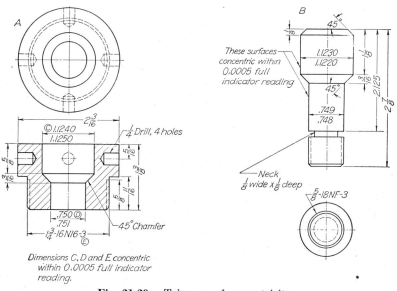

Fig. 21.29. Tolerance of concentricity.

mon axes in manufacture, will be concentric to a degree of precision more than adequate for functional requirements and no statement is required on the drawing concerning the allowable variation. However, mating pairs of two (or more) precise, close-fitting machined cylindrical surfaces must have the axes of adjoined cylinders closely coinciding in order to permit assembly of the parts; thus a method of giving the permissible deviation from concentricity is sometimes necessary. Since the center lines of adjoining cylinders coincide on the drawing, the tolerance cannot be given as a dimension. One method is to mark the diameters with reference letters and give the tolerance in note form as at *A*, Fig. 21.29. The reference letters may be dispensed with if the note is applied directly to the surfaces as at *B*.

21.28 Tolerance between centers. In any case where centers are arranged for interchangeable assembly, the tolerance on shafts, pins, etc., and also the tolerance on bearings or holes in the mating piece will affect the possible tolerance between centers. In Fig. 21.30, observe that smaller tolerances on the holes would necessitate a smaller tolerance on the center distances. A smaller allowance for the fit of the pins would make a tighter fit and reduce the possible tolerances for the center-to-center dimensions. Study carefully the dimensions of both pieces.

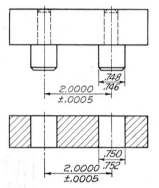

Fig. 21.30. Tolerance on centers.

21.29 Tolerance for angular dimensions. When it is necessary to give the limits of an angular dimension, the tolerance is generally bilateral, as $32° \pm \frac{1}{2}°$. When the tolerance is given in minutes, it is written $\pm 0°10'$, and when given in seconds it is written $\pm 0'30''$. Where the location of a hole or other feature is dependent upon an angular dimension, the length along the leg of the angle governs the angular tolerance permitted. A tolerance of $\pm 1°$ gives a variation of 0.035 in. for a length of 1 in. and may be used as a basis for computing the tolerance in any given problem.

As an example, assume an allowable variation of 0.007 in., then $(0.007/0.035) \times 1° = \frac{1}{5}°$ is the angular tolerance at 1 in. If the length is assumed as 2 in., then the tolerance would be one-half the tolerance computed for 1 in., or $\frac{1}{5}° \times \frac{1}{2} = \frac{1}{10}°$ or $0°6'$.

21.30 Surface quality. The proper functioning and wear life of a part frequently depends upon the smoothness quality of its surfaces. American Standard B46 defines the factors of surface quality and describes the meaning and use of symbols for use on drawings. Any surface, despite its apparent smoothness, will be found to have minute peaks and valleys, the height of which is termed *surface roughness* and which may or may not be superimposed on a more general *waviness*. The most prominent direction of tool marks and minute scratches is called *lay*.

· The degree of surface roughness may be measured as the maximum peak-to-valley height, average peak-to-valley height, or average deviation from the mean (root-mean-square value). The latter is usually preferred and may be measured with instruments such as the Profilometer.[1] The ability to make accurate measurements of roughness permits precise specification of the surface required. Figure 21.31 is a chart adapted from the U.S. Army Ordnance Standard (URAX6), which gives the range of roughness in microinches for surfaces produced by various means.

The following explanations pertaining to symbols for the control of surface quality are adapted from the ASA standard:

A surface whose quality is to be specified should be marked with a symbol having the general form of a check mark ($\checkmark$) so that the point of the symbol is (1) on the line indicating the surface, or (2) on a leader pointing to the surface.

[1] Physicists Research Co., Ann Arbor, Mich.

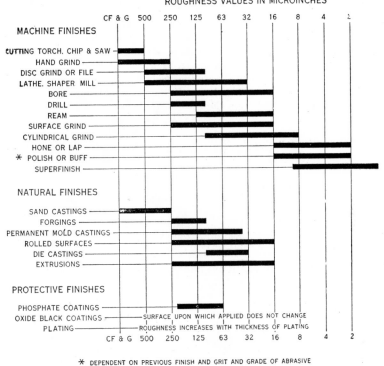

ROUGHNESS VALUES IN MICROINCHES

Fig. 21.31. Surface-roughness values.

Where it is desired to specify only the surface-roughness height, and the width of roughness or direction of tool marks is not important, the simplest form of the symbol should be used, Fig. 21.32A. The numerical value may be any one of the three roughness values mentioned above in connection with surface roughness, placed in the ∨ as shown.

Where it is desired to specify waviness height in addition to roughness height, a straight horizontal line should be added to the top of the simple symbol, Fig. 21.32B, and the numerical value of waviness height shown above this line.

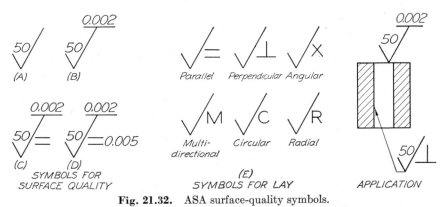

Fig. 21.32. ASA surface-quality symbols.

If the nature of the preferred lay is to be shown, it is indicated by the addition of a combination of lines as shown in Fig. 21.32C, D, and E.

The parallel and perpendicular part of the symbol indicates that the dominant tool marks on the surface are parallel or perpendicular to the boundary line of the surface in contact with the symbol. The complete symbol, including the roughness width placed to the right of the lay symbol, is shown in Fig. 21.32D.

The use of only one number to specify the height or width of roughness or waviness indicates the maximum value. Any lesser degree of roughness will be satisfactory. When two numbers separated by a dash are used, they indicate the maximum and minimum permissible values.

The surface-quality symbol should not be thought of as a finish mark in the same sense as the old symbol f and the newer V. These marks indicate the removal of material, whereas the surface-roughness symbol may be used to indicate the quality of a surface from which no material is to be removed as, for example, a die-cast or even a sand-cast surface. On the other hand, should a metal-removal process be required in order to obtain the surface quality specified, the surface-roughness symbol is used in place of the finish mark.

21.31   Positional and locational tolerances.[1]   The language of engineering drawing has developed along with the improvement of manufacturing

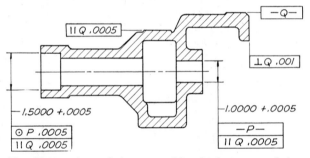

Fig. 21.33.   Army Ordnance positional-tolerance symbols.

methods. As quantity-production systems have been developed and accuracies improved, demands have been made for the drawings to depict the parts with greater exactness, particularly in the dimensioning. Examples of the trend in dimensioning are found in the methods of specifying tolerances, surface quality, and similar modern practices. Finished holes are now often specified by limit dimensions with, in addition, the surface-roughness specification, instead of the older practice of giving the size and operation, such as drilling, reaming, etc.

With improved manufacturing methods and higher precisions, a demand has developed for a workable method of controlling the parallelism, perpendicularity, concentricity, and symmetry of surfaces. Along this line, the Ordnance Department of the U.S. Army has developed a set of symbols for indicating positional tolerances. Figure 21.33 illustrates the procedure.

[1] Adapted from the Ordnance Department's "Manual on Dimensioning and Tolerancing" prepared by the inspection gage suboffice, Office of the Chief of Ordnance, A.S.F., U.S. Army.

The letter P, preceded and followed by dashes ($-P-$), connected to the diameter dimension of the small hole at the right, indicates that this hole is serving as a datum or reference surface with which one or more other surfaces will be checked for parallelism, perpendicularity, concentricity, or symmetry. Thus the concentricity symbol $\odot$, the datum letter P, and the tolerance value 0.0005 connected to the diameter dimension of the hole at the left indicate that this surface is to be concentric, with the datum surface $-P-$, within 0.0005 in. full indicator reading, or that the total permissible eccentricity (runout) is 0.0005 in.

The datum symbol $-Q-$ will be found assigned to the horizontal surface at the upper right while the adjoining vertical surface carries the perpendicularity symbol ($\perp$), the datum letter Q, and the tolerance 0.001;

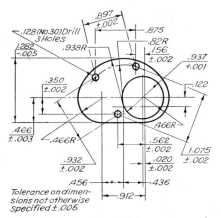

Fig. 21.34. Locational tolerances, usual method.

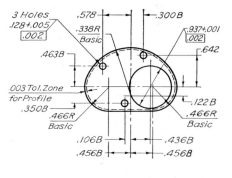

Fig. 21.35. Locational tolerances, Army Ordnance method.

therefore, this surface must be perpendicular to the datum surface $-Q-$ within 0.001 in. over its entire surface.

The method for specifying permissible errors in parallelism is similar to that used for concentricity and perpendicularity. Accordingly, the three surfaces in Fig. 21.33 carrying the parallelism symbol ($\parallel$) must each be parallel to the indicated datum surface $-Q-$ within 0.0005 in. over their entire surface.

The U.S. Army Ordnance Department has also developed a system for expressing *locational tolerances*.[1] The new system simplifies design calculations for the size and locational tolerances on mating parts, simplifies the appearance and readability of the drawing, and allows a maximum manufacturing variation without affecting the function of the parts.

Figure 21.34 illustrates the usual method for dimensioning a part, and Fig. 21.35 shows the Ordnance method. In the Ordnance system, dimensions for locating the centers of cylindrical shapes are given as basic values

[1] This system is based on ideas first proposed by G. A. Gladman of the National Physical Laboratory, Great Britain, and is now included, in essence, in proposed British standards.

followed by the letter *B*.   Beneath the size dimension for the cylinder, an additional positional tolerance value enclosed in a rectangle is given, which represents the permissible variation for the location of the cylinder and indicates that its center must lie within an imaginary circle of a diameter equal to the positional tolerance.   The center of this positional tolerance circle must, of course, be at the center located by the basic dimensions.   In Fig. 21.36, the symbol *P*.010 indicates that the centers of the small holes must be located by the dimensions given within a positional tolerance circle

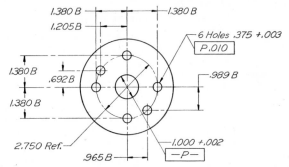

Fig. 21.36.   Locational tolerances, Army Ordnance method.

of 0.010 in. (diameter) with reference to the datum —*P*— (the large hole, whose position is basic).

An important advantage of the Ordnance system, compared with the conventional method, is that an increase in manufacturing variation is permitted without affecting the functioning of the parts.   In the conventional method, having direct tolerances given on location dimensions, the positional variation area is an inscribed square of the Ordnance positional tolerance circle.   Also, the effective area for gaging acceptable parts is usually restricted to the inscribed circle of the square.   Thus parts rejected by inspection according to the conventional system may prove to be acceptable by the Ordnance method.

The Ordnance tolerancing system may also be applied to the location of rectangular shapes.   The only difference is that the tolerance circle used with cylindrical shapes will be replaced by a tolerance rectangle within which the center of the form may vary.

PROBLEMS

Group I.   Dimensioned drawings from scale layouts

The illustrations are printed to scale, as indicated in each problem.   Transfer distances with dividers or by scaling and draw the objects to a convenient scale on a paper size to suit.   For proper placement of dimensions, more space should be provided between views than is shown in the illustrations.

1. Fig. 21.37.   Boom-pin rest.   Steel drop forging.   Shown half size, draw half size or full size.   Add top view if desired.   Show machining allowance with alternate position lines, and dimension as in Fig. 19.7.   All draft angles 7 deg.   Holes are drilled, corner notches milled.

2. Fig. 21.37. Same as Prob. 1, but make two drawings: (1) the unmachined forging dimensioned for the diemaker, and (2) the machined forging dimensioned for the machinist. Reference, Fig. 21.6.

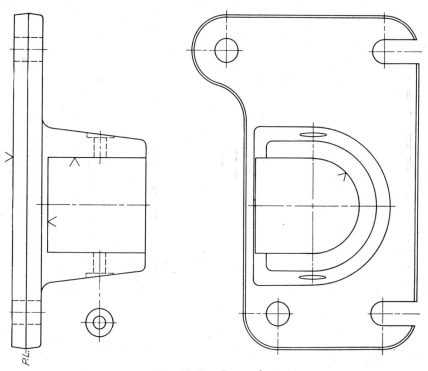

Fig. 21.37.   Boom-pin rest.

3. Fig. 21.38. Clutch lever. Aluminum drop forging. Shown half size, draw full size or twice size. Add top view if desired. Holes are drilled and reamed; ends of hub are finished; left-end lug is straddle milled; slot in lower lug is milled. Show machining allowance with alternate position lines and dimension as in Fig. 19.7. All draft angles 7 deg.

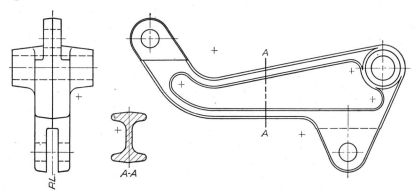

Fig. 21.38.   Clutch lever.

4. Fig. 21.38. Same as Prob. 3, but make two drawings: (1) the unmachined forging dimensioned for the diemaker, and (2) the machined forging dimensioned for the machinist. Reference, Fig. 21.6.

5. Fig. 21.39. Radiator mounting clip, LH, No. 16 (0.0625) steel sheet. Shown half size. Holes and slot are punched. Reference, Fig. 21.7.

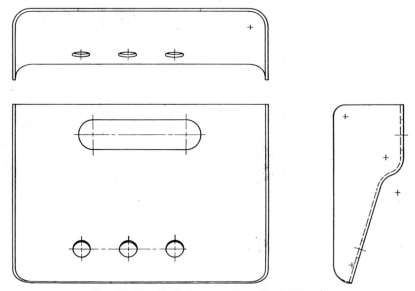

Fig. **21.39.** Radiator mounting clip, left hand.

6. Fig. 21.40. Pulley bracket. Shown half size. Aluminum sheet, 24ST, 0.032 thick. Reference, Fig. 21.7.

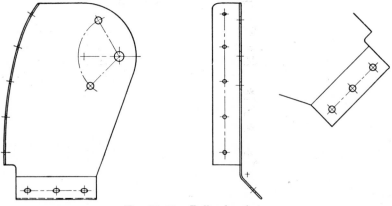

Fig. **21.40.** Pulley bracket.

Group II. Dimensioned drawings from an assembly or design drawing

The assembly drawings of Chap. 28 are well suited for exercises in dimensioning detail working drawings. The assembly shows the position of each part, and the function may be understood by a study of the motion, relationship, etc., of the different parts. Note particularly the mating and controlling surfaces and the logical reference surfaces for dimensions of location. Inasmuch as the dimensioning of an assembly drawing is crowded and probably does not even have the same views as will the detail drawing of one of the parts, disregard the position and selection of the assembly dimensions and use them only to obtain sizes. The following are suggested:

  7. Fig. 28.41. Detail drawing of shaft.
  8. Fig. 28.41. Detail drawing of bushing.
  9. Fig. 28.41. Detail drawing of bracket.
 10. Fig. 28.45. Detail drawing of body.
 11. Fig. 28.49. Detail drawing of hanger.
 12. Fig. 28.47. Detail drawing of rack.
 13. Fig. 28.47. Detail drawing of rack housing.
 14. Fig. 28.47. Detail drawing of cover.
 15. Fig. 28.39. Detail drawing of base.
 16. Fig. 28.71. Detail drawing of base.
 17. Fig. 28.71. Detail drawing of jaw.
 18. Fig. 28.71. Detail drawing of screw.
 19. Fig. 28.71. Detail drawing of screw bushing.
 20. Fig. 28.67. Detail drawing of frame (drop forging).
 21. Fig. 28.69. Detail drawing of base.
 22. Fig. 28.69. Detail drawing of frame.
 23. Fig. 28.70. Detail drawing of frame.
 24. Fig. 28.70. Detail drawing of ram.
 25. Fig. 28.70. Detail drawing of pinion shaft.
 26. Fig. 28.43. Detail drawing of base.
 27. Fig. 28.43. Detail drawing of cover.
 28. Fig. 28.43. Detail drawing of sleeve ball.
 29. Fig. 28.43. Detail drawing of stud ball.
 30. Fig. 28.65. Detail drawing of body.
 31. Fig. 28.65. Detail drawing, with development, of spring.

TEXT-FILMS

The following McGraw-Hill Text-Films have been correlated directly with Chaps. 20 and 21:

Dimensioning Techniques (silent filmstrip).

Stresses techniques, choice, and placement in standard dimensioning practice; illustrates and explains the various dimensioning symbols; demonstrates proper techniques of applying these symbols to various drawings.

Selection of Dimensions (20-min. sound motion picture).

Introduces the principles that govern the choice of dimensions; shows that these principles are based on (a) the functional characteristics of the object and (b) the manufacturing methods used in making the object.

22

Screw Threads

22.1 A screw thread is the operating element used on bolts, nuts, cap screws, wood screws, and the like, and also on shafts or similar parts employed either for transmitting power or for adjustment. Screw threads occur in one form or another on practically all engineering products. Consequently, in the making of working drawings, there is the repeated necessity to *represent* and *specify* screw threads.

22.2 Historical. The earliest records of the screw are found in the writings of Archimedes (278–212 B.C.). Although specimens of ancient Greek and Roman screws are so rare as to indicate that they were seldom used, in the later Middle Ages many are found, and it is known that both lathes and dies were used to cut threads. Most early screws, however, were made by hand, forging the head, cutting the slot with a saw, and fashioning the screw with a file. In colonial times, wood screws were blunt on the ends, the gimlet point not appearing until 1846. Iron screws were made for each threaded hole. There was no interchanging of parts, and nuts had to be tied to their own bolts. Sir Joseph Whitworth made the first attempt at a uniform standard in 1841. This was generally adopted in England but not in the United States.

22.3 Standardization. The initial attempt to standardize screw threads in the United States came in 1864 with the adoption of a report prepared by a committee appointed by the Franklin Institute. This system, designed by William Sellers, came into general use and was known as the "Franklin Institute thread," the "Sellers' thread," or the "United States thread." It fulfilled the need of a general-purpose thread for that period, but with the coming of the automobile, the airplane, and other modern equipment it was not adequate. Through the efforts of the various engineering societies, the Bureau of Standards, and others, the National Screw Thread Commission was authorized by Act of Congress in 1918 and inaugurated the present standards. This work has been carried on by the ASA and by the Interdepartmental Screw Thread Committee of the U.S. Departments of War, Navy, and Commerce. Later, these organizations, working in cooperation with representatives of the British and Canadian governments and standards associations, developed an agreement covering a general-purpose thread that fulfills the basic requirements for interchangeability of threaded products produced in the three countries. The "Declaration of Accord" establishing a "Unified Screw Thread" was signed in Washington, D.C., on November 18, 1948.

Essential features of the Unified and other threads are given in this chapter, while standards covering them completely are listed in the Appendix.

22.4   Screw-thread terminology

Screw thread (thread).   A ridge of uniform section in the form of a helix on the external or internal surface of a cylinder or cone.

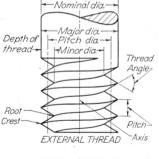
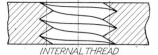

Straight thread.   A thread formed on a cylinder, Fig. 22.1.

Taper thread.   A thread formed on a cone, Fig. 25.7.

External thread (screw).   A thread on the external surface of a cylinder or cone, Fig. 22.1.

Internal thread (nut).   A thread on the internal surface of a cylinder or cone, Fig. 22.1.

Right-hand thread.   A thread which, when viewed axially, winds in a clockwise and receding direction. Threads are always right hand unless otherwise specified.

Left-hand thread.   A thread which, when viewed axially, winds in a counterclockwise and receding direction.   All left-hand threads are designated "LH."

Form.   The profile (cross section) of the thread. Figure 22.3 shows various forms.

Crest.   The edge or surface which joins the sides of a thread and is farthest from the cylinder or cone from which the thread projects, Fig. 22.1.

Fig. 22.1.   Screw-thread terminology.

Root.   The edge or surface which joins the sides of adjacent thread forms and coincides with the cylinder or cone from which the thread projects, Fig. 22.1.

Pitch.   The distance between corresponding points on adjacent thread forms measured parallel to the axis, Fig. 22.1.   This distance is a measure of the size of the thread form used.

Lead.   The distance a threaded part moves axially, with respect to a fixed mating part, in one complete revolution.   See "multiple threads" and Fig. 22.2.

Threads per inch.   The reciprocal of the pitch and the value specified to govern the size of the thread form.

Major diameter.   The largest diameter of a screw thread, Fig. 22.1.

Minor diameter.   The smallest diameter of a screw thread, Fig. 22.1.

Pitch diameter.   On a straight thread, the diameter of an imaginary cylinder, the surface of which cuts the thread forms where the width of the thread and groove are equal, Fig. 22.1.   The clearance between two mating threads is controlled largely by closely toleranced pitch diameters.

Depth of thread.   The distance between crest and root measured normal to the axis, Fig. 22.1.

Single thread.   A thread having the thread form produced on but one helix of the cylinder, Fig. 22.2 (see "multiple threads").   On a single thread, the lead and pitch are equivalent.   Threads are always single unless otherwise specified.

Multiple thread.   A thread combination having the same form produced on two or more helices of the cylinder, Fig. 22.2.   For a multiple thread, the lead is an integral

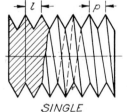

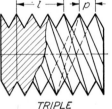

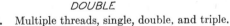

Fig. 22.2.   Multiple threads, single, double, and triple.

multiple of the pitch, that is, on a *double thread* the lead is twice the pitch, on a *triple thread*, three times the pitch, etc. A multiple thread permits a more rapid advance without a coarser (larger) thread form. Note that the helices of a double thread start 180° apart; those of a triple thread, 120° apart; and those of a quadruple thread, 90° apart.

22.5   Thread forms. Screw threads are used on fasteners, on devices for making adjustments, and for the transmission of power and motion. For these different purposes, a number of thread forms are in use, Fig. 22.3. The dimensions given are those of the basic thread forms. In practical usage, clearance must be provided between the external and internal threads.

The *sharp V*, formerly used to a limited extent, is rarely employed now; it is difficult to maintain sharp roots in quantity production. The

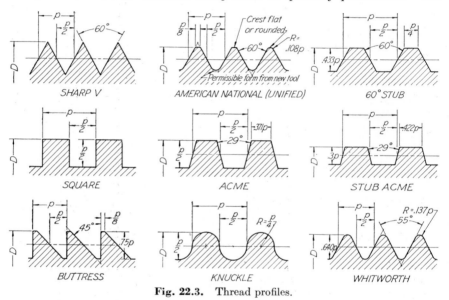

Fig. 22.3.   Thread profiles.

form is of interest, however, as the basis of more practical V-type threads; also, because of its simplicity, it is used on drawings as a conventional representation for other (V-type) threads.

V-type threads are employed primarily on fasteners and for making adjustments. For these purposes, the standard thread form in the United States is the *American National*. This form is also the basis for the "Unified Screw Thread" standard of the United States, Canada, and Britain, and as such is known as the *Unified* thread. As illustrated in Fig. 22.3, the form is that of the maximum external thread. Observe that, while the crest may be either flat or rounded, the root is rounded by design or as the result of tool wear. The American National thread is by far the most commonly used thread in this country.

The 60° *stub* form is sometimes preferred when, instead of multiple threads, a single National form thread would be too deep.

The former British standard was the *Whitworth* at 55° with crests and roots rounded. The *British Association Standard* at 47½°, measured in the metric system, is used for small threads. The *French* and the *International Metric Standards* have a form similar to the American National but are dimensioned in the metric system.

Pipe threads, also of V form, are discussed in Chap. 25.

For transmitting power the V shapes are not desirable, since part of the thrust tends to burst the nut. The *square thread* avoids this, as it transmits all the forces nearly parallel to the axis of the screw. It can have, evidently, only half the number of threads in the same axial space as a V thread of the same pitch, and thus in shear it is only half as strong. Because of manufacturing difficulties, the square-thread form is sometimes modified by providing a slight (5°) taper to the sides.

The *Acme* has generally replaced the square thread in use. It is stronger, more easily produced, and permits the use of a disengaging or split nut that cannot be used on a square thread.

The *Stub Acme* form results in a very strong thread suited to power applications where space limitation makes it desirable.

The *buttress* for transmitting power in only one direction has the efficiency of the square and the strength of the V thread. It is sometimes produced with a 7° slope on the perpendicular flank to simplify manufacture. Sometimes called the breechblock thread, it is used to withhold the pressure on breechblocks of large guns.

The *knuckle* thread is especially suitable when threads are to be molded, or rolled in sheet metal. It can be observed on glass jars and in a shallow form on the bases of ordinary incandescent lamps.

Internal screw threads are produced by cutting, while external threads may be made by cutting or rolling. Tests show that rolled threads are considerably stronger than cut threads. Through cold forging, rolling adds toughness and strength to the threaded portion of the metal.

22.6 Thread representation. The true representation of a screw thread is almost never used in making working drawings. In true representation, the crest and root lines, Fig. 22.4, appear as the projections of

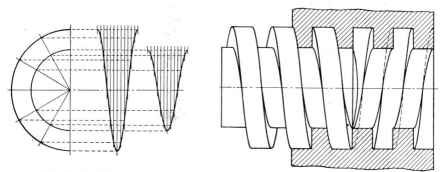

Fig. 22.4. True representation of a square thread, internal and external.

helices (see Helix, paragraph 5.65), the drawing of which is extremely laborious. For instances where true representation is desirable, that is, on advertising, elaborate display drawings, etc., templates can be made of cardboard or celluloid to assist in drawing the helices.

On practical working drawings, threads are represented with either a semiconventional or symbolic treatment which provides thread pictures adequate for manufacturing purposes. These methods of thread representation are discussed in the following paragraphs.

22.7 Semiconventional representation simplifies the drawing of the thread principally by conventionalizing the projection of the helix into a

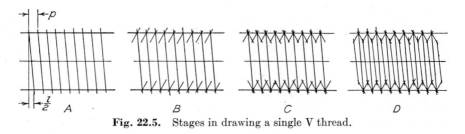

Fig. 22.5. Stages in drawing a single V thread.

straight line. Where applicable with certain thread forms, further simplifications are made. For example, the 29° angle of the Acme and 29° stub forms may be drawn at 30°, and the American National form is represented by the sharp V. In general, true pitch should be shown, although a small increase or decrease in pitch is permissible so as to have even units of measure in making the drawing. Thus, seven threads per inch may be increased

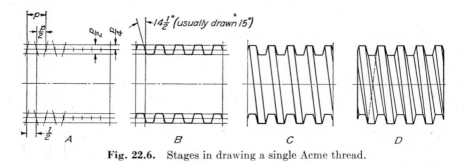

Fig. 22.6. Stages in drawing a single Acme thread.

to eight, or four and one-half may be decreased to four. The student must keep in mind that this is only to simplify the drawing and that the actual threads per inch must be specified in the dimensioning.

To draw a thread semiconventionally, we must know whether it is external or internal, the form, the major diameter, the pitch, its multiplicity, and whether it is right or left hand. Figure 22.5 illustrates the stages in drawing an American National or sharp V; Fig. 22.6, an Acme; and Fig.

22.7, a square thread. The V thread of Fig. 22.5 will illustrate the principle. At A the diameter is laid out, and on it the pitch is measured on the upper line. This thread is a single thread; therefore, the pitch is equal to the lead, and the helix will advance $p/2 = l/2$ in $180°$. This distance is laid off on the bottom diameter line, and the crest lines are drawn in. At

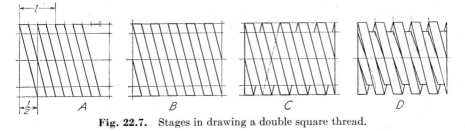

Fig. 22.7. Stages in drawing a double square thread.

B, one side of the V form is drawn and is completed at C. At D the root lines have been added. As can be seen from the three figures, 22.5, 22.6, and 22.7, the stages in drawing any thread semiconventionally are similar, the principal difference being in the thread form. The square thread of Fig. 22.7 is double, while that of Fig. 22.8 is single and left hand. Observe

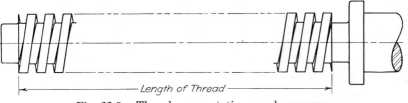

Fig. 22.8. Thread representation on a long screw.

in Fig. 22.8 that it is unnecessary to draw the threads on the whole length of a long screw. If the thread is left hand, the crest and root lines are slanted in the opposite direction to those shown in Figs. 22.5 to 22.7, as illustrated by the left-hand square thread of Fig. 22.8. Figure 22.9 illustrates semiconventional treatment for both external and internal V threads. Note that the crest and root lines are omitted on internal threads.

In general, threads should be represented semiconventionally except for the smaller sizes which are ordinarily pictured by means of the ASA thread symbols. It is suggested that threads of 1 in. and larger in actual measurement on the drawing be represented semiconventionally.

22.8 Thread symbols. The ASA provides two systems of thread symbols, "regular" and "simplified." It is recommended that these symbols be used for indicating the smaller threads (under 1 in.), and also that the regular symbols be used on assembly drawings and the simplified symbols on detail drawings.

22.9 The ASA regular thread symbols, Fig. 22.10, omit the profile on longitudinal views and indicate the crests and roots by lines perpendicular

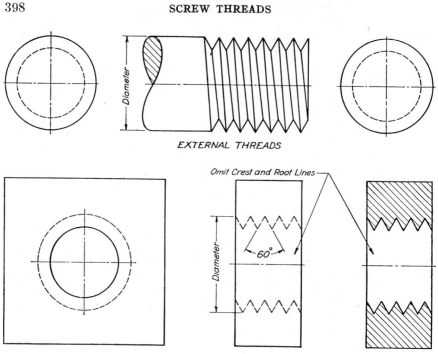

EXTERNAL THREADS

INTERNAL THREADS

Fig. 22.9. Semiconventional thread representation (suggested for V threads drawn 1 in. or over on both assembly and detail drawings).

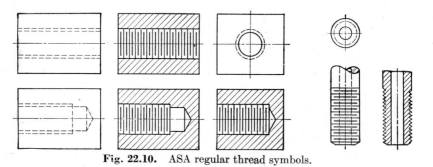

Fig. 22.10. ASA regular thread symbols.

to the axis. However, exceptions are made for internal threads not drawn in section and external threads drawn in section as shown by the figure.

22.10 The ASA simplified symbols, Fig. 22.11, omit both form and crest lines and indicate the threaded portion by dotted lines parallel to the axis at the approximate depth of thread. The simplified method does not have the descriptive effect of the regular symbol, but as it saves much time, it is preferred on detail drawings.

22.11 To draw the ASA symbols. The two sets of symbols should be carefully studied and compared. Note that the regular and simplified symbols are identical for hidden threads. Also note that the end view of

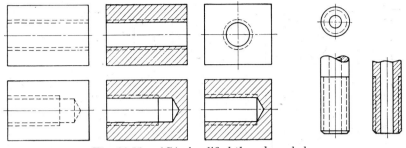

Fig. 22.11.   ASA simplified thread symbols.

an external thread differs from the end view of an internal thread, but that regular and simplified end-view symbols are identical.

No attempt needs be made to show either the actual pitch of the threads or their depth by the spacing of lines in the symbol.   Identical symbols may be used for several threads of the same diameter but of different pitch. It is possible only in the larger sizes to show the actual pitch and the true depth of thread without a confusion of lines that would defeat the purpose of the symbol.   The symbols should therefore be made so as to read clearly and look well on the drawing, without other considerations.

To draw a symbol for any given thread, only the major diameter and length of thread must be known, and for a blind tapped hole the depth of the tap drill is also needed.

A *regular or simplified symbol for a tapped hole* is drawn in the stages shown by Fig. 22.12.   As already stated, the lines representing depth of

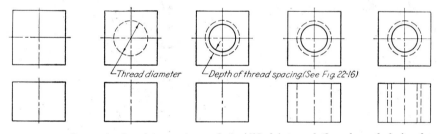

Fig. 22.12.   Stages in drawing regular and simplified internal thread symbols in plan and elevation.

thread are not drawn to actual scale, but are spaced so as to look well on the drawing and to avoid crowding of the lines.

A *regular symbol for a tapped hole in section* is drawn in the stages shown by Fig. 22.13.   The lines representing the crests are spaced by eye or scale to look well and need not conform to the actual thread pitch.   The lines representing the roots of the thread are equally spaced by eye between the crest lines and are usually drawn heavier.   Their length need not indicate the actual depth of thread, but should be kept uniform by using light guide lines.

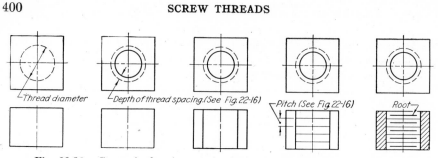

Fig. 22.13. Stages in drawing regular internal thread symbols in section.

A *simplified symbol for an external thread* is drawn in the stages shown by Fig. 22.14. The 45° chamfer extends to the root line of the thread. Note that in the end view the chamfer line is shown.

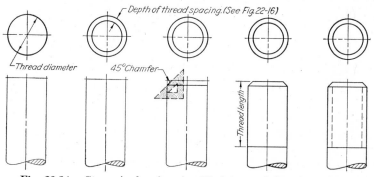

Fig. 22.14. Stages in drawing simplified external thread symbols.

A *regular symbol for external threads* is drawn in the stages shown by Fig. 22.15. The chamfer is 45° and to the depth of thread. Crest lines are spaced by eye or scale. Root lines are spaced by eye, are usually drawn heavier, and need not conform to actual thread depth.

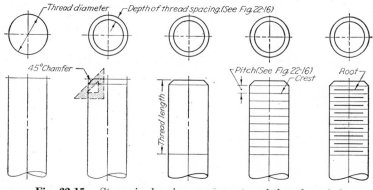

Fig. 22.15. Stages in drawing regular external thread symbols.

Line spacings. The table, Fig. 22.16, gives suggested values of "pitch" and "depth of thread" for purposes of drawing the ASA symbols. Figure

22.17 shows both regular and simplified symbols, full size, drawn according to the values given in Fig. 22.16. No distinction is made in the symbol between coarse and fine threads.

Major diameter of thread, D	Pitch (p) for drawing purposes	Depth of thread ($p/2$) for drawing purposes
$\frac{1}{8}$ and $\frac{3}{16}$	$\frac{1}{16}$ scant	$\frac{1}{32}$ scant
$\frac{1}{4}$ and $\frac{3}{8}$	$\frac{1}{16}$	$\frac{1}{32}$
$\frac{1}{2}$ and $\frac{5}{8}$	$\frac{1}{8}$	$\frac{1}{16}$
$\frac{3}{4}$ and $\frac{7}{8}$	$\frac{3}{16}$	$\frac{3}{32}$

Fig. 22.16. Suggested values for drawing thread symbols.

22.12 Threads in section. Figure 22.4 shows the true form of an internal square thread in section. Observe that the far side of the thread is visible, causing the root and crest lines to slope in the opposite direction

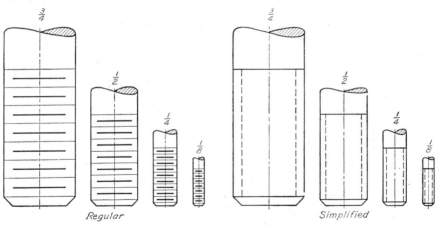

Regular   Simplified

Fig. 22.17. Thread symbols, drawing size.

from those on the external thread. Figure 22.9 shows the semiconventional treatment for V threads over 1 in. in diameter. Note that the crest and root lines are omitted. The regular and simplified symbols for threads in section are shown in Figs. 22.10 and 22.11. When two pieces screwed together are shown in section, the thread form should be drawn to aid in reading, Fig. 22.18. In the small diameters it is desirable to decrease the number of threads per inch, thus eliminating monotonous detail and greatly improving the readability of the drawing.

22.13 Unified and American (National) screw threads. The Unified thread standards adopted by the United States, Canada, and the United Kingdom for the bulk of threaded products basically constitutes the American Standard "Unified and American Screw Threads" (ASA B1.1–1949). The form of thread employed has been described in paragraph 22.5 and is essentially that of the former (1935) American Standard. Threads produced according to the former and present American Standards will interchange. Important differences between the two standards are in the liberalization of manufacturing tolerances, the provision of allowances for most classes of threads, and the changes in thread designations. The new American Standard contains, in addition to the Unified diameter-pitch combinations and thread classes (adopted in common by the three countries),

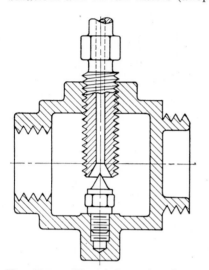

additional diameter-pitch combinations and two thread classes retained from the 1935 standard.

22.14 Thread series. Threads are classified in "series" according to the number of threads per inch used with a specific diameter. For example, an American (Unified) thread having 20 threads per inch applied to a $\frac{1}{4}$-in. diameter results in a thread belonging to the coarse-thread series, while 28 threads per inch on the same diameter gives a thread belonging to the fine-thread series.

In the United States, the thread forms which have been subjected to "series" standardization by the ASA include the Unified or American National, the Acme, Stub Acme, pipe

Fig. 22.18. Threads in section, drawing size.

threads, and the knuckle thread as used on electric sockets and lamp bases. Except for the Unified or American National, only one series is provided for each of the thread forms so standardized (see Appendix, page 651 for Acme and Stub Acme threads and page 674 for pipe threads).

The American Standard "Unified and American (National) Screw Threads" covers six series of screw threads and, in addition, certain other preferred special diameter-pitch combinations. In the descriptions of the series which follow, the letters "U" and "N" used in the series designations stand for the words "Unified" and "National (form)," respectively.

The *coarse-thread series*, designated "UNC" or "NC," is recommended for general use where conditions do not require a fine thread.

The *fine-thread series*, designated "UNF" or "NF," is recommended for general use in automotive and aircraft work and where special conditions require a fine thread.

The *extra-fine thread series*, designated "UNEF" or "NEF," is used particularly in aircraft work where an extremely shallow thread or a maximum number of threads within a given length is required.

The *8-thread series*, designated "8N," is a uniform-pitch series using eight threads per inch for all diameters concerned.

Bolts for high-pressure pipe flanges, cylinder-head studs, and similar fasteners against pressure require that an initial tension be set up by elastic deformation of the fastener and that the components be held together, so that the joint will not open when steam or other pressure is applied.   To secure a proper initial tension, it is not practicable that the pitch should increase with the diameter of the thread, as the torque required to assemble would be excessive.   Accordingly, for such purposes, the eight-thread series has come into general use in many classes of engineering work and as a substitute for the coarse-thread series.

The *12-thread series*, designated "12UN" or "12N," is a uniform-pitch series using 12 threads per inch for all diameters concerned.

Sizes of 12-pitch threads from ½ to 1¾ in. in diameter are used in boiler practice which requires that worn stud holes be retapped with the next larger size.   The 12-thread series is also widely used in machine construction for thin nuts on shafts and sleeves and provides continuation of the fine-thread series for diameters larger than 1½ in.

The *16-thread series*, designated "16UN" or "16N," is a uniform-pitch series, using 16 threads per inch for all diameters concerned.

This series is intended for applications requiring a very fine thread such as threaded adjusting collars and bearing retaining nuts.   It also provides continuation of the extra-fine thread series for diameters larger than 2 in.

Special threads, designated "UN," "UNS," or "NS," as covered in the standards include nonstandard or special combinations of diameter, pitch, and length of engagement.

The diameter-pitch combinations of the above series will be found on page 652 where the "Unified" combinations (combinations common to the standards of the United States, Canada, and Great Britain) are printed in bold type.

22.15   Unified and American screw-thread classes.   A class of thread is distinguished by the tolerance and allowance specified for the member threads and, therefore, is a control of the looseness or tightness of the fit between mating screws and nuts.   The Unified and American (National) and Acme are at present the only threads in this country standardized to the extent of providing several thread classes to control the fit.

The classes provided by the American Standard "Unified and American Screw Threads" are classes 1A, 2A, and 3A, applied to *external threads only;* classes 1B, 2B, and 3B, applied to *internal threads only;* and classes 2 and 3, applied to *both external and internal threads*.   These classes are achieved through toleranced thread dimensions given in the standards.

Classes 1A and 1B are intended for ordnance and other special uses where free assembly and easy production are important.   Tolerances and allowance are largest with this class.

Classes 2A and 2B are the recognized standards for the bulk of screws, bolts, and nuts produced and are suitable for a wide variety of applications.

A moderate allowance provides a minimum clearance between mating threads to minimize galling and seizure.

Classes 3A and 3B provide a class where accuracy and closeness of fit are important. No allowance is provided.

Classes 2 and 3, each applying to both external and internal threads, have been retained from the former (1935) American Standard. No allowance is provided with either class, and in general, tolerances are closer than with the corresponding new classes.

22.16 Unified threads. Not all the diameter-pitch combinations listed in the American Standard "Unified and American Standard Screw Threads" appear in the British and Canadian standards. Combinations used in common by the three countries are called "Unified" threads and are identified by the letter "U" in the series designation; they are printed in bold type in the table (see page 652). Unified threads may employ classes 1A and 1B, 2A and 2B, and 3A and 3B only. When one of these classes is used and the "U" does not appear in the designation, the thread conforms to the principles on which Unified threads are based.

The Unified and American National screw-thread table on page 652 indicates the classes for which each series has data tabulated in the standards. Threads of standard diameter-pitch combinations, but of a class for which data are not tabulated in the standard, are designated "UNS" if a Unified combination and "NS" if not.

22.17 Acme and Stub Acme threads. Acme and Stub Acme threads have been standardized by the ASA in one series of diameter-pitch combinations, page 651, Appendix. In addition, the standard provides for two general applications of Acme threads: general purpose and centralizing. The three thread classes, 2G, 3G, and 4G, standardized for the general-purpose applications, have clearances on all diameters for free movement. Centralizing Acme threads have a close fit on the major diameter to maintain alignment of the screw and nut and are standardized in five thread classes, 2C, 3C, 4C, 5C, and 6C. The Stub Acme has only one thread class for general usage.

22.18 Thread specification. The orthographic views of a thread are necessary in order to locate, dimensionally, the position of the thread on the part. In addition, the views describe whether the thread is external or internal. All other information, called the *specification*, is normally conveyed by means of either a note or dimensions and a note. In addition to appearing on drawings, the specification may be needed in correspondence, on stock and parts lists, etc.

Features of a thread on which information is essential for manufacture are form, nominal (major) diameter, threads per inch, and thread class or toleranced dimensions. In addition, if the thread is left hand, the letters "LH" must be included in the specification; also, if the thread is other than single, its multiplicity must be indicated.

In general, threads other than the Unified and American National,

Acme, and Stub Acme will require toleranced dimensions to control the fit, Fig. 22.19*E*.

Unified and American National threads are specified completely by note. The form of the specification always follows the same order—the nominal size is given first, then the number of threads per inch and the series desig-

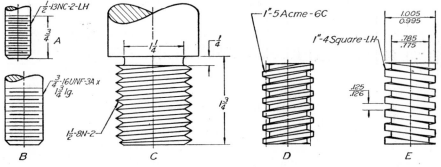

Fig. 22.19.   External thread specifications.

nation (UNC, NC, etc.), and then the thread class.   If the thread is left hand, the letters "LH" follow the class, Fig. 22.19*A*, *B*, *C*.

Examples:

¼-20UNC-3A	1-12UNF-2B-LH	2-8N-2	2-16UN-2B
¼-20NC-2	1-20NEF-3	2-12UN-2A	2-6NS-2A

Note that, when the Unified thread classes are employed, the letters "A" and "B" indicate whether the thread is external or internal.

Acme and Stub Acme threads are also specified by note.   The form of the specification follows that of the Unified, Fig. 22.19*D*.

Examples:

1¾-4Acme-2G (general purpose class 2 Acme, 1¾" major diameter, 0.25" pitch, single, right hand).

1-5Acme-4C-LH (centralizing class 4 Acme, 1" major diameter, 0.2" pitch, single. left hand).

2½-0.333p-0.666L-Acme-3G (general purpose class 3 Acme, 2½" major diameter 0.333" pitch, 0.666" lead, double, right hand).

¾-6 Stub Acme (Stub Acme, ¾" major diameter, 0.1667" pitch, right hand).

22.19   Tapped-hole specifications.   Always specify by note, giving the tap-drill diameter and depth of hole, followed by the thread specification and length of thread, Fig. 22.20.   For tap-drill sizes, see Appendix.   It is general commercial practice to use 75 per cent of the theoretical depth of thread for tapped holes.   This gives about 95 per cent of the strength of a full thread and is much easier to cut.

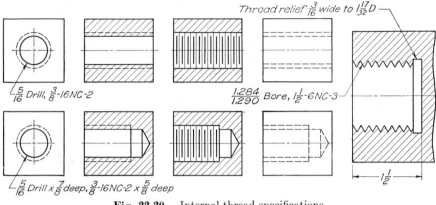

Fig. 22.20. Internal thread specifications.

22.20 Depth of tapped holes and entrance length for threaded rods, studs, cap screws, machine screws, and similar fasteners may be found by using an empirical formula based on the diameter of the fastener and the material tapped, see Fig. 22.21 and the accompanying table.

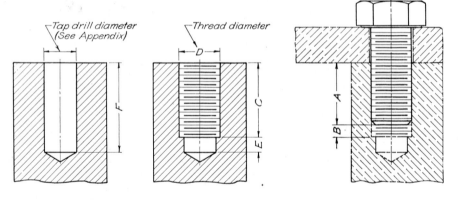

Fig. 22.21. Proportions for tapped holes.

Material	Entrance length for cap screws, etc., A	Thread clearance at bottom of hole, B	Thread depth, C	Unthreaded portion at bottom of hole, E	Depth of drilled hole, F
Aluminum.............	$2D$	$4/n$	$2D + 4/n$	$4/n$	$C + E$
Cast iron.............	$1\frac{1}{2}D$	$4/n$	$1\frac{1}{2}D + 4/n$	$4/n$	$C + E$
Brass................	$1\frac{1}{2}D$	$4/n$	$1\frac{1}{2}D + 4/n$	$4/n$	$C + E$
Bronze...............	$1\frac{1}{2}D$	$4/n$	$1\frac{1}{2}D + 4/n$	$4/n$	$C + E$
Steel................	D	$4/n$	$D + 4/n$	$4/n$	$C + E$

D = diameter of fastener
A = entrance length for fastener
B = thread clearance at bottom of hole
C = total thread depth

E = unthreaded portion at bottom of hole
n = threads per inch
F = depth of tap-drill hole

PROBLEMS

Group I. Helices

1. Draw three complete turns of a helix; diameter, 3 in.; pitch, $1\frac{1}{4}$ in.

2. Draw three complete turns of a conical helix, end and front views, with $1\frac{1}{2}$-in. pitch, whose large diameter is 4 in. and small diameter is $1\frac{1}{2}$ in.

Group II. Screw threads

3. Draw in section the following screw-thread forms, 1-in. pitch: American National, Acme, Stub Acme, square.

4. Draw two views of a square-thread screw and a section of the nut separated; diameter, $2\frac{1}{2}$ in.; pitch, $\frac{3}{4}$ in.; length of screw, 3 in.

5. Same as Prob. 4 but for V thread with $\frac{1}{2}$-in. pitch.

6. Draw screws 2 in. diameter and $3\frac{1}{2}$ in. long: single square thread, pitch $\frac{1}{2}$ in.; single V thread, pitch $\frac{1}{4}$ in.; double V thread, pitch $\frac{1}{2}$ in.; left-hand double square thread, pitch $\frac{1}{2}$ in.

7. Fig. 22.22. Working space, 7 by $10\frac{1}{2}$ in. Divide space as shown and in left space draw and label thread profiles, as follows: at A, sharp V, $\frac{1}{2}$-in. pitch; at B, American National (Unified), $\frac{1}{2}$-in. pitch; at C, square, 1-in. pitch; at D, Acme, 1-in. pitch. Show five threads each at A and B, and three at C and D.

In right space, complete the views of the object showing at E a $3\frac{1}{2}$-4UNC-2B threaded hole in section. The thread runs out at a $3\frac{17}{32}$-in.-diameter by $\frac{1}{4}$-in.-wide thread relief. The lower line for the thread relief is shown. At F show a $1\frac{3}{4}$-5UNC-3A thread. The thread is 1 in. long and runs out at a neck which is $1\frac{3}{8}$ in. diameter by $\frac{1}{4}$ in. wide. The free end of the thread should be chamfered at 45°. At G show the shank threaded $\frac{5}{8}$-18UNF-3A by 1 in. long; at H show $\frac{3}{8}$-16UNC-2B through tapped holes in section, four required. Completely specify all threads.

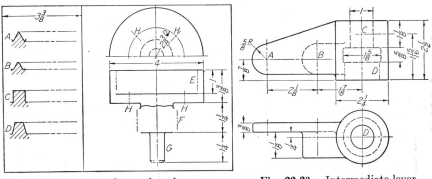

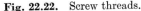
Fig. 22.22. Screw threads.

Fig. 22.23. Intermediate lever.

8. Fig. 22.23. Working space, 7 by $10\frac{1}{2}$ in. Complete the views and show threaded features as follows: at A, a $\frac{1}{2}$-20UNF-3B through tapped hole; at B, a $\frac{5}{8}$-11UNC-2B by $\frac{3}{4}$ in. deep tapped hole with tap drill $1\frac{1}{8}$ in. deep; at C, a $\frac{3}{8}$-16UNC-2B by $\frac{1}{4}$ in. deep tapped hole with the tap drill through to the 1-in. hole; at D, a $1\frac{1}{2}$-8N-2 threaded hole running out at the large cored hole. Completely specify all threads.

9. Fig. 22.24. Complete the views of the offset support by showing threaded holes as follows: at *A*, 1⅜-6UNC-2B; at *B*, ½-13NC-2; at *C*, ⅝-18UNF-3B. *A* and *C* are through holes. *B* is a blind hole to receive a stud. Material is cast iron. Specify the threaded holes.

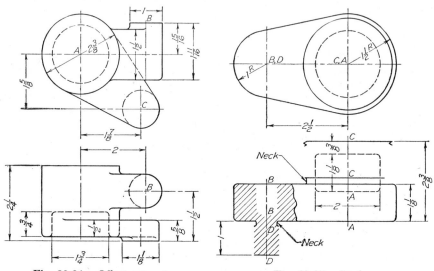

Fig. 22.24.   Offset support.   Fig. 22.25.   Rocker.

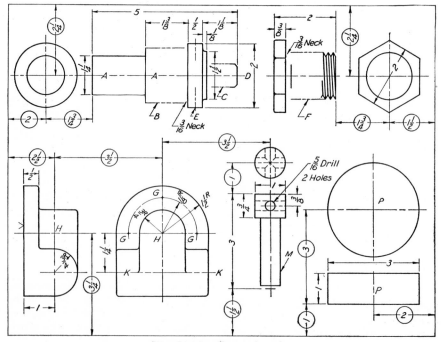

Fig. 22.26.   Screw threads.

10. Complete the views of the cast-steel rocker, Fig. 22.25, showing threads as follows: on center line AA, 2-8N-2; on center line BB, a $\frac{1}{2}$-20UNF-2B tapped hole, $\frac{5}{8}$ in. deep with tap drill $\frac{7}{8}$ in. deep; on center line CC, a $2\frac{3}{4}$-12UN-2A external thread; on center line DD, a $\frac{7}{8}$-14UNF-3A external thread.

11. Fig. 22.26 Minimum working space, $10\frac{1}{2}$ by 15 in. Complete the views of the objects and show threads and other details as follows: *upper left*, on center line AA show in section a $\frac{3}{4}$-10UNC-2B tapped hole, $1\frac{1}{2}$ in. deep, with tap-drill hole $2\frac{1}{2}$ in. deep. At B show a $1\frac{3}{4}$-8N-2 external thread in section. At C show a $\frac{3}{4}$-10UNC-2A thread in section. From D on center line AA show a $\frac{1}{4}$-in. drilled hole extending to the tap-drill hole. At E show six $\frac{1}{4}$-in. drilled holes $\frac{1}{4}$ in. deep equally spaced for spanner wrench. *Upper right*, at F show a $1\frac{1}{2}$-6UNC-2A thread. *Lower left*, at G show (three) $\frac{3}{8}$-16UNC-2B through tapped holes. At H show a $\frac{7}{8}$-9UNC-2B tapped hole $1\frac{1}{8}$ in. deep with the tap-drill hole going through the piece. On center line KK show a $\frac{7}{8}$-14UNF-3B through tapped hole. *Lower center*, at M show a $\frac{5}{8}$-18UNF-3A thread $1\frac{3}{4}$ in. long. *Lower right*, on center line P show a 2-4$\frac{1}{2}$UNC-2B hole in section. Completely specify all threads.

23

Threaded Fasteners

23.1 All engineering products, structures, etc., are composed of separate parts which must be held together by some means of fastening. Compared with permanent methods such as welding and riveting, threaded fasteners provide an advantage in that they may be removed, thus allowing disassembly of the parts. As distinguished from other fastening devices such as pins, rivets, keys, etc., a *threaded* fastener is a cylinder of metal having a screw thread on one end and, usually, a head on the other.

The quantity of threaded fasteners used each year is tremendous. Many varieties are obtainable, some standardized and others special. The stand-

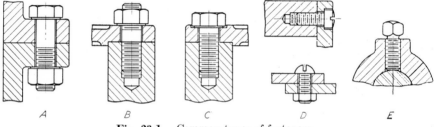

Fig. 23.1. Common types of fasteners.

ardization of such widely used products results in uniform and interchangeable parts obtainable without complicated and detailed specification and at low cost. Standardized fasteners should be employed wherever possible.

Most fasteners have descriptive names, as the "setscrew" which holds a part in a set or fixed position. The bolt derives its name from an early English use where it was employed as a fastener or pin for bolting a door. Five types, the bolt, stud, cap screw, machine screw, and setscrew, represent the bulk of threaded fasteners.

A *bolt*, Fig. 23.1*A*, having an integral head on one end and a thread on the other end, is passed through clearance holes in two parts and draws them together by means of a nut screwed on the threaded end.

A *stud*, Fig. 23.1*B*, is a rod threaded on each end. As used normally, the fastener passes through a clearance hole in one piece and screws permanently into a tapped hole in the other. A nut then draws the parts together.

A *cap screw*, Fig. 23.1*C*, passes through a clearance hole in one piece and screws into a tapped hole in the other. The head, an integral part of the screw, draws the parts together as the screw enters the tapped hole.

A *machine screw*, Fig. 23.1*D*, is a small fastener, used with a nut to function in the same manner as a bolt; or without a nut, to function as a cap screw.

A *setscrew*, Fig. 23.1*E*, screws into a tapped hole in an outer part, often a hub, and bears with its point against an inner part, usually a shaft.

410

23.2 American Standard square and hexagon bolts and nuts. Bolts with either square or hexagonal heads are sometimes called "machine bolts" to distinguish them from bolts of other head type, that is, carriage bolts, track bolts, etc. The present active standard covering square and hexagon bolts and nuts is the American Standard "Wrench-head Bolts and Nuts and Wrench Openings," last revised in 1941. To replace this, the proposed American Standard "Square and Hexagon Bolts and Nuts" was submitted to industry for comment in 1951. In all likelihood, the proposed standard will be adopted with slight, if any, change; hence it will be followed in this discussion as the latest information on the subject.

The standard provides two *series* as follows:

Regular boltheads and nuts are for general use. The dimensions and the resulting strengths are based on the theoretical analysis of the stresses and on results of numerous tests.

Heavy boltheads and nuts are for use where greater bearing surface is necessary. Therefore, for the same nominal size, they are larger in over-all dimensions than regular heads and nuts. They are used where a large clearance between the bolt and hole or a greater wrench-bearing surface is considered essential.

Square boltheads are standardized only in the regular series, while square nuts and hexagon boltheads and nuts are standardized in both regular and heavy. When specifying these fasteners, the word "heavy" is included if such a fastener is desired. Nothing need be said if a regular fastener is wanted.

The standard also provides two different types of *finish* for boltheads and nuts, which may be designated as "unfinished" and "semifinished."

Unfinished boltheads and nuts are, except for the threads, not machined on any surface. The bearing surface is plain.

Semifinished boltheads and nuts are machined or otherwise formed to provide a smooth bearing surface at right angles with the axis. For boltheads this will be a washer-faced bearing surface and for nuts either a washer face or a circular bearing surface produced by chamfering the corners.

Square boltheads and nuts, intended for less accurate types of work, are standardized in unfinished only, while hexagon boltheads and nuts are standardized in both unfinished and semifinished classes. In specifying a fastener, the finish is ignored if the unfinished class is wanted; if the semifinished is desired, the abbreviation "semifin" is included in the specification.

23.3 Square and hexagon bolt and nut information. The machine bolt, illustrated pictorially in hexagon form in Fig. 23.2, is widely used. This fastener is used, with a nut, to hold two or more pieces together by passing through clearance holes in each. Ordinarily, cold-drawn mild steel is used, although other materials may be specified.

The draftsman should be familiar with the following items:

General. *Nominal diameter.* The basic major diameter of the thread.

Width across flats (W). The distance separating parallel sides of the square or hexagon head or nut, corresponding with the nominal size of the wrench. This dimension (W) is obtainable from tables (see Appendix, page 655).

Tops of boltheads and nuts.   The tops of heads and nuts are flat with a chamfer to remove the sharp corners.   The angle of chamfer with the top surface is 25° for the square form and 30° for the hexagon form; both are drawn at 30°.   The diameter of the top circle is equal to the width across flats.

Washer face.   The washer face is a circular boss, turned or otherwise formed on the bearing surface of a bolthead or nut to make a smooth surface.   The diameter is equal to the width across flats.   The thickness is ⅟₆₄ in. for all fasteners.   A circular bearing surface may be obtained on a nut by chamfering the corners.   The angle of chamfer with the bearing face is 30°, and the diameter of the circle is equal to the width across flats.

Bolts. *Head form.*   The head form is *hexagon* in regular unfinished and semifinished and heavy unfinished and semifinished, *square* in regular unfinished only.

Bearing surface.   This surface is plain in unfinished, washer-faced in semifinished.

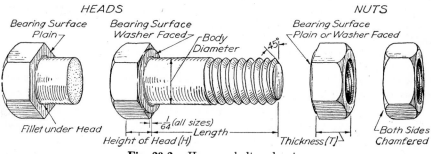

Fig. 23.2.   Hexagon bolt and nuts.

Height of head (H).   The height of the head is the over-all distance from the top to the bearing surface and includes the washer face where provided.   This dimension (H) is obtainable from tables (see Appendix, page 654).

Body diameter.   The body or shank diameter is normally equivalent to the major diameter of the thread.   Square bolts may be specified with "undersized body," which is approximately that of the thread pitch diameter.

Body (nominal) length.   This is the distance from the bearing surface to the extreme point.   Length increments vary with the diameter (see Appendix).

Thread length.   This is the distance from the extreme point to the last complete thread and varies with the diameter.   See footnote to the bolt table, Appendix.

Thread.   The thread shall be coarse series, class 2A.

Point.   The point of semifinished bolts shall be flat and chamfered or rounded.   It is usually drawn chamfered with the depth of chamfer conforming with the root of the thread.

Fillet under head.   This is a small fillet joining the head to the body; its radius varies with the size of the bolt and is usually omitted on the drawing.

Nuts. *Form.*   The nut form is *hexagon* in regular unfinished and semifinished and heavy unfinished and semifinished, *square* in regular and heavy unfinished only.   In addition, several types of special-purpose hexagon nuts are standardized (see paragraph 23.4).

Bearing surface.   This surface is plain in unfinished nuts, washer-faced or chamfered in semifinished.

Thickness of nut (T).   The thickness of a nut is the over-all distance from the top to the bearing surface and includes the thickness of the washer face where provided.

Thread.   The thread shall be coarse series, class 2B, for *unfinished* nuts and coarse-, fine-, or 8-pitch-thread series, class 2B, for *semifinished* nuts.

Tapped-hole countersink.   The tapped hole in semifinished nuts shall be countersunk slightly larger than the thread major diameter.   This is omitted on the drawing.

23.4   American Standard special-purpose nuts

Hexagon jam nuts.   Figs. 23.3 and 23.22.   Jam nuts are a common form of locking device.   They have the same dimensions (see Appendix, page 655) as corresponding plain nuts, excepting thickness, and are standardized in regular and heavy, unfinished and semi-finished, hexagon form only.

Semifinished hexagon slotted nuts, Figs. 23.3 and 23.22, are used with a cotter key or locking wire.   They have the same dimensions as corresponding plain nuts and are standardized in regular and heavy, semifinished, hexagon form only.

Semifinished hexagon thick nuts, Fig. 23.3, have the same dimensions as corresponding plain nuts, excepting thickness (see Appendix).   They are standardized in regular, semi-finished, hexagon form only.

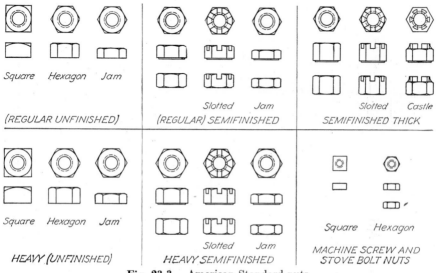

Fig. 23.3.   American Standard nuts.

Semifinished hexagon thick slotted nuts, Figs. 23.3 and 23.22, have the same dimensions as corresponding plain nuts, excepting thickness (see Appendix).   The thickness is the same as for unslotted thick nuts.   They are standardized in regular, semifinished, hexagon form only.

Semifinished hexagon castle nuts, Figs. 23.3 and 23.22, have the same over-all dimensions as corresponding thick nuts (see Appendix).   They are standardized in regular, semifinished, hexagon form only.

Machine-screw and stove-bolt nuts.   Fig. 23.3.   Hexagon machine-screw nuts have tops flat and are chamfered at 30°; bearing surfaces are normally plain but may be washer-faced, or chamfered, if so specified.   Square machine-screw nuts and stove-bolt nuts have flat tops and bottoms without chamfer.   The thread is *coarse-thread series* for square machine-screw or stove-bolt nuts, *coarse-* or *fine-thread series* for hexagon machine screw nuts, class 2B.   Most sizes are specified by number, see Appendix.

23.5   The drawing of fasteners may require considerable time when, for example, clearance conditions necessitate an accurately drawn fastener, using exact dimensions from tables.   Usually, however, their representation may be approximate or even symbolic, depending upon the note specifications that invariably accompany and exactly specify them.

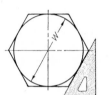

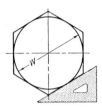

END VIEW OF HEXAGON BOLTHEAD

Draw a circle of diameter W and then draw the hexagon with T square and 30°–60° triangle.

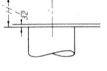

FACE VIEW OF HEXAGON BOLTHEAD

1. Establish the diameter, height of head, and washer-face thickness. The actual thickness of the washer face for all fasteners is $\frac{1}{64}$ in. but may be increased up to $\frac{1}{32}$ in. for the drawing.

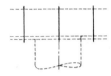

2. Draw, lightly, the vertical edges of the faces, projecting from the end view.

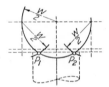

3. With radius of $W/2$ draw the circle arcs locating centers P_1 and P_2.

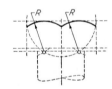

4. Draw chamfer arcs, using radii and centers shown.

5. Complete the views. Washer-face diameter is equal to W. For across-corners view, show 30° chamfer.

Fig. 23.4. Stages in drawing a hexagon head.

Before drawing a fastener, its *type, nominal diameter,* and *length,* if a bolt or screw, must be known. Knowing the type and diameter, other dimensions can be sought in the tables (see Appendix, page 654). Draftsmen experienced in drawing fasteners may establish satisfactory dimensions for a head or nut with memorized, simple formulas or through an instinctive understanding of the correct proportions.

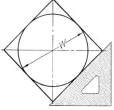

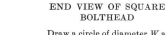

END VIEW OF SQUARE BOLTHEAD

Draw a circle of diameter W and then draw the square with T square and 45° triangle.

FACE VIEW OF SQUARE BOLTHEAD

1. Establish the diameter and the height of head.

2. Draw, lightly, the vertical edges of the faces, projecting from the end view.

3. Set compass to radius of $C/2$ and draw the circle arcs locating centers P_1 and P_2.	3. Set compass to radius of W and draw the circle arc locating the center P.

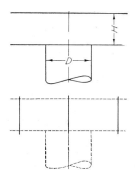

4. Draw chamfer arcs, using radii and centers shown.

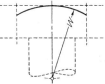

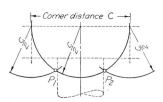

5. Complete the views. Show 30° chamfer on across-corners view.

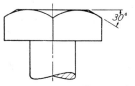

Fig. 23.5. Stages in drawing a square head.

Fasteners of hexagon or square form when viewed from the side show hyperbolic arcs resulting from the intersection of the chamfer cone and the plain sides. These arcs are always approximated with circle arcs. Experienced draftsmen will usually select appropriate radii and locate their centers by "trial and error," thus obtaining a well-proportioned drawing of the fastener. Since beginning students will require guidance in these matters, the following paragraph describes methods for drawing square and hexagon fasteners that give appropriate radii and centers.

23.6 To draw square and hexagon form fasteners. Square and hexagon heads and nuts are drawn "across corners" on all views showing the faces unless a special reason exists for drawing them "across flats." Figure 23.4 shows stages for drawing hexagon heads both "across corners" and

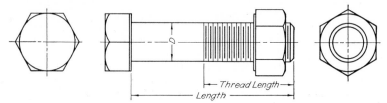

Fig. 23.6. American Standard regular hexagon semifinished bolt and nut.

"across flats," and Fig. 23.5 shows the same for square heads. The principles apply equally to the drawing of nuts. The following information must be known: (1) type of head or nut, (2) whether regular or heavy, (3) whether unfinished or semifinished, and (4) the nominal diameter. Using this information, additional data W (width across flats), H (height of head), and T (thickness of nut) are obtained from the tables (see Appendix, pages 654 and 655).

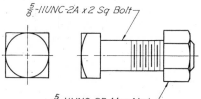

Fig. 23.7. ASA regular square bolt and regular unfinished hexagon nut.

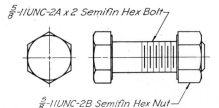

Fig. 23.8. ASA regular semifinished hexagon bolt and regular semifinished hexagon nut.

Figure 23.6 shows a regular semifinished hexagon bolt and nut, drawn by the method of Fig. 23.4, showing the head "across flats" and the nut "across corners." The length is selected from the bolt-length tables and the length of thread determined from the footnote to the bolt table, Appendix. Observe that the washer face shown in Fig. 23.4 will occur only with semifinished hexagon fasteners and is sometimes omitted from the drawings of these. Other views of bolts and nuts are shown in Figs. 23.7 to 23.10.

If an accurate drawing of the fastener is not essential, the W, H, and T dimensions of hexagon and square heads and nuts may be obtained from the nominal diameter and the following formulas; the resulting values will be quite close to the actual dimensions. For the regular series, $W = 1\frac{1}{2}D$,

$H = \frac{2}{3}D$, and $T = \frac{7}{8}D$; for the heavy series, $W = 1\frac{1}{2}D + \frac{1}{8}''$, $H = \frac{3}{4}D$, and $T = D$.

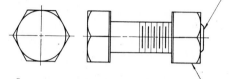

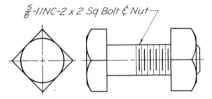

Fig. 23.9. ASA heavy semifinished hexagon bolt and heavy semifinished hexagon nut.

Fig. 23.10. ASA regular unfinished square bolt and square nut.

23.7 Specifying fasteners—ASA square and hexagon bolts and nuts. Standard fasteners are ordinarily specified by notes on the assembly drawing or parts list. The information needed includes the size (thread specification and nominal length) and the name; if the material is other than the mild steel ordinarily used, it must be stated.

Example: ¾-10UNC-2A × 4 Copper Heavy Semifinished Hexagon Bolt and ¾-10UNC-2B Regular Semifinished Hexagon Nut. This is abbreviated:
¾-10UNC-2A × 4 Copper Heavy Semifin Hex Bolt.
¾-10UNC-2B Semifin Hex Nut.

Figures 23.7 to 23.10, inclusive, show specifications for various ASA square and hexagon bolts and nuts. Remember that it is necessary to specify finish only when the fastener is semifinished (fasteners of the square form are always unfinished) also that the series designation is required only when the fastener is heavy (square bolts are standardized only in regular).

23.8 Studs. Fig. 23.11. The stud, a rod threaded on both ends, is used when through bolts are not suitable, for parts that must be removed frequently, such as cylinder heads, chest covers, etc. One end is screwed tightly into a tapped hole, and the projecting stud guides the removable piece to position. The end to be screwed permanently into position is called the "stud end" and the opposite end, the "nut end." The nut end is sometimes identified by rounding instead of chamfering. Studs have not been standardized by the ASA. The length of thread on the stud end is governed by the material tapped, see paragraph 22.20. The threads should jam at the top of the hole to prevent the stud from turning out when

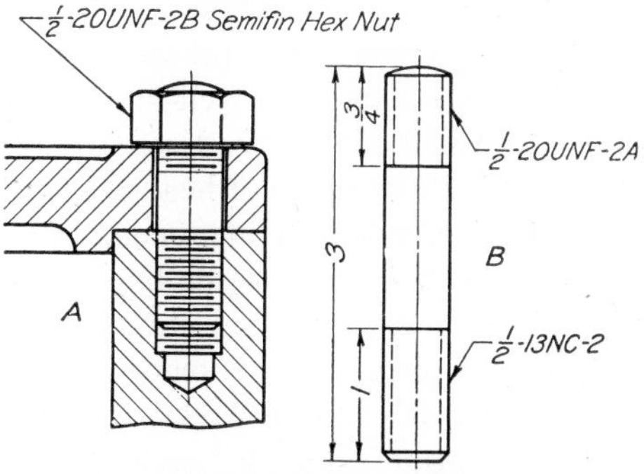

Fig. 23.11. Stud and nut.

the nut is removed.   The fit of the thread between the stud and tapped hole
should be tight.

The length of thread on the nut end should be such that there is no
danger of the nut binding before the parts are drawn together.   The name
"stud bolt" is often applied to a stud used as a through fastener with a
nut on each end.   The stud, a nonstandard part, is usually described on a
detail drawing, Fig. 23.11*B*.   The nut, being a standard part, is described
by note on the assembly drawing, Fig. 23.11*A*, or on the parts list.

23.9 Cap screws, Fig. 23.12, differ from bolts in that they are used
for fastening two pieces together by passing through a clearance hole in one
and screwing into a tapped hole in the other.   Cap screws are used on

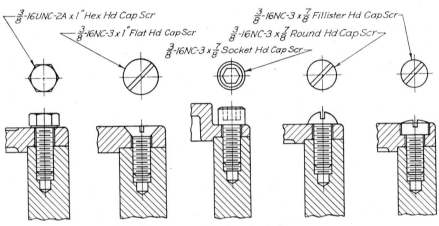

Fig. 23.12.   American Standard cap screws.

machine tools and other products requiring close dimensions and finished
appearances.   They are well-finished products; for example, the heads of
the slotted and socket head screws are machined, and all have chamfered
points.   The five types of heads shown in Fig. 23.12 are standard.   Detail
dimensions and length increments are given in the Appendix, page 657.
Threads are either coarse or fine and class 3 excepting the hexagon form
which is class 2A.   All are standardized in a single (regular) series except
the hexagon form which is made in both regular and heavy.   The hexagon
screw as standardized in ASA B18—1951 is a unified product resulting from
the combination of three previous products: the hexagon-head cap screw,
the automotive hexagon-head bolt, and the commercial close-tolerance
regular bolt.   Hence it may be identified by any of these names.   Sometimes it may be employed as a bolt with a nut, particularly in the automotive industry.   Hexagon cap screws have the same head dimensions and
thread lengths as semifinished hexagon bolts and are tabulated in the Appendix with these bolts.   The cap screw differs from the bolt by being held
to much closer body and eccentricity tolerances.   In addition, while the

hexagon screw may be washer-faced, as are semifinished bolts, it may also be double-chamfered instead.

The steps in drawing a hexagon-head cap screw are the same as for hexagon-head bolts. For other types of heads see Fig. 23.12 and obtain their sizes from tables in the Appendix. On the drawing it is not necessary to show clearance between the fastener and machine parts. However, clearance must be provided in the dimensioning. Specifications follow the same form as for bolts. See Fig. 23.12 for an example.

The nominal length of fasteners of any kind is the distance from the *largest diameter of the bearing surface* to the point; hence, with a flathead cap screw it is the over-all length.

23.10 Machine screws are small fasteners used principally in numbered diameter sizes. They are employed with a nut to function in the manner of a bolt or are used in a tapped hole like a cap screw. Threads are either coarse or fine and class 2. The finish is regularly bright, and the points are plain and sheared (unchamfered). The material used is commonly steel or brass. The nine standardized head shapes, Fig. 23.13, except for the hexagon, are available in slotted form as shown or with cross recesses, Fig.

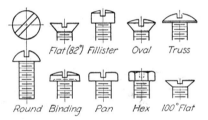

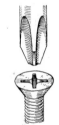

Fig. 23.13. American Standard machine screw heads.

Fig. 23.14. Recessed head and driver.

23.14. The size of the recess varies with the size of the screw. Two recess types occur: (1) intersecting slots with parallel sides converging to a sharp apex at the bottom of the recess (the same driver is used for all size recesses) and (2) large center opening, tapered wings, and a blunt bottom (five sizes of drivers needed).

The hexagon machine screw is not made with a cross recess but may be optionally slotted. Dimensions for drawing machine screw heads will be found in the Appendix, page 658. Machine screws are specified similarly to bolts and cap screws.

Examples: #10-24NC-2 × 2 Brass Slotted Flat Hd Mach Scr.
        #6-32NC-2 × ½ Recess Fil Hd Mach Scr.

23.11 Setscrews made of hardened steel are used for holding two parts in relative position, being screwed through one part and having the point set against the other. The American Standard square-head and headless screws are shown in Fig. 23.15. Types of points are shown in Fig. 23.16.

Headless setscrews are made to comply with the safety code of factory-inspection laws, which are very strict regarding the use of projecting screws on moving parts. Square-head setscrews have head proportions following the formulas of Fig. 23.15 and can be drawn by using the radii suggested there. A neck or a radius may be used under the head, and the points have the same dimensions as headless screws. Dimensions for headless setscrews are given in the Appendix, page 659.

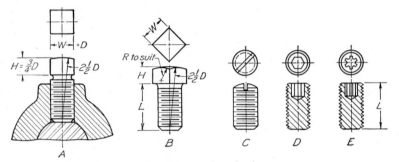

Fig. 23.15.   American Standard setscrews.

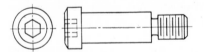

Fig. 23.16.   American Standard setscrew points.

The nominal length of square-head setscrews is the distance from under the head to the extreme point, and for headless setscrews it is the over-all length. The specification must include the type of point.

Examples: ¼-20UNC-2A × ¾ Sq Hd Cone Pt Setscrew.
                ½-13NC-3 × 2 Soc, Flat Pt Setscrew.

23.12 Shoulder screws, Fig. 23.17, are widely used for holding machine parts together and providing pivots, such as with cams, linkages, etc. They are also used with punch and die sets for attaching stripper plates

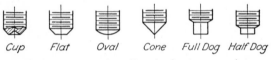

and are then commonly called "stripper bolts." Threads are coarse series, class 3. Detail dimensions are given in the Appendix, page 660.

Fig. 23.17.   American Standard shoulder screw.

23.13 American Standard round-head bolts, with nuts, are used only as through fasteners. The 11 head types in this group include carriage bolts, step bolts, round bolts, elevator bolts, and countersunk bolts. Several of the forms are for wood construction, having square sections, ribs, or fins under the head to prevent the fastener from turning. The heads of these fasteners are not machined or trimmed, hence may be somewhat irregular. The material is ordinarily mild steel. Threads are coarse series, class 2A; points are sheared, rounded, or flat and chamfered. Two body diameters are used: (1) a full-size body approximately equivalent to the nominal size, and (2) an undersize body approximating the pitch diameter of the thread. A table in the Appendix shows the form of heads and the proportions suitable for drawing purposes. Exact dimensions may be obtained from ASA B18.5—1951.

23.14 Plow bolts, Fig. 23.18, are used principally in agricultural equipment. The No. 3 and No. 7 heads are recommended for most new work.

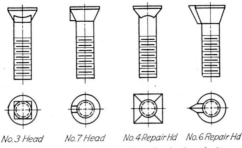

No.3 Head   No.7 Head   No.4 Repair Hd No.6 Repair Hd
Fig. 23.18. American Standard plow bolts.

Threads are coarse series, class 2A. For particulars and proportions, see ASA B.18.9—1950.

23.15 American Standard tapping screws. Tapping screws are hardened fasteners which form their own mating internal threads when driven into a hole of the proper size. For certain conditions and materials, these screws give a combination of speed and low production cost which makes them preferred. Many special types are available. The ASA has standardized head types conforming with all machine-screw heads except the binding and 100° flat heads. For drawing purposes, dimensions of machine-screw heads may be used. Sizes conform, in general, with machine-screw sizes. The ASA provides three types of threads and point combinations, Fig. 23.19. The threads are 60° with flattened crest and root; types A and B are interrupted threads, and all fasteners are threaded to the head. Full details will be found in ASA B18.6—1947.

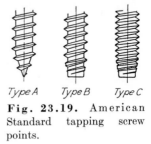

Type A   Type B   Type C
Fig. 23.19. American Standard tapping screw points.

23.16 Fasteners for wood. Many forms of threaded fasteners for use in wood are available. Some are illustrated in Fig. 23.20. Threads are interrupted, 60° form, with a gimlet point. The ASA has standardized lag bolts having square heads and also wood screws having flat, round, and oval heads. Lag boltheads follow the same dimensions and, in general, the same nominal sizes as regular square bolts. Specific information will be found in ASA B18—1951. Wood screws follow the same head dimensions and, in general, the same nominal sizes as the corresponding flat-, round-, and oval-head machine screws. The nominal sizes, however, are carried to higher numbers. See table in Appendix. Like machine screws, wood screw heads may be plain slotted or have either style of cross recess. Several kinds of finish are available, for example, bright steel, blued, nickel-plated, etc. Material is usually steel or brass.

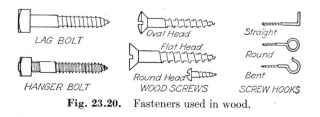

Fig. 23.20.　Fasteners used in wood.

23.17　Other forms of threaded fasteners. Many other forms of threaded fasteners, most of which have not been standardized, are in common use. Figure 23.21 illustrates some of these.

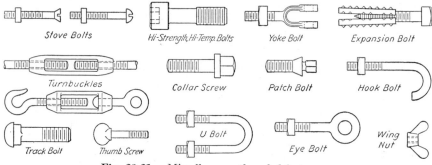

Fig. 23.21.　Miscellaneous threaded fasteners.

23.18　Lock nuts and locking devices. Fig. 23.22. Many different locking devices are used to prevent nuts from working loose. A screw thread holds securely unless the parts are subject to impact and vibration, as in a railroad-track joint or an automobile engine. A common device is the *jam nut A*. *Slotted nuts L* and *castle nuts M*, to be held with a cotter or wire, are commonly used in automotive and allied work. For additional information on jam, slotted, and castle nuts, see paragraph 23.4.

At *B* is shown a *round nut* locked by means of a setscrew. A brass plug is placed under the setscrew to prevent damage to the thread. This is a common type of adjusting nut used in machine-tool practice. *C* is a lock nut, in which the threads are deformed after cutting. Patented *spring washers* such as are shown at *D*, *E*, and *F* are common devices. Special patented nuts with plastic or fiber inserts or with distorted threads are in common use as locking devices. The locking action of *J, K, N,* and *O* should be evident from the figure.

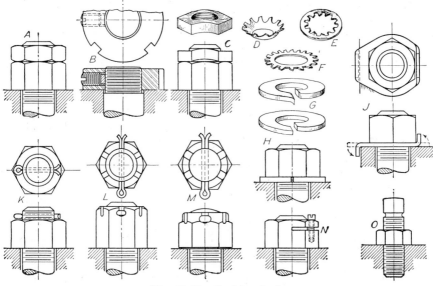

Fig. 23.22. Locking devices.

23.19   ASA Standard plain and lock washers. There are four standard ASA spring lock washers: light, medium, heavy, and extra heavy; these are shown at *G* and *H,* Fig. 23.22, and are specified by giving nominal diameter and series.

Example: ½ Heavy Lock Washer.

ASA plain washers are also standardized in four series, light, medium, heavy, and extra heavy, and are specified by giving nominal diameter and series.

Example: ⁷⁄₁₆ Light Plain Washer.

Dimensions of ASA plain and lock washers will be found in the Appendix, pages 666 and 667.

PROBLEMS

1. Draw one view of regular semifinished hexagon bolt and nut, across corners; diameter, 1 in.; length, 5 in.

2. Same as Prob. 1 for a heavy unfinished bolt and nut.

3. Same as Prob. 1 for a square bolt and nut.

4. Draw four ½- by 1½-in. cap screws, each with a different kind of head. Specify each.

5. Fig. 23.23. Show the pieces fastened together on center line EE with a $\frac{3}{4}$-in. hex-head cap screw and light lock washer. On center line AA show a $\frac{5}{8}$- by $1\frac{1}{2}$-in. shoulder screw.

6. Fig. 23.24. Show pieces fastened together with a $\frac{3}{4}$-in. square bolt and heavy square nut. Place nut at bottom.

7. Fig. 23.25. Fasten pieces together with a $\frac{3}{4}$-in. stud and regular semifinished hexagon nut.

8. Fig. 23.26. Fasten pieces together with a $\frac{3}{4}$-in. fillister-head cap screw.

9. Fig. 23.23. Fasten pieces together with a $\frac{3}{4}$-in. stud and regular semifinished hexagon nut and light lock washer. On center line AA show a $\frac{5}{8}$- by $1\frac{1}{2}$-in shoulder screw.

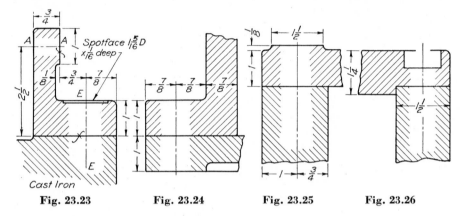

Fig. 23.23   Fig. 23.24   Fig. 23.25   Fig. 23.26

10. Fig. 23.24. Fasten pieces together with a 1-in. square bolt and unfinished hexagon nut. Draw bolthead across flats and nut at bottom across corners.

11. Fig. 23.25. Fasten pieces together with a $\frac{3}{4}$-in. hexagon cap screw.

12. Fig. 23.26. Fasten pieces together with a $\frac{5}{8}$-in. socket-head cap screw.

13. Draw one view of a round-head square-neck (carriage) bolt; diameter, 1 in.; length, 5 in.; with regular square nut.

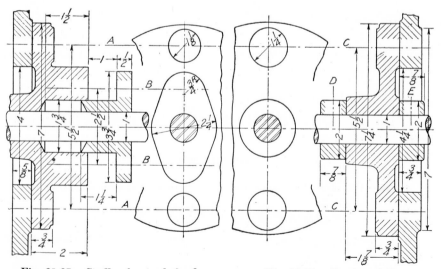

Fig. 23.27. Stuffing box and gland.   **Fig. 23.28.** Bearing plate.

14. Draw one view of a round-head rib-neck (carriage) bolt; diameter, ¾ in.; length, 4 in.; with regular square nut.

15. Draw two views of a shoulder screw; diameter, ¾ in.; shoulder length, 5 in.

16. Draw two views of a socket-head cap screw; diameter, 1¼ in.; length, 6 in.

17. Fig. 23.27. Draw the stuffing box and gland, showing the required fasteners. At *A* show ½-in. hexagon-head cap screws (six required). At *B* show ½-in. studs and regular semifinished hexagon nuts. Specify fasteners.

18. Fig. 23.28. Draw the bearing plate, showing the required fasteners. At *C* show ½-in. regular semifinished hexagon bolts and nuts (four required). At *D* show ½-in. socket setscrew. At *E* show ½-in. square-head setscrew. Setscrews to have cone points. Specify fasteners.

Problems 17 and 18 may be drawn together on an 11- by 17-in. sheet, or on separate sheets, showing full diameter of flanges.

19. Fig. 23.29. Draw the ball-bearing head, showing the required fasteners. At *A* show ½- by 1¾-in. regular semifinished hexagon bolts and nuts (six required), with heads to left and across flats. Note that this design prevents the heads from turning. At *B* show 5⁄16- by ¾-in. fillister-head cap screws (four required). At *C* show a ⅜- by ½-in. slotted flat-point setscrew with fiber disk to protect threads of spindle. Specify fasteners.

20. Fig. 23.30. Draw the plain-bearing head, showing the required fasteners. At *D* show ½- by 2-in. studs and regular semifinished hexagon nuts (six required); spotface 1 in. diameter by 1⁄16 in. deep. At *E* show ⅜- by 1-in. hexagon-head cap screws (four required). At *F* show a 7⁄16- by ⅞-in. square-head cup-point setscrew. At *G* show a ⅛-27NPT hole with a pipe plug. Show the 11⁄32-in. tap drill through for gun packing the gland. Specify fasteners.

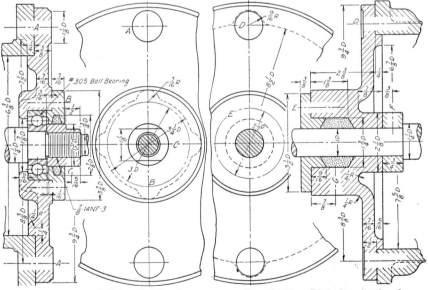

Fig. 23.29. Ball-bearing head.   **Fig. 23.30.** Plain-bearing head.

Problems 19 and 20 may be drawn together on an 11- by 17-in. sheet, or on separate sheets, showing full diameter of flanges.

24

Keys, Rivets, and Springs

24.1 Keys. In the making of machine drawings there is frequent occasion for representing key fasteners, used to prevent rotation of wheels, gears, etc., on their shafts. A key is a piece of metal, Fig. 24.1, placed so

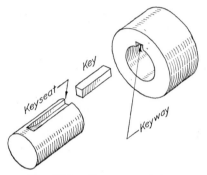

that part of it lies in a groove, called the *keyseat*, cut in a shaft. The key then extends somewhat above the shaft and fits into a *keyway* cut in a hub. Thus, after assembly, the key is partly in the shaft and partly in the hub, locking the two together so that one cannot rotate without the other.

24.2 Key types. The simplest key, geometrically, is the square key, placed *half* in the shaft and *half* in the hub, Fig. 24.2. A flat key is rectangular in cross section and is used

Fig. 24.1. Key nomenclature.

in the same manner as the square key. The gib-head key, Fig. 24.3, is tapered on its upper surface and is driven in to form a very secure fastening. Both square and flat (parallel and tapered stock) keys have been standardized by the ASA. Tables of standard sizes are given in the Appendix, page 661.

The Pratt and Whitney key, Fig. 24.4, is a variation on the square key. It is rectangular in cross section and has rounded ends. It is placed two-

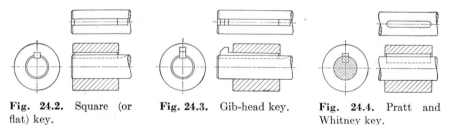

Fig. 24.2. Square (or flat) key.

Fig. 24.3. Gib-head key.

Fig. 24.4. Pratt and Whitney key.

thirds in the shaft and one-third in the hub. The key is proportioned so that the keyseat is square and the keyway is half as deep as it is wide.

Perhaps the most common key is the Woodruff, Fig. 24.5. This key is a flat segmental disk with either a flat (*A*) or round (*B*) bottom. The keyseat is semicylindrical and cut to a depth so that *half* the *width* of the key extends above the shaft and into the hub. Tables of dimensions are given on page 662, Appendix. A good basic rule for proportioning a Woodruff key to a given shaft is to have the width of the key one-fourth the diameter of the shaft and its radius equal to the radius of the shaft, selecting the standard key that comes nearest to these proportions. In drawing Woodruff keys, care should be taken to place the center for the arc above the top of the key to a distance equal to one-half the thickness of the saw used in splitting the blank. This amount is given in column E of the table in the Appendix.

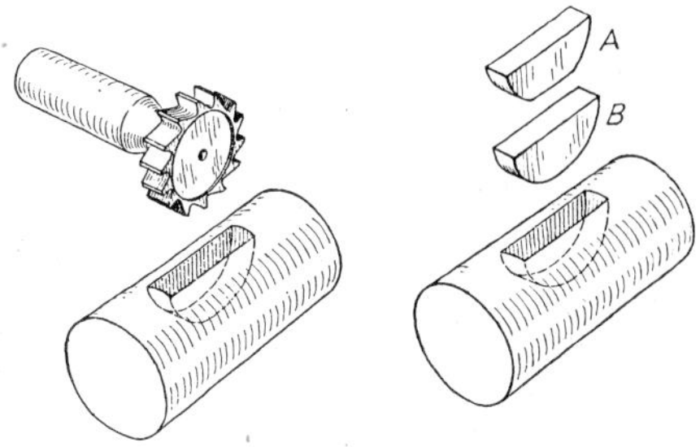

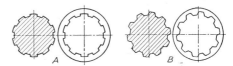

Fig. 24.5. Woodruff keys, cutter, and keyseat.

Figure 24.6 shows three keys for light duty: the saddle key (A), the flat key (B), and the pin or Nordberg key (C), which is used at the end of a shaft, as, for example, in fastening a handwheel.

Figure 24.7 shows some forms of heavy-duty keys. A is the Barth key, B the Kennedy key, and C the Lewis key for driving in one direction. In the latter two the line of shear is on the diagonal.

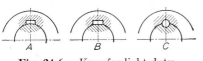

Fig. 24.6. Keys for light duty.

For very heavy duty, keys are not sufficiently strong and splines (grooves) are cut in both shaft and hub, arranged so that they fit one within the other, Fig. 24.8. A and B are two forms of splines widely used instead of keys. B is the newer ASA involute spline (B5.15—1946).

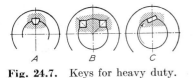

Fig. 24.7.   Keys for heavy duty.

Fig. 24.8.   Splined shafts and hubs.

24.3 Specification of keys. Keys are specified by note or number, depending upon the type.

Square and flat keys are specified by a note giving the width, height, and length.
Examples: ½ Square Key 2½ Lg.
    ½ × ⅜ Flat Key 2½ Lg.

Plain taper stock keys are specified by giving the width, the height at the large end, and the length. The height at the large end is measured at the distance W (width) from the large end. The taper is 1 to 96. See Appendix, page 661.
Examples: ⅜ × ⅜ × 1½ Square Plain Taper Key.
    ½ × ⅜ × 1¼ Flat Plain Taper Key.

Gib-head taper stock keys are specified by giving, except for name, the same information as for square or flat taper keys. See Appendix, page 661.
Examples: ¾ × ¾ × 2¼ Square Gib-head Taper Key.
    ⅞ × ⅝ × 2½ Flat Gib-head Taper Key.

Pratt and Whitney keys are specified by number or letter. See Appendix, page 664.
Example: Pratt and Whitney Key No. 6.
Woodruff keys are specified by number. See Appendix, page 662.

Dimensions and specifications of other types of keys may be found in handbooks or manufacturers' catalogues.

24.4 Dimensioning keyseats and keyways. The dimensioning of the seat and way for keys depends upon the purpose for which the drawing is intended. For unit production, when the keys are expected to be fitted by the machinist, nominal dimensions may be given, as in Fig. 24.9. For

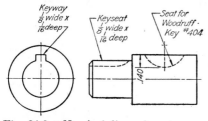

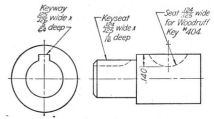

Fig. 24.9. Nominal dimensions (square and Woodruff keys).

Fig. 24.10. Limit dimensions (square and Woodruff keys).

quantity production, the limits of width (and depth if necessary) should be given as in Fig. 24.10. Pratt and Whitney keyseats and keyways are dimensioned as in Fig. 24.11. Note that the *length* of the keyseat is given to correspond with the specification of the key. If interchangeability is important and when careful gaging is necessary, the dimensions should be given as in Fig. 24.12 and the values expressed with limits.

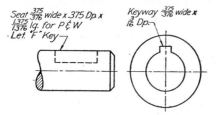

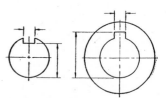

Fig. 24.11. Dimensioning *P* and *W* key-seat and keyway.

Fig. 24.12. Dimensions for interchangeable manufacture.

24.5 Rivets. Rivets are used for making permanent fastenings, generally between pieces of sheet or rolled metal. They are round bars of steel or wrought iron with a head formed on one end and are often put in place red hot so that a head may be formed on the other end by pressing or hammering. Rivet holes are punched, punched and reamed, or drilled larger than the diameter of the rivet, and the shank of the rivet is made just long enough to give sufficient metal to fill the hole completely and make the head.

Large rivets are used in structural-steel construction and in boiler and tank work. In structural work, only a few kinds of heads are normally

needed: the button, high button, and flat-top countersunk heads, Fig. 24.13.
The standard rivet symbols used in structural work are given on page 559.

For boiler and tank work the button, cone, round-top countersunk, and
pan heads are used. Plates are connected by either lap or butt joints.
In Fig. 24.14, *A* is a single-riveted lap joint and *B* a double-riveted lap joint.
C is a single-strap and *D* a double-strap butt joint.

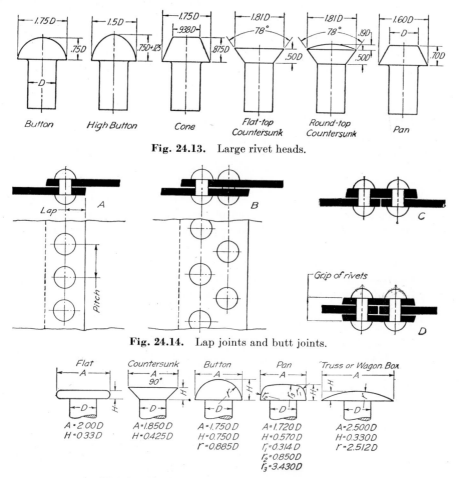

Fig. 24.13. Large rivet heads.

Fig. 24.14. Lap joints and butt joints.

Fig. 24.15. American Standard small rivet heads.

Large rivets are available in diameters of $\frac{1}{2}$ to $1\frac{3}{4}$ in., by increments of
even $\frac{1}{8}$ in. The length needed is governed by the "grip," as shown at
Fig. 24.14*D*, plus the length needed to form the head. Length of rivets for
various grip distances may be found in the handbook "Steel Construction"
published by the American Institute of Steel Construction.

Small rivets are used for fabricating light structural shapes and sheet
metal. ASA small rivet heads are shown in Fig. 24.15. Small rivets are

available in diameters of $\frac{3}{32}$ to $\frac{7}{16}$ in., by increments of even $\frac{1}{32}$ in. to $\frac{3}{8}$ in. diameter.

Tinners', coopers', and belt rivets are used for fastening thin sheet metal, wood, leather, rubber, etc. Standard heads and proportions are given in the Appendix, page 665.

24.6   Springs.   A spring may be defined as an elastic body designed to store energy when deflected. Springs are classified according to their geometrical form: helical or flat.

24.7   Helical springs are further classified as (1) compression, (2) extension, or (3) torsion, according to the intended action.   On working drawings helical springs are drawn either as a single-line convention, as in Fig. 24.16,

Compression Spring   Torsion Spring   Extension Spring

Fig. 24.16.   Single-line representation of springs.

or semiconventionally, as shown in Figs. 24.17, 24.18, and 24.19, by laying out the diameter (D) and pitch (P) of coils, then drawing a construction circle for the wire size at the limiting positions and conventionalizing the helix with straight lines.   Helical springs may be wound of round, square, or special section wire.

Compression springs are wound with the coils separated so that the unit may be compressed, and the ends may be either open or closed and may be

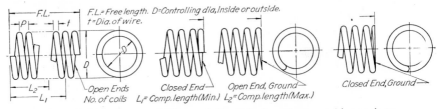

Fig. 24.17.   Representation and dimensioning of compression springs.

left plain or ground, as shown in Fig. 24.17.   The information that must be given for a compression spring is as follows:

1. Controlling diameter: (*a*) outside, (*b*) inside, (*c*) operates inside a tube, or (*d*) operates over a rod.
2. Wire or bar size.
3. Material (kind and grade).
4. Coils: (*a*) total number, (*b*) right or left hand.
5. Style of ends.
6. Load at deflected length of ___.
7. Load rate between ___ inches and ___ inches.
8. Maximum solid height.
9. Minimum compressed height in use.

Extension springs are wound with the loops in contact so that the unit may be extended, and the ends are usually made as a loop, as shown in Fig. 24.18. Special ends are sometimes required and are described by the

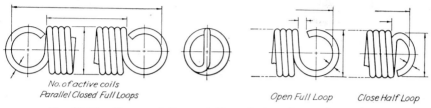

No. of active coils
Parallel Closed Full Loops

Open Full Loop   Close Half Loop

Fig. 24.18. Representation and dimensioning of extension springs.

ASA. The information that must be given for an extension spring is as follows:

    1. Free length: (a) over-all, (b) over coil, or (c) inside of hooks.
    2. Controlling diameter: (a) outside diameter, (b) inside diameter, or (c) operates inside a tube.
    3. Wire size.
    4. Material (kind and grade).
    5. Coils: (a) total number, (b) right or left hand.
    6. Style of ends.
    7. Load at inside hooks.
    8. Load rate, pounds per 1-in. deflection.
    9. Maximum extended length.

Torsion springs are wound with either closed or open coils, and the load is applied torsionally (at right angles to the spring axis). The ends may

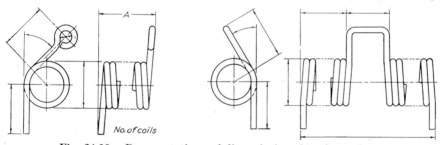

No. of coils

Fig. 24.19. Representation and dimensioning of torsion springs.

be shaped as hooks or as straight torsion arms, as indicated in Fig. 24.19. The information that must be given for a torsion spring is as follows:

    1. Free length (dimension A, Fig. 24.19).
    2. Controlling diameter: (a) outside diameter, (b) inside diameter, (c) operates inside a hole, or (d) operates over a rod.
    3. Wire size.
    4. Material (kind and grade).
    5. Coils: (a) total number, (b) right or left hand.
    6. Torque, pounds at __ degrees of deflection.
    7. Maximum deflection (degrees from free position).
    8. Style of ends.

24.8   Flat springs.   A flat spring may be classified as any spring made of flat or strip material.   Flat springs, Fig. 24.20, may be classified as (1) simple flat springs, formed so that the desired force will be applied when the spring is deflected in a direction opposite to the force; (2) power springs, made as a straight piece and then coiled inside an enclosing case; (3) Belleville springs, stamped of thin material and shaped so as to store energy

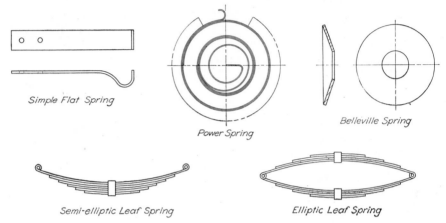

Simple Flat Spring

Power Spring

Belleville Spring

Semi-elliptic Leaf Spring   Elliptic Leaf Spring

Fig. 24.20.   Flat springs.

when deflected; and (4) leaf springs, in either elliptic or semielliptic form, made of several pieces of varying length, shaped so as to straighten when a load is applied.   The information that must be given for a flat spring is as follows:

1. A drawing showing the detailed shape and dimensions of the spring.
2. Material and heat-treatment.
3. Finish.

PROBLEMS

Group I.   Keys (key sizes will be found in Appendix)

   1. Fig. 24.21.   Draw hub and shaft as shown, with a Woodruff key in position.
   2. Fig. 24.22.   Draw hub and shaft as shown, with a square key 2 in. long in position.
   3. Fig. 24.23.   Draw hub and shaft as shown, with a gib-head key in position.
   4. Fig. 24.24.   Draw hub and shaft as shown, with a Pratt and Whitney key in position.

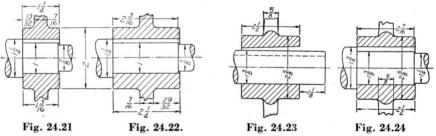

Fig. 24.21   **Fig. 24.22.**   **Fig. 24.23.**   **Fig. 24.24**

Group II. Rivets

5. Fig. 24.25. Draw top view and section of a single-riveted butt joint 10⅝ in. long. Pitch of rivets is 1¾ in. Use cone-head rivets.

6. Fig. 24.26. Draw a column section made of 15-in. by 33.9-lb channels with cover plates as shown, using ⅞-in. rivets (dimensions from the handbook of the American Institute of Steel Construction). Use buttonhead rivets on left side and flat-top countersunk head rivets on right side so that the outside surface is flush.

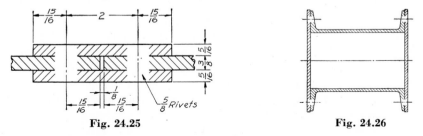

Fig. 24.25   **Fig. 24.26**

Group III. Springs

7. Draw a compression spring as follows: inside diameter, ¾ in.; wire size, ⅛ in. diameter; coils 14, right hand; squared and ground ends; free length, 3½ in.

8. Draw a compression spring as follows: outside diameter, 1 in.; wire size, ⁹⁄₃₂ in. diameter; coils 12, left hand; open ends, not ground; free length, 4 in.

9. Draw an extension spring as follows: free length over coils, 2 in.; outside diameter, 1⅛ in.; wire size, ⅛ in. diameter; coils 11, right hand; ends parallel closed loops.

10. Draw an extension spring as follows: free length inside hooks, 2¾ in.; inside diameter, ¾ in.; wire size, ⅛ in. diameter; coils 11, left hand; ends parallel closed half loops.

11. Draw a torsion spring as follows: free length over coils ¾ in.; inside diameter, 1⅛ in.; wire size, ⅛ in. diameter; coils 5, right hand; ends straight and turned to follow radial lines to center of spring and extend ½ in. from outside diameter of spring.

Piping Drawings

25.1 A familiarity with pipe and pipe fittings is necessary not only for making piping drawings but because pipe is often used as a construction material. A knowledge of pipe threads is also essential, because in the making of machine drawings there is frequently the need to represent and specify tapped holes to receive pipe for liquid or gas supply lines.

25.2 Kinds of pipe. Standard pipe of steel or wrought iron up to 12 in. in diameter is designated by its nominal inside diameter, which differs somewhat from the actual inside diameter. Early pipe manufacturers made the walls in the smaller sizes much too thick and in correcting this error in design took the excess from the inside to avoid changing the sizes of fittings. Three weights of pipe—standard, extra strong, and double extra strong—are in common use. In the same nominal size all three have the same outside diameter, that of standard-weight pipe, the added thickness for the extra and double extra strong being on the inside. Thus the outside diameter of 1-in. pipe in all three weights is 1.315 in., the inside diameter of standard 1-in. pipe is 1.05 in., of 1-in. extra strong, 0.951 in., and of XX, 0.587 in. The ASA in *ASA Bulletin* B36.10—1939 gives a means of specifying wall thicknesses by a series of schedule numbers which indicate approximate values for the expression $1,000 \times (P/S)$, where P is pressure and S the allowable stress. Recommended values for S may be obtained from the ASME Boiler Code, the American Standard Code for Pressure Piping (ASA, B31.1), etc. The designer computes the exact value of wall thickness as required for a given condition and selects from the schedule numbers the one nearest to the computed values. In the ASA system, pipe is designated by giving nominal pipe size and wall thickness, or nominal pipe size and weight per foot.

All pipe over 12 in. in diameter is designated as OD (outside-diameter) pipe and is specified by its outside diameter and thickness of metal. Boiler tubes in all sizes are known by their outside diameters.

Brass and copper pipe have the same nominal diameters as iron pipe but have thinner wall sections. There are two standard weights: regular and extra strong. Commercial lengths are 12 ft, with longer lengths made to order.

Seamless flexible metal tubing is used for conveying steam, gases, and liquids in all types of equipment such as locomotives, diesel engines, hydraulic presses, etc., where vibration is present, where outlets are not in alignment, and where there are moving parts.

Copper tubing is available in nominal diameters of ⅛ to 12 in. and in four weights known as classes K, L, M, and O. Class K is extra-heavy hard, class L is heavy hard, class M is standard hard, and class O is light hard.

Lead pipe and lead-lined pipe are used in chemical work. Cast-iron pipe is used for water and gas in underground mains and for drains in buildings.

Many other kinds of pipe are in more or less general use and are known by trade names, such as hydraulic pipe, merchant casing, API (American Petroleum Institute) pipe, etc. Details may be found in manufacturers' catalogues.

25.3 Pipe fittings. Pipe fittings are the parts used in connecting and "making up" pipe. They are usually cast iron or malleable iron, except

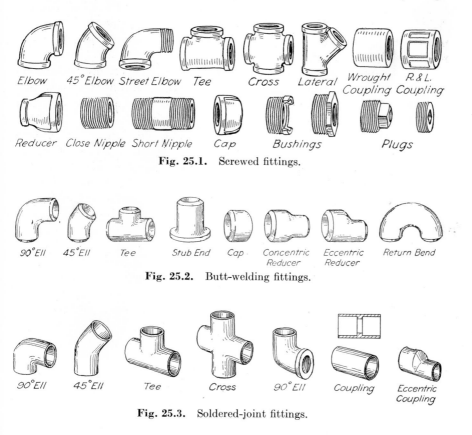

Elbow   45° Elbow   Street Elbow   Tee   Cross   Lateral   Wrought   R. & L.
                                                                  Coupling Coupling

Reducer   Close Nipple Short Nipple   Cap   Bushings   Plugs

Fig. 25.1. Screwed fittings.

90° Ell   45° Ell   Tee   Stub End   Cap   Concentric   Eccentric   Return Bend
                                              Reducer   Reducer

Fig. 25.2. Butt-welding fittings.

90° Ell   45° Ell   Tee   Cross   90° Ell   Coupling   Eccentric
                                                          Coupling

Fig. 25.3. Soldered-joint fittings.

couplings, which are wrought or malleable iron. Brass and other alloys are employed for special uses. Standard pipe fittings are *screwed fittings*, Fig. 25.1 and pages 675 and 676, Appendix; *flanged fittings*, page 678, Appendix; *welded-joint fittings*, Fig. 25.2 and page 679, Appendix; *soldered-joint fittings*, Fig. 25.3; and *bell-and-spigot fittings*. *Tube couplings* are usually patented arrangements, in general requiring the flaring of the ends of the tubing. Manufacturers' catalogues should be consulted for details and methods of specifying. *Elbows* are used to change the direction of a pipe line either 90° or 45°. The *street elbow* has male threads on one end, thus eliminating one pipe joint if used at a fitting. *Tees* connect three pipes, and *crosses* connect four. *Laterals* are made with the third opening at 45° or 60° to the straight run.

Straight sections of pipe are made in 12- to 20-ft lengths and are connected by *couplings*. These are short cylinders, threaded on the inside. A right-hand coupling has right-hand threads at both ends. To close a system of piping, although a union is preferable, a *right-and-left coupling* is sometimes used. A *reducer* is similar to a coupling but has the two ends threaded for different sized pipe. Pipes are also connected by screwing them into cast-iron flanges and bolting the flanges together. Unless the pressures are very low, flanged fittings are recommended for all systems requiring pipe over 4 in. in diameter.

Nipples are short pieces of pipe threaded on both ends. If the threaded portions meet, the fitting is a *close nipple;* if there is a short unthreaded portion, it is a *short nipple.* Long and extra-long nipples range in length up to 24 in.

A *cap* is used to close the end of a pipe. A *plug* is used to close an opening in a fitting. A *bushing* is used to reduce the size of an opening. *Unions* are used to close systems and to connect pipes that are to be taken down occasionally. A screwed union, Fig. 25.4, is composed of three pieces, two of which, A and B, are screwed firmly on the ends of the pipes

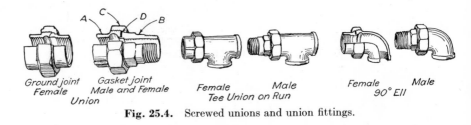

Fig. 25.4. Screwed unions and union fittings.

to be connected. The third piece C draws them together, the gasket D forming a tight joint. Unions are also made with ground joints or with special metallic joints instead of gaskets. Several forms of screwed unions and union fittings are shown in Fig. 25.4. Flange unions in a variety of forms are used for large sizes of pipe.

25.4 Valves. Figure 25.5 shows a few types of valves used in piping. A is a gate valve, used for water and other liquids, as it allows a straight flow. B is a plug valve, opened and closed with a quarter turn; C, a ball-check valve; and E, a swing-check valve permitting flow in one direction. For heavy liquids the ball-check valve is preferred. D is a globe valve, used for throttling steam or fluids; F is a butterfly valve, opened and closed with a quarter turn, but not steamtight, and used only as a check or damper.

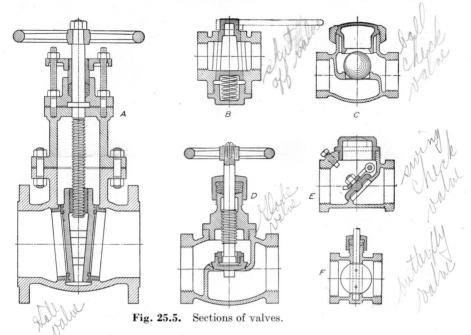

Fig. 25.5.   Sections of valves.

25.5 Specification of fittings. Fittings are specified by giving the nominal pipe size, material, and name.

Examples: 2″ M.I. Elbow.   1½″ Brass Tee.

When a fitting connects more than one size of pipe, the size of the largest run opening is given first, followed by the size at the opposite end of the run.   The diagrams of Fig. 25.6 show the order of specifying reducing

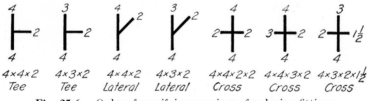

4×4×2	4×3×2	4×4×2	4×3×2	4×4×2×2	4×4×3×2	4×3×2×1½
Tee	Tee	Lateral	Lateral	Cross	Cross	Cross

Fig. 25.6.   Order of specifying openings of reducing fittings.

fittings.   The word "male" must follow the size of the opening if an external thread is wanted.

Example: 2 × 1 (male) × ¾ M.I. Tee.

Valves are specified by giving the nominal size, material, and type.

Example: 1″ Iron Body Brass-mounted Globe Valve.   (If a particular valve is required it is best to give, in addition, "Manufacturer's No.___ or equal.")

25.6 Pipe threads. When screwed fittings are used or when a connection must be made to a tapped hole, pipe is threaded on the ends for the purpose. The ASA provides two types of pipe thread: tapered and straight. The normal type employs a taper internal and taper external thread. This thread (originated in 1882 as the Briggs Standard) is illustrated in Fig. 25.7. The threads are cut on a taper of $\frac{1}{16}$ in. per inch, measured on the diameter, thus fixing the distance a pipe enters a fitting and ensuring a tight joint. Taper threads are recommended by the ASA for all uses with the exception of the following five types of joints: type 1, pressure-tight joints for pipe

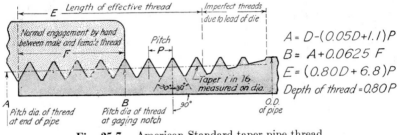

$$A = D-(0.05D+1.1)P$$
$$B = A+0.0625\,F$$
$$E = (0.80D+6.8)P$$
$$\text{Depth of thread} = 0.80P$$

Fig. 25.7. American Standard taper pipe thread.

couplings; type 2, pressure-tight joints for grease-cup, fuel, and oil fittings; type 3, free-fitting mechanical joints for fixtures; type 4, loose-fitting mechanical joints with lock nuts; type 5, loose-fitting mechanical joints for hose coupling. For these joints straight pipe threads may be used. The number of threads per inch is the same in taper and straight pipe threads. Actual diameters vary for the different types of joints. When needed they may be obtained from the ASA bulletins. A common practice is to use a taper external thread with a straight internal thread, on the assumption that the materials are sufficiently ductile to allow the threads to adjust

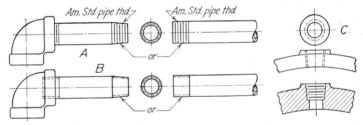

Fig. 25.8. Conventional pipe threads.

themselves to the taper thread. All pipe threads are assumed to be tapered unless otherwise specified.

Pipe threads are represented by the same conventional symbols as bolt threads. The taper is so slight that it does not show unless exaggerated. It need not be indicated unless it is desired to call attention to it, as in Fig. 25.8. In plan view, as at C, the dotted circle should be the actual outside diameter of the pipe specified. The length of effective thread is $E = (0.80D + 6.8)P$, Fig. 25.7.

25.7 Specification of threads. Pipe threads are specified by giving the nominal pipe diameter, number of threads per inch, and the standard letter symbol to denote the type of thread. The following ASA symbols are used:

```
  NPT  = taper pipe thread.
 NPTF  = taper pipe thread (dryseal).
  NPS  = straight pipe thread.
 NPSC  = straight pipe thread in couplings.
 NPSI  = intermediate internal straight pipe thread (dryseal).
 NPSF  = internal straight pipe thread (dryseal).
 NPSM  = straight pipe thread for mechanical joints.
 NPSL  = straight pipe thread for locknuts and locknut pipe threads.
 NPSH  = straight pipe thread for hose couplings and nipples.
 NPTR  = taper pipe thread for railing fittings.
```

Examples: $\frac{1}{2}$-14NPT. $\qquad\qquad$ $2\frac{1}{2}$-8NPTR.

The specification for a tapped (pipe-thread) hole must include the tap drill size.

Example: $\frac{59}{64}$ Drill, $\frac{3}{4}$-14NPT.

Dimensions of ASA taper pipe threads (NPT) are given on page 674, Appendix. Dimensions of other pipe threads are given in ASA B2.1 and in manufacturers' catalogues.

25.8 Piping drawings. Two general systems are used: (1) *scale layout* and (2) *diagrammatic.* Scale layouts are used principally for large pipe (usually flanged), as in boiler and power-plant work where lengths are critical and especially when the pipe is not cut and fitted in the field. Also, smaller pipe may be thus detailed when the parts are cut and threaded and then shipped to the job. Figure 25.9 is an example of a scale layout. The

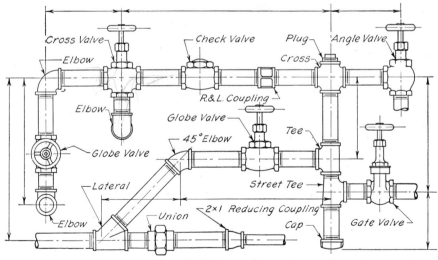

Note: All fittings 2"M.I. unless otherwise noted.
All valves 2" Iron body.

Fig. 25.9. Scale layout of piping.

fittings may be specified on the drawing as in Fig. 25.9 or on a bill of material. On small-scale drawings such as architectural plans, plant layouts, etc., or on sketches, the diagrammatic system is used in which the fittings are shown by symbols (page 683, Appendix) and the runs of pipe are shown by a single line, regardless of the pipe diameters, as shown in Fig. 25.10.   When lines carry either different liquids or different states of a liquid, they are identified

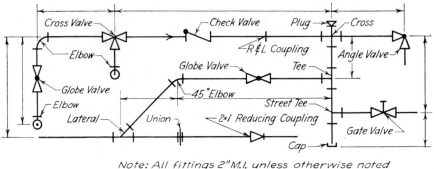

Note: All fittings 2"M.I. unless otherwise noted
All valves 2" Iron body.

Fig. 25.10.   Piping drawing, diagrammatic.

by coded line symbols.   The standard code for hot water, steam, cold water, etc., is given on page 683, Appendix.   The single line should be made heavier than the other lines of the drawing.

The arrangement of views is generally in orthographic projection, Fig. 25.11A.   Sometimes, however, it is clearer to swing all the piping into one plane and make only one "developed view" as at B.   Isometric and oblique diagrams, used either alone or in conjunction with orthographic or developed drawings, are very often employed in representing piping, as at C.

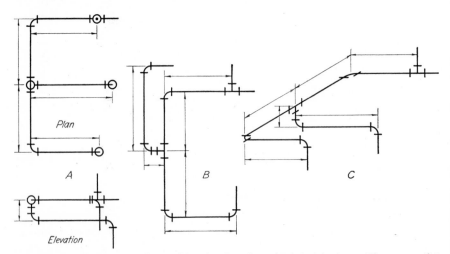

Fig. 25.11.   Piping in orthographic, developed, and pictorial views (diagrammatic).

25.9 Dimensioning a pipe drawing. The dimensions on a piping drawing are principally *location* dimensions, all of which are made to center lines, both in single-line diagrams and in scale layouts, as shown in Figs. 25.9 and 25.10. Valves and fittings are located by measurements to their centers, and the allowances for make-up are left to the pipe fitter. In designing a piping layout, care should be taken to locate valves so that they are easily accessible and have ample clearance at the handwheels. The *sizes* of pipe should be specified by notes telling the nominal diameters, never by dimension lines on the drawing of the pipes. The fittings are specified by note, as described in paragraph 25.5. Very complete notes are an important essential of all piping drawings and sketches.

When it is necessary to dimension the actual length of a piece of pipe, the distance can be calculated by using the over-all fitting dimensions and accounting for the entrance length of the pipe threads.

Dimensions for standard pipe and for various fittings are given in the Appendix.

PROBLEMS

Group I. Pipe fittings

1. In the upper left-hand corner of one sheet draw a 2-in. tee (full size). Plug one outlet. In the second, place a 2- by 1½-in. bushing; in the remaining outlet use a 2-in. close nipple and on it screw a 2- by 1½-in. reducing coupling. Lay out remainder of sheet so as to include the following 1½-in. fittings: coupling, globe valve, R&L coupling, angle valve, 45° ell, 90° ell, 45° Y, cross, cap, three-part union, flange union. Add extra pipe, nipples, and fittings so that the system will close at the reducing fitting first drawn.

2. Make a one-view drawing of a 1½-in. globe valve. Use an 8½- by 11-in. sheet. See Appendix for proportions.

3. Same as Prob. 2 for a 1½-in. angle globe valve.

4. Same as Prob. 2 for a 1¼-in. gate valve.

Group II. Piping layouts to scale

5. Fig. 25.12. (*a*) Make a scale layout of the sodium hydroxide

$$(NaOH + H_2O)$$

lines of the hydrogen generator. Show cross section of the headers, one cylinder of the pump, a portion of the sodium hydroxide tank, and a portion of the top of one generator. (*b*) Make a scale layout of the hydrogen (H_2) line of the hydrogen generator. Show a portion of each generator with the lines in place. Use 11- by 17-in. paper. Scale, $3'' = 1'-0''$. Use standard pipe, malleable fittings, brass valves. Make a bill of material listing all pipe, valves, and fittings needed.

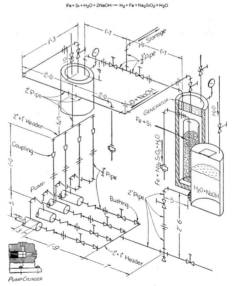

SCHEMATIC DIAGRAM OF HYDROGEN GENERATOR

$Fe + Si + H_2O + 2NaOH \rightarrow H_2 + Fe + Na_2SO_2 + H_2O$

Fig. 25.12. Hydrogen generator.

The operation of the unit is as follows: After the generators have been charged with ferrosilicon (Fe + Si), a mixture of sodium hydroxide (NaOH) and water (H_2O) is pumped into the generators. When the ferrosilicon, sodium hydroxide, and water are together in the generator, they react to form hydrogen (H_2) and a sludge (Fe, Na_2SiO_2 and H_2O). As the hydrogen gas forms, the internal pressure of the generator is built up. To keep the reaction going, additional water and sodium hydroxide solution has to be pumped into the generators against this pressure. As the hydrogen gas is formed, it is piped to a storage tank. The sludge is siphoned off periodically to prevent excessive accumulation that might retard the reaction.

A four-cylinder pump is used to provide a more uniform flow of fluid than would be obtained if a large single-cylinder pump were used. The four cylinders of the pump are connected to one intake line and to one exhaust line through headers (manifolds). Instead of building an intake and an exhaust valve into the cylinders of the pump, standard ball-type check valves are used and are connected as near as possible to the pump cylinders by means of standard pipe and fittings.

6. Fig. 25.13. Make a scale layout of the gas-burner installation. Specify fittings and give center-line dimensions. Use 11- by 17-in. paper. Scale, $3'' = 1'-0''$.

7. Fig. 25.14. Make a scale layout of a Grinnell industrial heating unit, closed return, gravity system. Use center-line distances and placement of fittings as shown in the diagram. Use 3-in. supply main, 2-in. pipe and fittings to unit, ¾-in. pipe and fittings from unit to 2-in. return main. Add all necessary notes and dimensions. Use an 11- by 17-in. sheet. Scale, $3'' = 1'-0''$.

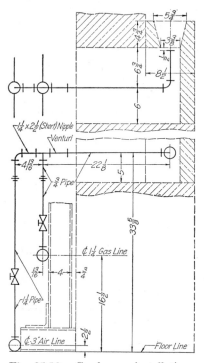

Fig. 25.13. Gas-burner installation.

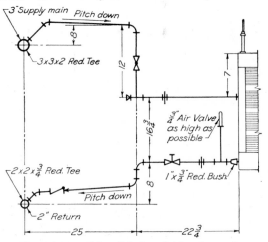

Fig. 25.14. Grinnell industrial heating unit.

Group III. Piping layouts, diagrammatic

8. Fig. 25.15. *A* is a storage tank for supplying the mixing tanks *B*, *C*, and *D* and is located directly above them. The capacities of the mixers are in the ratios of 1, 2, and 3. Design (in one view) a piping system with sizes such that, neglecting frictional losses, the three tanks will fill in approximately the same time. So arrange the piping that any one of the tanks can be cut out or removed for repairs without disturbing the others. Use single-line conventional representation. Dimension to center lines and specify the fittings.

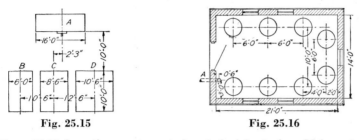

Fig. 25.15   Fig. 25.16

9. Figure 25.16 shows the arrangement of a set of mixing tanks. Make an isometric drawing of an overhead piping system to supply water to each tank. Water supply enters the building through a 2½-in. main at point *A*, 3 ft below floor level. Place all pipe 10 ft above floor level, except riser from water main and drops to tanks, which are to end with globe valves 5 ft above floor level. Arrange the system to use as little pipe and as few fittings as possible. Neglecting frictional losses, sizes of pipe used should be such that they will deliver approximately an equal volume of water to each tank if all were being filled at the same time. The pipe size at the tank should not be less than ¾ in. Dimension and specify all pipe and fittings.

10. Make a drawing of the system of Prob. 9. Show the layout in a developed view. Dimension from center to center and specify all pipe and fittings.

11. Make a list of the pipe and fittings to be ordered for the system of Prob. 9. Arrange the list in a table, heading the columns as below:

Size	Pipe lengths	Valves		Fittings		Material	Remarks (make, kind of threads, etc.)
		Number	Kind	Number	Kind		

12. Make an oblique drawing of a system of piping to supply the tanks in Fig. 25.16. All piping except risers shall be in a trench 1 ft below floor level. Risers should not run higher than 6 ft above floor level. Other conditions as in Prob. 9.

13. Figure 25.17 shows the outline of the right-hand half of a bank of eight heat-treating furnaces. *X* and *Y* are the leadins from the compressed-air and fuel mains. Draw the piping layout, using single-line representation, to distribute the air and fuel to the furnaces. The pipe sizes should be reduced proportionately as the oven leads are taken off. Each tail pipe should be removable without disturbing the other leads or closing down the other furnaces. Dimension the piping layout and make a bill of material for the pipe and fittings.

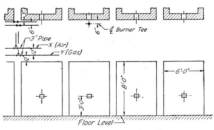

Fig. 25.17. Heat-treating furnaces.

26

Welding Drawings

26.1 The subject of welding is of particular interest to the draftsman for two reasons. First, welding is being used more and more extensively for permanent fastenings in places where formerly rivets or bolts were employed. Second, the method of designing and fabricating welded machine parts that have heretofore been made as castings or forgings is gaining rapidly in favor. As to the strength of welded connections, it is possible to make a welded joint stronger than the members joined.

26.2 **Welding processes** are classified according to the manner in which the welded joint is completed: (1) pressure welding (forging) and (2) non-pressure welding (fusion and brazing). Actually all welding is a fusion process, but by long usage, fusion welding is understood to include the arc, gas, and thermit processes.

In arc welding, pieces of metal to be welded are brought to the proper welding temperature at point of contact by the heat liberated at the arc terminals so that the metals are completely fused into each other.

In gas or oxyacetylene welding a high-temperature flame is produced by igniting a mixture of two gases, usually oxygen and acetylene.

Resistance welding is a heat and squeeze process. The parts to be welded, while being forced together by mechanical pressure, are raised to the temperature of fusion by the passage of a heavy electrical current through the junction.

26.3 **Classification of welded joints.** Figure 26.1 shows the basic types of joints, which are classified by the method of assembly of the parts. The applicable welds are listed underneath each joint.

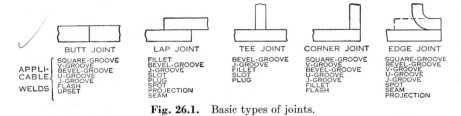

APPLI-CABLE WELDS	BUTT JOINT	LAP JOINT	TEE JOINT	CORNER JOINT	EDGE JOINT
	SQUARE-GROOVE V-GROOVE BEVEL-GROOVE U-GROOVE J-GROOVE FLASH UPSET	FILLET BEVEL-GROOVE J-GROOVE SLOT PLUG SPOT PROJECTION SEAM	BEVEL-GROOVE J-GROOVE FILLET SLOT PLUG	SQUARE-GROOVE V-GROOVE BEVEL-GROOVE U-GROOVE J-GROOVE FILLET FLASH	SQUARE-GROOVE BEVEL-GROOVE V-GROOVE U-GROOVE J-GROOVE SPOT SEAM PROJECTION

Fig. 26.1. Basic types of joints.

26.4 **Types of welds.** Figure 26.2 shows in cross section the fundamental types of welds. For bead and fillet welds, the pieces are not prepared by cutting before making the weld, and the essential difference in V, bevel, U, and J welds is in the preparation of the parts joined. Pairs of the fundamental welds such as double V, double bevel, etc., make a further variety. Almost any combination is possible for complicated connections.

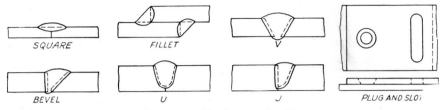

Fig. 26.2.   Fundamental welds.

26.5   The individual basic weld symbols originate either from the preparation of the pieces making up the joint or, where no preparation is necessary, from the section shape of the weld.   Figure 26.3 shows the fundamental welds and the basic symbols specifying these welds.

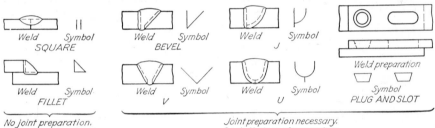

Fig. 26.3.   Fundamental welds and individual basic symbols.

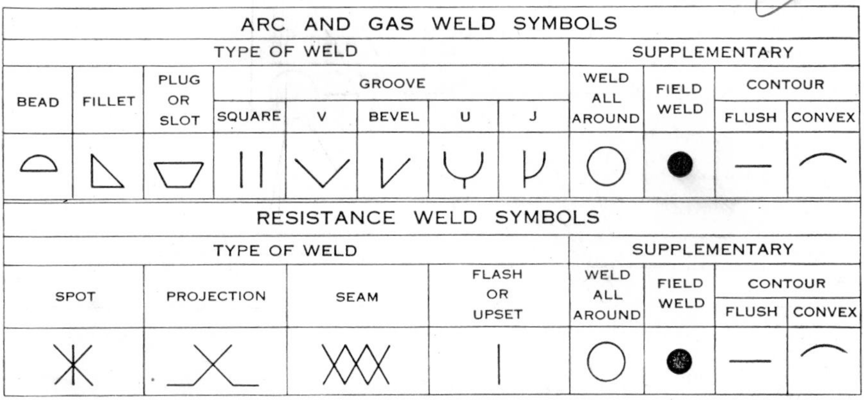

ARC AND GAS WELD SYMBOLS											
TYPE OF WELD								SUPPLEMENTARY			
BEAD	FILLET	PLUG OR SLOT	GROOVE					WELD ALL AROUND	FIELD WELD	CONTOUR	
			SQUARE	V	BEVEL	U	J			FLUSH	CONVEX
⌒	◿	⏢	||	V	V	Ụ	Ụ	◯	●	—	⌒
RESISTANCE WELD SYMBOLS											
TYPE OF WELD					SUPPLEMENTARY						
SPOT		PROJECTION	SEAM		FLASH OR UPSET	WELD ALL AROUND	FIELD WELD	CONTOUR			
								FLUSH	CONVEX		
✕		⋅✕	XXX		|	◯	✦	—	⌒		

Fig. 26.4.   American Standard weld symbols.

Figure 26.4 shows the American Standard basic arc, gas, and resistance weld symbols, including supplementary symbols.

26.6   Sizes of welds.   In addition to specifying the type of weld to be made, a description of the size is also necessary.   Thus, the *basic weld symbol* plus *size specifications* are the elements included in a complete welding symbol. Figure 26.5 shows weld sizes. The dimensions of root opening, depth of preparation, and included angle are the important sizes to specify for grooved welds. The size of a 45° fillet weld is the dimension shown.

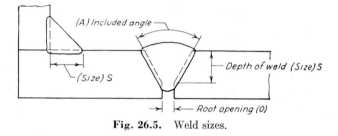

Fig. 26.5. Weld sizes.

Unequal-leg fillet welds are specified by giving the size of both legs, as described in Art. II-2b.[1] Sizes of plug and slot welds are given as specified in Arts. V and VI.

26.7 The complete welding symbol. Figure 26.6 shows the basic form of the welding symbol and gives the position of the various marks and dimensions. There is a distinction between the terms *weld symbol* (paragraph 26.5) and *welding symbol*.

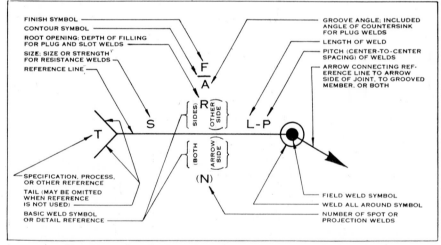

Fig. 26.6. Standard location of elements of a welding symbol.

The *weld symbol* is the ideograph (Fig. 26.4) used to indicate the desired type of weld. The assembled *welding symbol* consists of the following eight elements, or such of these elements as are necessary: (1) reference line, (2) arrow, (3) basic weld symbols, (4) dimensions and other data, (5) supplementary symbols, (6) finish symbols, (7) tail, (8) specification process or other references.

[1] References to Articles refer to the Instructions for Use of Welding Symbols, pages 450 to 460.

Figure 26.7 summarizes the important points dealing with the specification of welds and the location of weld symbols.   Figure 26.7 also gives some general directions for drawing the symbols and shows how the symbols appear when completed.

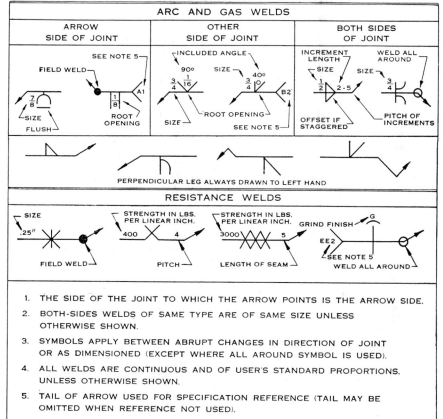

Fig. 26.7.   Location of weld symbols and specifications.

Figure 26.8 classifies welded joints and shows the symbols for each.

The arrow (see Fig. 26.8) points to the grooved member at a point near the weld.   The side of the weld pointed to is always called the arrow side. For nonsymmetrical welds (bevel and *J*), in order to show *which* piece is to be prepared, the leader must be made with a definite break pointing toward the piece to be prepared, as shown by the bevel and *J* welds in Fig. 26.8 and described in Art. I-15.   The tail of the arrow is used to hold a reference only when specification of strength, type of rod, etc., is to be given.   The individual basic symbols are placed on the basic form to describe any possible combination of welds for a complete joint.   Every simple weld that is a part of the complete joint must be specified.

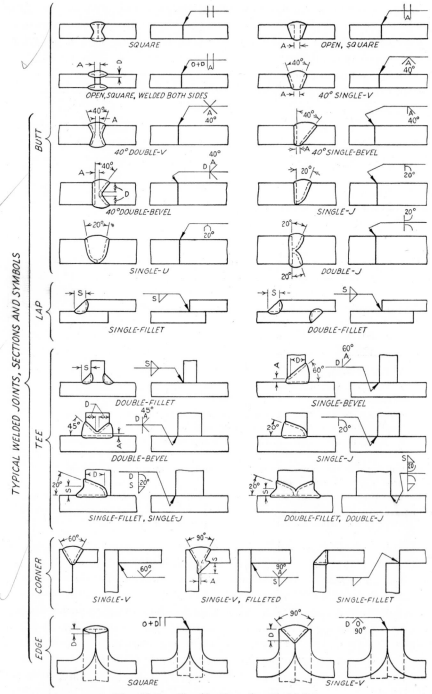

Fig. 26.8. Classification of welded joints.

26.8   Welding drawings.   A welding drawing shows a unit or part made of several pieces of metal, with each welded joint described and specified. Figure 26.9 shows the detail drawing of a part made of cast iron, and Fig. 26.10 shows a part identical in function, but made up by welding.   A comparison of the two drawings shows the essential differences both in construction and in drawing technique.   Note the absence of fillets and rounds in

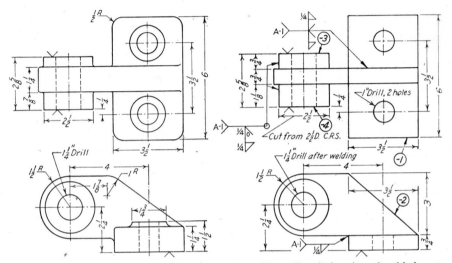

Fig. 26.9.   Detail drawing of casting.   **Fig. 26.10.**   Detail drawing of welded part.

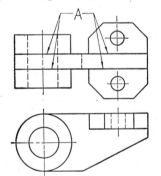

Fig. 26.11.   Joint lines shown.

the welding drawing.   Note also that all the pieces making up the welded part are dimensioned so that they may be cut easily from standard stock.

All joints between the individual pieces of the welded part must be shown, even though the joint would not appear as a line on the completed part. The lines marked A in Fig. 26.11 illustrate this principle.   Each individual piece should be identified by number, Fig. 26.10.

26.9   Use of the symbols.   The following instructions should be followed for placement and form of the symbols.   Some practices to avoid are also given.

INSTRUCTIONS FOR USE OF WELDING SYMBOLS[1]

I. General Provisions

1. Location significance of arrow

   a. In the case of groove, fillet, and flash or upset welding symbols, the arrow shall connect the welding symbol reference line to one side of the joint, and this side shall be considered the *arrow side* of the joint.   The side opposite the arrow side of the joint shall be considered the *other side* of the joint.   (Fig. 26.6.)

   b. In the case of plug, slot, spot, seam and projection welding symbols, the arrow shall connect the welding symbol reference line to the outer surface of one of the members of the joint at the center line of the desired weld.   The member to which the arrow points shall be considered the *arrow-side* member.   The other member of the joint shall be considered the *other-side* member.   (Art. V-1*a*.)

   c. When a joint is depicted by a single line on the drawing and the arrow of a welding symbol is directed to this line, the arrow side of the joint shall be considered as the near side of the joint in accordance with the usual conventions of drafting.   (Fig. 26.8.)

   d. When a joint is depicted as an area parallel to the plane of projection in a drawing and the arrow of a welding symbol is directed to near area, the *arrow-side* member of the joint shall be considered as the near side of the joint in accordance with the usual conventions of drafting.   (Fig. 26.8.)

2. Location of weld with respect to joint

   a. Welds on the arrow side of the joint shall be shown by placing the weld symbol on the side of the reference line toward the reader, thus:

   b. Welds on the other side of the joint shall be shown by placing the weld symbol on the side of the reference line away from the reader thus:

   c. Welds on both sides of the joint shall be shown by placing weld symbols on both sides of the reference line, toward and away from the reader, thus:

   d. Spot, seam, flash and upset weld symbols have no arrow-side or other-side significance in themselves, although supplementary symbols used in conjunction therewith may have such significance.   Spot, seam, flash and upset weld symbols shall be centered on the reference line, thus:

3. Method of drawing symbols

   a. Symbols may be drawn mechanically or freehand, as desired.

4. Use of inch, degree and pound marks

   a. Inch, degree and pound marks may be used on welding symbols or not, as desired, except that inch marks shall be used for indicating the diameter of spot and projection welds and the width of seam welds, when such welds are specified by linear dimension.

5. Location of specification, process or other references

   a. When a specification, process or other reference is used with a welding symbol, the reference shall be placed in the tail, thus:

6. Use of symbols without references

   a. When desired, symbols may be used without specification, process or other references in the following instances:

   (1) When a note such as the following appears on the drawing: "Unless otherwise designated, all welds are to be made in accordance with Specification No. _____."

   (2) When the welding procedure to be used is prescribed elsewhere.

[1] Adapted from ASA Z32.2.1—1949.

7. Use of general notes

a. When desired, general notes such as the following may be placed on a drawing to provide detailed information pertaining to the predominating welds, and this information need not be repeated on the symbols.

"Unless otherwise indicated, all fillet welds are $\frac{5}{16}$ inch size."

"Unless otherwise indicated, root openings for all groove welds are $\frac{3}{16}$ inch."

8. Use of weld-all-around symbol

a. Welds extending completely around a joint shall be indicated by means of the weld-all-around symbol, thus:

9. Use of field weld symbol

a. Field welds (welds not made in a shop or at the place of initial construction) shall be indicated by means of the field weld symbol, thus:

10. Extent of welding denoted by symbols

a. Symbols apply between abrupt changes in the direction of the welding or to the extent of hatching or dimension lines, except when the weld-all-around symbol is used.

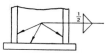

11. Weld proportions

a. All welds shall be continuous and of user's standard proportions unless otherwise indicated.

12. Finishing of welds

a. Finishing of welds, other than cleaning, shall be indicated by suitable contour and finish symbols.   (Art. II-9.)

13. Location of weld symbols

a. Weld symbols, except spot and seam, shall be shown only on the welding symbol reference line and not on the lines of the drawing

b. Spot and seam weld symbols may be placed directly on drawings at the locations of the desired welds, thus:

14. Construction of fillet, and bevel- and J-groove welding symbols

a. Fillet and bevel- and J-groove weld symbols shall be shown with the perpendicular leg *always* to the left, thus:

15. Use of break in arrow of bevel- and J-groove welding symbols

a. When a bevel- or J-groove weld symbol is used, the arrow shall point with a definite break toward the member which is to be chamfered, thus: (In cases where the member to be chamfered is obvious, the break in the arrow may be omitted.)

16. Reading of information on welding symbols

a. Information on welding symbols shall be placed to read from left to right along the reference line in accordance with the usual conventions of drafting, thus:

17. Combined weld symbols

a. For joints having more than one weld, a symbol shall be shown for each weld, thus:

18. Designation of special types of welds

a. When the basic weld symbols are inadequate to indicate the desired weld, the weld shall be shown by a cross section, detail or other data, with a reference thereto on the welding symbol, observing the usual location significance, thus:

II. Fillet Welds

1. General

a. Dimensions of fillet welds shall be shown on the same side of the reference line as the weld symbol, thus:

b. When no general note governing the dimensions of fillet welds appears on the drawing, the dimensions of fillet welds on both sides of the joint shall be shown as follows:

(1) When both welds have the same dimensions, one or both may be dimensioned, thus:

(2) When the welds differ in dimensions, both shall be dimensioned thus:

c. When there appears on the drawing a general note governing the dimensions of fillet welds, such as "All fillet welds $\frac{5}{16}$ in. size unless otherwise noted," the dimensions of fillet welds on both sides of the joint shall be indicated as follows:

(1) When both welds have dimensions governed by the note, neither need be dimensioned, thus:

(2) When the dimensions of one or both welds differ from the dimensions given in the general note, both welds shall be dimensioned, thus:

2. Size of fillet welds

a. The size of a fillet weld shall be shown to the left of the weld symbol, thus:

b. The size of a fillet weld with unequal legs shall be shown in parentheses to the left of the weld symbol, as shown. Weld orientation is not shown by the symbol and shall be shown on the drawing when necessary.

3. Length of fillet welds

a. The length of a fillet weld, when indicated on the welding symbol, shall be shown to the right of the weld symbol, thus:

b. When fillet welding extends for the full distance between abrupt changes in the direction of the welding, no length dimension need be shown on the welding symbol.

c. Specific lengths of fillet welding may be indicated by symbols in conjunction with dimension lines, thus:

4. Extent of fillet welding

a. When it is desired to show the extent of fillet welding graphically, one type of hatching with definite end lines shall be used, thus:

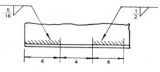

b. Fillet welding extending beyond abrupt changes in the direction of the welding shall be indicated by means of additional arrows pointing to each section of the joint to be welded, as shown in Art. I-10, except when the weld-all-around symbol is used.

5. Dimensioning of intermittent fillet welding

a. The pitch (center-to-center spacing) of intermittent fillet welding shall be shown as the distance between centers of increments on *one* side of the joint.

b. The pitch (center-to-center spacing) of intermittent fillet welding shall be shown to the right of the length dimension, thus:

c. Chain intermittent fillet welding shall be shown thus:

d. Staggered intermittent fillet welding shall be shown thus:

6. Termination of intermittent fillet welding

a. When intermittent fillet welding is used by itself, the symbol indicates that increments shall be located at the ends of the dimensioned length.

b. When intermittent fillet welding is used between continuous fillet welding, the symbol indicates that spaces equal to the pitch minus the length of one increment shall be left at the ends of the dimensioned length. (Art. II-3.)

7. Combination of intermittent and continuous fillet welding

a. Separate symbols shall be used for intermittent and continuous fillet welding when the two are used in combination. (Art II-3*c*.)

8. Fillet welds in holes and slots

a. Fillet welds in holes and slots shall be shown by means of fillet weld symbols.

9. Surface contour of fillet welds

a. Fillet welds that are to be welded approximately flat-faced without recourse to any method of finishing shall be shown by adding the flush-contour symbol to the weld symbol, observing the usual location significance, thus:

b. Fillet welds that are to be made flat-faced by mechanical means shall be shown by adding both the flush-contour symbol and the user's standard finish symbol[1] to the weld symbol, observing the usual location significance, thus:

c. Fillet welds that are to be mechanically finished to a convex contour shall be shown by adding both the convex-contour symbol and the user's standard finish symbol[1] to the weld symbol, observing the usual location significance, thus:

III. Groove Welds

1. General

a. Dimensions of groove welds shall be shown on the same side of the reference line as the weld symbol, thus:

b. When no general note governing the dimensions of groove welds appears on the drawing, the dimensions of double-groove welds shall be shown as follows:

(1) When both welds have the same dimensions, one or both may be dimensioned, thus:

---

[1] Finish symbols used herein indicate the method of finishing (C = chipping; G = grinding; M = machining) and not the degree of finish.

(2) When the welds differ in dimensions, both shall be dimensioned, thus:

c. When there appears on the drawing a general note governing the dimensions of groove welds, such as "All V-groove welds shall have a 60° groove angle unless otherwise noted," the dimensions of double-groove welds shall be indicated as follows:

(1) When both welds have dimensions governed by the note, neither need be dimensioned, thus:

(2) When the dimensions of one or both welds differ from the dimensions given in the general note, both welds shall be dimensioned, thus:

2. Size of groove welds

a. The size of groove welds shall be shown to the left of the weld symbol, thus: (groove depth plus root penetration)

b. The size of groove welds with no specified root penetration shall be shown as follows:

(1) The size of single-groove and symmetrical double-groove welds which extend completely through the member or members being joined need not be shown on the welding symbol.

(2) The size of groove welds which extend only partly through the member or members being joined shall be shown on the welding symbol.

c. The size of groove welds with specified root penetration shall be indicated by showing both the depth of chamfering and the root penetration, separated by a plus mark and placed to the left of the weld symbol. The depth of chamfering and the root penetration shall read in that order from left to right along the reference line, thus:

3. Groove dimensions

a. Root opening of groove welds shall be the user's standard unless otherwise indicated. Root opening of groove welds, when not the user's standard, shall be shown inside the weld symbol, thus:

b. Groove angle of groove welds shall be the user's standard, unless otherwise indicated. Groove angle of groove welds, when not the user's standard, shall be shown thus:

c. Groove radii and root faces of U- and J-groove welds shall be the user's standard unless otherwise indicated. When groove radii and root faces of U- and J-groove welds are not the user's standard, the weld shall be shown by a cross section, detail or other data, with a reference thereto on the welding symbol, observing the usual location significance, thus:

4. Designation of back and backing welds

Bead-type back and backing welds of single-groove welds shall be shown by means of the bead weld symbol. (Art. IV-2.)

5. Surface contour of groove welds

a. Groove welds that are to be welded approximately flush without recourse to any method of finishing shall be shown by adding the flush-contour symbol to the weld symbol, observing the usual location significance, thus:

b. Groove welds that are to be made flush by mechanical means shall be shown by adding both the flush-contour symbol and the user's standard finish symbol[1] to the weld symbol, observing the usual location significance, thus:

c. Groove welds that are to be mechanically finished to a convex contour shall be shown by adding both the convex-contour symbol and the user's standard finish symbol[1] to the weld symbol, observing the usual location significance, thus:

IV. Bead Welds

1. General

a. The single bead weld symbol shall be used to indicate bead-type back or backing welds of single-groove welds.

b. The dual bead weld symbol shall be used to indicate surfaces built up by welding.

2. Use of bead weld symbol to indicate bead-type back or backing welds

a. Bead welds used as back or backing welds of single-groove welds shall be shown by placing a single bead weld symbol on the side of the reference line opposite the groove weld symbol, thus:

b. Dimensions of bead welds used as back or backing welds shall not be shown on the welding symbol. If it is desired to specify these dimensions, they shall be shown on the drawing.

3. Surface contour of back or backing welds

a. Back or backing welds that are to be welded approximately flush without recourse to any method of finishing shall be shown by adding the flush-contour symbol to the bead weld symbol, thus:

b. Back or backing welds that are to be made flush by mechanical means shall be shown by adding both the flush-contour symbol and the user's standard finish symbol[1] to the bead weld symbol, thus:

c. Back or backing welds that are to be mechanically finished to a convex contour shall be shown by adding both the convex-contour symbol and the user's standard finish symbol[1] to the bead weld symbol, thus: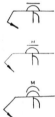

4. Use of bead weld symbol to indicate surfaces built up by welding

a. Surfaces built up by welding, whether by single- or multiple-pass bead welds, shall be shown by the dual bead weld symbol, thus:

b. The dual bead weld symbol does not indicate the welding of a joint, and hence has no arrow- or other-side significance. This symbol shall be drawn on the side of the reference line toward the reader, and the arrow shall point clearly to the surface on which the weld is to be deposited.

c. Dimensions used in conjunction with the dual bead weld symbol shall be shown on the same side of the reference line as the weld symbol, thus:

5. Size (height) of surfaces built up by welding

a. The size of a surface built up by welding shall be indicated by showing the minimum height of the weld deposit to the left of the weld symbol, thus:

[1] Finish symbols used herein indicate the method of finishing (C = chipping; G = grinding; M = machining) and not the degree of finish.

b. When no specific height of weld deposit is desired, no size dimension need be shown on the welding symbol.

6. Extent, location and orientation of surfaces built up by welding

a. When the entire area of a plane or curved surface is to be built up by welding, no dimension other than size (height of deposit) need be shown on the welding symbol.

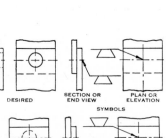

b. When a portion of the area of a plane or curved surface is to be built up by welding, the extent, location and orientation of the area to be built up shall be indicated on the drawing.

V. Plug Welds

1. General

a. Holes in the arrow-side member of a joint for plug welding shall be indicated by placing the weld symbol on the side of the reference line toward the reader, thus:

b. Holes in the other-side member of a joint for plug welding shall be indicated by placing the weld symbol on the side of the reference line away from the reader, thus:

c. Dimensions of plug welds shall be shown on the same side of the reference line as the weld symbol, thus:

d. The plug weld symbol shall not be used to designate fillet welds in holes. (Art. II-8.)

2. Size of plug welds

a. The size of a plug weld shall be shown to the left of the weld symbol, thus:

3. Angle of countersink

a. Included angle of countersink of plug welds shall be the user's standard unless otherwise indicated. Included angle of countersink, when not the user's standard, shall be shown thus:

4. Depth of filling

a. Depth of filling of plug welds shall be complete unless otherwise indicated. When the depth of filling is less than complete, the depth of filling, in inches, shall be shown inside the weld symbol, thus:

5. Spacing of plug welds

a. Pitch (center-to-center spacing) of plug welds shall be shown to the right of the weld symbol, thus:

6. Surface contour of plug welds

a. Plug welds that are to be welded approximately flush without recourse to any method of finishing shall be shown by adding the flush-contour symbol to the weld symbol, thus:

b. Plug welds that are to be made flush by mechanical means shall be shown by adding both the flush-contour symbol and the user's standard finish symbol[1] to the weld symbol, thus:

VI. Slot Welds

1. General

a. Slots in the arrow-side member of a joint for slot welding shall be indicated by placing the weld symbol on the side of the reference line toward the reader, thus:

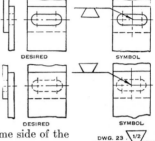

b. Slots in the other-side member of a joint for slot welding shall be indicated by placing the weld symbol on the side of the reference line away from the reader, thus:

c. Dimensions of slot welds shall be shown on the same side of the reference line as the weld symbol, thus:

d. The slot weld symbol shall not be used to designate fillet welds in slots.   (Art. II-8.)

2. Depth of filling

a. Depth of filling of slot welds shall be complete unless otherwise indicated.   When the depth of filling is less than complete, the depth of filling, in inches, shall be shown inside the weld symbol, thus: ▪

3. Details of slot welds

a. Length, width, spacing, included angle of countersink, orientation and location of slot welds cannot be shown on the welding symbol.   These data shall be shown on the drawing or by a detail with a reference thereto on the welding symbol, observing the usual location significance, thus:

4. Surface contour of slot welds

a. Slot welds that are to be welded approximately flush without recourse to any method of finishing shall be shown by adding the flush-contour symbol to the weld symbol, thus:

b. Slot welds that are to be made flush by mechanical means shall be shown by adding both the flush-contour symbol and the user's standard finish symbol[1] to the weld symbol, thus:

VII. Spot Welds

1. General

a. Spot weld symbols have no arrow- or other-side significance in themselves, although supplementary symbols used in conjunction therewith may have such significance. (Art. VII-6.)   Spot weld symbols shall be centered on the reference line.   (Art. VII-4.)

b. Dimensions of spot welds may be shown on either side of the reference line.

[1] Finish symbols used herein indicate the method of finishing (C = chipping; G = grinding; M = machining) and not the degree of finish.

2. Size of spot welds

  a. Spot welds shall be dimensioned by either size or strength, as follows:

  (1) The size of spot welds shall be designated as the diameter of the weld expressed decimally in hundredths of an inch, and shall be shown, with inch marks, to the left of the weld symbol, thus:

  (2) The strength of spot welds shall be designated as the minimum acceptable shear strength in pounds per spot, and shall be shown to the left of the weld symbol, thus:

3. Spacing of spot welds

  a. The pitch (center-to-center spacing) of spot welds shall be shown to the right of the weld symbol, thus:

  b. When spot weld symbols are shown directly on the drawing, spacing shall be shown by dimensions.

4. Extent of spot welding

  a. When spot welding extends less than the distance between abrupt changes in the direction of the welding, or less than the full length of the joint (Art. I-10), the extent shall be dimensioned, thus:

5. Number of spot welds

  a. When a definite number of spot welds is desired in a certain joint, the number shall be shown in parentheses either above or below the weld symbol, thus:

6. Flush spot-welded joints

  a. When the exposed surface of one member of a spot-welded joint is to be flush, that surface shall be indicated by adding the flush-contour symbol to the weld symbol, observing the usual location significance, thus:

<h2 style="text-align:center">VIII. Seam Welds</h2>

1. General

  a. Seam weld symbols have no arrow- or other-side significance in themselves, although supplementary symbols used in conjunction therewith may have such significance. (Art. VIII-7.) Seam weld symbols shall be centered on the reference line.

  b. Dimensions of seam welds may be shown on either side of the reference line.

2. Size of seam welds

  a. Seam welds shall be dimensioned by either size or strength as follows:

  (1) The size of seam welds shall be designated as the width of the weld expressed decimally in hundredths of an inch, and shall be shown, with inch marks, to the left of the weld symbol, thus:

  (2) The strength of seam welds shall be designated as the minimum acceptable shear strength in pounds per linear inch, and shall be shown to the left of the weld symbol, thus:

3. Length of seam welds

  a. The length of a seam weld, when indicated on the welding symbol, shall be shown to the right of the weld symbol, thus:

b. When seam welding extends for the full distance between abrupt changes in the direction of the welding (Art. I-10), no length dimension need be shown on the welding symbol.

c. When seam welding extends less than the distance between abrupt changes in the direction of the welding, or less than the full length of the joint (Art. I-10), the extent shall be dimensioned, thus:

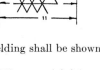

4. Dimensioning of intermittent seam welding

a. The pitch (center-to-center spacing) of intermittent seam welding shall be shown as the distance between centers of the weld increments.

b. The pitch (center-to-center spacing) of intermittent seam welding shall be shown to the right of the length dimension, thus:

5. Termination of intermittent seam welding

a. When intermittent seam welding is used by itself, the symbol indicates that increments shall be located at the ends of the dimensioned length.

b. When intermittent seam welding is used between continuous seam welding, the symbol indicates that spaces equal to the pitch minus the length of one increment shall be left at the ends of the dimensioned length.

6. Combination of intermittent and continuous seam welding

a. Separate symbols shall be used for intermittent and continuous seam welding when the two are used in combination.

7. Flush seam-welded joints

a. When the exposed surface of one member of a seam-welded joint is to be flush, that surface shall be indicated by adding the flush-contour symbol to the weld symbol, observing the usual location significance, thus:

IX. Projection Welds

1. General

a. Embossments on the arrow-side member of a joint for projection welding shall be indicated by placing the weld symbol on the side of the reference line toward the reader, thus:

b. Embossments on the other-side member of a joint for projection welding shall be indicated by placing the weld symbol on the side of the reference line away from the reader, thus:

c. Proportions of projections shall be shown by a detail or other suitable means.

d. Dimensions of projection welds shall be shown on the same side of the reference line as the weld symbol, thus:

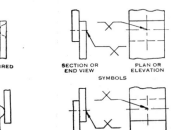

2. Size of projection welds

a. Projection welds shall be dimensioned by either size or strength, as follows:

(1) The size of projection welds shall be designated as the diameter of the weld expressed decimally in hundredths of an inch, and shall be shown, with inch marks, to the left of the weld symbol, thus:

(2) The strength of projection welds shall be designated as the minimum acceptable shear strength in pounds per weld, and shall be shown to the left of the weld symbol, thus:

3. Spacing of projection welds

a. The pitch (center-to-center spacing) of projection welds shall be shown to the right of the weld symbol, thus:

4. Extent of projection welding

a. When projection welding extends less than the distance between abrupt changes in the direction of the welding, or less than the full length of the joint, the extent shall be dimensioned, thus:

5. Number of projection welds

a. When a definite number of projection welds is desired in a certain joint, the number shall be shown in parentheses, thus:

6. Flush projection-welded joints

a. When the exposed surface of one member of a projection welded joint is to be made flush, that surface shall be indicated by adding the flush-contour symbol to the weld symbol, observing the usual location significance, thus:

X. Flash and Upset Welds

1. General

a. Flash and upset weld symbols have no arrow-side or other-side significance in themselves although supplementary symbols used in conjunction therewith may have such significance (Art. X-2). Flash or upset weld symbols shall be centered in the reference line.

b. Dimensions of flash and upset welds shall not be shown on the welding symbol.

2. Surface contour of flash and upset welds

a. Flash and upset welds that are to be made flush by mechanical means shall be shown by adding both the flush-contour symbol and the user's standard finish symbol[1] to the weld symbol, observing the usual location significance, thus:

b. Flash and upset welds that are to be mechanically finished to a convex contour shall be shown by adding both the convex-contour symbol and the user's standard finish symbol[1] to the weld symbol, observing the usual location significance, thus:

PROBLEMS

The draftsman should be so thoroughly familiar with the welding symbols that he can write and read them without hesitation. Problems 1 and 2 give practice in reading, Probs. 3 and 4 in writing. Problems 5 to 9 give practice in the use of the symbols on working drawings.

1, 2. Figs. 26.12, 26.13. Make full-size cross-sectional sketches (similar to Figs. 26.14 and 26.15) of the joints indicated. Dimension each sketch.

3, 4. Figs. 26.14, 26.15. Sketch members and show welding symbol for each complete joint. Estimate weld size from plate thickness.

[1] Finish symbols used herein indicate the method of finishing (C = chipping; G = grinding; M = machining) and not the degree of finish.

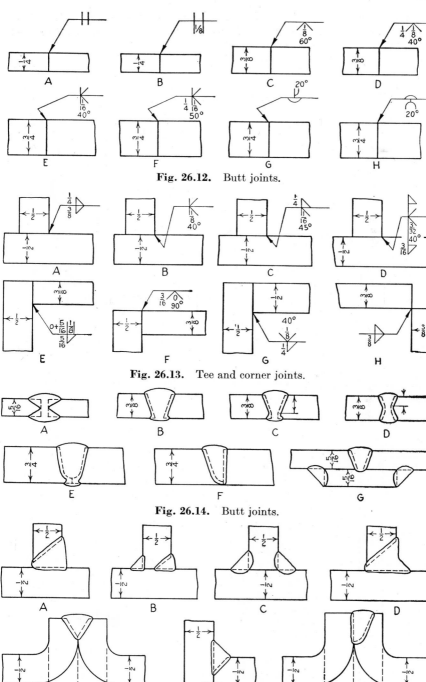

Fig. 26.12.   Butt joints.

Fig. 26.13.   Tee and corner joints.

Fig. 26.14.   Butt joints.

Fig. 26.15.   Tee, corner, and edge joints.

5, 6. Figs. 26.16, 26.17. Make complete welding drawing for each object. These problems are printed quarter size. Draw full size by scaling or transferring with dividers.

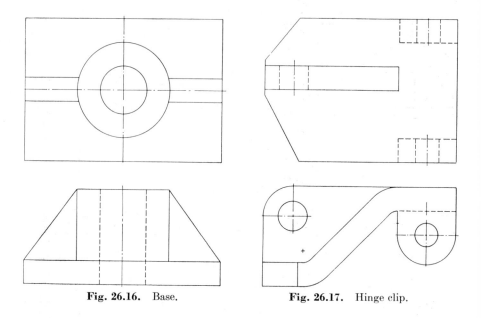

Fig. 26.16. Base. **Fig. 26.17.** Hinge clip.

7. Fig. 26.18. Draw the views given, add welding symbols, dash numbers for identification of the individual pieces, and complete the materials list.

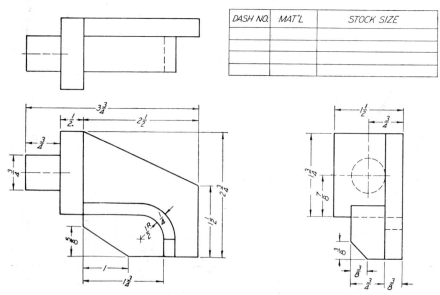

DASH NO.	MAT'L	STOCK SIZE

Fig. 26.18. Pivoted spacer.

8. Fig. 26.19. Draw the views given and add welding symbols and dash numbers. Make a materials list similar to the one used in Prob. 7.

9. Fig. 26.20. Draw the views given and add welding symbols and dash numbers. Make a materials list. Determine length of material for rim.

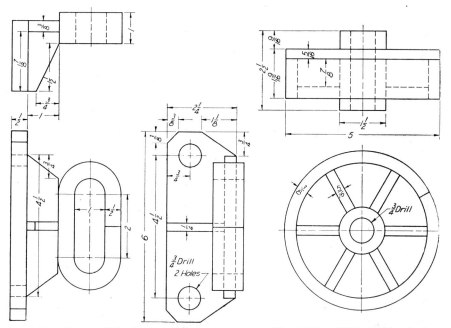

Fig. 26.19. Belt-tightener bracket.   **Fig. 26.20.** Ribbed-disk wheel.

27

Gears and Cams

27.1 Gears. The representation and specification of gears are of such common occurrence that the nomenclature, basic proportions, and formulas for calculation should be familiar to the engineer and draftsman.

Briefly, gears are an adaptation of rolling cylinders and cones, designed to ensure positive motion. There are numerous variations, but the basic forms, Fig. 27.1, are *spur gears*, for transmitting power from one shaft to another parallel shaft; *spur gear* and *rack*, for changing rotary motion to linear motion; *bevel gears*, for shafts whose axes intersect; and *worm gears*, for nonintersecting shafts at right angles to each other.

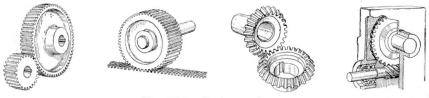

Fig. 27.1. Basic gear forms.

27.2 Gear teeth. The teeth of gears are projections designed to fit into the tooth spaces of the mating gear, Fig. 27.2, and contact mating teeth along a common line known as the "pressure line." The most common form for the tooth flank is the *involute*, and when so made the gears are known as involute gears. The angle of the pressure line determines the particular involute the flank will have. The ASA has standardized two pressure angles, $14\frac{1}{2}°$ and 20°. A composite $14\frac{1}{2}°$ tooth and a 20° stub tooth are also used (see ASA B6.1).

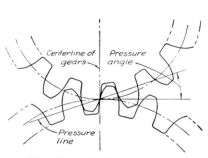

Fig. 27.2. Mating gear teeth.

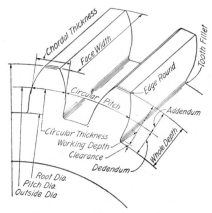

Fig. 27.3. Gear nomenclature.

27.3 Letter symbols and formulas for spur gearing. The names of the various portions of a spur gear and the teeth are given in Fig. 27.3. The ASA standard letter symbols and formulas for calculation are as follows:

N = number of teeth = $P_d \times D$.

P_d = diametral pitch = number of teeth on the gear for each inch of pitch diameter = N/D.

D = pitch diameter = N/P_d.

p = circular pitch = length of the arc of the pitch-diameter circle subtended by a tooth and a tooth space = $\pi D/N = \pi/P_d$.

t = circular (tooth) thickness = length of the arc of the pitch-diameter circle subtended by a tooth = $p/2 = \pi D/2N = \pi/2P_d$.

t_c = chordal thickness = length of the chord subtended by the circular thickness arc = $D \sin (90°/N)$.

a = addendum = radial distance between the pitch-diameter circle and the top of a tooth = a constant$/P_d$ = for standard $14\frac{1}{2}°$ or 20° involute teeth, $1/P_d$.

b = dedendum = radial distance between the pitch-diameter circle and the bottom of a tooth space = a constant$/P_d$ = for standard $14\frac{1}{2}°$ or 20° involute teeth, $1.157/P_d$.

c = clearance = radial distance between the top of a tooth and the bottom of a mating tooth space = a constant$/P_d$ = for standard $14\frac{1}{2}°$ or 20° involute teeth, $0.157/P_d$.

h_t = whole depth = radial distance between the top and bottom of a tooth = $a + b$ = for standard $14\frac{1}{2}°$ or 20° involute teeth, $2.157/P_d$.

h_k = working depth = greatest depth a tooth of one gear extends into a tooth space of a mating gear = $2a$ = for standard $14\frac{1}{2}°$ or 20° involute teeth, $2/P_d$.

D_O = outside diameter = diameter of the circle containing the top surfaces of the teeth = $D + 2a = (N + 2)/P_d$.

D_R = root diameter = diameter of the circle containing the bottom surfaces of the tooth spaces = $D - 2b = (N - 2.314)/P_d$.

F = face width = width of tooth flank.

f = tooth fillet = fillet joining the tooth flank and the bottom of the tooth space = $0.157/P_d$ max.

r = edge round = radius of the circumferential edge of a gear tooth (to break the sharp corner).

n = revolutions per unit of time.

In addition to the above basic letter symbols, subscripts G and P are used to denote gear and pinion, respectively. (When one of two mating gears is smaller than the other, it is known as the pinion.)

m = gear ratio = m_G for the gear = $N_G/N_P = n_P/n_G = D_G/D_P$.
    = m_P for the pinion = $N_P/N_G = n_G/n_P = D_P/D_G$.

(The pitch diameter and number of teeth are inversely proportional to speed.)

27.4 Spur-gear calculations. There are many different combinations producing various individual problems, but the following is typical and will illustrate the procedure:

Assume that the center distance and speeds are known.
Center distance = 7 in.
Speed of gear 500 rpm, speed of pinion 1,500 rpm.
Then $m_G = n_P/n_G = 1,500/500 = 3/1 = D_G/D_P$.
Therefore, $3D_P = D_G$.

From the center distance, $D_P + D_G = 14$ in.
Substituting for D_G in terms of D_P,
$D_P + 3D_P = 14$.   Solving, $D_P = 3\frac{1}{2}$ in.
Solving for $D_G = 3D_P = 3 \times 3\frac{1}{2} = 10\frac{1}{2}$ in.
At this time, the diametral pitch will have to be assumed.
Assume $P_d = 5$.
Then, $N_P = P_d \times D_P = 5 \times 3\frac{1}{2} = 17\frac{1}{2}$, which is obviously impossible since a gear could not have a half tooth.
Assuming $P_d = 6$,
$N_P = 6 \times 3\frac{1}{2} = 21$
$N_G = 6 \times 10\frac{1}{2} = 63$

Now, all the values such as addendum, dedendum, outside diameter, etc., can be calculated from the equations given in paragraph 27.3.   Note that if, in a given problem, the two pitch diameters are known, the center distance will have to be found; if one pitch diameter is known and the center distance given, the second pitch diameter must be solved for; etc.

27.5   To draw a spur gear.   Fig. 27.4.   To draw the teeth of a standard involute-toothed spur gear by an approximate circle-arc method, lay off the

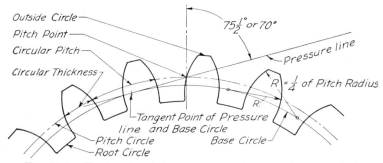

Fig. 27.4.   To draw involute spur gear teeth, approximate method.

pitch circle, root circle, and outside circle.   Start with the pitch point and divide the pitch circle into distances equal to the circular thickness. Through the pitch point draw a line of $75\frac{1}{2}°$ with the center line for a $14\frac{1}{2}°$ involute tooth (for convenience the draftsman uses 75°), or 70° for a 20° tooth.   Draw the base circle tangent to the pressure line.   With compasses set to a radius equal to one-fourth the radius of the pitch circle, describe arcs through the division points on the pitch circle, keeping the needle point on the base circle.   Darken the arcs for the tops of the teeth and bottoms of the spaces and add the tooth fillets.   For 16 or fewer teeth the radius value of one-fourth pitch radius *must be increased* to suit, in order to avoid the appearance of excessive under-cut.   For a small number of teeth, the radius may be as large as or equal to the pitch radius.

This method of drawing gear teeth is useful on display drawings, but on working drawings the tooth outlines are not drawn.   Figure 27.5 illustrates the method of indicating the teeth and dimensioning a working drawing of a spur gear.

The dimensions necessary for the teeth of cut gears are outside diameter, number of teeth, diametral pitch, and width of face. The standard letter symbols, paragraph 27.3, are seldom used on drawings. In Fig. 27.5, T indicates teeth and P is the diametral pitch.

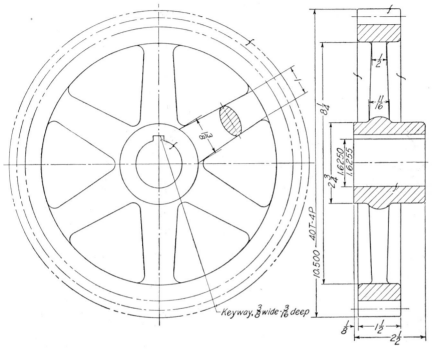

Fig. 27.5. Working drawing of a spur gear.

27.6 To draw a rack. Fig. 27.6. To draw the teeth of a standard involute rack by an approximate method, draw the pitch line and lay off the addendum and dedendum distances. Divide the pitch line into spaces equal to the circular thickness of the mating gear. Through these points of

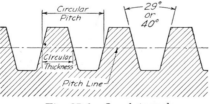

Fig. 27.6. Involute rack.

division draw the tooth faces at $14\frac{1}{2}°$ ($15°$ is used by draftsmen). Draw tops and bottoms and add the tooth fillets. For standard $20°$ full-depth or stub teeth use $20°$ instead of $14\frac{1}{2}°$. Specifications of rack teeth (to be given on a detail drawing) are axial (linear) pitch (equal to circular pitch of the mating gear), number of teeth, diametral pitch, whole depth.

27.7   Bevel gears. For bevel gears the theoretical rolling surfaces become cones. The pitch diameter (D) of the gear, as shown in Fig. 27.7A, is the base diameter of the cone. The addendum and dedendum are calculated in the same way as for a spur gear and are measured on a cone, called the "back cone," whose elements are normal to the face-cone elements, Fig. 27.7A. The diametral pitch, circular pitch, etc., are the same as for a spur gear.

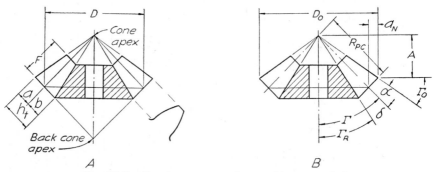

Fig. 27.7.   Bevel gear proportions and letter symbols.

In addition to the letter symbols and calculations for spur gears, the dimensions shown in Fig. 27.7B, with formulas for calculating, are needed:

Γ = pitch-cone angle = angle between a pitch-cone element and the cone axis. tan Γ = $D_G/D_P = N_G/N_P$ (gear) = $D_P/D_G = N_P/N_G$ (pinion).

R_{PC} = pitch-cone radius = length of an element of the pitch cone. R_{PC} = $D/2 \sin \Gamma$.

α = addendum angle = angle between the pitch cone and the outside of a tooth. tan α = a/R_{PC}.

δ = dedendum angle = angle between the pitch cone and the bottom of a tooth space. tan δ = b/R_{PC}.

Γ_O = face angle = angle between a line *normal* to the gear axis and the outside (face) of the teeth. Γ_O = $90° - (\Gamma + \alpha)$. (Note that this angle is the complement of the angle an element of the outside cone makes with the axis.)

Γ_R = root-cone angle = cutting angle = angle between the axis and an element of the root cone. Γ_R = $\Gamma - \delta$.

a_N = angular addendum = addendum distance measured *normal* to the gear axis. a_N = $a \cos \Gamma$.

D_O = outside diameter = outside diameter at the base of the teeth. D_O = $D + 2a_N$.

A = apex distance = altitude of the outside-diameter cone. A = $(D_o/2) \tan \Gamma$.

27.8   To draw a bevel gear. Fig. 27.8. To draw the teeth of an involute-toothed bevel gear by an approximate method (the Tredgold method), draw the center lines, intersecting at O. Across the center lines lay off the pitch diameters, and project them parallel to the center lines until the projectors intersect at the pitch point P. From the pitch point, draw the pitch-circle diameters for each gear, and from their extremities, draw the "pitch cones" to the vertex or "cone center" O. Lay off the addendum and dedendum distances for each gear on lines through the pitch points perpendicular to the cone elements. Extend one of these normals for each gear to intersect the axis, as at B and C, making the "back cones." With B as center, swing arcs 1, 2, and 3 for the top, pitch line, and bottom, respectively, of a developed tooth. On a radial center line AB, draw a tooth, by the method of Fig. 27.4. Start the plan view of the gear by projecting points 1, 2, and 3 across to its vertical center line and drawing circles through the points. Lay off the radial center lines for each tooth.

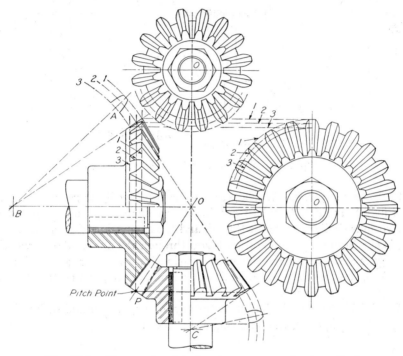

Fig. 27.8. To draw involute bevel gears, approximate method.

With dividers take the circular thickness distances from A and transfer them to each tooth. This will give three points on each side of each tooth through which a circle arc, found by trial, will pass, giving the foreshortened contour of the large end of the teeth in this view. From this point the drawing becomes a problem in projection drawing. Note that in every view the lines converge at the cone center O and that, by finding three points on the contour of each tooth, circle arcs can be found by trial which will be sufficiently close approximations to give the desired effect.

This method is used for finished display drawings. Working drawings for cut bevel gears are drawn without tooth outlines and are dimensioned as shown in Fig. 27.9, from the calculations given in paragraph 27.7. For a cast gear the tooth outline must be given for the patternmaker.

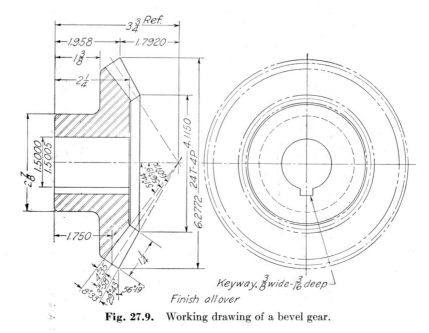

Fig. 27.9.   Working drawing of a bevel gear.

27.9 Worm gears.   Worm gears are used primarily to get great reductions in relative speed and to obtain a large increase in effective power. The worm is similar to a screw thread, and the computing of pitch diameter, etc., is also similar.   On a section taken through the axis of the worm, the worm gear and worm have the same relationship as a spur gear and rack. Therefore, the tooth shape, addendum, dedendum, etc., will be the same as for a spur gear and rack.

In addition to the calculations necessary for a spur gear and rack (addendum, dedendum, etc.), the following are needed:

Worm

l = lead of worm threads.
N_W = multiplicity of worm threads.
p_{XW} = axial pitch = l/N_W.
D_W = pitch diameter of worm.
λ = lead angle. $\tan \lambda = l/\pi D$.

Worm gear

C = center distance between worm and wheel.
D_G = pitch diameter of worm gear.
D_{tp} = pitch throat diameter = pitch diameter of wheel = D_G.
D_{to} = outer throat diameter = pitch diameter plus twice the addendum = $D_G + 2a$.
D_{ti} = inner throat diameter = pitch diameter minus twice the dedendum = $D_G - 2b$
R_{tp} = pitch throat radius = pitch radius of worm = $D_W/2$.
R_{to} = outer throat radius = $(D_W/2) - a$.
R_{ti} = inner throat radius = $(D_W/2) + b$.
C_{R_t} = center of throat radius = $C = (D_G/2) + (D_W/2)$.

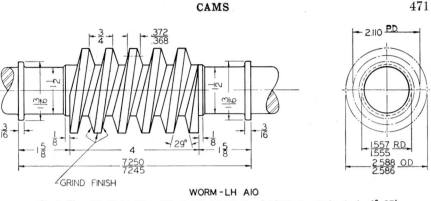

WORM – LH A10

Single Thread to Match Worm Wheel A9. 24:1 Ratio. 3.921 Centers. Helix Angle 6°-27'.
Material AISI 3120. Heat Treatment SAE Ⅲ $\frac{1}{16}$ Case. Scleroscope 75-90.

Fig. 27.10. Working drawing of a worm.

27.10 To draw worm gears. In assembly, a worm and worm gear are generally shown with the worm in section and the worm gear drawn as a conventional end view like the end view of Fig. 27.11. The detail drawings are made up as in Figs. 27.10 and 27.11. The calculated dimensions described in paragraph 27.9 are given as shown on the figures.

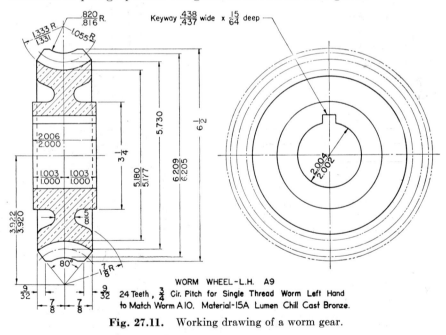

WORM WHEEL-L.H. A9

24 Teeth , $\frac{3}{8}$ Cir. Pitch for Single Thread Worm Left Hand
to Match Worm A10. Material-15A Lumen Chill Cast Bronze.

Fig. 27.11. Working drawing of a worm gear.

27.11 Cams. A cam is a machine element with surface or groove formed to produce special or irregular motion in a second part, called a "follower." The shape of the cam is dependent upon the motion required and the type of follower that is used. The type of cam is dictated by the required relationship of the parts and the motions of both.

27.12 Types of cams. The direction of motion of the follower with
respect to the cam axis determines two general types, as follows: (1) radial
or disk cams, in which the follower moves in a direction perpendicular to the
cam axis; and (2) cylindrical or end cams, in which the follower moves

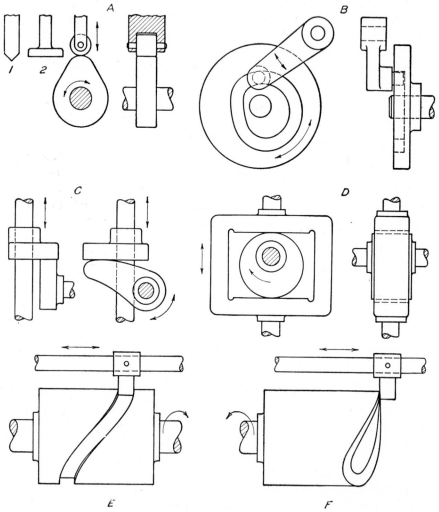

Fig. 27.12. Types of cams.

parallel to the cam axis. Figure 27.12 shows at *A* a *radial cam*, with a
roller follower held against the cam by gravity or by a spring. As the cam
revolves, the follower is raised and lowered. Followers are also made with
pointed ends and with flat ends. *B* shows a *face cam*, with a roller follower
at the end of an arm or link, the follower oscillating as the cam revolves.
When the cam itself oscillates, the *toe* and *wiper* are used, as at *C*. The toe,
or follower, may also be made in the form of a swinging arm.

A *yoke* or *positive-motion cam* is shown at D, the enclosed follower making possible the application of force in either direction. The sum of the two distances from the center of the cam to the points of contact must always be equal to the distance between the follower surfaces. The cylindrical *groove cam* at E and the *end cam* at F both move the follower parallel to the cam axis, force being applied to the follower in both directions with the groove cam, and in only one direction with the end cam.

27.13 Kinds of motion. Cams may be designed to move the follower with constant velocity, acceleration, or harmonic motion. In many cases, combinations of these motions, together with surfaces arranged for sudden rise or fall, or to hold the follower stationary, go to make up the complete cam surface.

27.14 Cam diagrams. In studying the motion of the follower, a diagram showing the height of the follower for successive cam positions is useful and is frequently employed. The cam position is shown on the abscissa, the full 360° rotation of the cam being divided, generally, every 30°

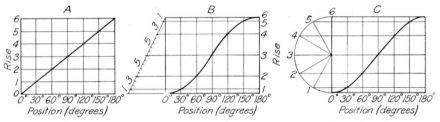

Fig. 27.13. Methods of plotting cam diagrams; three kinds of motion.

(intermediate points may be used if necessary). The follower positions are shown on the ordinate, divided into the same number of parts as the abscissa. These diagrams are generally made to actual size.

Constant velocity gives a uniform rise and fall and may be plotted as at A, Fig. 27.13, by laying off the cam positions on the abscissa, measuring the total follower movement on the ordinate and dividing it into the same number of parts as the abscissa. As the cam moves one unit of its rotation, the follower likewise moves one unit, producing the straight line of motion shown.

With constant acceleration, the distance traveled is proportional to the square of the time, or the total distance traveled is proportional to 1, 4, 9, 16, 25, etc., and if the increments of follower distance are made proportional to 1, 3, 5, 7, etc., the curve may be plotted as shown at B. Using a scale, divide the follower rise into the same number of parts as the abscissa, making the first part one unit, the second three units, and so on. Plot points at the intersection of the coordinate lines, as shown. The curve at B accelerates and then decelerates to slow up the follower at the top of its rise.

Harmonic motion (sine curve) may be plotted as at C by measuring the rise and drawing a semicircle, dividing it into the same number of parts as the abscissa, and projecting the points on the semicircle as ordinate lines. Points are plotted at the intersection of the coordinate lines, as shown.

Figure 27.14 is the cam diagram for the cam of Fig. 27.16. The follower rises with harmonic motion in 180°, drops halfway down instantly, and then returns with uniform motion to the point of beginning.

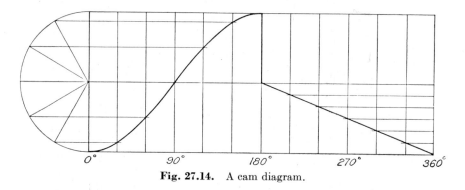

Fig. 27.14. A cam diagram.

27.15 Timing diagrams. When two or more cams are used on the same machine and their functions are dependent on each other, the "timing" and relative motions of each may be studied by means of a diagram showing each follower curve. The curves may be superimposed, but a better method is to place one above the other as in Fig. 27.15.

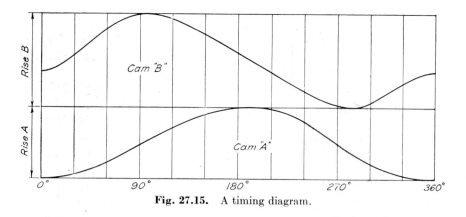

Fig. 27.15. A timing diagram.

27.16 To draw a plate cam. The principle involved in drawing a cam is the same for all types. Illustrating with the cam of Fig. 27.16, for which the diagram of Fig. 27.14 was made, the point C is the center of the shaft, and A is the lowest and B the highest position of the center of the roller follower.

Divide the rise into six parts harmonically proportional. Divide the semicircle ADE into as many equal parts as there are spaces in the rise, and draw radial lines.   With C as center and radius $C1$, draw an arc intersecting the first radial line at $1'$.   In the same way locate points $2'$, $3'$, etc., and draw a smooth curve through them.   If the cam is revolved in the direction of the arrow, it will raise the follower with the desired harmonic motion.

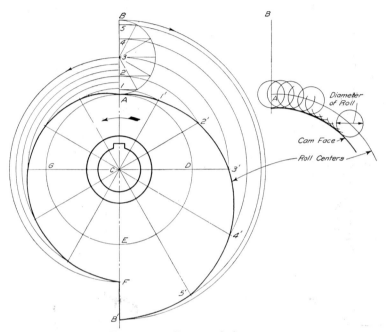

Fig. 27.16.   Layout of plate cam.

Draw $B'F$ equal to one-half AB.   Divide $A3$ into six equal parts and the arc EGA into six equal parts.   Then for equal angles the follower must fall equal distances.   Circle arcs drawn as indicated will locate the required points on the cam outline.

This outline is for the center of the roller; allowance for the roller size may be made by drawing the roller in its successive positions and then drawing a tangent curve as shown in the auxiliary figure.

27.17 To draw a cylindrical cam.   The drawing of a cylindrical cam differs somewhat from that of a plate cam, as, in addition to the regular views, it generally includes a developed view, from which a template is made.   Assume that the follower is to move upward $1\frac{1}{2}$ in. with harmonic motion in 180°, and then return with uniform acceleration.   Top and front views of the cylinder are drawn, Fig. 27.17, and the development of the surface is laid out.   Divide the surface as shown, also the top view to show the positions of points plotted.   Divide the rise for harmonic motion by drawing the semicircle and projecting the points.   Refer to Fig. 27.13C. Divide the return for acceleration as shown.   Refer to Fig. 27.13B.   The curve thus obtained is for the center of the follower.   Curves drawn tangent to circles representing positions of the follower will locate the working surfaces of the cam. The development made as described is the drawing used to make the cam.

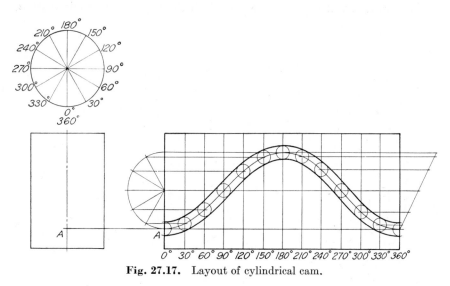

Fig. 27.17. Layout of cylindrical cam.

PROBLEMS

Group I. Spur gears

1. Make an assembly drawing of a pair of spur gears, from the following information: On an 11- by 17-in. sheet locate centers for front view of gear B $4\frac{1}{2}$ in. from right border and $3\frac{1}{2}$ in. from bottom border. Gear A is to the left of gear B. Center distances between gears are 5.250 in. Gear A revolves at 300 rpm and has four spokes, elliptical in cross section, 1-in. major and $\frac{1}{2}$-in. minor axes; inside flange diameter, $4\frac{3}{8}$ in.; hub 2 in. diameter, $1\frac{1}{2}$ in. long. Gear B revolves at 400 rpm and is disk type with $\frac{1}{2}$-in. web; inside flange diameter, $3\frac{1}{4}$ in.; hub, 2 in. diameter, $1\frac{1}{2}$ in. long. Material is cast steel; face width, 1 in.; diametral pitch, 4; shaft diameters, 1 in.; $\frac{1}{4}$-in. Woodruff keys. Draw front view and sectional top view.

2. Figure 27.18 shows a gear box for a reducing mechanism using spur gears. Using the scale shown on the drawing, transfer the necessary distances to obtain the net available space for the gears and design gears as follows: center distance, 4 in.; gear A revolves at 900 rpm, gear B, 1,500 rpm; diametral pitch, 4; face width, 1 in. Use standard $14\frac{1}{2}°$ involute teeth. Calculate the necessary values (shown in table). Draw the top view in section. Show four teeth on each gear on front view and complete the view with conventional lines.

3. Fig. 27.18. Same as Prob. 2 but for $A = 525$ rpm, $B = 675$ rpm. Use $20°$ involute teeth.

4. Make working drawings for the gears of Prob. 2.

5. Make working drawings for the gears of Prob. 3.

6. A broken spur gear has been measured and the following information obtained: number of teeth, 33; outside diameter, $4\frac{3}{8}$ in.; width of face, 1 in.; diameter of shaft, $\frac{7}{8}$ in.; length of hub, $1\frac{1}{4}$ in. Make a drawing of a gear blank with all dimensions and information necessary for making a new gear. Dimensions not given above may be made to suit as the drawing is developed.

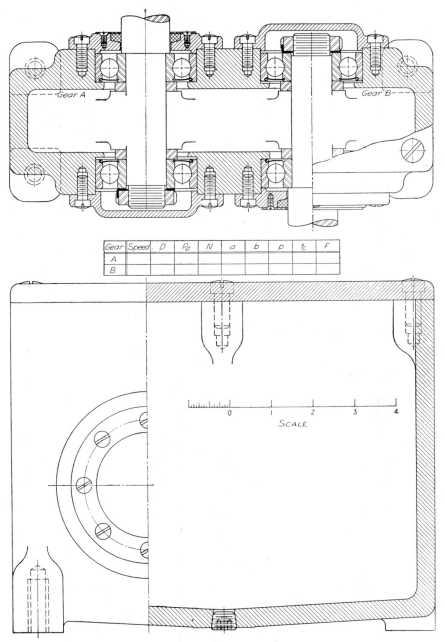

Gear	Speed	D	P_d	N	a	b	p	t_c	F
A									
B									

SCALE

Fig. 27.18.   Spur-gear reducer.

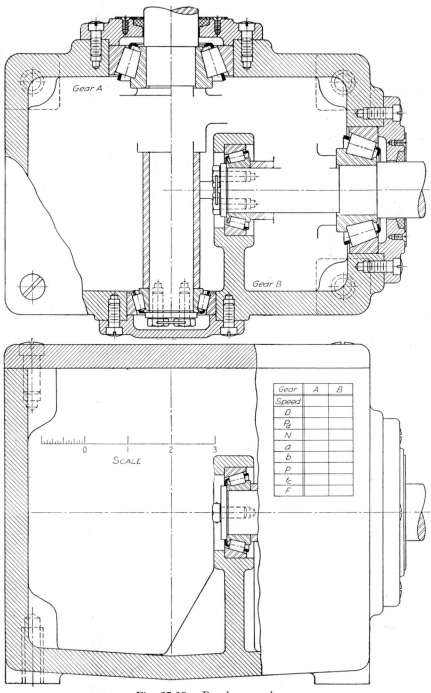

Fig. 27.19.   Bevel-gear reducer.

7. Make a drawing for a spur gear. The only information available is as follows: root diameter, 7.3372 in.; outside diameter, 8.200 in.; width of face, $1\frac{1}{8}$ in.; diameter of shaft, $1\frac{3}{8}$ in.; length of hub, 2 in.

Group II. Racks

8. Draw a spur gear and rack as follows: gear, 4-in. pitch diameter, 20 teeth, face width, 1 in.; standard $14\frac{1}{2}°$ involute teeth. Rack is to move laterally 5 in. Compute axial pitch, addendum and dedendum for rack and draw the rack and gear in assembly showing all teeth on rack and four teeth on gear.

9. Same as Prob. 8 but gear is 5-in. pitch diameter, has 25 teeth and $\frac{7}{8}$-in. face width, with 20° standard involute teeth.

Group III. Bevel gears

10. Figure 27.19 shows a gear box for a reducing mechanism using bevel gears. Using the scale shown on the drawing, transfer the necessary distances to obtain net available space for the gears and design gears as follows: gear A has 6-in. pitch diameter, diametral pitch, 4; speed, 350 rpm; face width, 1 in. Gear B has a speed of 600 rpm. Use standard $14\frac{1}{2}°$ involute teeth. Compute the necessary values (shown in table). Draw top view in section and front view as an external view showing all teeth.

11. Fig. 27.19. Same as Prob. 10 but gear A has $5\frac{1}{2}$-in. pitch diameter and 22 teeth; speed, 750 rpm. Gear B has a speed of 1,100 rpm. Use standard 20° involute teeth. Face width is 1 in.

12. Make working drawings for the bevel gears of Prob. 10, refer to paragraph 27.7 to compute values needed.

13. Make working drawings for the bevel gears of Prob. 11, refer to paragraph 27.7 to compute values needed.

Group IV. Spur and bevel gear trains

14. Fig. 27.20. Make an assembly drawing of gear train, as follows: A and B are bevel gears, with $\frac{7}{8}$-in. face width and 6-in. pitch diameter. A is 3-in. pitch diameter, revolves at 150 rpm. B revolves at 100 rpm. C and D are spur gears with 8-in. pitch diameter, 1-in. face width. C engages D, which revolves at 40 rpm. All shafts are 1 in. Draw A in full section, B with lower half in section, C and D in full section, quarter-end view of gear B in space indicated, and end views of C and D.

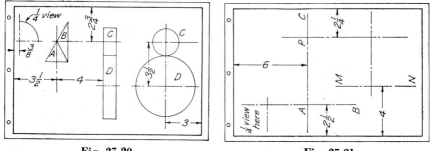

Fig. 27.20   Fig. 27.21

15. Fig. 27.21. A 3-in. diameter, 3 diametral pitch bevel gear R on shaft AB running 1,120 rpm drives another bevel gear S on shaft AC at 840 rpm. On shaft AC centered at P, an 8-in. diameter, 4 diametral pitch spur gear T drives a pinion U at 1,680 rpm. All shaft diameters are 1 in.; face widths, 1 in. Hub diameters of R and S are $1\frac{3}{4}$ in. Gear C has four spokes, elliptical, $\frac{5}{8}$ by 1 in.; hub, $1\frac{7}{8}$-in. diameter; thickness of flange, $\frac{1}{2}$ in. Draw gear R with upper half in section; S, T, and U in full section. Put quarter-end view of R in space indicated and end views of T and U on center line MN.

Group V. Worm gears

16. Make an assembly drawing of a pair of worm gears, as follows: center distance, 6 in.; pitch diameter of worm gear, $8\frac{1}{2}$ in.; face width of worm gear, $1\frac{7}{8}$ in.; pitch diameter of worm, $3\frac{1}{2}$ in.; standard $14\frac{1}{2}°$ involute worm teeth. Single-threaded worm, left hand 4 in. long, 1 in. lead. Show appropriate spindle ends for worm and suitable hub for worm gear. Make assembly drawing as a half section through axis of worm.

17. Make detail drawings of the worm gear and worm of Prob. 16. Refer to paragraph 27.9 and Figs. 27.10 and 27.11 for calculation of necessary dimensions.

Group VI. Cams

18. Make a drawing for a plate cam to satisfy the following conditions: On a vertical center line, a point A is $\frac{7}{8}$ in. above a point O, and a point B is $1\frac{3}{4}$ in. above A. With center at O, revolution clockwise, the follower starts at A and rises to B with uniform motion during one-third revolution, remains at rest one-third revolution, and drops with uniform motion the last one-third revolution to the starting point. Diameter of shaft, $\frac{3}{4}$ in.; diameter of hub, $1\frac{1}{4}$ in.; thickness of plate, $\frac{1}{2}$ in.; length of hub, $1\frac{1}{4}$ in.; diameter of roller, $\frac{1}{2}$ in.

19. Make a drawing for a face cam using the data of Prob. 18.

20. Make a drawing for a toe-and-wiper cam. The toe shaft is vertical, $\frac{3}{4}$ in. in diameter. Starting at a point 1 in. directly above center of wiper shaft, the toe is to move upward 2 in. with simple harmonic motion, with 135° turn of the shaft. Wiper has $1\frac{1}{4}$-in.-diameter hub, is $1\frac{1}{4}$ in. long; has $\frac{3}{4}$-in.-diameter shaft. Design toe to suit.

21. Make a drawing for a positive-motion cam. Starting at a point 1 in. above center of cam shaft, upper follower surface is to move upward 1 in. with simple harmonic motion in 180° turn of cam. Return is governed by necessary shape of cam. Follower is $\frac{1}{2}$ in. thick on $\frac{1}{2}$-in. vertical shaft. Cam is $\frac{1}{2}$ in. thick on $\frac{3}{4}$-in.-diameter shaft; hub, $1\frac{1}{4}$-in. diameter, $1\frac{1}{4}$ in. long.

22. Make a drawing, with development, for a cylindrical cam. The $\frac{1}{2}$-in.-diameter roller follower is to move 2 in. leftward with constant velocity in 180° turn of cylinder and return with simple harmonic motion. Cam axis is horizontal; cylinder, 4-in. diameter, 4 in. long on 1-in. shaft. Follower is pinned to $\frac{5}{8}$-in. shaft 3 in. center to center from cylinder.

28

Working Drawings

28.1 Definition. A working drawing is any drawing used to give information for purposes of manufacture, construction, or erection of a machine or structure. Complete knowledge for the production of a machine or structure is given by a *set* of working drawings conveying all the facts fully and explicitly, so that further instruction is not required.

The description given by the set of drawings will thus include:

1. The full graphical representation of the shape of each part (shape description).
2. The figured dimensions of all parts (size description).
3. Explanatory notes, general and specific, on the individual drawings, giving the specifications of material, heat-treatment, finish, etc. Often, particularly in architectural and structural work, the notes of explanation and information concerning details of materials and workmanship are too extensive to be included on the drawings and so are made up separately in typed or printed form and called the *specifications*, thus the term "drawings and specifications."
4. A descriptive title on each drawing.
5. A description of the relationship of each part to the others (assembly).
6. A parts list or bill of material.

A set of drawings will include, in general, two classes: (1) *detail drawings* giving the information included in items 1 to 4, and (2) an *assembly drawing*, item 5, giving the location and relationship of the parts.

28.2 Engineering procedure. In designing a new machine or structure, the first drawings are usually in the form of freehand sketches on which the original ideas, scheming, and inventing are worked out. These are either accompanied or followed by calculations to prove the suitability of the design. Working from the sketches and calculations, the design department produces a *design assembly* (also called a "design layout" or "design drawing"), Fig. 28.1. This is a preliminary pencil drawing on which more details of the design are worked out. It is accurately made with instruments, full size if possible, and shows the shape and position of the various parts, but little attempt is made to show all the intricate detail. Only the essential dimensions, such as basic calculated sizes, are given. On the drawing, or separately as a set of written notes, will be the designer's general specifications for materials, heat-treatments, finishes, clearances or interferences, etc., and any other information needed by the draftsman in making up the individual drawings of the separate parts.

Working from the design drawing and notes, a draftsman (detailer) then makes up the individual detail drawings illustrated by the detail drawing of Fig. 28.2, taken from the design drawing of Fig. 28.1. On the detail drawing, all the views necessary for complete shape description are provided,

481

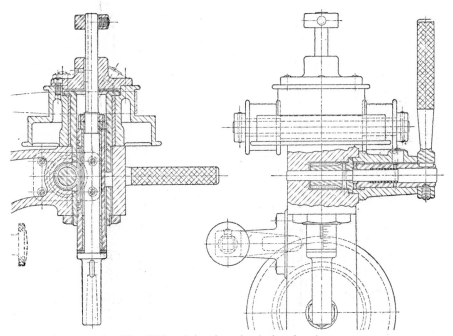

Fig. 28.1.   A portion of a design drawing.

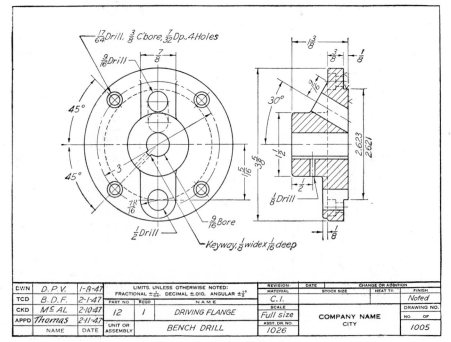

Fig. 28.2.   A detail drawing.

and all the necessary dimensions and manufacturing directions are given. Dimension values for nonmating surfaces are obtained by scaling the design drawing, and the more critical values are had from the design notes and from drafting-room standards. The detailer will correlate the dimensions of mating parts and give all necessary manufacturing information.

The set of drawings is completed by making an assembly drawing and a parts list or bill of material.

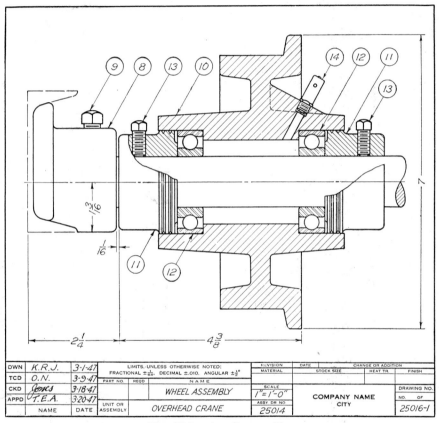

Fig. 28.3. A unit assembly.

If the machine is to be quantity produced, "operation" or "job" sheets will be prepared describing the separate manufacturing steps required and indicating the use and kind of special tools, jigs, fixtures, etc. The tool-design group, working from the detail drawings and the operation sheets, designs and makes the drawings for the special tools needed.

28.3 Assembly drawings. An assembly drawing is, as its name implies, a drawing of the machine or structure put together, showing the relative positions of the different parts.

Under the term "assembly drawings" are included preliminary design drawings and layouts, piping plans, unit assembly drawings, installation diagrams, and final complete drawings used for assembling or erecting the machine or structure.

The design drawing, as already indicated, is the preliminary layout on which the scheming, inventing, and designing are accurately worked out. The *assembly drawing* is in some cases made by tracing from the design drawing. More often it is drawn from the dimensions of the detail drawings. This provides a valuable check on the correctness of the detail drawings.

The assembly drawing may give the over-all dimensions and the distances between centers or from part to part of the different pieces, thus fixing the relation of the parts to each other and aiding in the erection of the

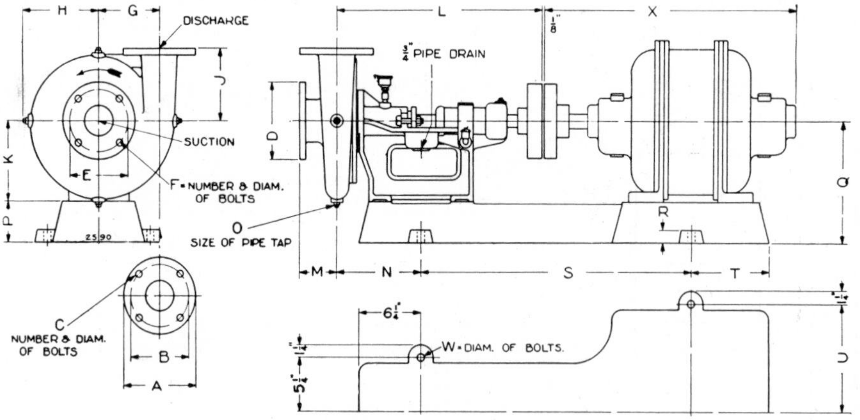

CODE WORD	PIPE SIZES DISCH.	PIPE SIZES SUCT'N.	A	B	C	D	E	F	G	H	J	K	L	M	N	O	P	Q	R	S	T	U	W	X
			DIMENSIONS IN INCHES																					
JAY	1 1/2"	2"	TAPPED OPENINGS						5 13/16	6 7/8	6 1/2	7 3/4	20 3/8	3 1/4	8 3/4	3/8								
JABBER	2"	2 1/2"	6	4 3/4	4-5/8	7	5 1/2	4-5/8	5 29/32	7 1/4	6 1/2	7 3/4	20 7/16	3	8 1/4	3/8								
JACKET	3"	3"	7 1/2	6	4-5/8	7 1/2	6	4-5/8	6 1/4	7 11/16	7	7 3/4	20 11/16	3 3/4	8 1/2	3/8	ABOVE DIMENSIONS DETERMINED BY SIZE OF MOTOR AND BASE USED							
JACK	4"	4"	9	7 1/2	8-5/8	9	7 1/2	8-5/8	7 11/16	8 3/4	7 3/4	8 13/16	22 11/16	4 1/2	10	1/2								
JACOBUS	5"	5"	10	8 1/2	8-3/4	10	8 1/2	8-3/4	8 1/8	9 1/8	8 1/4	8 13/16	22 15/16	5	10 1/4	1/2								

Fig. 28.4. An outline assembly drawing, tabular.

machine. It should not be overloaded with detail, particularly invisible detail. Unnecessary hidden lines should not be used on any drawing, least of all on an assembly drawing.

Assembly drawings usually have reference letters or numbers designating the different parts. These "piece numbers," sometimes enclosed in circles (called "balloons" by draftsmen), Fig. 28.3, with a leader pointing to the piece, are used in connection with the details and bill of material.

A *unit assembly drawing* or subassembly, Fig. 28.3, is a drawing of a related group of parts used for showing the assembly of complicated machinery where it would be practically impossible to show all the features on one drawing. Thus, in the drawing of a lathe, there would be included unit assemblies of such groups of parts as the headstock, tailstock, gearbox, etc.

An *outline assembly drawing* is used to give a general idea of the exterior shape of a machine or structure and contains only the principal dimensions, Fig. 28.4. When it is made for catalogues or other illustrative purposes,

dimensions are often omitted.   These drawings are frequently used to give
the information required for the installation or erection of equipment and
are then called *installation drawings.*

An *assembly working drawing* gives complete information for producing a
machine or structure on one drawing.   This is done by providing adequate
orthographic views together with dimensions, notes, and a descriptive title.
Figure 28.45 may be considered an example.

A *diagram drawing* is an assembly showing, symbolically, the erection or
installation of equipment.   Erection and piping and wiring diagrams are
examples.   Diagram drawings are often made in pictorial form.

28.4   Detail drawings.   A detail drawing is the drawing of a single
piece, giving a complete and exact description of its form, dimensions, and

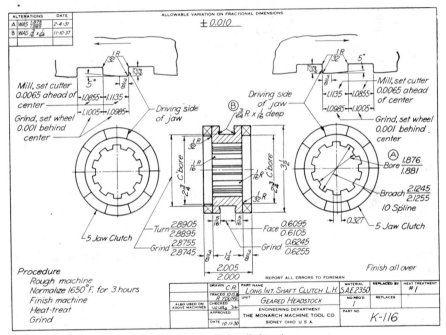

Fig. 28.5.   A detail drawing.

construction.   A successful detail drawing will tell the workman *simply* and
directly the shape, size, material, and finish of each part; what shop operations are necessary; what limits of accuracy must be observed; the number
of parts wanted; etc.   It should be so exact in description that, if followed,
a satisfactory part will result.   Figure 28.5 illustrates a commercial detail
drawing.

Detailing practice will vary somewhat according to the industry and the
requirements of the shop system.   For example, structural details are often
grouped together on one sheet, while in modern mechanical practice a
separate sheet is used for each part.

If the parts are grouped on one sheet, the detailed pieces should be set, if possible, in the same relative position as on the assembly and, to facilitate reading, placed as nearly as possible in natural relationship. Parts of the same material or character are usually grouped together as, for example, forgings on one sheet, castings on another, and parts machined from stock on another. A subtitle must be provided for each part, giving the part number, material, number required for each assembly, etc.

The accepted and best system in mechanical work is to have each piece, no matter how small, on a separate sheet. As described in paragraph 19.3, if the single-drawing system is followed, one drawing will be used by all shops. If the multiple system is used, a separate drawing must be made for each shop; thus there may be a *pattern drawing*, a *casting drawing*, and a *machining drawing*, all for a single cast part. A detail drawing should be a complete unit for the purpose intended and should not be dependent in any way upon any other detail drawing.

28.5 Tabular drawings. A tabular drawing, either assembly or detail, is one on which the dimension values are replaced with reference letters, an accompanying table on the drawing listing the corresponding dimensions for a series of sizes of the machine or part, thus making one drawing serve for the range covered. Some companies manufacturing parts in a variety of sizes use this tabular system of size description, but a serious danger with it is the possibility of misreading the table. Figure 28.4 illustrates a tabular assembly drawing.

28.6 Standard drawings. To avoid the difficulties experienced with tabular drawings, some companies are now making a "standard drawing," complete except for the actual figured dimensions. This drawing is reproduced by offset printing or black-and-white reproduction on vellum paper, and the reproductions are dimensioned separately for the various sizes of parts. This method gives a separate, complete drawing for each size of

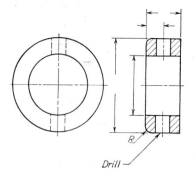

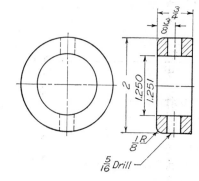

Fig. 28.6. A standard drawing.   Fig. 28.7. A standard drawing filled in.

part, and when a new size is needed the drawing is easily and quickly made. Figure 28.6 shows a standard drawing, and Fig. 28.7 the drawing filled in, making a completed working drawing.

28.7   Standard parts.   Purchased or company standard parts may be specified by name and size or by number and, consequently, will not need to be detailed.   All standard parts, such as bolts, screws, antifriction bearings, etc., are shown on the assembly drawing and are given a part number.   The complete specifications for their purchase are given in the parts list.

Sometimes, however, a part is made by *altering* a standard or previously produced part.   In this case a detail drawing is made, showing and specifying the original part with changes and dimensions for the alteration.

28.8   The bill of material, or parts list, is a tabulated statement, usually placed on a separate sheet in the case of quantity production (as in Fig. 28.37), or on the assembly drawing in other cases, as illustrated in Fig. 28.50. This table gives the piece number, name, quantity, material, and sometimes the stock size of raw material, detail drawing numbers, weight of each piece, etc.   A final column is usually left for remarks.   The term "bill of material" is usually used in structural and architectural drawing.   The term "parts list" more accurately applies in machine-drawing practice.   In general, the parts are listed in the order of their importance with the larger parts first and ending with the standard parts such as screws, pins, etc.

The blank ruling for a bill of material should not be crowded.   Lines should never be spaced closer than $\frac{1}{4}$ in.; $\frac{5}{16}$ or $\frac{3}{8}$ in. is better, with the height of the lettering not more than half the space and centered between lines.   Instead of being lettered, bills of material are frequently typed on forms printed on thin paper.   Intensifying the impression by carbon paper on the back increases the opacity of the typing, and a clearer blueprint will result.

28.9   Set of drawings.   A *complete set* of working drawings consists of detail sheets and assembly sheets, the former giving all necessary information for the manufacture of each of the individual parts which cannot be purchased, and the latter showing the parts assembled as a finished unit or machine.   The set includes the bill of material or parts list and may also contain special drawings for the purchaser, such as foundation plans or oiling diagrams.

28.10   Making a working drawing—basic concepts.   Although pictorial drawings are used to some extent in special cases, the basis of all working drawings is orthographic projection.   Thus, to represent an object completely, at least two views are ordinarily necessary, often more.   The only general rule is, *make as many views as are necessary to describe the object clearly,* **and no more.**   Instances may occur in which the third dimension is so evident as to make one view sufficient, as, for example, in the drawing of a shaft or bolt.   In other cases perhaps a half-dozen views might be required to describe a piece completely.   Sometimes half, partial, or broken views may be used to advantage.

As previously stated, select for the front view the face showing the largest dimension, preferably the obvious front of the object when in its functioning position, and then decide what other views are necessary. A vertical cylindrical piece, for example, would require only a front and a top view; a horizontal cylindrical piece, only a front and a side view. Determine which side view to use, or whether both are needed. The one with the fewest hidden lines should be preferred. In some cases the best representation may be to use *both* side views with all unnecessary dotted lines omitted. See whether an auxiliary view or a note will save one or more other views and whether a section will be better than an exterior view. One statement may be made with the force of a rule: *If anything in clearness can be gained by violating a principle of projection, violate it.*

Paragraphs 13.20 to 13.33 give a number of examples of conventions that are in violation of theoretical representation but are in the interest of clearness. The draftsman must remember that his responsibility is to the reader of the drawing and that he is not justified in saving himself any time or trouble at the expense of the drawing by making it less plain or easy to read. The time so saved by the draftsman may be lost to the company a hundredfold in the shop, where the drawing is used not once but repeatedly.

There is a *style* in drawing, just as there is in literature, which indicates itself in one way by ease of reading. Some drawings stand out, while others, which may contain all the information, are difficult to decipher. Although dealing with mechanical thought, there is a place for some artistic sense in mechanical drawing. The number, selection, and disposition of views; the omission of anything unnecessary, ambiguous, or misleading; the size and placement of dimensions and lettering; and the contrast of lines are elements concerned in the *style.*

In commercial drafting, *accuracy* and *speed* are the two requirements. The drafting room is an expensive department, and time is thus an important element. The draftsman must therefore have a ready knowledge not only of the principles of drawing but of the conventional methods and abbreviations and of any device or system that will save time without sacrificing clearness.

The usual criticism of the beginner by the employer is the result of the former's lack of appreciation of the necessity for *speed.*

28.11 Materials used for working drawings. Working drawings go to the shop in the form of blueprints, black-line prints, or other similar forms of reproduction, and the drawings must therefore be made on translucent material, either directly or as tracings. Pencil drawings may be made on tracing paper or on pencil cloth; inked drawings, on tracing paper or on tracing cloth.

Tracing paper is a thin translucent material commonly called "vellum." Considerable time and expense may be saved by making the original pencil drawing on this material. Excellent prints may be had if the lines are of sufficient blackness and intensity.

Pencil cloth is a transparentized fabric with one or both sides of its surface prepared to take pencil, so that the original drawing may be made on it and prints made either from the pencil drawing or after it has been inked. Some of the newer cloths are moisture resistant, others are really waterproof. Pencil cloth is made for pencil drawings, and perfect blueprints can be made from drawings made on it with sharp, hard pencils. Ink lines, however, do not adhere well and have a tendency to chip or rub off in cleaning.

Tracing cloth is a fine-thread fabric sized and transparentized with a starch preparation. The smooth side is considered by the makers as the working side, but most draftsmen prefer to work on the dull side, which will take pencil marks. The cloth should be fastened down smoothly over the pencil drawing and its selvage torn off. To remove the traces of grease that sometimes prevent the flow of ink, it should then be dusted with chalk or prepared pounce (a blackboard eraser may be used) and rubbed off with a cloth. Carbon tetrachloride is an effective cleaning agent. Rub a moistened cloth over the surface—any excess will evaporate in a moment.

A *plastic material* known as Kodatrace[1] similar to film backing is now available for both pencil and ink drawings. It is evenly translucent, has a fine matte surface, good lasting qualities, and requires no special storage precautions.

28.12 Drawing sizes. Drawing paper and cloth are available in rolls of various widths and in standard trimmed sizes. Most drafting rooms use standard sheets, printed with border and title block. The recommended sizes shown in the accompanying table, based on multiples of $8\frac{1}{2}$ by 11 in. and 9 by 12 in., permit the filing of prints in a standard letter file.

Finished Flat Sheet Sizes

Table 1			Table 2		
Designation	Width	Length	Designation	Width	Length
A	$8\frac{1}{2}$	11	A	9	12
B	11	17	B	12	18
C	17	22	C	18	24
D	22	34	D	24	36
E	34	44	E	36	48
F[1]	28	40	F[1]	28	40

[1] Not a multiple of the basic size. To be used when width of *E* size is not adaptable.

Figure 28.8 illustrates the most common trimmed sizes. Larger drawings may be made on rolled stock of standard width, with the length as a multiple of 11 or 12 in., not to exceed 144 in.

28.13 Order of penciling. After the scheming, inventing, and calculating have been done and the design drawing has been completed, the order of procedure for making the detail drawings is:

1. Select a suitable standard sheet, or lay off a sheet to standard size, with the excess paper to the right, as a convenient space for making sketches and calculations, and block out the space for the title.

2. Decide what scale is to be used, choosing one large enough to show all dimensions without crowding, and plan the arrangement of the sheet by making a little preliminary

[1] Trade name, Eastman Kodak Co., Rochester, N.Y.

freehand sketch, estimating the space each view will occupy and placing the views to the best advantage for preserving, if possible, a balance in the appearance of the sheet. Be sure to leave sufficient space *between* views for the dimensions.

3. Draw the center lines for each view, and on these "block in" the views by laying off the principal dimensions and outlines, using *light, sharp, accurate* pencil lines. Center lines are drawn for the axes of symmetry of all symmetrical views or parts of views. Thus every cylindrical part should have a center line—the projection of the axis of the piece. Every circle should have two center lines intersecting at its center.

4. Draw the views beginning with the most dominant features and progressing to the subordinate. The different views should be carried on together, projecting a character-

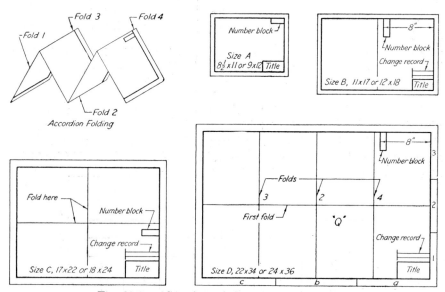

Fig. 28.8. ASA trimmed sizes of paper and cloth.

istic shape as shown on one view to the other views, *not* finishing one view before starting another. Draw the lines to the final finished weight (wherever possible), using a minimum of construction. *Never* make a drawing lightly and then "heavy" it later.

5. Finish the projections, putting in last the minor details. Check the projections and make sure that all views are complete and correct.

6. Draw all necessary dimension lines; then put in the dimensions.

7. Draw guide lines for the notes and then letter them.

8. Lay out the title.

9. Check the drawing carefully.

The overrunning lines of the constructive stage should not be erased before tracing or inking. These extensions are often convenient in showing the stopping points. All unnecessary erasing should be avoided as it abrades the surface of the paper so that it catches dirt more readily.

As an aid in stopping tangent arcs in inking, it is desirable to mark the tangent point on the pencil drawing with a short piece of the normal to the curve at the point of tangency. Figure 28.9 illustrates the stages of penciling.

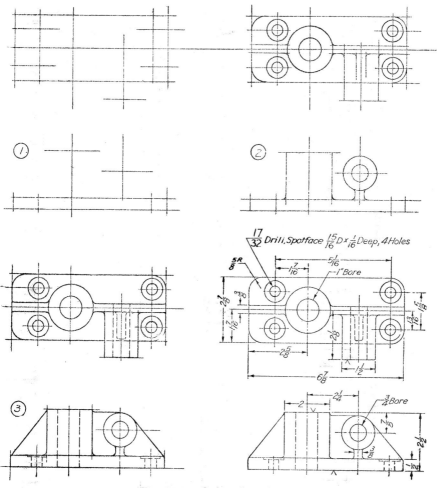

Fig. 28.9. Order of penciling.

28.14 Order of inking. To ensure good printing, the ink should be perfectly black and the ruling pens in good condition. Red ink should not be used unless it is desired to have some lines inconspicuous on the print. Blue ink will not print well. Sometimes, on maps, diagrams, etc., it is desirable to use colored inks on the tracing to avoid confusion of lines; in such cases, the addition of a little Chinese white will render them sufficiently opaque to print.

Ink lines may be removed from tracing cloth by rubbing with a hard pencil eraser, slipping a triangle under the tracing to give a harder surface. The rubbed surface should afterward be burnished with a burnisher or with the fingernail. In tracing a part that has been section-lined, a piece of white paper may be slipped under the cloth and the section lining done without reference to the section lines underneath.

Tracing cloth is very sensitive to atmospheric variations, often changing overnight so as to require restretching. If a large tracing cannot be finished during the day, some views should be finished and no figure left with only part of its lines traced.

In making a large tracing it is well to cut off the required piece from the roll and lay it exposed, flat, for a short time before fastening it down.

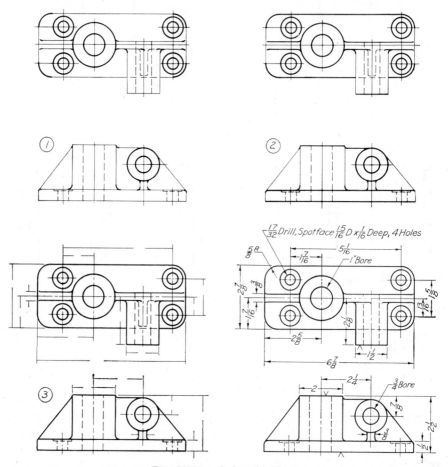

Fig. 28.10. Order of inking.

Water will ruin a tracing on starch-coated cloth, and moist hands or arms should not come in contact with it. The habit should be formed of keeping the hands off drawings. In both drawing and tracing on large sheets, it is a good plan to cut a mask of drawing paper to cover all but the view being worked on. Unfinished drawings should always be covered overnight.

Tracings may be cleaned of pencil marks and dirt by wiping with a cloth moistened with benzine or carbon tetrachloride. To prevent smearing when using this method of cleaning, borders and titles should be printed in an ink not affected by benzine.

Order of inking

1. Ink all full-line circles, beginning with the smallest, then circle arcs.
2. Ink dotted circles and arcs in the same order as full-line circles.
3. Ink any irregular curved lines.
4. Ink straight full lines in this order: horizontal, vertical, and inclined.
5. Ink straight dotted lines in the same order.
6. Ink center lines.
7. Ink extension and dimension lines.
8. Ink arrowheads and dimensions.
9. Section-line all areas representing cut surfaces.
10. Letter notes and titles. (On tracings, draw pencil guide lines first.)
11. Ink the border.
12. Check the inked drawing.

Figure 28.10 shows the stages of inking.

28.15 Title blocks. The title of a working drawing is usually located in the lower right-hand corner of the sheet, the size of the space varying with the amount of information to be given. The spacing and arrangement are designed to provide the information most helpful in a particular line of work.

In general, the title of a machine drawing should contain the following information:

1. Name of company and its location.
2. Name of machine or unit.
3. Name of part (if a detail drawing).
4. Drawing number.
5. Part number (if a detail drawing).
6. Number of parts required (for each assembly).
7. Scale.
8. Assembly-drawing number (given on a detail drawing to identify the part in assembly).
9. Drafting-room record: names or initials of draftsman, tracer, checker, approving authority; each with date.
10. Material.

To these, depending upon the need of the information, may be added:

11. Stock size.
12. Heat-treatment.
13. Finish.
14. Name of purchaser, if special machine.
15. Drawing "supersedes" and "superseded by."

Form of title. Every drafting room has its own standard form for titles. In large offices the blank form is often printed in type on the tracing paper or cloth. Figures 28.11 and 28.12 are characteristic examples.

A form of title that is used to some extent is the *record strip*, a strip marked off across either the lower part or right end of the sheet, containing the information required in the title and space for the record of orders, revisions, changes, etc., that should be noted, with the date, as they occur. Figure 28.13 illustrates one form.

It is sometimes desired to keep the records of orders and other private information on the tracing but not to have them appear on the print.   In

					THE HOOVER COMPANY		
					NORTH CANTON, OHIO		
					SCALE		
					DATE		
					DR. BY	TR. BY	
CHG NO.	MADE BY CHKD BY	REQ NO.	DATE	CHANGE	CH. BY	APP. BY	

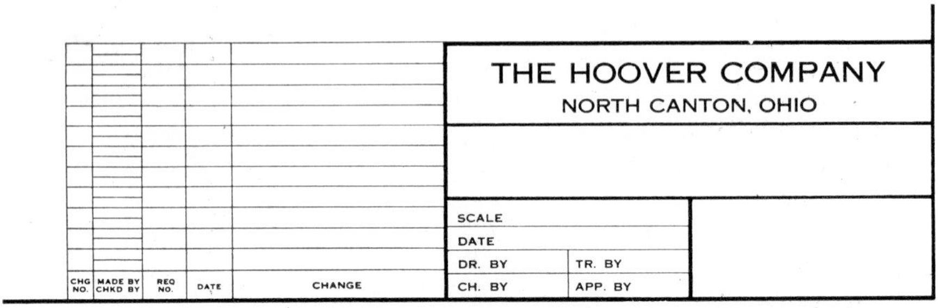

Fig. 28.11.   A printed title form.

such cases a record strip is put outside the border and trimmed off the print before sending it out.

To letter a title.   The title should be lettered freehand in single-stroke capitals, either vertical or inclined, but not both styles in the same title. Write out the contents on a separate piece of paper, then refer back to paragraph 2.17, where full instructions have been given.

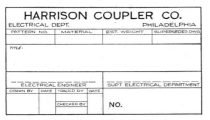

Fig. 28.12.   A printed title form.

28.16   Zoning.   As an aid in locating some item on a large drawing, the lower and right borders may be ruled and marked as shown on the D size drawing of Fig. 28.8.   Item Q would be located in zone $b2$.   A separate column in the change-record block is often used to indicate the position of each drawing change.

28.17   Checking.   When a working drawing is finished, it must be checked by an experienced person, who, in signing his name to it, becomes responsible for any errors.   This is the final "proofreading" and cannot be

UNIT				REVISION	DATE		CHANGE OR ADDITION	
				NAME OF PIECE				
DR.	DATE	SYMBOL OF MACHINES USED ON			SUPERSEDES DRAW.	STOCK CASTING		
CH.						DROP FORGING		
TR.		THE LODGE & SHIPLEY MACHINE TOOL CO.			SUPERSEDED BY DRAW.	MATERIAL	PIECE No.	
TR. CH.		Form 796 CINCINNATI, OHIO. U. S. A.						

Fig. 28.13.   A strip title.

done by the one who has made the drawing nearly so well as by another person.   In small offices all the work is checked by the chief draftsman, and draftsmen sometimes check each other's work; in large drafting rooms one or more checkers who devote all their time to this kind of work are employed.

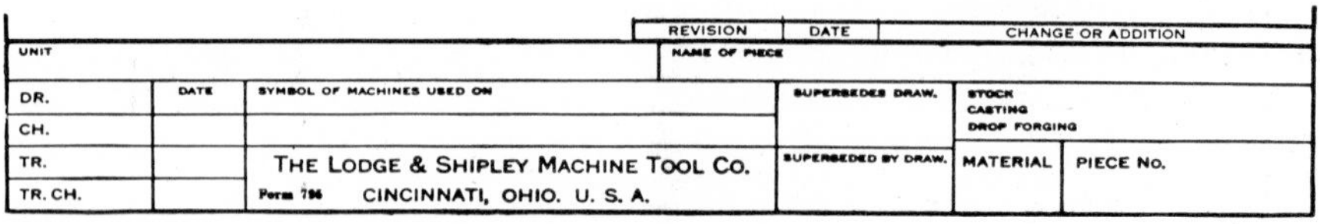

All notes, computations, and checking layouts should be preserved for future reference.

Students may gain experience in this work by checking each other's drawings.

To be effective, checking must be done in an absolutely systematic way and with thorough concentration.

28.18   Order of checking.   Each of the following items should be gone through separately.   As each dimension or feature is verified, a check mark in colored pencil should be placed on or above it and corrections indicated with a different colored pencil.

1. Put yourself in the position of those who are to read the drawing and find out it it is easy to read and tells a straight story.   Always do this before checking any individual features; in other words, before you have had time to become accustomed to the contents.

2. See that each piece is correctly designed and illustrated and that all necessary views are shown but none that is not necessary.

3. Check all the dimensions by scaling and, where advisable, by calculation also. Preserve the calculations.

4. See that dimensions for the shop are given as required by the shop and that the shop is not left to do any adding or subtracting in order to get a needed dimension.

5. Check for tolerances.   See that they are neither too "fine" nor too "coarse" for the particular conditions of the machine, so as neither to increase unnecessarily the cost of production nor, on the other hand, to impair accuracy of operation or duplication.

6. Go over each piece and see that finishes are properly specified.

7. See that every specification of material is correct and that all necessary ones are given.

8. Look out for "interferences."   This means that each detail must be checked with the parts that will be adjacent to it in the assembled machine to see that proper clearances have been allowed.

9. When checking for clearances in connection with a mechanical movement, lay out the movement to scale, figure the principal angles of motion, and see that proper clearances are maintained in all positions, drawing small mechanisms to double size or larger.

10. See that all the small details such as screws, bolts, pins, rivets, etc., are standard and that, where possible, stock sizes have been used.

11. Check every feature of the title, or record strip, and bill of material.

12. Review the drawing in its entirety, adding such explanatory notes as will increase its efficiency.

28.19   Alterations.   Once a drawing has been printed and the prints have been released to the shop, any alterations or changes should be recorded on the drawing and new prints issued.   If the changes are extensive, the drawing may be *obsoleted* and a new drawing made which *supersedes* the old drawing.   Many drawing rooms have "change-record" blocks printed in conjunction with the title, where minor changes are recorded, Fig. 28.11. The change is identified in the record and on the face of the drawing with a letter.

New designs may be changed so often that the alterations cannot be made fast enough to reach the shop when needed.   In this case, sketches showing the changes are rapidly made, reproduced, and sent to the shop where they are fastened to each print of the drawing. These sketches, commonly known as "engineering orders," are later incorporated on the drawing.

Portions of a drawing may be canceled by drawing closely spaced parallel lines, usually at 45°, over the area to be voided.

28.20 Working sketches. Facility in making, freehand, an orthographic drawing is an essential part of the equipment of every engineer. Such routine men as tracers and detailers may get along with skill and speed in mechanical execution, but the designer must be able to record his ideas freehand. In all inventive mechanical thinking, in all preliminary designing, in all explanation and instructions to draftsmen, freehand sketching is the mode of expression. Its mastery means the mastery of the language, and it is gained only after full proficiency in drawing with instruments is acquired. It is the mastery which the engineer, inventor, designer, chief draftsman, and contractor, with all of whom time is too valuable to spend in mechanical execution, must have.

Working sketches may be made in either orthographic or pictorial form. Chapter 8 gives the fundamentals for orthographic freehand drawings, and Chap. 18 discusses pictorial sketching.

28.21 Kinds of working sketches. Working sketches may be divided into two general classes: first, those made before the structure is built and, second, those made after the structure is built.

In the first class are included the sketches made in connection with the designing of the structure, which may be classified as (1) *scheme* or *idea* sketches, used in studying and developing the arrangement and proportion of parts; (2) *computation sketches*, made in connection with the figured calculations for motion and strength; (3) *executive sketches*, made by the chief engineer, inventor, or consulting engineer, to give instructions for special arrangements or ideas which must be embodied in the design; (4) *design sketches*, used in working up the schemes and ideas into such form that the design drawing can be started; and (5) *detail sketches*, made as substitutes for detail drawings.

The second class includes (1) *detail sketches*, drawn from existing parts, with complete notes and dimensions, from which duplicate parts may be constructed directly, or from which working drawings may be made, Fig. 28.14; (2) *assembly sketches*, made from an assembled machine to show the relative positions of the various parts, with center and location dimensions, or sometimes for a simple machine, with complete dimensions and specifications; and (3) *outline* or *diagrammatic sketches*, generally made for the purpose of location: sometimes, for example, to give the size and location of pulleys and shafting, piping, or wiring, that is, information for use in connection with the setting up of machinery; sometimes to locate a single machine, giving the over-all dimensions, sizes, and center distances for foundation bolts, and other necessary information.

28.22 Making a working sketch. In making a working sketch the principles of projection and the rules of practice for working drawings are to

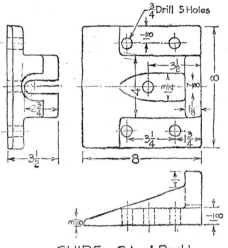

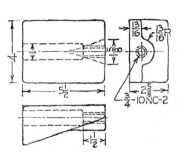

BLOCK · C.I.- 1 Req'd.

$\frac{3}{4}$" Cap Screw 3$\frac{3}{4}$"Lg. -1 Req'd
Washer for Screw - 1 Req'd.

GUIDE - C.I. - 1 Req'd.

Fig. 28.14. A detail sketch (leveling block).

be remembered and applied. A systematic order should be followed for both idea sketches and sketches from objects, as listed below:

1. Visualize the object.
2. Decide on the treatment, orthographic or pictorial.
3. Determine the view or views.
4. Determine the size of the sketch.
5. Locate the center lines.
6. Block in the main outlines.
7. Complete the detail.
8. Add dimension lines and arrowheads.
9. Put on the dimensions.
10. Letter notes and title, with date.
11. Check the drawing.

Before a good graphical description of an object or idea can be developed, it is essential that the mental image of it be definite and clear. The clearness of the sketch is a direct function of this mental picture. Hence the first step is to concentrate on visualization, leading directly to the second step, determination of the best method of representation. This will probably not be just the same as would be made in a scale drawing. For exam-

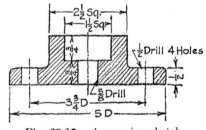

Fig. 28.15. A one-view sketch.

ple, a note in regard to thickness or shape of section will often be used to save a view, Fig. 28.15; thus one view of a piece that is circular in cross section would be sufficient. In other cases additional part views and extra sections may be sketched rather than complicate the regular views with added lines that might confuse the sketch, although the same lines might be perfectly clear in a measured drawing. The third step is to determine the view (pictorial) or views (orthographic). Draw the object in its functioning position, if possible, but if another position will show the features to better advantage, use it. A machine should, of course, be represented right-side up, in its natural working position. If symmetrical about an axis, often one-half only need be sketched. If a whole view cannot be made on one page, it may be put on two, each part being drawn up to a break line used as a datum line.

The fourth step is to proportion the size of the sketch to the sheet. Have it large enough to show all detail clearly, but allow plenty of room for dimensions, notes, and memorandums. Small parts may be sketched larger than full size. Do not try to crowd all the views on one sheet of paper. Use as many sheets as may be required, but name each view, indicating the direction in which it is taken. Sometimes one view alone will require a whole sheet.

Sketches are often made on coordinate paper ruled faintly in sixteenths, eighths, or quarters of an inch, used either simply as an aid in drawing straight lines and judging proportions, or for drawing to approximate scale by assigning suitable values to the unit spaces. The latter use is more applicable to design sketches than to sketches from the object.

In drawing on plain paper, the location of the principal points, centers, etc., should be so judged that the sketches will fit the sheet, and the whole sketch, with as many views, sections, and auxiliary views as are necessary to describe the piece, will be drawn in as nearly correct proportion as the eye can determine, *without taking any measurements.*

28.23 Dimension lines. After the sketching of a piece is finished, it should be gone over and dimension lines for all the dimensions needed for the construction added, drawing extension lines and arrowheads carefully and checking to see that none is omitted.

28.24 Measuring and dimensioning. The measurements for the dimensions indicated on the drawing may now be added. If the sketch is of an existing part, a flexible rule or steel scale will serve for getting most of the dimensions. Never use a draftsman's scale for measuring castings, as it will be soiled and have its edges marred.

Always measure from finished surfaces, if possible. Judgment must be exercised in measuring rough castings so as not to record inequalities.

28.25 Checking the sketch. The final step is to check the sketch. It is a curious fact that when a beginner omits a dimension it is usually a basic, vital one, as that of the center height of a machine or an over-all length.

Sketches are not always made on paper having a printed title, but essentially the same information as for an instrument drawing should be recorded in some convenient place on the sheet. All notes and special directions should be checked for accuracy along with the drawing proper. In general, follow the order of checking given in paragraph 28.17.

28.26 Reproduction of drawings. As has already been indicated, working drawings go to the shop in the form of prints made from the original drawings. Several different printing processes are in use, all of which give the best results from tracings inked on tracing cloth or paper. However, quite satisfactory prints may be obtained from pencil drawings on translucent paper when the penciling is done skillfully, with uniform opaque lines. In fact, most of the drawings of industry are not inked; only those of a permanent nature such as maps, charts, etc., and tracings that must be printed a great many times are inked.

Blueprints. The simplest and most generally used copying process is the blueprinting process, in which the prints are made by exposing a piece of sensitized paper and a tracing in close surface contact with each other to sunlight or electric light in a printing frame or machine made for the purpose. On exposure to the light a chemical action takes place, which when fixed by washing in water gives a strong blue color. The parts protected from the light by the black lines of the tracing wash out, leaving the white paper.

Vandyke paper is a thin sensitized paper which turns dark brown when exposed to light and properly "fixed." A reversed negative of a tracing may be made on it by exposing it to light with the inked side of the drawing next to the sensitized side of the paper; then this negative can be printed on blueprint paper, giving a positive print with blue lines on white.

B W prints and Directo prints have black lines on a white ground and are made directly from the original tracing, either in a blueprinting machine (and developed by hand) or in a special machine made for the purpose. They are used extensively when positive prints are desired.

Ozalid prints. This process is based on the chemical action of light-sensitive diazo compounds. It is a contact method of reproduction in which the exposure is made in either a regular blueprinting machine or an ozalid "whiteprint" machine, and the exposed print is developed dry with ammonia vapors in a developing machine. Standard papers giving black, blue, and maroon lines on a white ground are available. Dry developing has the distinct advantage of giving prints without distortion, and it also makes possible the use of transparent papers, cloth, and foils which effects savings in drafting, as these transparent replicas can be changed by additions or erasures and prints made from them without altering the original tracing.

Photostat prints are extensively used by large corporations. By this method a print with white lines on a dark background is made directly from any drawing or tracing, to any desired reduction or enlargement, through the use of a large specially designed camera. This print may be again photostated, giving a brown-black line on a white ground. This method is extremely useful to engineers for drawings to be included in reports and for matching drawings of different scales which may have to be combined into one.

Duplicating tracings. Tracings having all the qualities of ordinary inked ones are made photographically from pencil drawings by using a sensitized tracing cloth.

Lithoprinting. When a number of copies of a drawing (50 or more) are needed, they may be reproduced by lithoprinting, a simplified form of photolithography, at comparatively small cost.

Copying methods, such as those of the mimeograph, ditto machine, and other forms of the hectograph or gelatin pad, are often used for small drawings.

28.27 Filing and storing of drawings. Drawings are filed in steel or wooden cabinets made for the purpose. Many engineering offices store their drawings in fireproof vaults and remove them only for making alterations or for printing. Photographic copies are sometimes made as a separate permanent record. Drawings are always filed flat or rolled. Prints, however, are folded for filing or mailing. The usual method is the "accordion" fold illustrated in Fig. 28.8. To aid in the filing of accordion-folded prints, a supplementary number block may be added, as shown.

28.28 Individual fields. The foregoing paragraphs of this chapter have described the usual methods employed in the drafting rooms of industry. However, it must be realized that each major branch of engineering (or divisions within a major branch) will have some special practices. As examples, a civil engineer in sanitary work will deal with drainage, water treatment, etc., while his brother civil engineer in structural work will be concerned with steel, concrete, etc., in fabricating bridges, roadways, etc.

To meet these varied requirements, every engineer must have a basic graphical training, but there must naturally be a corresponding variation in the emphasis placed on some phases of graphical work.

In preparation for aircraft drawing, the requisites are a thorough knowledge of orthographic projection and engineering geometry; an acquaintance with shop practice, including riveted construction and welding; experience in the use of sheet-metal stamped shapes; and, desirably, a facility in using perspective and other pictorial methods. Training in engineering geometry is especially important since more than usual emphasis is placed on the theory, drawing, and dimensioning of warped surfaces. Drawings used in the aircraft industry may be classified under three general divisions: (1) preliminary design drawings, (2) layout drawings, and (3) production drawings.

Agricultural engineers should have a good basic training with attention paid to working drawings of machines and farm buildings.

In preparation for ceramic engineering, emphasis should be placed on mechanical and structural drafting practice.

The study of drawing in preparation for chemical engineering involves all the basic principles considered in this and previous chapters. The chemical engineer should be informed on piping and on the various forms of equipment used in industrial chemistry, such as mixing, grinding, filtering, drying, and conveying machinery.

Civil engineers should be well trained in the making of piping, welding, structural, architectural, map, and topographic drawings.

Electrical engineers need the basic equipment in the language of drawing as do mechanical or other engineers. In its application in their profession it may be divided into two general classes: working drawings, as of electrical machinery; and diagrammatic or symbolic drawings, such as wiring diagrams, etc. In electrical working drawings the principles and conventions of this chapter are all applicable. Diagrammatic drawings, using conventional symbols for electrical equipment and connections, form an important class of electrical drawings. Electrical symbols, wiring symbols, and radio symbols are given in the Appendix.

Industrial and mechanical engineers should have a broad training in working-drawing practice including structural and architectural drawings and should be thoroughly familiar with drawing practices for gears, cams, welded construction, and jigs and fixtures.

Metallurgical, mining, and petroleum engineers should have a good basic training in engineering drawing and geometry.

It is evident that a welding engineer should be thoroughly familiar with welding-drawing practice, in addition to his basic training.

28.29 Special practices. Drawings made for unusual purposes may call for special methods not commonly employed in regular drafting. Chapter 35 describes a number of drafting procedures such as stretching paper, water-color and India-ink washes, etc., to be used whenever occasion demands.

One practice with which all engineers should be familiar is the method of locating machines and equipment in a plant. Generally a drawing of the building is made and the machines are located by making scale drawings of them, cutting them out, and shifting them around on the building plan to get the best arrangement. When the final positions are decided upon, a drawing is made showing the machines and the "route lines" for materials and products. Some of the drawing time required for this work may be saved by making the building drawing on beaverboard, attaching the machine cutouts to the drawing with a paper-stapling machine, and then photostating the complete assembly. The photostat is made to half the scale of the "master board" and is used as any plant layout drawing would be. The master boards are filed away in special cases so that when changes are necessary the machines may be relocated and a new photostat made.

PROBLEMS

The first part of any working-drawing problem consists of the selection of views, the choice of suitable scales, and the arrangement of the sheet. In classwork a preliminary sketch layout should be submitted for approval before the drawing is commenced.

In dimensioning these problems the principles given in Chaps. 20 and 21 should be followed carefully. Before applying finish marks, study the problem to determine which surfaces should be so marked. On parts that are to fit accurately, the class of fit is to be assumed or assigned, and limit dimensions are to be figured from the nominal sizes given, using the ASA tables of allowances and tolerances in the Appendix. The illustration for the problem is to be taken as the preliminary sketch or design drawing from which to make the actual working drawings for the shop. Because of restricted space, the illustrations are often crowded; do not, therefore, follow them as examples of good spacing or of the best placing of dimensions. The dimensions used are intended primarily for drawing purposes and are not necessarily those which should be selected for the working drawing.

Group I. Detail drawings. *Problems* 1 to 18. Figs. 28.16 to 28.33.

This group includes problems involving sectional views, auxiliaries, and conventional representation. Several methods of part production will be found: casting, forging, forming of sheet metal, and plastic molding.

Group II. An assembly drawing from the details. *Problems* 19 to 23. Figs. 28.34 to 28.38.

Group III. Detail drawings from the assembly. *Problems* 24 to 41. Figs. **28.39 to** 28.52.

Group IV. A set of drawings from an exploded pictorial. *Problems* 42 to 49. Figs. 28.53 to 28.59.

Group V. A set of drawings from a pictorial assembly. *Problems* 50 to 55. Figs. 28.60 to 28.65.

Group VI. A set of drawings from the design drawing. *Problems* 56 to 66. Figs. 28.66 to 28.76.

Group VII. Working sketches. *Problems* 67 to 72.

Group I. Detail drawings

1. Fig. 28.16. Make complete working drawing with necessary sectional views. Cast iron.

2. Fig. 28.17. Working drawing of friction-shaft bearing. Cast iron.

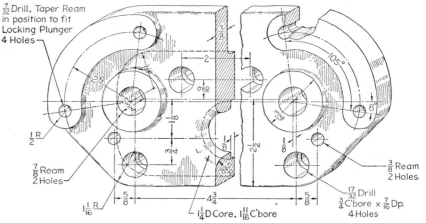

Fig. 28.16. Gear-shifter bracket.

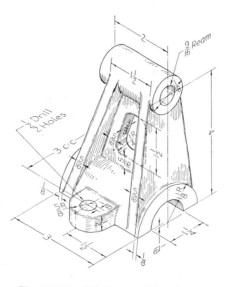

Fig. 28.17. Friction-shaft bearing.

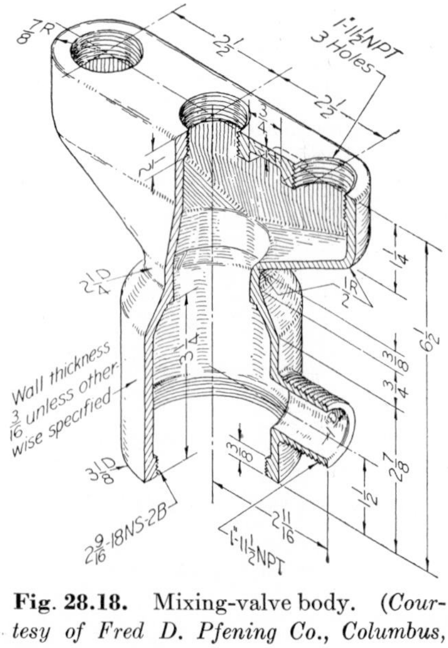

Fig. 28.18. Mixing-valve body. (*Courtesy of Fred D. Pfening Co., Columbus, Ohio.*)

3. Fig. 28.18.   Working drawing of mixing-valve body.   Cast brass.
4. Fig. 28.19.   Working drawing of conveyer hanger.   Determine what views and part views will best describe the piece.   Cast steel.

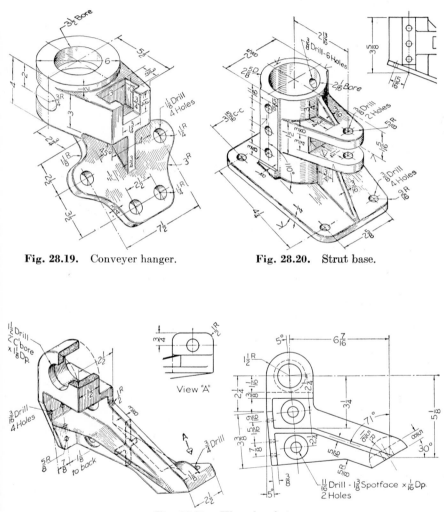

Fig. 28.19.   Conveyer hanger.   **Fig. 28.20.**   Strut base.

Fig. 28.21.   Hinge bracket.

5. Fig. 28.20.   Working drawing of strut base.   Determine what views and part views will best describe the piece.   Cast aluminum.
6. Fig. 28.21.   Draw given front view.   Add part views and auxiliaries to best describe the piece.   Cast aluminum.

7. Fig. 28.22. Working drawing of valve cage. Cast bronze.

8. Fig. 28.23. Determine what views and part views will best describe the piece. Malleable iron.

9. Fig. 28.24. Working drawing of water-pump cover. Aluminum alloy die casting.

10. Fig. 28.25. Working drawing of slotted spider. Malleable iron.

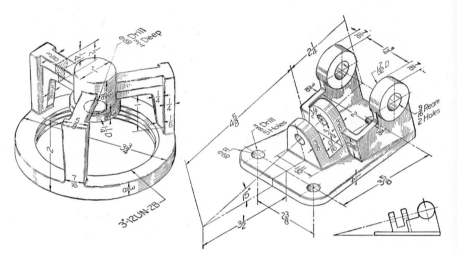

Fig. 28.22. Valve cage.   **Fig. 28.23.** Brace plate.

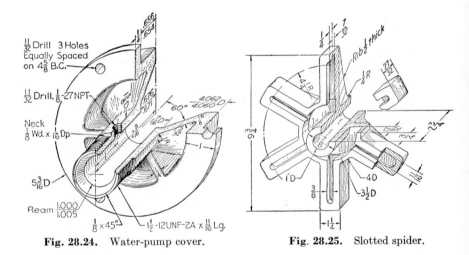

Fig. 28.24. Water-pump cover.   **Fig. 28.25.** Slotted spider.

11. Fig. 28.26. Make working drawing of relief-valve body. Cast brass.

12. Fig. 28.27. Working drawing of breaker. Steel.

13. Fig. 28.28. Working drawing of meter case. Molded bakelite.

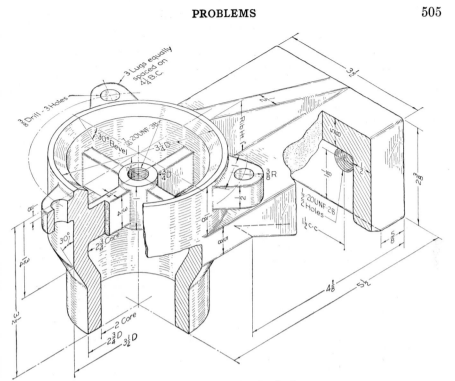

Fig. 28.26.   Relief-valve body.

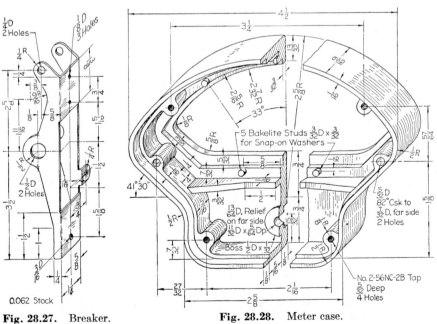

0.062 Stock

Fig. 28.27.   Breaker.   **Fig. 28.28.**   Meter case.

14. Fig. 28.29. (*a*) Make detail working drawings on same sheet, one for *rough* forging and one for *machining;* or (*b*) make one detail drawing for forging and machining. Alloy steel.

15. Fig. 28.30. Make working drawing of buffer stand. Steel drop forging. Drawings same as Prob. 14.

16. Fig. 28.31. Working drawing of puller body. Press forging, steel. Drawings same as Prob. 14.

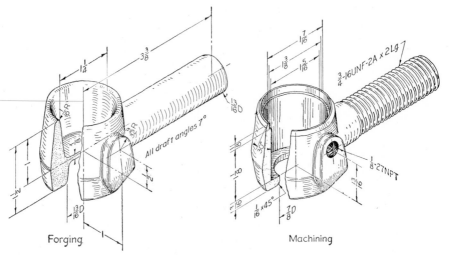

Forging   Machining

Fig. 28.29. Steering knuckle.

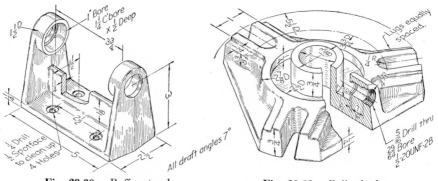

Fig. 28.30. Buffer stand.   **Fig. 28.31.** Puller body.

17. Fig. 28.32. Working drawing of automotive connecting rod. Drop forging, alloy steel. Drawings same as Prob. 14.

18. Fig. 28.33. Working drawing of torque-tube support. Drop forging, aluminum alloy. Drawings same as Prob. 14.

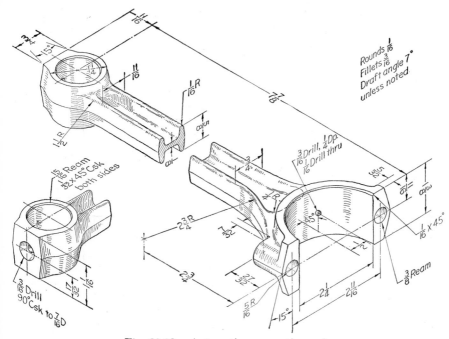

Fig. 28.32. Automotive connecting rod.

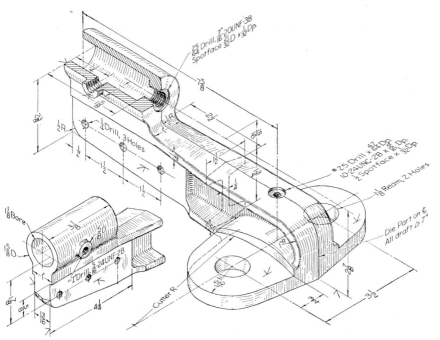

Fig. 28.33. Torque-tube support.

Group II. An assembly drawing from the details

19. Fig. 28.34. Make an assembly drawing of the crane hook from details given. Standard parts 7 to 10 are not detailed; see Appendix or handbook for sizes.

20. Fig. 28.35. Make an assembly drawing, front view in section, of caster.

21. Fig. 28.35. Redesign caster for ball-bearing installation.

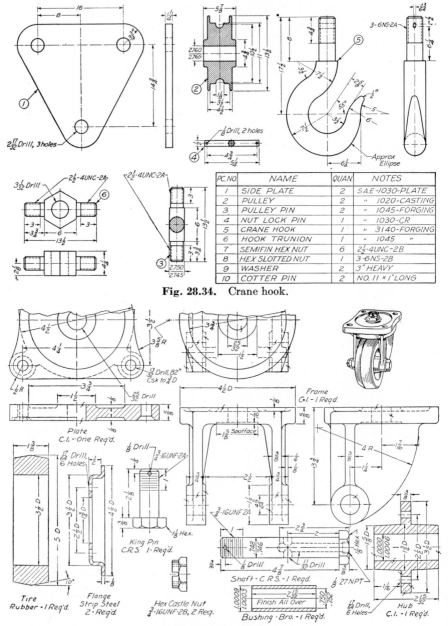

PC.NO.	NAME	QUAN.	NOTES
1	SIDE PLATE	2	S.A.E.-1030-PLATE
2	PULLEY	2	" 1020-CASTING
3	PULLEY PIN	2	" 1045-FORGING
4	NUT LOCK PIN	1	" 1030-CR
5	CRANE HOOK	1	" 3140-FORGING
6	HOOK TRUNION	1	" 1045 "
7	SEMIFIN HEX NUT	6	2¼-4UNC-2B
8	HEX SLOTTED NUT	1	3-6NS-2B
9	WASHER	2	3" HEAVY
10	COTTER PIN	2	NO. 11 × 1" LONG

Fig. 28.34. Crane hook.

Fig. 28.35. Caster.

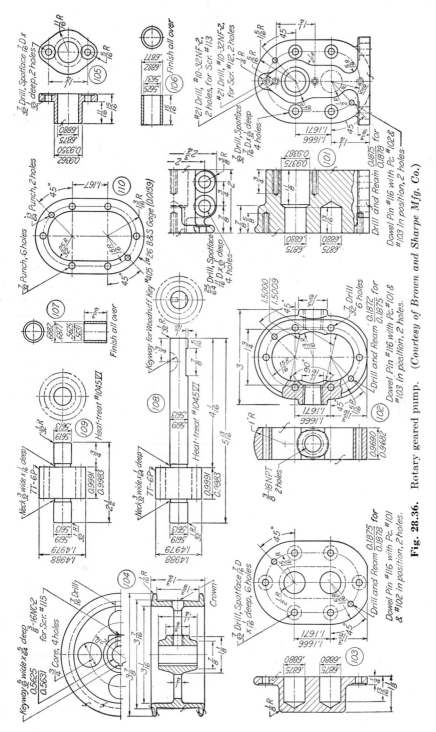

Fig. 28.36. Rotary geared pump. (Courtesy of Brown and Sharpe Mfg. Co.)

22. Fig. 28.36.   Make an assembly drawing of the Brown and Sharpe rotary geared pump, with top view, longitudinal section, and side view.   Show direction of rotation of shafts and flow of liquid with arrows.   Give dimensions for base holes to be used in setting; also give distance from base to center of driving shaft and size of shaft and key. Refer to Chap. 27 for method of drawing the teeth of the gears, pieces 108 and 109.   For parts not detailed, see parts list, Fig. 28.37.

PARTS LIST

BROWN AND SHARPE No. 1 ROTARY GEARED PUMP

PC. NO	DRAW. SIZE	NAME	QUAN	MAT.	STOCK		USED ON		REMARKS
					DIA.	LENG	NAME	PC. NO	
101		Base	1	C.I.					
102		Body	1	C.I.					
103		Cover	1	C.I.					
104		Pulley	1	C.I.					
105		Gland	1	C.I.					
106		Gland Bushing	1	Bro.					
107		Gear Bushing	4	Bro.					
108		Driving Gear	1	S.A.E. #1045	1 9/16	5 7/8			
109		Driven Gear	1	S.A.E. #1045	1 9/16	2 9/16			
110		Gasket	2	Sheet Copper			Body	102	#26 B&S Gage (0.0159)
111		#10-32 x 1 5/8 Slotted Hex. Hd. Mach. Scr. & Nut	4				Cover	103	
112		#10-32 x 1 5/8 Slotted Hex. Hd. Cap Scr.	2				Cover	103	
113		#10-32 x 7/8 Slotted Hex. Hd. Cap Scr.	2				Gland	105	
114		Woodruff Key #405	1				Driving Gear	108	
115		3/8 x 3/8 Headless Set Scr., 3/8-16NC-2	1				Pulley	104	
116		5/16 x 1 7/16 Dowel Pin	2	C.R.S.			Cover	103	
		Packing	To Suit						Garlock Rotopac #239

Fig. 28.37.   Parts list for rotary geared pump.

23. Fig. 28.38.   From detail sketches, make assembly and detail drawings of Uni-pump centrifugal pump, as made by the Weinman Pump Mfg Co., in which the pump casing is mounted directly on a driving motor, making a compact and efficient design. Cross sections of the volute taken at intervals of 45° should be shown by removed sections, either successive or superimposed, and similar sections should be made through the impeller.   At 3,425 rpm this pump delivers 520 gal per min against a head of 160 ft.

The detail drawings should be made up as a set of drawings with each part drawn on a separate sheet.   Choose a standard sheet size so that the part may be drawn either full or half size.   Dimensioning should be for quantity production with limit dimensions given wherever the function of the parts requires such dimensions.   See Chap. 21 for the method of selecting the various fits needed.   Drawings of cast parts may be made either in the "single drawing" or "multiple drawing" system as described in Chap. 19.

The assembly drawing should show, by dimensions, the relationship between intake and exhaust openings.   The sizes of intake and exhaust openings should be given.   The mounting flange should also be dimensioned and the number and size of holes in this flange should be specified.

Complete the set of drawings by making a parts list.   See Fig. 28.37 for items and style.

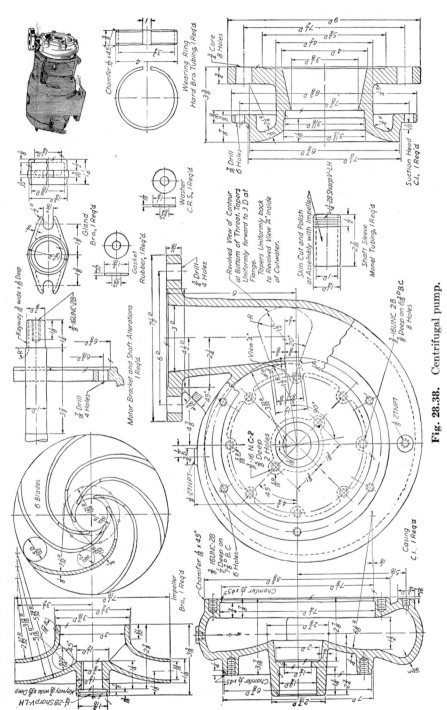

Fig. 28.38. Centrifugal pump.

Group III.   Detail drawings from the assembly

    24. Fig. 28.39.   Make detail drawings of the jig table.   Parts, cast iron.

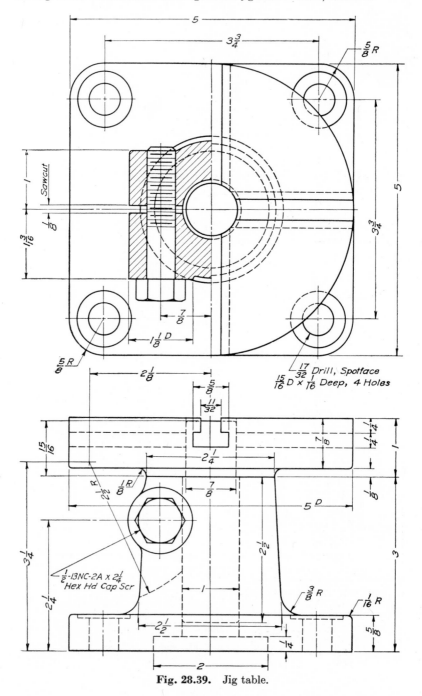

Fig. 28.39.   Jig table.

25. Fig. 28.40.   Make detail drawings of the door catch.

26. Fig. 28.41.   Make detail drawings of the belt drive.   Pulley and bracket, cast iron; gear and shaft, steel; bushing, bronze.

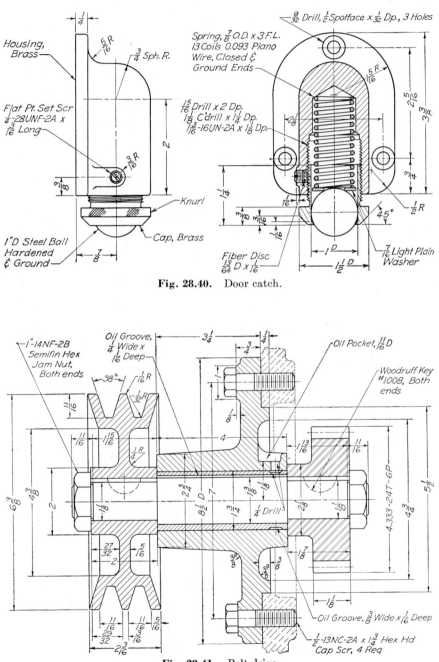

Fig. 28.40.   Door catch.

Fig. 28.41.   Belt drive.

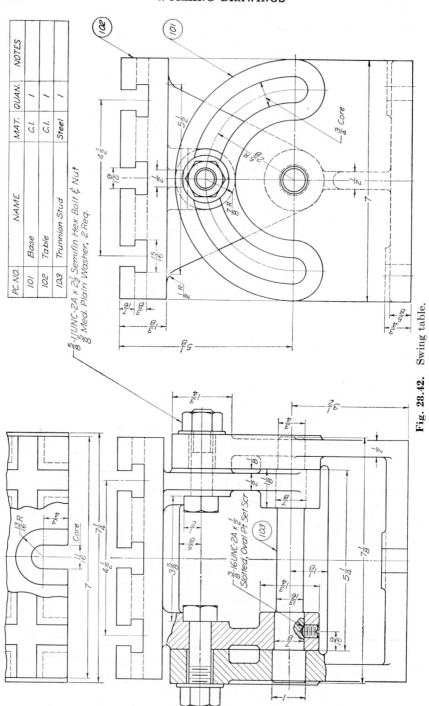

PC.NO.	NAME	MAT.	QUAN.	NOTES
101	Base	C.I.	1	
102	Table	C.I.	1	
103	Trunnion Stud	Steel	1	

$\frac{5}{8}$-11UNC-2A x 2$\frac{1}{2}$ Semifin Hex Bolt & Nut
$\frac{5}{8}$ Med. Plain Washer, 2 Req.

$\frac{3}{16}$-16UNC-2A x $\frac{1}{2}$
Slotted, Oval Pt Set Scr

Fig. 28.42. Swing table.

27. Fig. 28.42. Make detail drawings of swing table.
28. Fig. 28.43. Make detail drawings of sealed ball joint.
29. Fig. 28.44. Make detail drawings of belt tightener. Bracket, pulley, and collar, cast iron; bushing, bronze; shaft, steel.

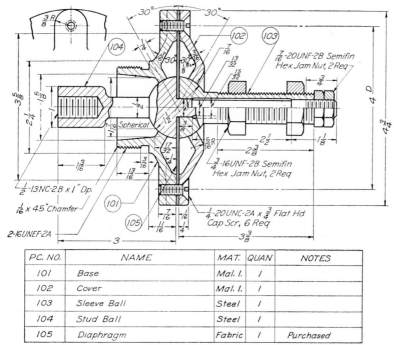

PC. NO.	NAME	MAT.	QUAN	NOTES
101	Base	Mal. I.	1	
102	Cover	Mal. I.	1	
103	Sleeve Ball	Steel	1	
104	Stud Ball	Steel	1	
105	Diaphragm	Fabric	1	Purchased

Fig. 28.43. Sealed ball joint.

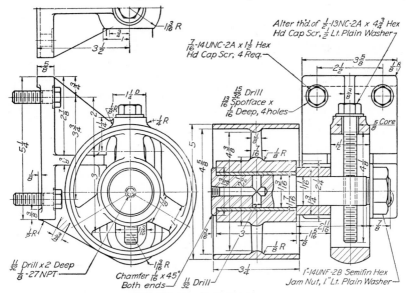

Fig. 28.44. Belt tightener.

30. Fig. 28.45.   Make detail drawings of rotary pressure joint.
31. Fig. 28.46.   Make detail drawings of ball-bearing idler pulley.

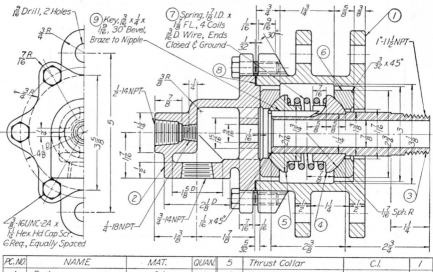

PC.NO.	NAME	MAT.	QUAN.					
1	Body	C.I.	1	5	Thrust Collar		C.I.	1
2	Head	C.I.	1	6	Seal Ring		No.61 Graphitar	2
3	Nipple Tube	Steel	1	7	Spring		Stainless Steel	1
4	Nipple Body	C.I.	1	8	Gasket		Durabla	1
				9	Key		Steel	1

Fig. 28.45.   Rotary pressure joint.   (*Courtesy of The Johnson Corp., Three Rivers, Mich.*)

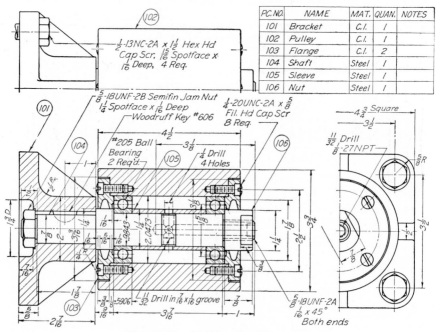

PC.NO.	NAME	MAT.	QUAN.	NOTES
101	Bracket	C.I.	1	
102	Pulley	C.I.	1	
103	Flange	C.I.	2	
104	Shaft	Steel	1	
105	Sleeve	Steel	1	
106	Nut	Steel	1	

Fig. 28.46.   Ball-bearing idler pulley.

PC. NO.	NAME		MAT.	QUAN.	NOTES
101	Butterfly Housing		Mal.I.	1	
102	Rack Housing		Mal.I.	1	
103	Butterfly	(.0625"thick)	Steel	1	#16 U.S.S. Gage
104	Butterfly Shaft		Steel	1	
105	Pinion		Steel	1	
106	Rack		Steel	1	16 Pitch
107	Key Screw		Steel	1	
108	Cover	(.0625"thick)	Steel	1	#16 U.S.S. Gage

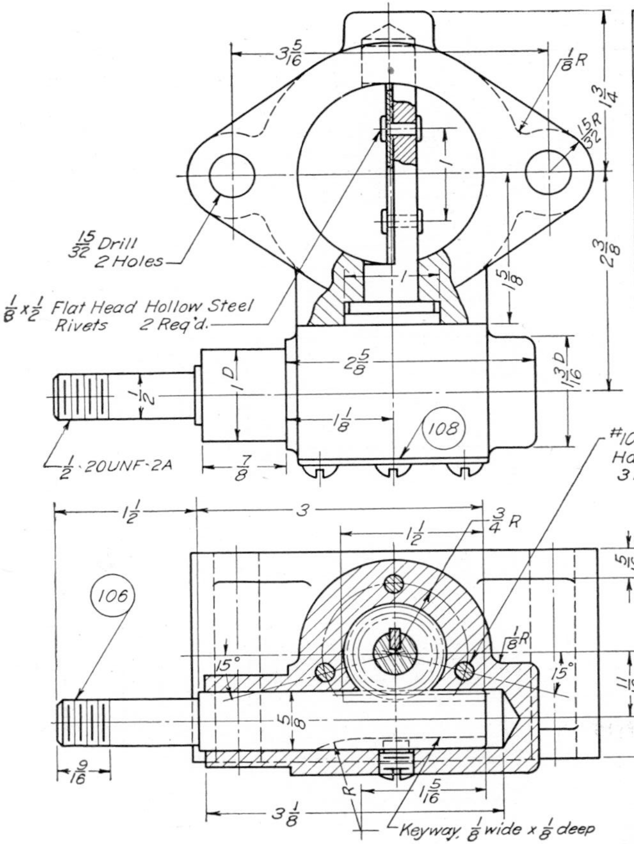

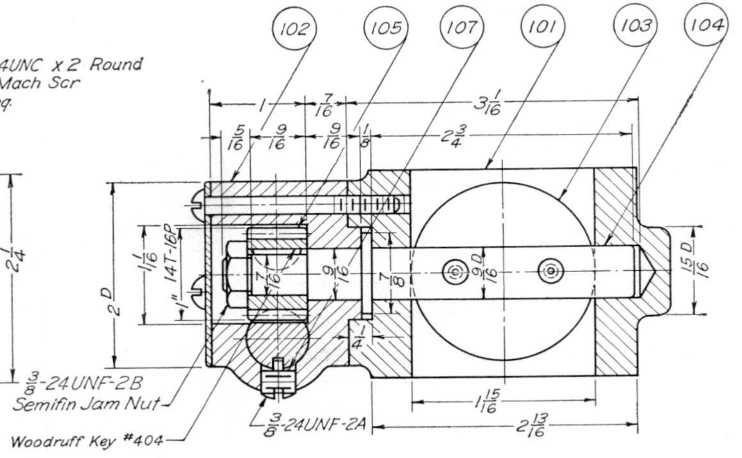

Fig. 28.47. Butterfly valve.

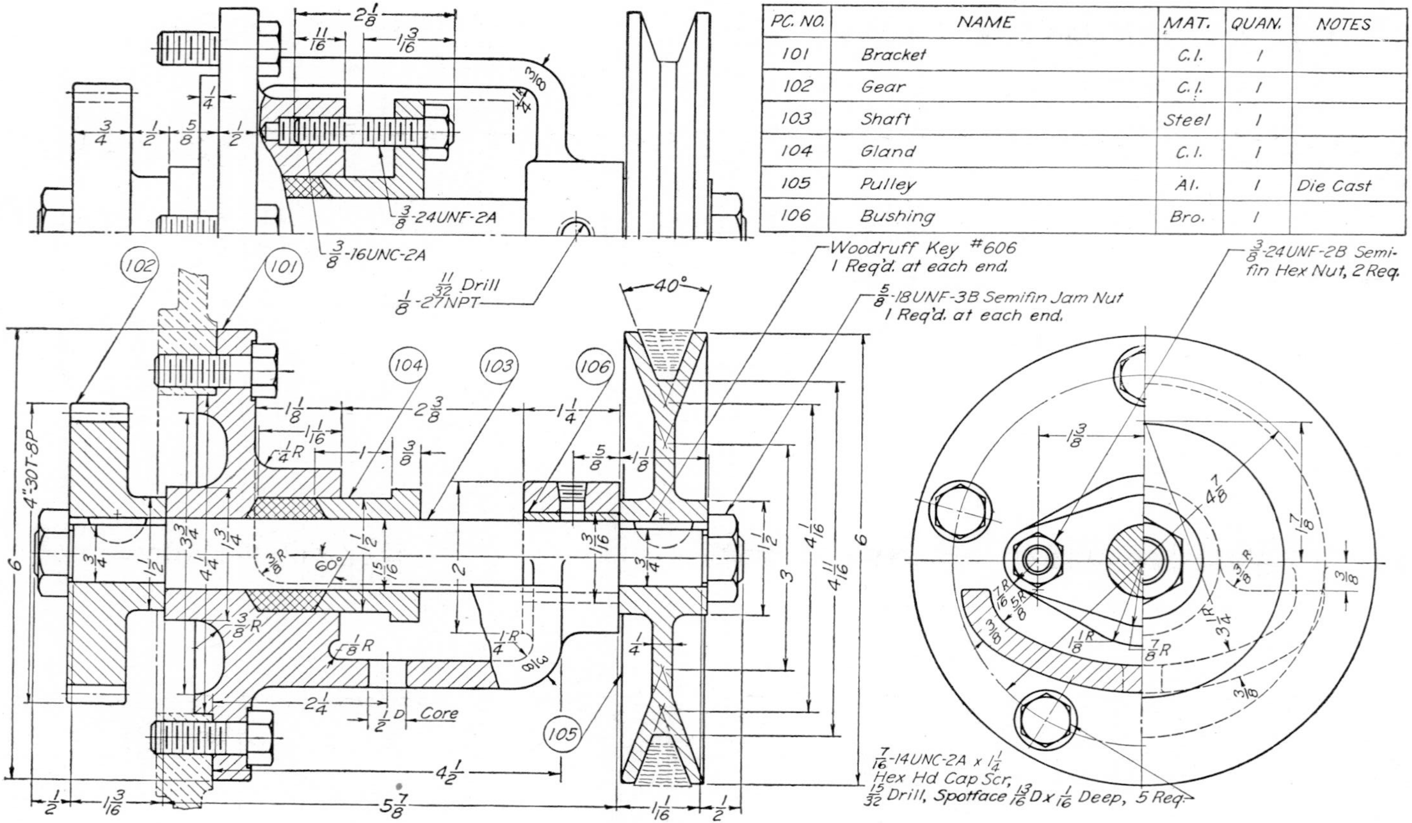

Fig. 28.48. V-belt drive.

PC. NO.	NAME	MAT.	QUAN.	NOTES
101	Bracket	C.I.	1	
102	Gear	C.I.	1	
103	Shaft	Steel	1	
104	Gland	C.I.	1	
105	Pulley	Al.	1	Die Cast
106	Bushing	Bro.	1	

32. Fig. 28.47. Make detail drawings of butterfly valve. Refer to Chap. 27 for method of detailing gear and rack.

33. Fig. 28.48. Make detail drawings for V-belt drive.

34. Fig. 28.49. Make detail drawings of rail-transport hanger. Rail is 10-lb. ASCE.

35. Fig. 28.49. Redesign for 21-lb ASCE rail. Use standard 2½-in. pipe for support.

36. Fig. 28.50. Make detail drawings of double-acting air cylinder. Length of stroke to be assigned. Fix length of cylinder to allow for clearance of 1 in. at ends of

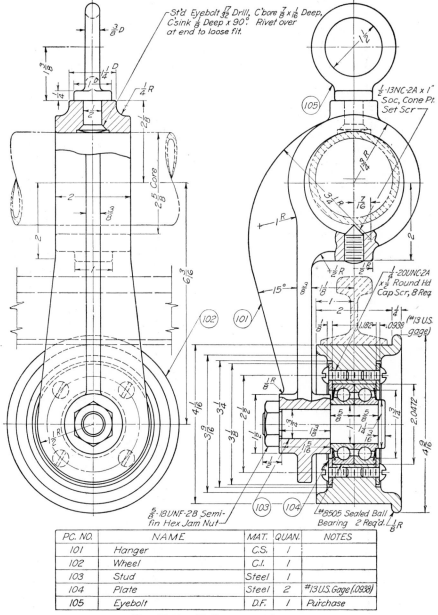

PC. NO.	NAME	MAT.	QUAN.	NOTES
101	Hanger	C.S.	1	
102	Wheel	C.I.	1	
103	Stud	Steel	1	
104	Plate	Steel	2	#13 U.S. Gage (.0938)
105	Eyebolt	D.F.	1	Purchase

Fig. 28.49. Rail-transport hanger.

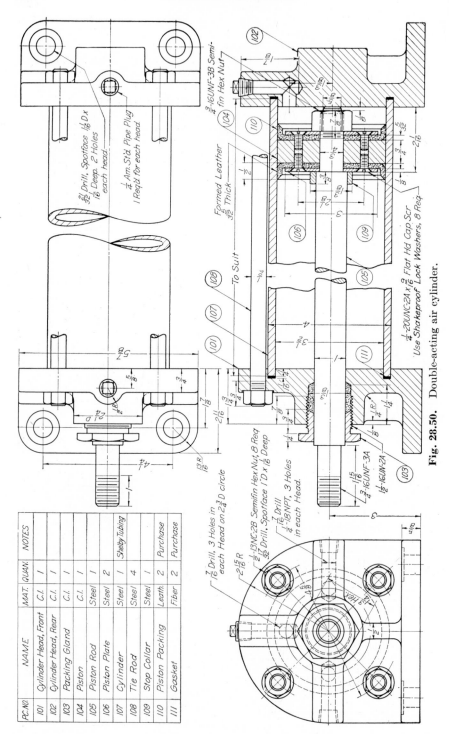

Fig. 28.50. Double-acting air cylinder.

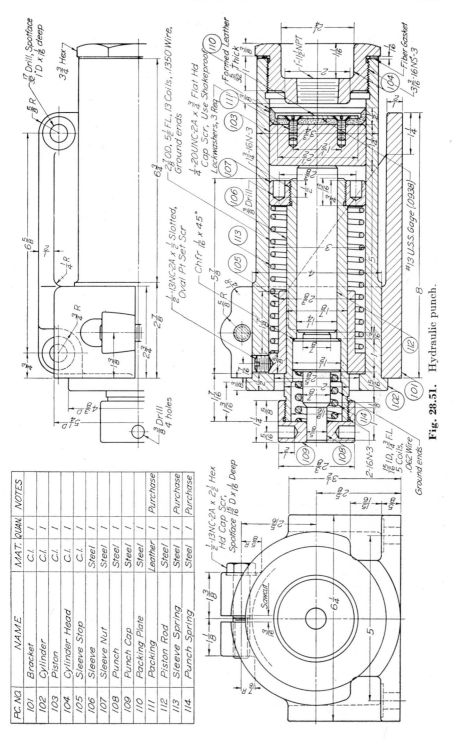

Fig. 28.51. Hydraulic punch.

PC. NO.	NAME	MAT.	QUAN.	NOTES
101	Bracket	C.I.	1	
102	Cylinder	C.I.	1	
103	Piston	C.I.	1	
104	Cylinder Head	C.I.	1	
105	Sleeve Stop	C.I.	1	
106	Sleeve	Steel	1	
107	Sleeve Nut	Steel	1	
108	Punch	Steel	1	
109	Punch Cap	Steel	1	
110	Packing Plate	Steel	1	
111	Packing	Leather	1	Purchase
112	Piston Rod	Steel	1	
113	Sleeve Spring	Steel	1	Purchase
114	Punch Spring	Steel	1	Purchase

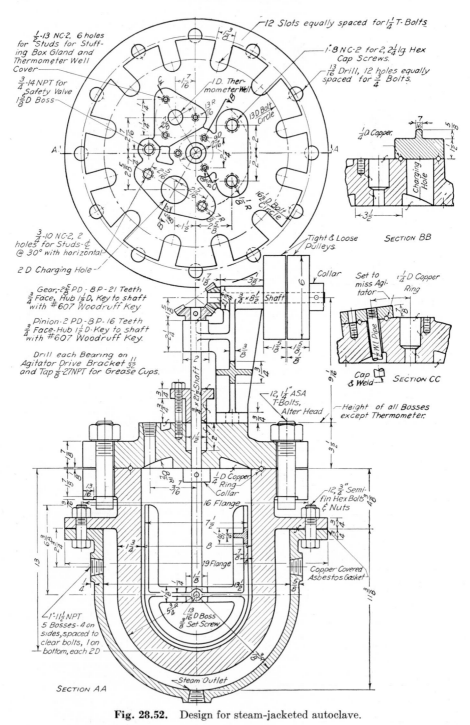

Fig. 28.52.   Design for steam-jacketed autoclave.

stroke. Note that pieces 101 and 102 are identical except for the extra machining of the central hole in piece 101 for the shaft, packing, and gland. Make separate drawings for this piece, one for the pattern shop, and two for the machine shop.

37. Fig. 28.51. Make detail drawings of hydraulic punch. In action, the punch assembly proper advances until the cap, piece 109, comes against the work. The assembly (piece 106 and attached parts) is then stationary, and the tension of the punch spring (piece 114) holds the work as the punch advances through the work and returns.

38. Fig. 28.51. Redesign for a punch diameter of ¾ in. and stroke 1½ in.

39. Fig. 28.52. Make detail drawings for steam-jacketed laboratory autoclave. An autoclave is an apparatus used when chemical action under pressure is required. It may be built with a steam jacket as in Fig. 28.52, or without. Stirring devices may or may not be provided, depending on the use. The autoclave shown has a 2-gal capacity and is designed for 800-lb. working pressure.

40. Fig. 28.52. Design an autoclave of 10-gal capacity. Provide an agitator to revolve at 125 rpm, driven from a motor running at 1,200 rpm. Calculate the size of pulley and bevel gears. Figure wall thickness for 900-lb pressure. On the steam-jacket shell add three lugs for supporting legs. Provide openings in cover for safety valve, pressure gage, and thermometer well. Use T bolts, calculating area and referring to handbook for corresponding bolt size. Make complete assembly drawing.

41. Make detail drawings of autoclave from Prob. 40, including design of supporting legs.

Group IV. A set of drawings from an exploded pictorial

The problems in this group have been arranged for complete exercises in the making of a set of working drawings. Remember that the dimensions given on the pictorial views are to be used only to obtain distances or information needed. In some cases the data needed for a particular part may have to be obtained from the mating part.

The detail drawings should be made with each part on a separate sheet. Drawings of cast or forged parts may be made either in the "single drawing" or the "multiple drawing" system as described in Chap. 19.

The assembly drawing should include any necessary dimensions such as number, size, and spacing of mounting holes, that might be required by a purchaser or needed for checking with the machine on which a subassembly is used.

For the style and items to be included in the parts list, see Figs. 28.37 and 28.76.

42. Fig. 28.53. Make a complete set of drawings for pivot hanger, including detail drawings, assembly drawing, and parts list. All parts are steel. This assembly is comprised of a yoke, base, collar, and standard parts.

43. Fig. 28.54. Make a complete set of drawings for pump valve. The valve seat, stem, and spring are brass; the disk is hard-rubber composition. In operation, pressure of a fluid upward against the disk raises it and allows flow. Pressure downward forces the disk tighter against the seat and prevents flow.

44. Fig. 28.55. Make a complete set of working drawings for the antivibration mount.

45. Fig. 28.56. Make a complete set of working drawings for the cartridge-case trimmer. Note that some of the dimensions will have to be obtained from the mating part. A tabular drawing may be made of the case holder, covering holders for various cartridge cases. The dimensions to be tabulated are (a) holder length, (b) diameter and (c) taper of hole.

46. Fig. 28.57. Make a complete set of working drawings of the hydraulic check valve. Spring is stainless steel; gasket is soft aluminum; all other parts are steel.

47. Fig. 28.58. Make a complete set of working drawings of the boring-bar holder. All parts are steel. Note that the *body* is made in one piece, then split with a ⅛-in.-wide cut (exaggerated in the picture). The holder may be seen in use in Fig. 19.11.

48. Fig. 28.58. Design three boring bars (see Fig. 19.11) to fit the boring-bar holder and make a tabular drawing.

49. Fig. 28.59. Make a complete set of working drawings of the ratchet wrench.

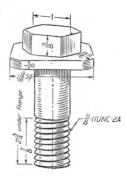

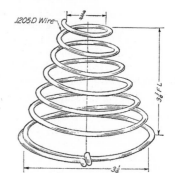

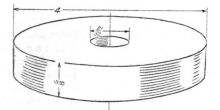

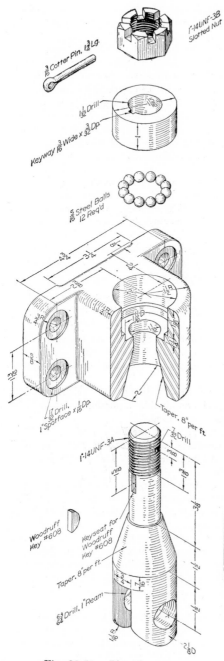

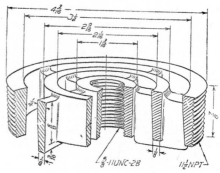

Fig. 28.53. Pivot hanger.

Fig. 28.54. Pump valve.

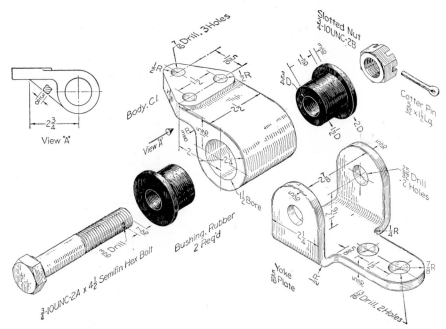

Fig. 28.55. Antivibration mount.

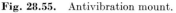

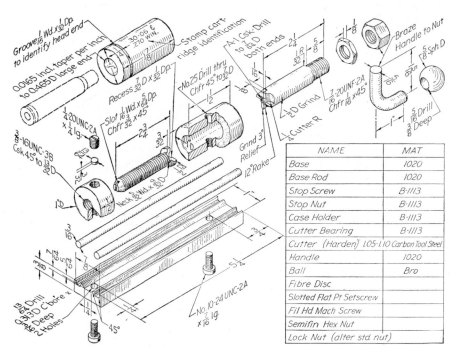

NAME	MAT
Base	1020
Base Rod	1020
Stop Screw	B-1113
Stop Nut	B-1113
Case Holder	B-1113
Cutter Bearing	B-1113
Cutter (Harden)	1.05-1.10 Carbon Tool Steel
Handle	1020
Ball	Bro
Fibre Disc	
Slotted Flat Pt Setscrew	
Fil Hd Mach Screw	
Semifin Hex Nut	
Lock Nut (alter std nut)	

Fig. 28.56. Cartridge-case trimmer. (*Courtesy of L. E. Wilson, Cashmere, Wash.*)

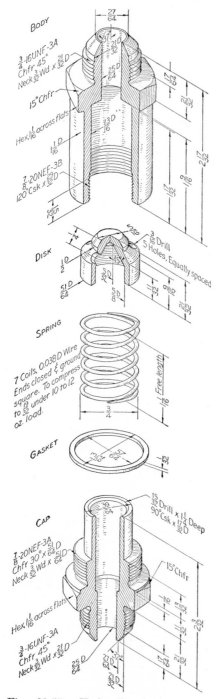

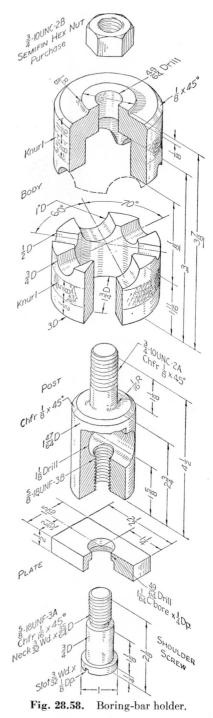

Fig. 28.57. Hydraulic check valve. (*Courtesy of Kohler Co., Kohler, Wis.*)

Fig. 28.58. Boring-bar holder.

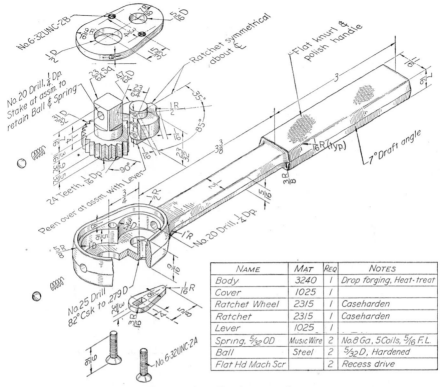

Fig. 28.59. Ratchet wrench.

NAME	MAT	REQ	NOTES
Body	3240	1	Drop forging, Heat-treat
Cover	1025	1	
Ratchet Wheel	2315	1	Caseharden
Ratchet	2315	1	Caseharden
Lever	1025	1	
Spring, 5/32 OD	Music Wire	2	No.8 Ga, 5 Coils, 5/16 F.L.
Ball	Steel	2	5/32 D, Hardened
Flat Hd Mach Scr		2	Recess drive

Group V.   A set of drawings from a pictorial assembly

50. Fig. 28.60.   Make a complete set of working drawings of the high-tension coil mount.

51. Fig. 28.61.   Make a complete set of working drawings of the pipe clamp.   The flange is cast steel.

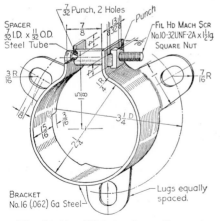

Fig. 28.60.   High-tension coil mount.

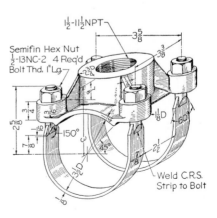

Fig. 28.61.   Pipe clamp.

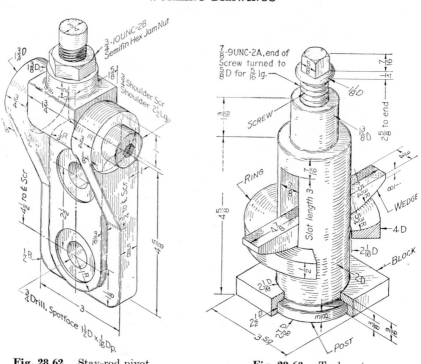

Fig. 28.62.   Stay-rod pivot.

Fig. 28.63.   Tool post.

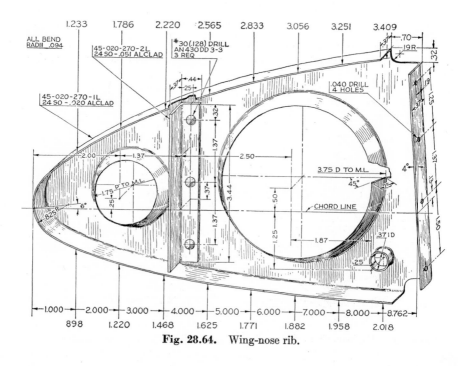

Fig. 28.64.   Wing-nose rib.

52. Fig. 28.62. Make a complete set of working drawings of the stay-rod pivot. Parts are malleable iron.

53. Fig. 28.63. Make a complete set of working drawings of the tool post. All parts are steel.

54. Fig. 28.64. Make a unit-assembly working drawing of the wing-nose rib.

55. Fig. 28.65. Make assembly and details of liquid-flow thermostat to double size. In detailing the bimetallic spring, use a development to show the shape before coiling. The width changes uniformly from $1\frac{1}{2}$ in. at the base to $\frac{7}{16}$ in. at the end.

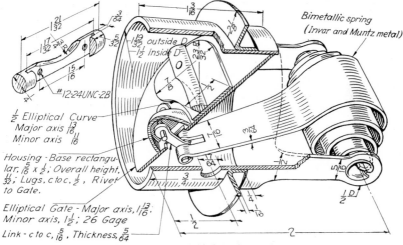

Fig. 28.65. Liquid-flow thermostat.

Group VI. A set of drawings from the design drawing

In working from a design drawing most dimensions are obtained by scaling. However, for dimensions where close fits are involved, limits and tolerances will have to be applied to the scaled *basic* size, as explained in Chap. 21. In some of the following problems appropriate limits have been given on the design drawing.

56. Fig. 28.66. Make a complete set of working drawings from the full-size isometric design drawing. Remember that measurements can be made only on isometric axes.

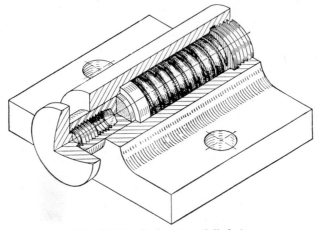

Fig. 28.66. Spring stop (full size).

All parts are steel.   Spring is $\frac{7}{16}$ in., outside diameter, $1\frac{1}{4}$ in. free length, nine coils, 0.062-in. music wire, ground ends.

57. Fig. 28.67, saw-hole punch.   From design drawing, shown one-half size, make complete set of drawings.   Frame is 1035 steel drop forging.   Screw is 1025 CRS.   Screw handle is 1020 CRS, ends are upset.   Punch and die are 1085 HR, heat-treat SAE No. 66. Transfer outer curve of handle from design drawing, draw other curves parallel.   Dimension handle curve by giving width across narrowest and widest points and the end radius. Locate these positions lengthwise.   Use note "fair curve through points dimensioned." Dimensioning of section provides for the inner curves.

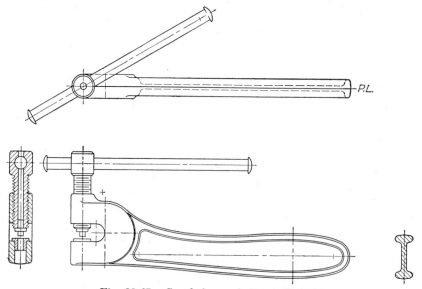

Fig. 28.67.   Saw-hole punch (one-half size).

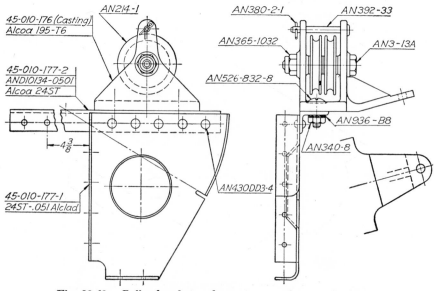

Fig. 28.68.   Pulley bracket and support assembly (one-half size).

58. Fig. 28.68. Make a set of drawings of the pulley bracket and support assembly from the design drawing, printed half size.

59. Fig. 28.68. Make a unit-assembly working drawing from the design drawing, printed half size. Add parts list.

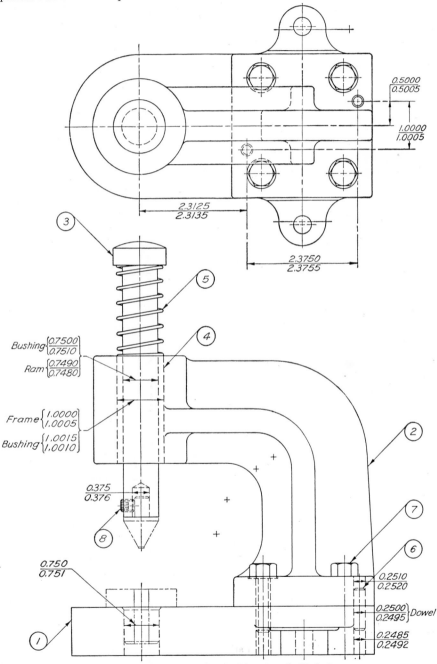

Fig. 28.69. Marking machine (one-half size).

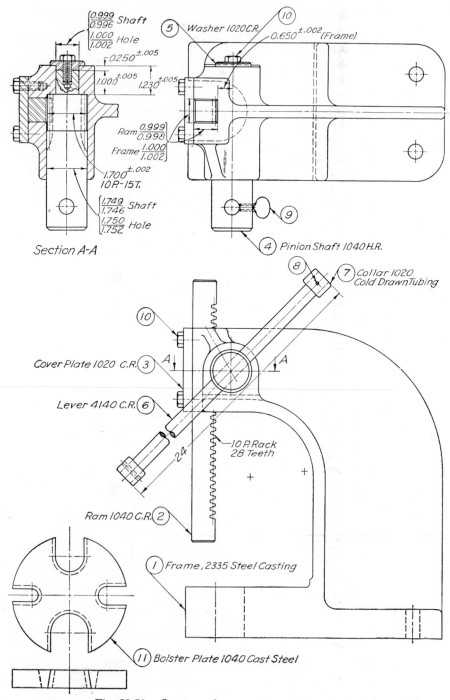

Fig. 28.70. One-ton arbor press (one-quarter size).

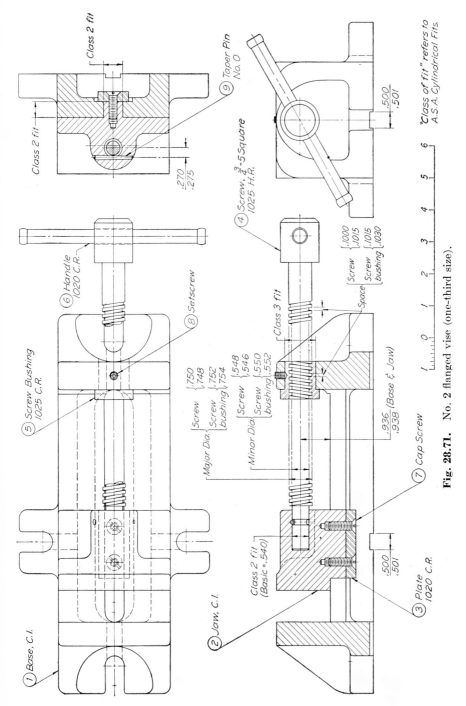

Fig. 28.71. No. 2 flanged vise (one-third size).

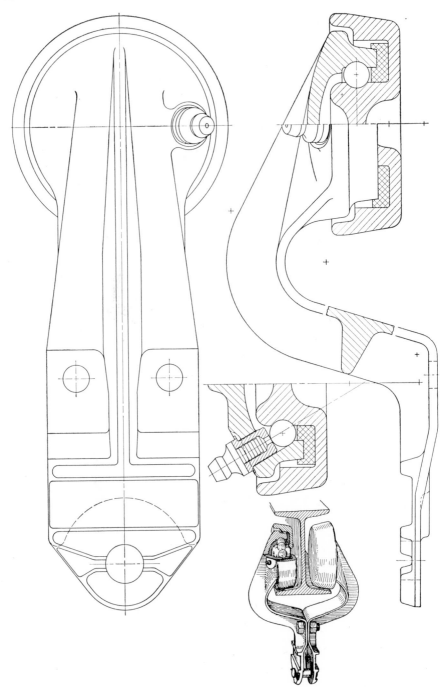

Fig. 28.72. Conveyer trolley (full size). (*Courtesy of Link Belt Co., Chicago, Ill.*)

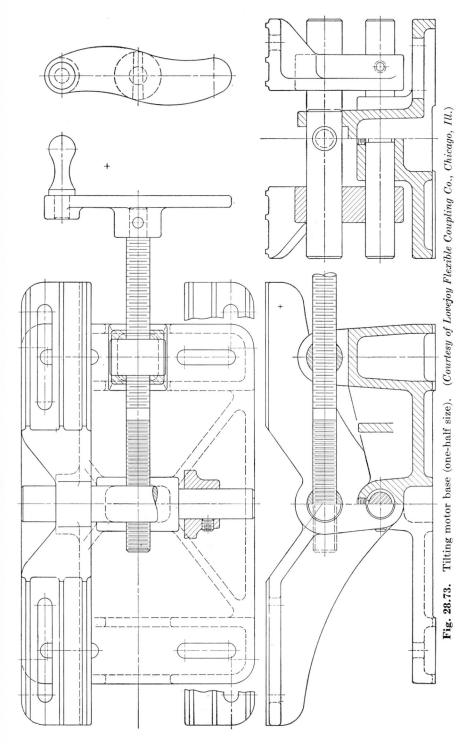

Fig. 28.73. Tilting motor base (one-half size). (Courtesy of Lovejoy Flexible Coupling Co., Chicago, Ill.)

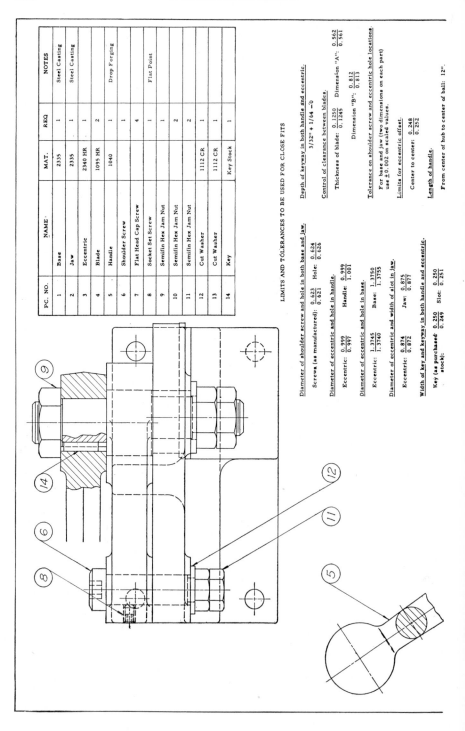

PC. NO.	NAME	MAT.	REQ	NOTES
1	Base	2335	1	Steel Casting
2	Jaw	2335	1	Steel Casting
3	Eccentric	2340 HR	1	
4	Blade	1095 HR	2	
5	Handle	1040	1	Drop Forging
6	Shoulder Screw		1	
7	Flat Head Cap Screw		4	
8	Socket Set Screw		1	Flat Point
9	Semifin Hex Jam Nut		1	
10	Semifin Hex Jam Nut		2	
11	Sumifin Hex Jam Nut		2	
12	Cut Washer	1112 CR	1	
13	Cut Washer	1112 CR	1	
14	Key	Key Stock	1	

LIMITS AND TOLERANCES TO BE USED FOR CLOSE FITS

Diameter of shoulder screw and hole in both base and jaw.
Screws (as manufactured): 0.623/0.621   Hole: 0.624/0.626

Diameter of eccentric and hole in handle.
Eccentric: 0.999/0.997   Handle: 0.999/1.001

Diameter of eccentric and hole in base.
Eccentric: 1.3745/1.3740   Base: 1.3750/1.3755

Diameter of eccentric and width of slot in jaw.
Eccentric: 0.874/0.872   Jaw: 0.875/0.877

Width of key and keyway in both handle and eccentric.
Key (as purchased stock): 0.250/0.249   Slot: 0.250/0.251

Depth of keyway in both handle and eccentric.
$3/32" + 1/64 -0$

Control of clearance between blades.
Thickness of blade: 0.1250/0.1245   Dimension "A": 0.562/0.561
Dimension "B": 0.812/0.813

Tolerance on shoulder screw and eccentric hole locations.
For base and jaw (two dimensions on each part) use ± 0.002 on scaled values.

Limits for eccentric offset.
Center to center: 0.248/0.252

Length of handle.
From center of hub to center of ball: 12".

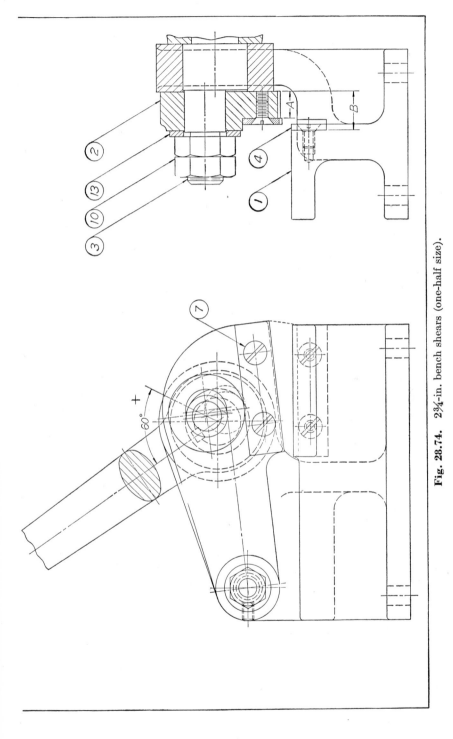

Fig. 28.74. 2¾-in. bench shears (one-half size).

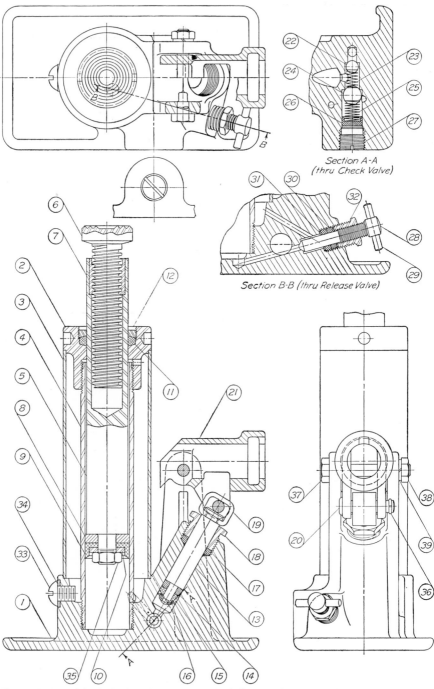

Section A-A
(thru Check Valve)

Section B-B (thru Release Valve)

Fig. 28.75. 1½-ton hydraulic jack (one-half size). (*Courtesy of Hein-Warner Corp.,
Waukesha, Wis.*)

60. Fig. 28.69, marking machine. From design drawing, shown half size, make complete set of drawings. Base, piece 1, is malleable-iron casting. Frame, piece 2, is cast iron. Ram, piece 3, is 1020 HR; bushing, piece 4, is 1020 cold-drawn tubing; heat-treatment for both is carburize at 1650 to 1700°F, quench direct, temper at 250 to 325°F. Spring, piece 5, is piano wire, No. 20 (0.045) gage, six coils, free length 2 in., heat-treatment is "as received." Marking dies and holders are made up to suit objects to be stamped.

61. Fig. 28.70, arbor press. From design drawing, shown one-quarter size, make complete set of drawings. All necessary information is given on the design drawing.

62. Fig. 28.71, No. 2 flanged vise. From design drawing, make complete set of drawings, including details, parts list, and assembly. Design drawing is shown one-third size. All necessary information is given on the design drawing.

63. Fig. 28.72, conveyer trolley for 3-in. I beam. From design drawing, make complete set of drawings including details, assembly, and parts list. Design drawing is full size. Detail drawings are required for the bracket, wheel, seal, lubricator adapter, and clevis pin; all other parts are standard.

Parts required for each two-wheel assembly are two brackets, two wheels, two felt seals, 22 balls (11 required per side), two lubricant fittings, two adapters for lubricant fittings, two $\frac{1}{4}$-20UNC-2A semifinished hexagon bolts together with nuts and lock washers, one clevis pin, and two $\frac{7}{64}$ in.-by 1-in. cotter pins. All parts, excepting seal, are steel. Brackets and wheels are drop-forged of high-carbon steel with bearing raceways induction hardened. Balls are $\frac{9}{32}$ in. diameter, hardened and ground. Clevis pin is $\frac{3}{8}$ in. diameter by 1 in. long, drilled for cotter pins and is high-carbon steel, hardened.

64. Fig. 28.73, tilting motor base. Design drawing is half size. Make complete set of drawings. Base, motor, rails, and handle are cast iron. Handle knob, screw, base nut shaft, rail nut shaft, and pivot shaft are steel. Screw is $\frac{1}{2}$ in. diameter with *NC* and *NF* threads.

65. Fig. 28.74, bench shears. Design drawing is half size. Make a complete set of drawings. For dimensions where close fits are involved, either the decimal limits or the tolerance to be applied to the scaled basic size are given on the design drawing. Heat-

PC. NO.	NAME	REQ.	MAT.	PC. NO.	NAME	REQ.	MAT.
1	Base	1	Mal. Iron	21	Handle Socket	1	Mal. Iron
2	Top Nut	1	Steel	22	Suction Valve Ball	1	Steel
3	Reservoir Tube	1	Steel	23	Suction Valve Spring	1	Piano Wire
4	Ram Cylinder	1	Steel	24	Discharge Valve Ball	1	Steel
5	Ram	1	Steel	25	Discharge Valve Spring	1	Piano Wire
6	Ram Extension Screw	1	Steel	26	Check Valve Seal	1	Neoprene
7	Ram Extension Screw Bushing	1	Steel	27	Check Valve Plug	1	Steel
8	Ram Spacer	1	Formica	28	Release Valve Screw	1	Steel
9	Ram Cup	1	Neoprene	29	Release Valve Screw Pin	1	Steel
10	Ram Cup Retainer	1	Steel	30	Release Valve Packing	2	Neoprene-Duck
11	Ram Packing	1	Neoprene-Duck	31	Release Valve Packing Washer	2	Steel
12	Ram Packing Nut	1	Steel	32	Release Valve Packing Nut	1	Steel
13	Pump Piston	1	Steel	33	Filler Screw	1	Steel
14	Pump Piston Backing Washer	1	Formica	34	Filler Screw Washer	1	Fiber
15	Pump Piston Cup	1	Neoprene	35	Ram Cup Nut	1	Steel
16	Pump Piston Cup Retainer	1	Steel	36	1/4" Pin Ring	1	Steel
17	Pump Piston Packing	1	Neoprene-Duck	37	Handle Socket Bolt	1	Steel
18	Pump Piston Packing Nut	1	Steel	38	Jam Nut	1	Steel
19	Pump Piston Clip	1	Steel	39	Lock Washer	1	Steel
20	Pump Piston Pin	1	Steel				

Fig. 28.76. Parts list for hydraulic jack.

treatments should be specified as follows: for base and jaw, "normalize at 1550°F"; for eccentric, "as received"; for blade, "to Rockwell C57-60"; for handle, none. Finish for blades, "grind." Washers are special but may be specified on the parts list by giving inside diameter, outside diameter, and thickness. The key may be specified on the parts list by giving width, thickness, and length.

66. Figs. 28.75 and 28.76, $1\frac{1}{2}$-ton hydraulic jack. Design drawing is half size. Make a complete set of drawings. The thread pitches may be scaled from the design drawing. Suction valve spring, piece No. 23, is $\frac{1}{4}$ in. outside diameter, $\frac{3}{8}$ in. free length, six coils, No. 5 gage piano wire. Discharge valve spring, piece No. 25, is $\frac{5}{16}$ in. outside diameter, 1 in. free length, eight coils, No. 5 gage piano wire.

Group VII. Working sketches

67. Make a selection of one of the problems in Group I and make a detail working sketch.

68. Make a selection of one of the problems in Group II and make an assembly sketch.

69. Select a single part from one of the assemblies of Groups III to V and make a working sketch.

70. Select a single part from one of the figures, 28.18 to 28.59, and make a pictorial working sketch.

71. Make a selection of one of the problems in Group III and make detail working sketches.

72. Make a selection of one of the problems in Group IV or V and make a complete set of working sketches.

29

Jigs and Fixtures

29.1 **Jigs and fixtures** are devices for holding the work and guiding the tools for machining operations on pieces made in interchangeable quantity production. Their use makes possible more rapid as well as more accurate manufacturing at a reduction of cost. In general the distinction between a jig and a fixture is that a jig clamps or is clamped to the work and guides the various tools into position, while a fixture is fastened to the machine and holds the piece in a definite position but does not guide the cutting tool. The object to be machined, usually termed "the production" or "the subject," may, for example, require the drilling of several holes or their drilling and tapping, drilling and counterboring, or drilling and reaming. The particular jig designed to aid in these operations would be called a "drill jig," "drill-and-tap jig," "drill-and-counterbore jig," or "drill-and-ream jig." If the operation to be performed is to face the end of a cylinder, the device for holding the production would be called a "facing fixture." If the production is to be held while a hole is bored in it on a lathe, the holding device would be a "boring fixture."

29.2 **Production cost.** Whether or not to use a jig depends on two items: first, the number of pieces to be machined and, second, the accuracy demanded. The cost of producing the part individually should be figured carefully and compared to the cost of producing with a jig, in each case measuring time from the starting of one piece to the starting of the next piece, and using the current wage scale of the kind of operators required. The estimated cost of making the jig will then answer the question. In the same way the saving in time by the use of a more expensive jig over a cheaper one should be studied.

29.3 **Jig borers.** When relatively few pieces are to be drilled, it may be cheaper to machine them individually, either on a drill press

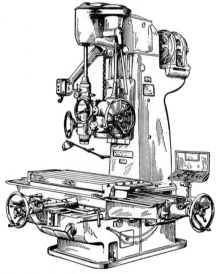

Fig. 29.1. Jig borer. (*Courtesy of Pratt and Whitney.*)

or, very much more accurately, on a jig borer, Fig. 29.1. If many are required, such as parts for automobiles and similar large-quantity work, a jig

541

is indispensable for accuracy, speed, interchangeability, and reduction of cost. The correct procedure, therefore, is to use the jig borer to construct a jig (the purpose for which the jig borer was designed) and use the jig for accurate, interchangeable products done on machines cheaper and speedier than the jig borer and operated by almost unskilled labor.

In a job shop making parts to be cast and finished but assembled at another place, orders might call for from ten to a hundred or a thousand machines, with repeat orders later, and the jigs would assure the same degree of accuracy in all the production pieces.

29.4 Principles of design. To illustrate some of the principles of jig design, a simple jig for drilling two $\frac{3}{4}$-in. holes and reaming one 1-in. hole in

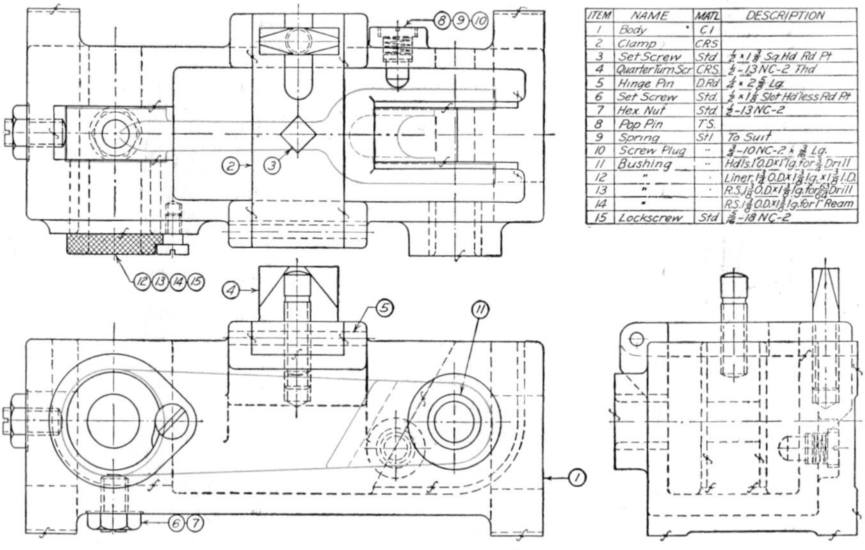

ITEM	NAME	MAT'L	DESCRIPTION
1	Body	CI	
2	Clamp	CRS	
3	Set Screw	Std	$\frac{1}{2}\times1\frac{3}{8}$ Sq. Hd Rd Pt
4	Quarter Turn Scr.	CRS.	$\frac{1}{2}$-13 NC-2 Thd
5	Hinge Pin	D. Rd	$\frac{1}{4}\times2\frac{5}{8}$ Lg.
6	Set Screw	Std.	$\frac{1}{2}\times1\frac{1}{8}$ Slot Hd'less Rd Pt
7	Hex. Nut	Std.	$\frac{1}{2}$-13 NC-2
8	Pop Pin	T.S.	
9	Spring	Stl	To Suit
10	Screw Plug	"	$\frac{3}{4}$-10 NC-2 $\times\frac{3}{16}$ Lg.
11	Bushing	"	Hdls. 1" O.D. × 1" lg. for $\frac{3}{4}$ Drill
12	"	"	Liner, $1\frac{3}{4}$ O.D. × $1\frac{3}{8}$ lg. × $1\frac{3}{8}$ I.D.
13	"	"	R.S. $1\frac{3}{8}$ O.D. × $1\frac{3}{8}$ lg. for $\frac{63}{64}$ Drill
14	"		R.S. $1\frac{3}{8}$ O.D. × $1\frac{3}{8}$ lg. for 1" Ream
15	Lockscrew	Std	$\frac{5}{16}$-18 NC-2

Fig. 29.2. Jig for pawl carrier.

a pawl carrier is shown in Fig. 29.2. These principles, which should be followed as far as possible, are

1. The production must go into the jig easily and quickly.
2. The production must be located accurately.
3. The bushings must be accessible to the operator.
4. The production must be securely clamped in the jig.
5. The production must be removable easily and quickly.

Note incidentally that it is universal practice in jig drawing to show the production in *red*, while the jig itself, in *black*, is drawn, as to visibility, as if the production was not in place.

In this example, and in all other designs, four main points of design involved in the above principles must be observed. Briefly these are

1. Locating the production.
2. Clamping the production.
3. Selecting bushings of correct style and size.
4. Designing the jig body to accommodate the production and satisfy the principles.

By following these four cardinal points, a drill jig can be designed that will satisfy the requirements of commercial production. Each point involves careful study to decide upon the most suitable of many methods to use in combination with the others. Several types in each division will be discussed, but the reader will understand that he is not confined to these only, in designing some particular piece of work.

29.5 Locating the production. The shape of the production, previous milling and finishing before drilling, and other points of design will influence the type of locator best suited for the production. Location must be thoroughly considered, as it is perhaps the most important of the four points, from the standpoint of accuracy in the jig.

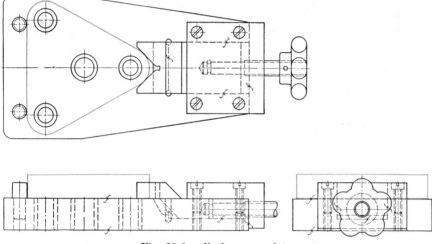

Fig. 29.3. Jig for cover plate.

Finished surfaces are often used to locate—a finished surface of the production is placed against a finished surface of the jig; or, when necessary, even an unfinished surface of the production is placed against a finished surface of the jig. Location surfaces may take the form of pads, counterbores, or two finished surfaces at right angles to each other.

Pins give an easy and relatively inexpensive method of location and at the same time a very accurate one. A finished or an unfinished surface of the production is held against a pin and a finished surface, or against either two or three pins, by a clamp or screws, Fig. 29.3.

In the jig of Fig. 29.6, two pins, one circular and the other flattened, are used to locate. Both pins are accurate to the size necessary to fit into two previously drilled or reamed holes in the production. (One pin must be flattened because the center-to-center distances of the holes may vary enough to make a fit impossible with two round pins.) The round pin locates along the line of centers, and both pins locate at right angles to the line of centers, since the flats of the flattened pin are always placed perpendicular to the line of centers. Note that the pins are made so that they can be pressed into the fixture only up to the shoulder. The ends are chamfered, preferably at 30°, to allow easy entry into the production.

Small pins are usually made of tool steel, hardened and ground. Large pins may be made of cold-rolled steel, pack-hardened, and ground. They should not be cyanided, as this does not give sufficient depth of hardening, and the grinding of a cyanided piece is not successful. The shoulder of the

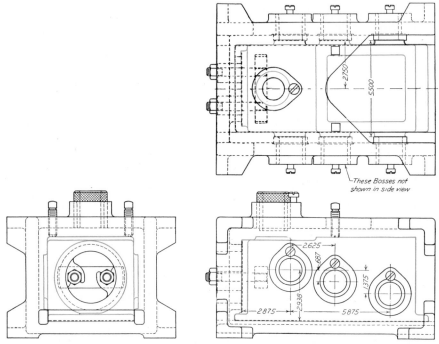

Fig. 29.4. Drill-and-ream jig for gear case.

pin is pressed against a finished surface or into a light spot face or counterbore to a suitable depth.

Bushings serve as locators in certain designs, as illustrated in Fig. 29.4. This jig is to serve in drilling and reaming holes in a gear case, on which the out-to-out distance between bosses is an accurate dimension with limits; hence the surfaces of these bosses provide good points for location, and the accurately located shoulder bushings are designed to come to contact with them. Location of the subject in the other directions is by using finished surfaces, against which it is clamped by screws and a bar clamp.

V blocks are often used in jig design, both as locators and as clamps. An example was seen in Fig. 29.3. The jig of Fig. 29.5 employs a V whose purpose is mainly for location, though it also serves as a "backstop" in clamping, while the setscrews are the clamps proper. A V block is more easily made as a separate piece, secured to the body of the jig by screws and dowel pins. Fastening the V block without dowel pins, by using slotted holes for the cap screws, might be necessary in case the circular boss on the production varied considerably in diameter with different castings.

Accurate holes for pins. A small plate jig is often used to drill a recurring series of holes in making a large jig, Fig. 29.6, or in a production itself.

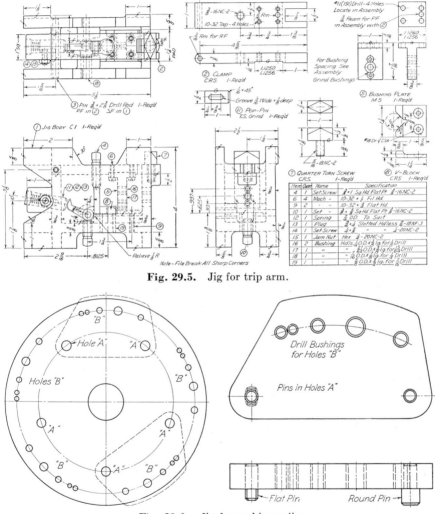

Fig. 29.5. Jig for trip arm.

Fig. 29.6. Jig for making a jig.

The small jig carries two locating pins, one round and the other flattened, for reasons already mentioned in paragraph 29.5. On the large jig the holes marked *A* have been previously drilled and reamed, either with the jig borer or on a radial boring machine, to match the pins of the small jig, through whose use the series of holes may then be drilled with far more accuracy and speed than if each hole had to be located individually.

Center locators. The jig of Fig. 29.7 uses a center locator. If the hole in the production is of such size that it has been bored on a lathe and the piece faced at the same time, this method of locating is indicated. The shank for locating is of such diameter that the hole is a slip fit over it. Either a class 2 or 3 ASA fit could be used, depending upon the accuracy of drilling required.

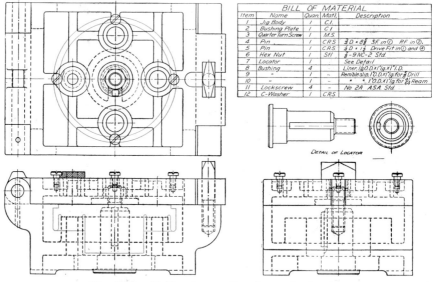

BILL	OF	MATERIAL		
Item	Name	Quan.	Matl.	Description
1	Jig Body	1	C.I.	
2	Bushing Plate	1	C.I.	
3	Quarter Turn Screw	1	M.S.	
4	Pin	1	C.R.S.	¾ D × 8⅞ S.F. in ① R.F. in ②.
5	Pin	1	C.R.S.	½ D × 1½ Drive Fit in ① and ④
6	Hex Nut	1	Stl	⅝ - 9 N.C-2 Std.
7	Locator	1		See Detail
8	Bushing	4	"	Liner.1⅛ O.D.×1"lg.×1"I.D.
9	"	1	"	Rem'ble.slip.1"O.D.×1"lg.for⅜ Drill
10	"	1	"	" ". 1"O.D.×1"lg.for⅜ Ream
11	Lockscrew	4	"	No.2A A.S.A. Std
12	C-Washer	1	C.R.S.	

DETAIL OF LOCATOR

Fig. 29.7.   Drill-and-ream jig using center locator.

Keyways serve as locators in cases where it is necessary to drill holes that must be in a particular position. In a jig designed for a coupling where the holes must be in the center of the bosses and at the same time be located with respect to the keyway, the center locator would include a key to slip into the keyway of the subject.

29.6   Clamps and clamping. Some of the more commonly used clamps for fastening the subject securely in the jig are the following:

1. Bar clamp.
2. Slotted clamp.
3. Setscrews and studs.
4. C washer.
5. V slide.

6. Spiral-rise cam.
7. Star knob and stud.
8. Adjustable pins.
9. Hydraulic piston.

The jigs illustrated in this chapter show several of these methods of clamping. The important point to observe is that *the clamp must not distort the production, as such distortion introduces inaccuracy in the drilled holes upon release of the clamping pressure. Clamping must be applied at a point on the production that will withstand the strain introduced,* and as close as possible to the point drilled. This last cannot always be made to apply, but it should be considered carefully.

Clamps suffer the most wear of any part of a jig, and cyanide hardening is advisable. When there is a possibility of marring a finished surface, a soft-nosed clamp should be employed.

Slotted clamps are widely used. To get proper action they should have the stud at the center or closer to the production than to the tail of the clamp. Studs and nuts are preferred over cap screws, as they do not wear out the body of the jig and may be replaced cheaply.

Setscrews are cheap and highly efficient as a means of holding the production securely, Fig. 29.5. In clamping four sides of an object, the setscrews on two sides will have lock nuts, and those on the other two sides will be used for locking and unlocking the piece.

Use may be made of a stud and nut in combination with a C washer in cases where the production slips over the stud or a locating pin, Fig. 29.7.

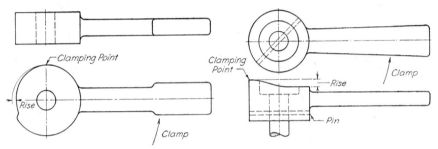

Fig. 29.8.   Spiral-rise cam clamps.

V slide. The principal precaution in the use of the V slide in clamping is to see that its length is at least equal to its width, to avoid having an unstable action. Its thickness depends upon the production and whether the slide is fixed or movable. In the latter case the size of the control screw will have a bearing on the thickness.

Spiral-rise cam clamps are useful in quantity production where quick clamping and unclamping with little thought required from the operator are the prime requisites. The maximum variation in the production pieces at the point of clamping must be known, from which the rise of the cam is computed, in order that the cam face will clamp the production with a 90° turn of the handle. Figure 29.8 shows two types of locking cams which give locking action in either of two directions from the axis.

Star knobs and studs are an adaptation of the setscrew principle for hand operation.

Adjustable pins are used to support fragile sections of the production. Correct designs are shown in Fig. 29.9. They should be locked into position by a setscrew.

Hydraulic pistons are for heavy work and work requiring special clamping. Their design is of too specialized a nature to be included here.

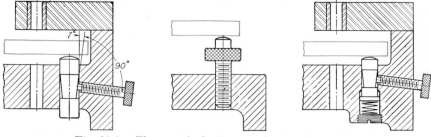

Fig. 29.9.   Three methods of supporting fragile sections.

29.7 American Standard bushings.   Drill bushings are standardized items, made in five different styles, Fig. 29.10.   They are available in six to eight lengths in each style for use with all the numbered, lettered, and fractional drill sizes up to 2 in.

The plain stationary press-fit bushings, used when the bushing is expected to last during the life of the jig, are made in two types: the *headless* and the *head type.*   The headless type is used when the center distance of holes is too close for a bushing with a head and when it is desirable to have the top of the bushing flush with the top of the jig plate.   Both are used without liners.

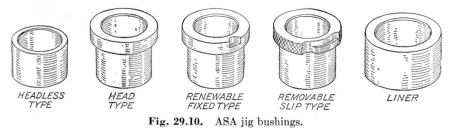

| HEADLESS TYPE | HEAD TYPE | RENEWABLE FIXED TYPE | REMOVABLE SLIP TYPE | LINER |

Fig. 29.10.   ASA jig bushings.

Renewable bushings, with liners, are used in cases either where the bushing will wear enough for replacement or where it is necessary to interchange bushings in one hole.   There are two types: the *renewable fixed* and the *renewable-slip*[1] type.   Renewable fixed bushings are used for one operation only.   Renewable slip bushings are used where two or more operations, requiring different inside diameters, are performed in a single jig without removing the production from the jig, such as where drilling is followed by reaming, spot facing, counterboring, tapping, etc.   They should be used in combination with a liner and lock screw unless the design cannot possibly allow the additional space required by the liner.

Bushings are specified by giving, in order, (1) type, (2) outside diameter, (3) length, (4) drill size.

For correct installation, design drawings should show clearly the bell-mouthed end of the bushing as the entry end for the drill.   For accurate drilling the other end should be not more than one drill diameter from the

[1] Also called *removable-slip* type.

production. The thickness of the production, type of material being drilled, and design of the jig will all influence the minimum distance between the end of the bushing and the production. Chip clearance must be considered to avoid drill binding and the creation of unusual pressures. Sometimes the bushing is designed to touch the production, and the chips are carried up and out at the top.

Some shops prefer to use the type of bushings that have $\frac{1}{64}$-in. grinding stock on the outside diameter, for fitting the bushing to the hole.

Bushings for special work should be described by following the tables of standard wall thicknesses, size of head, etc., and specifying the proper finish and heat-treatment.

29.8 The jig body. Jig bodies are of two general classes: the open body and the closed or box type. In general, open jigs have drill bushings in the same plane, parallel to one another. The second, box-shaped type is for drilling holes from various planes and directions. Occasionally there may be an overlap in the nomenclature of the two general types.

On account of the required rigidity, cast iron has been the usual material for jig bodies, but welded steel is now being used successfully.

Judgment should be given to the weight of the body. For ease of handling it should have no excess weight but must not be lightened at any expense of the stiffness and rigidity necessary for accuracy. It is often possible, however, to core out metal in various places without decreasing strength. For the comfort and safety of the operator, corners should be rounded and all burrs and sharp edges removed by filing. For convenience in moving, small jigs may be equipped with handles, and large ones with hooks for handling with a crane.

Finished feet should be provided on the sides opposite the drill bushings. For proper machining, small lugs are often placed on other sides to act as stops. The jig feet are generally part of the casting but in some cases are inserts. Four should always be used in preference to three, because with four feet any unevenness in setting, such as a chip under one foot, will at once draw the attention of the operator, by rocking.

On the inside of the jig and at other places where machining is to be done, particular care should be taken to allow proper clearance for the machining tools. Points of location should, if possible, be visible to the operator.

Small jigs do not need to be clamped to the table, but large jigs and all fixtures should be provided with means of clamping securely to the machine on which they are used.

29.9 Summary. Fourteen points in jig design.

1. Provide best method of locating.
2. Provide best method of clamping.
3. Select correct types of bushings.
4. Have bushings accessible to operator.
5. Design for quick loading and unloading.
6. Design for ability to withstand abuse without affecting accuracy.

7. Keep in mind the safety of the operator.

8. Provide clearance for drills after passing through the work.

9. Provide for chip clearance and easy removal of chips.

10. Design so that cheaper parts wear out first.

11. See that finished surfaces will not be marred by clamping devices.

12. Provide means for lifting heavy jigs.

13. If loose parts are unavoidable, chain them to the body of the jig.

14. Consider the cost of materials and labor, but do not attempt to cut the cost of the jig at the expense of efficiency of the design.

29.10   Making a jig drawing.   The drafting-room procedure in designing a jig or fixture should follow approximately this order:

1. Sketch the design freehand, to get the proper choice of views and an idea of space requirements.   This original sketch will take into account previously finished surfaces of the production.

2. Allowing ample space between views, carefully draw the production in red in its several views.

3. Build the jig around the production, following the correct principles of location, clamping, bushings, and body design.

4. Dimension the drawing of the jig, using decimal dimensions for all locators and bushings, following the system of base-line dimensioning, from zero coordinate axes. See Fig. 21.20.

5. Give each part an item number.

6. Prepare a bill of material of all items in sequence.

7. Check the drawing.

29.11   Fixtures.   Two examples are given here to illustrate the many uses of fixtures in quantity production.   Figure 29.11 is a fixture to aid in

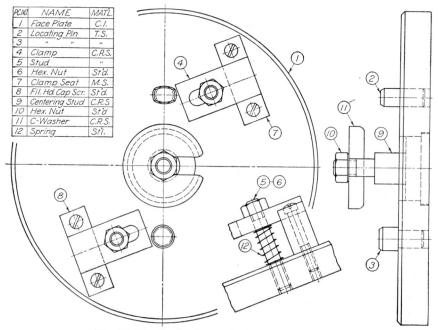

PC.NO.	NAME	MATL.
1	Face Plate	C.I.
2	Locating Pin	T.S.
3	" "	"
4	Clamp	C.R.S.
5	Stud	"
6	Hex. Nut	St'd.
7	Clamp Seat	M.S.
8	Fil. Hd. Cap Scr.	St'd.
9	Centering Stud	C.R.S.
10	Hex. Nut	St'd
11	C-Washer	C.R.S.
12	Spring	St'l.

Fig. 29.11.   Lathe fixture for boring and facing.

boring the hole and facing the projection and bottom of the flange of Fig. 13.57. The flange locates over the pins. The center clamp is removed, and slotted clamps are used while the hole and projection are being machined. To complete the finishing of the bottom, the clamps are slid back and the center clamp is put in place.

Figure 29.12 is a fixture for holding the toggle-shaft support of Fig. 9.81 in boring the hole and facing the end. The bracket locates over two pins and is held in place by the clamp.

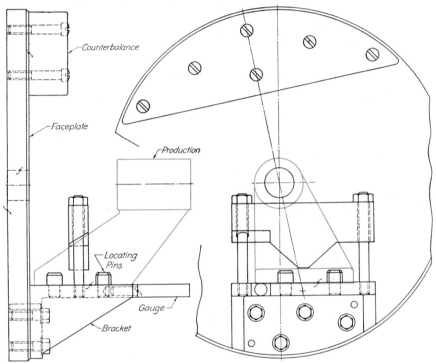

Fig. 29.12. Counterbalanced boring-and-facing fixture.

Both these fixtures clamp to the faceplate of the lathe, the entire fixture and production rotating. Being unbalanced, the offset bracket fixture requires a counterbalance to reduce vibration and aid in accuracy of work. To compute the size of the counterbalance, the center of gravity and the moment of the fixture and production together about the working center must be found. From this the area and thickness of counterbalance and its working distance from the center may be calculated to find an equivalent moment to balance that on the opposite side of center. Common practice is to provide a slightly oversize counterbalance thickness, which allows the shop to complete the balance by removal of metal. This is a timesaver and permits slight changes that may take place in some parts used in the fixture.

In designing fixtures for milling, slotting, saw cutting, and similar operations the same principles of location and clamping as those given for jig designing are followed.   To obtain secure clamping, finished bases should be provided with two square keys for aligning the fixture with the T slots in the milling table, as well as with slots at each end for T bolts.

If a previous operation has been performed on the subject, a gaging surface should be provided, if at all possible, to which the cutter may be set, thus obtaining accurately the required distance between the two finished surfaces.

PROBLEMS

The "tooling-up" procedure in machining a casting from its unfinished state to the finished product has an important bearing on the total cost and requires careful thought as to the proper sequence of operations.   In the following problems consider the entire casting as rough, and prepare a shop procedure schedule, listing the tools in their successive order, so that each operation may have a direct relationship to the preceding one. Give the tools the progressive numbers T-1; T-2; etc.

1. Design a drill-and-ream jig for Fig. 20.21.   Locate on a finished pad the lug in a finished slot and the finished end of the cylinder, 4 in. long, against a finished boss of the jig.   Clamp from the top and back with one setscrew each.   Provide plain bushings for the base holes in the pad and two liners with removable drill-and-ream bushings for the larger holes.   Two lengths of removable bushings will be required, the longer being to reach within a drill diameter of the cylinder $2\frac{3}{4}$ in. long.   Design a box-type body with feet opposite the sides in which bushings are placed.   The right side of the body will be open to permit loading.   Spot-face the holes outside the jig.

2. Design a drill jig for special nut, Fig. 21.29A.   Locate over a center locator on a finished pad through the $1\frac{1}{8}$-in. hole, the locator reducing in size sufficiently to use a nut and C washer for clamping on the $1\frac{3}{4}$-in.-diameter end.   Nut should be small enough to clear the hole when loading and unloading.   Provide bushings in an open-type body.

Alternative method.   Use the same method of locating but provide only one drill bushing and an index pin 90° from the bushing.   Drill one hole, index this hole to the pin, drill the next hole, etc.

3. Design a drill-and-ream jig for the base plate, Fig. 21.21.   The body may consist of two rectangular plates somewhat larger than the production, separated $\frac{5}{8}$ in. more than the thickness of the production.   This thickness may be taken as $\frac{1}{2}$ in.   Locate against three pins, two on the flat side and one at the right end, the pins being in the top plate and located in the jig at the time of locating the bushing holes on the jig borer.   Clamp in place against the pins and down to the finished surface upon which the production rests. Provide the proper bushings in the top plate of the jig.

4. Fig. 28.41.   Design a drill jig for the $\frac{1}{4}$-in. oilhole.   Locate on a horizontal locator through the large center hole of the production, using a nut and C washer for removal. Index the production with a pin through one of the capscrew holes, so that the drill will enter the oil reservoir in the casting at the proper place.

5. Fig. 13.57.   Design a boring-and-facing fixture for flange.   Refer to the design shown in Fig. 29.11.   Assume that the top flat surface has been finished and the $\frac{3}{4}$-in. holes reamed prior to the operation of boring and facing in this fixture.   For boring the $2\frac{5}{8}$- and 2-in. diameter holes, use the two clamps, the center stud and washer being removed.   For facing, remove or slip the clamps out of place and use the centering stud with washer and nut.   On a production line, two fixtures could be made using those parts necessary for successive operations in each fixture.

6. Fig. 9.79.   Design a boring-and-facing fixture for plunger bracket.   Refer to the design shown in Fig. 29.12.   Assume that the base is finished and that the base holes are reamed to size.   Use these for locating over two pins, one flat and one round, and clamp down to the projecting shelf with a clamp as shown, or equivalent.   This fixture should be counterbalanced to reduce vibration and obtain greater accuracy.

30

The Elements of Structural Drawing

30.1 By the term "structural drawing" is meant the drawings of steel, masonry, wood, concrete, etc., for structures such as buildings, bridges, and dams. Structural drawings differ from other drawings only in certain details and practices which have developed as peculiar to the materials worked with and the method of their fabrication. The differences are so well established that it is essential for any engineer to know something of the methods of representation in use in structural work.

30.2 Classification of structural drawings. Structural drawings may be classified as follows:[1]

(1) *General plan.* This will include a profile of the ground; location of the structure; elevations of ruling points in the structure; clearances; grades; direction of flow, high water, and low water (for a bridge); and all other data necessary for designing the substructure and superstructure.

(2) *Stress diagram.* This will give the main dimensions of the structure, the loading, stresses in all members for the dead loads, live loads, wind loads, etc., itemized separately; total maximum stresses and minimum stresses; sizes of members; typical sections of all built members showing arrangement of material; and all information necessary for detailing the various parts of the structure.

(3) *Shop drawings.* Shop detail drawings should be made of all steel and ironwork, and detail drawings should be made of all timber, masonry, and concrete work.

(4) *Foundation or masonry plan.* The foundation or masonry plan should contain detail drawings of all foundations, walls, piers, etc., that support the structure. The plans should show the loads on the foundations, the depth of footings, the spacing of piles where used, the proportions for the concrete, the quality of masonry and mortar, the allowable bearing on the soil, and all data necessary for accurately locating and constructing the foundations.

(5) *Erection diagram.* The erection diagram should show the relative location of every part of the structure, shipping marks for the various members, all main dimensions, number of pieces in a member, packing of pins, size and grip of pins, and any special feature or information that may assist the erector in the field. The approximate weight of heavy pieces will materially assist the erector in designing his falsework and derricks.

(6) *Falsework plans.* For ordinary structures it is not common to prepare falsework plans in the office, this important detail being left to the erector in the field. For difficult or important work, erection plans should be worked out in the office and should show in detail all members and connections of the falsework and also give instructions for the successive steps in carrying out the work. Falsework plans are especially important for concrete and masonry arches and other concrete structures and for forms for all walls, piers, etc. Detail plans of travelers, derricks, etc., should also be furnished the erector.

(7) *Bills of material.* Complete bills of material showing the different parts of the structure with their marks and shipping weights should be prepared. This is necessary to permit checking of shipping weights and shipment and arrival of materials.

(8) *Rivet list.* The rivet list should show the dimensions and number of all field rivets, field bolts, spikes, etc., used in the erection of the structure.

[1] From Milo S. Ketchum, "Structural Engineers' Handbook," 3d ed., McGraw-Hill Book Co., Inc., New York.

(9) *List of drawings.* A list should be made showing the contents of all drawings belonging to the structure.

30.3   Structural-steel shapes.   Steel structures are made up of "rolled shapes" fastened together with rivets, bolts, or welds.   The function of structural-steel drawings is to show how these shapes are to be fabricated in the shop and then erected to form the various members of bridges, buildings, etc.   Sections of the common shapes are shown in Fig. 30.1.   Dimensions for detailing these and other less common shapes may be found in the Ameri-

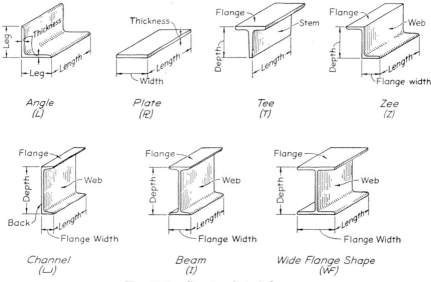

Fig. 30.1.   Structural steel shapes.

can Institute of Steel Construction handbook.   Dimensions for detailing common sizes of channels, I beams, wide flange sections, and angles are given in the Appendix.

In designating rolled-steel shapes on drawings, the AISC standard abbreviations and order of specifications are used, as follows:

Plates.   Pl 18 × ½ × 4'-2 (width × thickness × length).

Equal angles.   L3 × 3 × ¼ × 7'-6 (size of legs × thickness × length).

Unequal angles.   L6 × 4 × ⁵⁄₁₆ × 10'-0 (size of long leg × size of short leg × thickness × length).

Standard channels.   9 ⌐ 13.4 × 12'-4 (depth of section × weight per foot × length).

Standard I beams.   12 I 31.8 × 14'-6 (depth of section × weight per foot × length).

Wide flange sections.   14 W⁻48 × 16'-3 (nominal depth of section × weight per foot × length).

Tees.   T5 × 3 × 11.5 × 8'-0 (width of flange × depth × weight per foot × length).

Structural tees.   Cut from W⁻ section: ST 5 W⁻10.5 × 4'-7 (depth × weight per foot × length).

Cut from I beam: ST 5 I 12.5 × 5'-4 (depth × weight per foot × length).

Zees.   Z6 × 3½ × 15.7 × 9'-10 (depth × width of flange × weight per foot × length).

30.4   Drawings of steel structures.   The general drawings include the general plan, the stress diagram, and the erection diagram and correspond in many respects to the design drawings of the mechanical engineer.   In some cases the design is worked out completely by the engineer, who gives the sizes and weights of members and the number and spacing of all rivets, but in most cases the general dimensions, positions, and sizes of the members and the number of rivets are shown, leaving the details to be worked out in the shop or to be given on separate complete shop drawings.

In order to show the details clearly, the structural draftsman often uses two scales in the same view, one for the center lines or skeleton of the structure, showing the shape, and a larger one for the parts composing it.   The scale used for the skeleton is determined by the size of the structure as compared with the sheet; $\frac{1}{4}''$, $\frac{3}{8}''$, and $\frac{1}{2}''$ to $1'\text{-}0''$ are commonly used.   Figure 30.2 is a typical shop drawing of a small roof truss, giving complete details. Such drawings are made about the stress-diagram lines (used in calculating the stresses and sizes of the members), which are then employed as the gravity lines of the members and form the skeleton, as illustrated separately to small scale in the box on the figure.   The intersections of these lines are called "working points" and are the points from which all distances are figured.   The length of each working line is computed accurately, and from it the intermediate dimensions are obtained.

The design diagram is often put on the same sheet, as with the drawing of the truss.

30.5   Detailing practice for structural steel.   Separate drawings made to a sufficiently large scale to carry complete information are called "shop detail drawings," Fig. 30.3.   When possible, the drawings of all members are shown in the same relative position which they will occupy in the completed structure: vertical, horizontal, or inclined.   Long vertical or inclined members may be drawn in a horizontal position, a vertical member always having its lower end at the left, and an inclined member drawn in the direction it would fall.   Except in plain building work, a diagram to small scale (showing by a heavy line the relative position of the member in the structure) should be drawn on every detail sheet.

In steel construction, a member may be composed of either a single rolled shape or a combination of two or more rolled shapes.   Figure 30.3 is a shop detail drawing of a member made from a single rolled shape.   Figures 30.2, 30.4, and 30.5 are shop detail drawings of members made up of several rolled shapes.   These figures will illustrate detailing practice.   Note in Fig. 30.2 that only one-half of the truss is shown.   When thus drawn it is always the left end, looking toward the side on which the principal connections are made.

The scale of shop drawings is usually $\frac{1}{4}'' = 1'\text{-}0$ to $1'' = 1'\text{-}0$.   Often, for long members, the cross section will be drawn to a larger scale than the length.   Sometimes it is even advantageous to pay no attention to scaled length but to draw the member as though there were breaks in the length

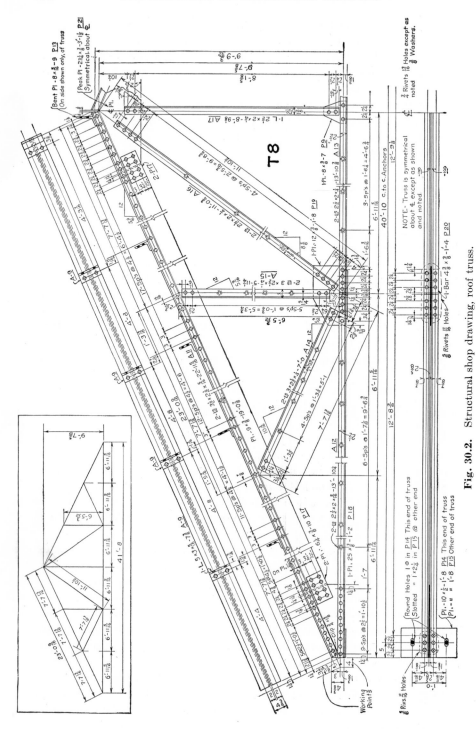

Fig. 30.2.   Structural shop drawing, roof truss.

(but not shown on the drawing, as in Fig. 30.5) so that rivet spacings at the ends (and intermediately) can be drawn to the same scale as the cross section.

Dimensions are always placed above the dimension line, and the dimension lines are not broken but are continuous. Length dimensions are expressed in feet and inches. All inch symbols are omitted unless there is the possibility of misunderstanding, thus 1 bolt should be 1″ bolt to distinguish between size and number. Inch symbols are omitted even though

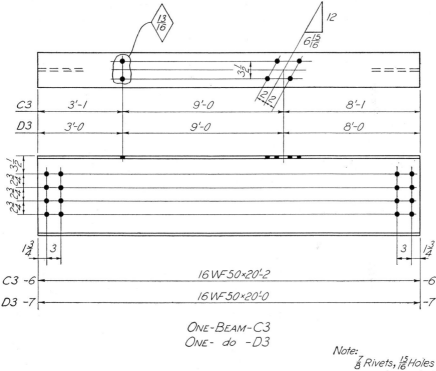

Fig. 30.3. Structural shop drawing, beam.

the dimensions are in feet and inches, and dimensions should be hyphenated thus: 7'-0, 7'-0½, 7'-4. Plate widths and section depths of rolled shapes are given in inches. Care should be taken that dimensions are given to commercial sizes of materials.

Rolled shapes are specified by abbreviated notes, as described in paragraph 30.3. The specification is given either along with the length dimension as in Fig. 30.3 or near and parallel to the shape as in Fig. 30.4.

Erection marks are necessary in order to identify the member. These are indicated on the drawing by letters and numbers in the subtitle. The erection diagram then carries these marking numbers and identifies the position of the member. Figure 30.19 shows an example of an erection diagram with marking numbers.

The erection mark also identifies the member in the shop and serves as a shipping mark. The mark is composed of a letter and number. Capital letters are used, *B* for beam, *C* for column, *T* for truss, etc. The number gives the specific member in an assembly.

Assembly marks are used when the same shape is used in more than one place on a member. The member is completely specified *once* followed by the assembly mark (lower-case letters, to distinguish from erection marks). The complete specification is then not repeated but only the assembly mark given. As an example, see the angles "$2 \llcorner 4 \times 3\frac{1}{2} \times \frac{3}{8} \times 8\frac{1}{2}$(a)," in Fig. 30.4.

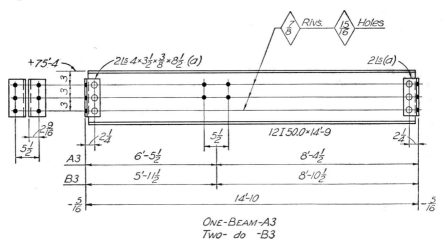

Fig. 30.4. Structural shop drawing, beam.

Different members may be detailed together on the same drawing when they differ only in length, spacing of rivets or holes, or when one member has special holes or has an extra piece added. Figures 30.3 and 30.4 both show two beams detailed on the same drawing. Note that the different lengths are given with the erection mark at the end of the dimension line.

When one of two similar members has a hole or other feature on one member only, the special feature is indicated by drawing a freehand circle around the detail with a leader to a note such as, "on A-3 only."

Distances to center lines of another connecting member are given, as in Figs. 30.3 and 30.4, by placing the distance, preceded by a minus sign (−), at the end of the length dimension. These distances to center are a great aid in checking the details with an assembly or layout drawing.

Inclinations of members and inclined center lines, cuts, etc., are indicated by their tangents. As in Figs. 30.2 and 30.3, a small right triangle is drawn with its hypotenuse parallel to the line or on the line whose inclination is to be specified. The long leg of the triangle is always specified as 12.

Rivets and holes are dimensioned in the view that shows them as circles. Dimensions pertaining to a row of rivets should be given in a single line as in

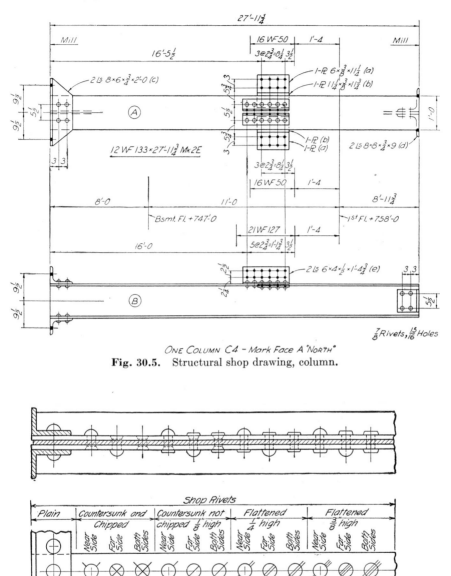

Fig. 30.5. Structural shop drawing, column.

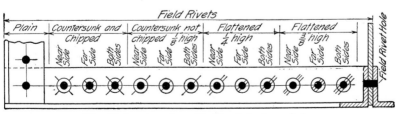

Fig. 30.6. American Standard rivet symbols.

Fig. 30.2. Gage dimensions, even though standard, should always be given. The size of rivets and holes is given in a general note as in Fig. 30.3.

The length of rivets is not usually given on the drawing; the workman picks a rivet length long enough to go through the members and protrude far enough so that the head may be formed.

Common practice is to make rivet holes $\frac{1}{16}$ in. larger than the rivets, see Figs. 30.3 to 30.5.

If some of the rivets or holes for a member are of a different size, these are indicated by the size in a diamond, as in Figs. 30.3 and 30.4.

Rivet symbols are used because it is impossible to show the details of head form on a small-scale drawing. The ASA symbols for indicating various kinds of heads are given in Fig. 30.6.

The size of most structures prevents their being completely fabricated in the shop. Therefore, portions as large as transportation facilities or ease of handling will allow are assembled and then connected to other portions in the field. Shop rivets are indicated by an open circle, the size of the rivet head. Holes for field rivets are indicated by "blacked-in" circles the diameter of the hole, see Figs. 30.3, 30.4, 30.5, and 30.6. Rivets are drawn to scale. Figure 30.7 shows the proportions of rivet heads with respect to the diameter.

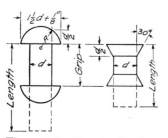

Fig. 30.7. Structural rivet proportions.

Rivet spacing is an important item in detailing, and there are a number of conditions that control the placement. Rivets spaced too close together or too close to a projecting part cannot be properly driven. Rivets placed too close to the edge or end of a member may weaken the member.

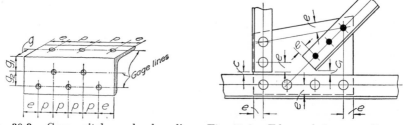

Fig. 30.8. Gage, pitch, and edge distances.   **Fig. 30.9.** Edge and clearance distances.

Rivets are spaced along "gage" lines, parallel to the axis of the member and at certain "pitch" distances along the gage line, Fig. 30.8. The minimum distance between rivets in any direction is three rivet diameters. The minimum edge distance (e), Fig. 30.9, from sheared edges of a member is $1\frac{1}{2}$ rivet diameters. Distance to a rolled edge may be slightly less than $1\frac{1}{2}$ diameters and is usually controlled by the location of the gage line. Whenever possible the same edge distance is used on all members, and the distance is then given in a general note such as "edge distance $1\frac{1}{4}$ except as noted."

Gage-line distances and minimum driving clearances for common rolled shapes are given in the Appendix.

Standard beam connections are given on page 680.

Clearances between various members of a structure are necessary so that there will be no interferences, because of manufacturing inaccuracies. More clearance should be allowed for field erection than for shop fabrication. Field clearance (C_1, Fig. 30.9) should be approximately $\frac{1}{2}$ in., and shop clearance (C) should be about $\frac{1}{4}$ in. Note the clearances shown between the angles (fastened with a gusset plate) in Fig. 30.9.

Elevations, sections, and other views are placed in relation to each other by the rules of third-angle projection, except that when a view is given under a front view, as in Fig. 30.2, it is made as a section taken above the lower flange, looking down, instead of as a regular bottom view looking up. Large sections of materials are shown with uniform crosshatching. Small-scale sections are blacked-in solid, with white spaces left between adjacent parts, see paragraph 13.4.

Bent plates should be developed and the "stretchout" length of bent forged bars given. The length of a bent plate may be taken as the inside length of the bend plus half the thickness of the plate for each bend.

A bill of material always accompanies a structural drawing. This may be put on the drawing, but the best practice is to attach it as a separate "bill sheet," generally on $8\frac{1}{2}$- by 11-in. paper.

Lettering is done in rapid single stroke, either inclined or vertical.

Checking is usually indicated by a red-pencil check mark placed under the dimension, note, or specification.

General notes should accompany the general drawing or appear in some cases in the title of the shop drawing. Items included are painting, shipping instructions, etc.

30.6 Timber structures. The representation of timber-framed structures involves no new principles but requires particular attention to details. Timber members are generally rectangular in section and are specified to nominal sizes in even inches as $8'' \times 12''$. The general drawing must give center and other important distances accurately. Details drawn to larger scale give specific information as to separate parts. The particulars of joints, splices, methods of fastening, etc., should be detailed.

Two scales may sometimes be used to advantage on the general drawing, as was done in Fig. 30.10. Complete notes are an essential part of such drawings, especially when an attempt at dimensioning the smaller details would result in confusion.

Joints in timber structures may be fastened with nails or spikes, wood screws, bolts, or ring-shaped or flat *connectors*, similar in action to a dowel or key. Some common types are shown in Fig. 30.11. *A* is a split ring, assembled in grooves in each piece and held together with a bolt, as indicated at *B*. The sharp projections on the alligator connector *C* are forced into the members by pressure. The *claw-plate* connector *D* is used either in pairs, back to back, for timber-to-timber connections, or single for timber to metal. A typical assembly is shown at *E*. The Kubler wood dowel connector *F* fits into a bored hole in each timber face, and a bolt holds the parts together.

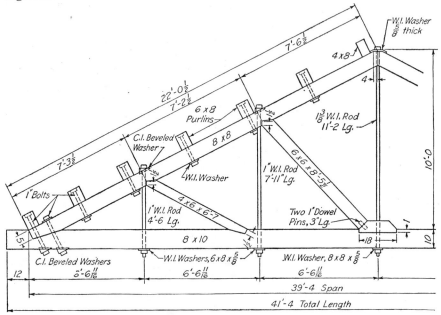

Fig. 30.10.   Structural shop drawing, timber truss.

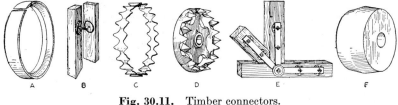

Fig. 30.11.   Timber connectors.

The Forest Products Laboratory publication, "Wood Handbook," gives basic information on wood as a material of construction, including the connectors, and is available at small cost from the Superintendent of Documents, Washington, D.C.

30.7   Masonry structures.   In drawing masonry the symbols used bear some resemblance to the material represented. Figure 30.12 gives those in common use and shows the stages followed to secure uniformity of effect in rendering earth and concrete. Drawings for piers, foundations for machines, and other structures are met with in all kinds of engineering work. Grade levels, floor levels, and other fixed heights should be given, together with accurate location dimensions for foundation bolts. All materials should be marked plainly with name or notes.

30.8   Reinforced concrete is an important division of masonry construction needing careful attention in representation and specification. It is

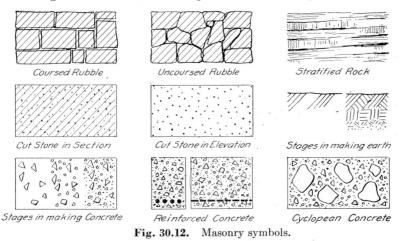

Fig. 30.12.   Masonry symbols.

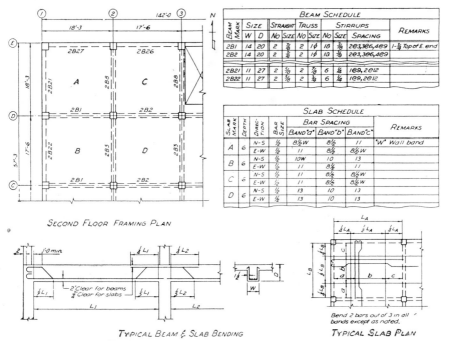

Fig. 30.13.   Reinforced concrete, general plan.

almost impossible to show the shape and location of reinforcing bars in concrete by the usual orthographic views, without the use of a systematic scheme of conventional symbols and marking.

Figure 30.13 shows a portion of the general structural plan for the first floor of a building. By means of the plan, the tabular data, the general notes, and the specifications, the engineer completely specifies the reinforced-concrete floor of the building. The location of the reinforced beams is given on the plan; the size of the beam and reinforcing to be used are indicated in the beam schedule; and the typical beam sections give the basic information for bending of the reinforcing bars. The type of floor slab used is indicated on the plan and in the slab schedule by the letters A, B, etc. The slab schedule, in conjunction with the typical slab plan, indicates the direction and spacing of reinforcing.

General notes on the drawing or in the specifications cover such items as maximum strength of concrete, grade of steel, minimum cover, etc.

The general drawing of Fig. 30.13, although completely specifying the reinforced-concrete construction, does not give the exact details of how the bars are bent and placed. The contractor supplying the steel makes

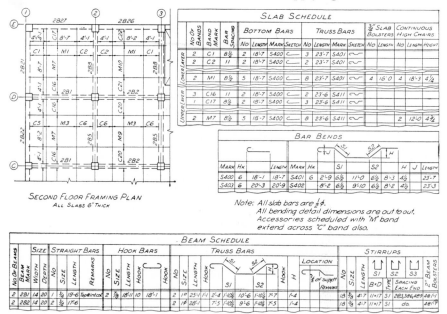

Fig. 30.14. Reinforced concrete, detail plan.

another drawing, Fig. 30.14, showing in detail the bending, spacing, etc., for all the steel.

Walls, columns, and other portions of reinforced structures are represented similarly to the beams and floor slabs illustrated.

PROBLEMS

1. Fig. 30.15. Make a shop drawing of the triple-effect evaporator support. Assume complete shop fabrication. Use ⅝-in. rivets.

2. Fig. 30.15. Make a shop drawing of the triple-effect evaporator support. Assume shop fabrication of all parts except the long channels and the 3- by 3- by ¼-in. angle brace; use ⅝-in. shop rivets and ⅝-in. field bolts.

3. Fig. 30.15. Same as Prob. 2, but redesign for welded construction.

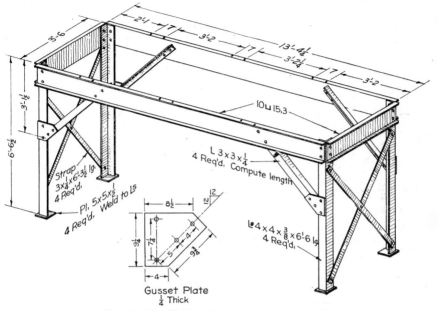

Fig. 30.15. Triple-effect evaporator support.

4. Fig. 30.16. Make a shop drawing of the column base. Assume complete assembly in the shop. Use ¾-in. rivets. Open holes are for 1-in. anchor bolts.

5. Fig. 30.16. Make a shop bill of material listing all parts used in Prob. 4.

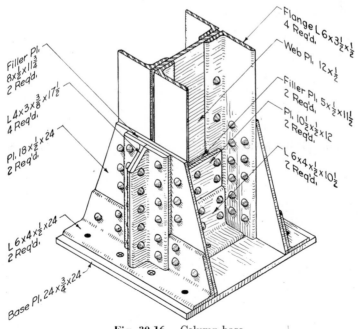

Fig. 30.16. Column base.

6. Fig. 30.17.   Make a shop drawing for the crane-trolley-frame support.   Assume fabrication as indicated in the figure.   One end is shown; the other end is similar.   Use ⅝-in. rivets wherever possible.

7. Fig. 30.17.   Make a shop bill of material listing all parts used in Prob. 6.

8. Fig. 30.10.   Redesign, using (wherever possible) fasteners shown in Fig. 30.11.

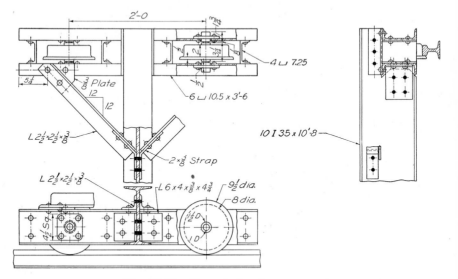

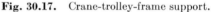

Fig. 30.17.   Crane-trolley-frame support.

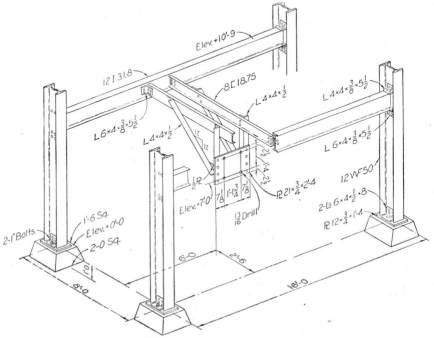

Fig. 30.18.   Motor support.

9. Fig. 30.18.   Make a shop drawing for the motor support.   Assume shop fabrication as follows: (a) 8-in. channels, 4- by 4- by ½-in. angles, ½-in. plate, and 6- by 4- by ⅜-in. beam connectors (angles), two members required, one right hand, one left hand; (b) 21 by ¾ by 2′-4 plate; (c) 12-in. I beam, two required with 4- by 4- by ⅜-in. beam connectors temporarily bolted in place.   Assume columns to be part of the existing structure.   Use ¾-in. rivets and ¾-in. bolts.

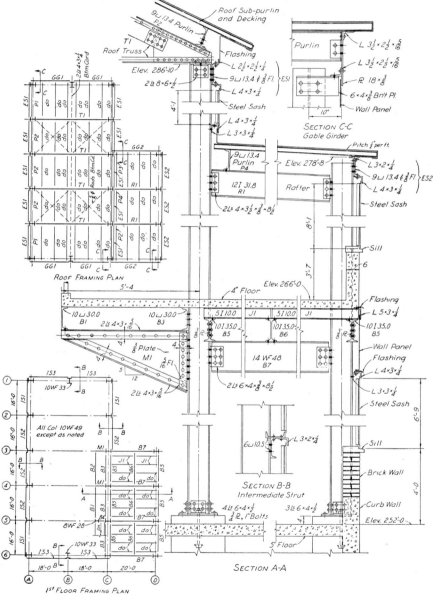

Fig. 30.19.   Steel-frame mill building.

10. Fig. 30.18.   Make an erection drawing for the motor support.   Assume columns to be part of the existing structure.

11. Fig. 30.19.   Make a shop drawing of roof truss $T1$ for the steel-frame mill building.   This drawing is to be similar to the drawing shown in Fig. 30.2.   For truss $T1$, use the same size members and the same roof pitch as is used for truss $T8$, Fig. 30.2. Detail only the left half of the truss to a scale suitable for 11- by 17-in. paper.

12. Fig. 30.19.   Prepare shop drawings for the following steel members used in fabricating the steel mill building: (*a*) bracket $M1$; (*b*) beams $B1$ and $B3$ (one detail for both); (*c*) beam $B5$ (assume $\frac{3}{8}$-in. plate to be shop fabricated to column); and (*d*) beam $B6$.   Assume shop and field fabrication indicated in Fig. 30.19.   Use $\frac{3}{4}$-in. rivets.   These details, along with the shipping list and general notes, may be drawn on 11- by 17-in. paper to a scale of $1'' = 1'$-0.

13. Fig. 30.19.   Prepare shop drawings for the following steel members used in fabricating the steel mill building: (*a*) bracket $M1$, and (*b*) column $C4$.   Assume shop and field fabrication indicated in Fig. 30.19.   Use $\frac{3}{4}$-in. rivets.   Three faces of the column will have to be shown.

14. Fig. 30.19.   Make a shop drawing of column $D4$.   Assume shop and field fabrication as indicated.   Use $\frac{3}{4}$-in. rivets.

15. Fig. 30.19.   Make a shop drawing of beam $B7$.

16. Fig. 30.19.   Make a shop drawing of rafter $R1$.

17. Fig. 30.19.   Make a general structural plan, similar to Fig. 30.13, of the concrete floor at elevation 266'-0.   Use $\frac{1}{2}$-in. round reinforcing bars spaced 9 in. on centers, alternate bars are bent for the floor.   In 6-in. wall, use $3\frac{1}{2}$-in. round bars in bottom and $\frac{3}{8}$-in. round vertical bars at 18 in. hooked 18 in. into floor slab.

18. Fig. 30.19. Make a reinforcing detail drawing, similar to Fig. 30.14, for Prob. 17.

31

The Elements of Architectural Drawing

31.1   Architecture is defined as the art or science of building; especially the art of building houses, churches, bridges, and other structures, for the purposes of civil life.   From this definition architecture is properly placed, professionally, between engineering and the fine arts.   It is entirely beyond the scope of this book to cover architectural designing, that phase of architecture based primarily upon the study of the fine arts; however, *engineers will work with architects in the building of structures and should, therefore, understand some of the procedures followed in an architectural drafting room.*

Structural engineers will determine the design of columns, beams, floor slabs, etc.; mechanical engineers will prepare designs for heating and ventilating equipment; electrical engineers will determine lighting requirements, and in the field of power they will design the electrical system of the structure properly to meet the requirements of the client; and all engineers will be concerned with structures that are designed to house themselves and their activities.

31.2   Characteristics of architectural drawing.   In applying engineering drawing to architecture, the architect uses peculiarities of expression with which all engineers should be familiar, since they will often be required to read and work with architectural drawings.   Presentation techniques, as in a profiled section, Fig. 31.1, or unusual views, such as the reflected plan, Fig. 31.2, and even the occasional use of first and second angles of projection may be foreign

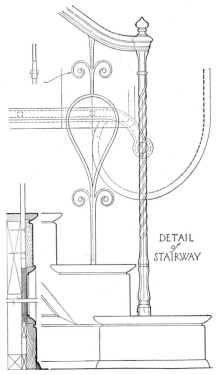

DETAIL
of
STAIRWAY

Fig. 31.1.   Stairway detail, showing profiled section and superimposed plan view.

to the engineer whose previous experience has not required collaboration with an architect.   To prepare himself fully for such an association, careful study of architectural drawings, together with the reasons for their variation from the more usual engineering drawings, will be invaluable to an engineering student.

The general principles of drawing are the same for all kinds of technical work; however, an architect's drafting will usually indicate a more spon-taneous approach to the drawing problem than that shown by other engi-neers. Preliminary studies, presentation drawings, building models, and the working drawings require varying techniques and drafting skills; thus, with more adaptability than his fel-low engineers, an architect must be capable of doing both freehand and instrument drawing, using all the materials and techniques at a drafts-man's disposal.

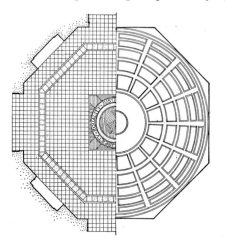

Half Floor Plan   Half Ceiling Plan

Fig. 31.2.   Floor plan and reflected plan of a domed ceiling.

31.3 Preliminary studies. The design for a building is initiated by the client presenting his requirements to the architect. This may be accom-plished in conferences, or through the use of written material; at times a combination of both procedures will be used. If the building is for indus-trial purposes, the engineers of indus-try will present flow sheets of the manufacturing processes to be em-ployed in the proposed structure. Close cooperation between the engi-neering and architectural personnel is absolutely necessary to ensure that the resultant building meets the need of the industry. Similarly, for all types of buildings, the client-architect contacts will result in the determina-tion of a program of minimum requirements, maximum allowable costs, architectural style, building materials, etc.

The architect then establishes a structural grid in keeping with the func-tion and structural requirements of the building.[1] With this grid as a background several solutions to the problem are developed, usually in rough sketch form on tracing paper. A selection of the better solutions is made for further study in plan, elevation, and section.

Throughout this phase of the work sketches will be kept relatively small, although care will be taken to maintain proper proportions. The smallness of these "thumbnail sketches" forces the designer to consider the essential elements only, for a study of detail is impossible at a small scale. Prelimi-nary plans, showing two schemes for a one-floor house, are reproduced in Fig. 31.3 at approximately the scale of the original studies.

31.4 Presentation drawings. The object of presentation drawings is to give realistic and effective representations of proposed designs, for illus-

[1] Various modular dimensions for the grid may be employed, but in residential work a 4'-0'' square seems most adaptable, whereas in commercial work, with reinforced concrete or steel construction, 20'-0'' or larger is advantageous.

trative or competitive purposes. They are generally drawn in perspective, then rendered in water color, ink, crayon, or pencil, giving the effect of color, light, and shade. Such accessories as human figures, adjacent buildings, foliage, etc., are introduced for scale, an idea of relative size. Should the

Fig. 31.3. Preliminary-plan studies.

presentation show one or more floor plans, the "scale" of the plan is indicated by the inclusion of furniture and floor designs on the interior, and walks, drives, and the planting of the grounds immediately surrounding the building. Examples of presentation drawings are shown in Fig. 31.4.

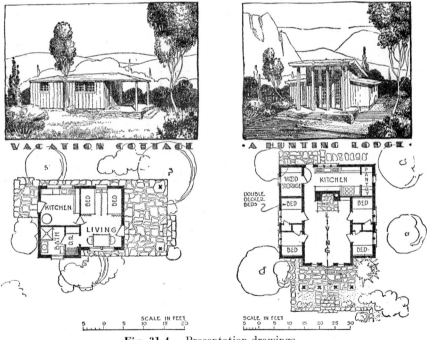

Fig. 31.4. Presentation drawings.

31.5 Models. The use of building models, for presentation purposes, is widespread throughout the architectural profession. They are made in the drafting room, using drawing paper, illustration board, balsa wood, etc.

The different walls and roof surfaces are laid out in developed form, rendered, folded, and then mounted on a rigid base. It is particularly important that all features, such as moldings, railings, plantings, etc., be kept to scale. The advantage of such a presentation, in showing the appearance of the completed building from any station point, is of obvious value, when compared with the single station point of a presentation drawing.

For reproduction purposes a photograph of the model, superimposed on one of the actual site, makes an effective presentation.

31.6   Materials of construction.   At some time previous to the preparation of the working drawings and specifications, the selection of building materials must be made.   Items that will influence the selection will include appearance, initial cost, erection time, and maintenance.   Conventional symbols for the more common building materials are shown in Fig. 31.5.

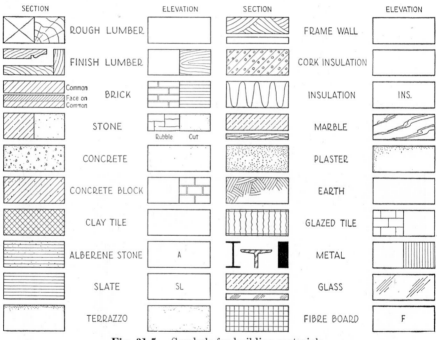

Fig. 31.5.   Symbols for building materials.

31.7   Size coordination of building materials and equipment.   Size coordination of a building's many parts may be accomplished by cutting and fitting during field operations or by shop fabrication.   In actual practice a combination of both techniques is usually employed; however, it will be apparent that tighter fits and lower costs result from shop-fabrication methods replacing the more wasteful procedures inherent in the majority of field operations.

Considerable study and research have resulted in the ASA approving a 4-in. unit as the standard module for building materials.   From a practical standpoint, it must be understood that not all manufacturers are producing materials sized in 4-in. increments; nor is such standardization ever likely to occur. *Standardization, for the purpose of size coordination of building materials and equipment, is achieved by a judicious selection from the available sizes, followed by a tying of the resulting details into the modular grid.*

31.8 Grid position of details. A symmetrical location of walls and openings, with respect to the horizontal grid, is desirable in order to effect standardization. In the instance of wall locations, it will be seen in Fig. 31.6 that only one reference to the grid is possible if the walls are (1) cen-

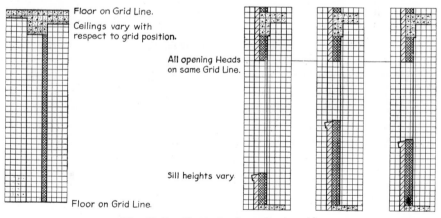

Fig. 31.6. Grid positioning of walls.

tered on the grid lines, or (2) centered between grid lines. Any other system of positioning walls results in numerous possibilities of grid referencings. It will be seen, in (3) through (6), that four possible grid positions may be had if one face of each wall is positioned on a grid line.

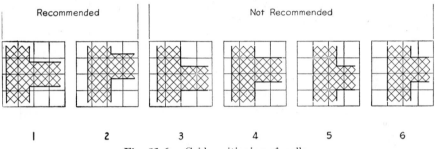
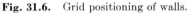

Fig. 31.7. Vertical referencing to grid.

Vertical referencing is usually restricted to maintaining floor levels on grid lines. Openings need not be symmetrical in their vertical positioning, since head and sill details are different; however, different sized openings are usually positioned with all heads on the same grid line, for any one story. Necessary adjustments due to variations in floor thicknesses are made at the intersections of the walls and ceilings, Fig. 31.7.

31.9 Nominal vs. actual size. Two systems of dimension notation are currently being used in the many architectural offices. The majority of such establishments show actual values in nearly all instances; however, the more modern procedure of grid referencing allows, and in fact makes preferable, the use of nominal values on all small-scale layout drawings.

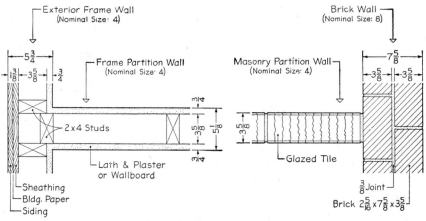

Fig. 31.8. Nominal versus actual sizes, frame and masonry walls.

A study of Fig. 31.8 will serve to illustrate the difference between nominal and actual sizes. Nominal thicknesses of walls are established by the nominal size of the structural members. Since 2- by 4-in. studding is used in both the exterior and partition frame walls shown, the 4-in. size is assigned as their nominal thickness. The actual size of a 2 by 4 is $1\frac{5}{8}$ by $3\frac{5}{8}$ in. The glazed tile in the masonry partition wall is actually $3\frac{5}{8}$ by $11\frac{5}{8}$ by $3\frac{5}{8}$ in. and nominally 4 by 12 by 4 in. (allowances for a $\frac{3}{8}$-in. mortar joint having been made in each of the three dimensions). A $\frac{3}{8}$-in. mortar joint is again designed for in the sizing of modular brick; actual dimensions are $2\frac{5}{16}$ by $7\frac{5}{8}$ by $3\frac{5}{8}$ in., while nominally they are $2\frac{2}{3}$ by 8 by 4 in. It will be noted that interior and exterior treatment, or finish, is not considered in the assignment of the nominal size to any wall thickness; the structural members alone are so considered.

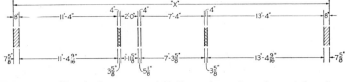

Fig. 31.9. Nominal versus actual dimension values, layout drawings.

Comparison of the line of actual dimensions with the line of nominal dimensions in Fig. 31.9 will show the comparative ease in determining total dimensions (such as X) when nominal values are used in preference to actual quantities. A detail, dimensioned with actual values and referenced to the grid, completes the information required for the proper use of nominal values, thus simplifying the arithmetic processes ever-present in checking, estimating from, and the field use of architectural drawings.

31.10 Dimensioning. The correct dimensioning of an architectural drawing requires a knowledge of building-construction methods: The dimensions should be placed so as to be most convenient for the workman, given to and from accessible points, and selected so that commercial variation in the sizes of materials will not affect the principal dimensions. In general, it will be found that dimensions are given to the faces of masonry walls, the outside face of the studs in an exterior wall, and the center of the studs in a partition wall. Columns and beams are located by dimensioning to their center lines, as are window and door openings in frame walls (in masonry walls the openings are dimensioned). Compared with the dimensioning techniques used in the other engineering fields, architectural working drawings will appear overdimensioned. No usable dimension should be omitted on an architectural drawing, even though that dimension could be determined by the addition and/or subtraction of other dimensions on the sheet.

Legibility is a matter of prime importance in the subject of dimensioning. All numerals must be carefully drawn, since a crease in the paper, a smudge, or a poor print of the drawing could result in the misreading of a dimension value. (The draftsman should be particularly mindful of the numerals 3 and 5.)

In the dimensioning of drawings that have been laid out in the modular system, it is essential that the grid referencings be clearly indicated since the grid will usually be omitted from small-scale drawings. *An arrowhead is used at the end of the dimension line when the dimension is to a point on a grid line, and a dot is used for all points not on grid lines* (Fig. 31.10). Regardless of whether actual or nominal values are shown, the architect does not find the

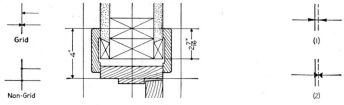

Fig. 31.10. Dimension line terminals for grid and nongrid dimensions.   **Fig. 31.11.** Arrowheads.

graceful but slim arrowhead, used by other engineers, suitable for his use. In Fig. 31.11 (1), the reader will see that the dimensions might be taken to either the solid or dotted line; but in (2), where a more bulky arrowhead is used, no question arises as to which line the dimensions refer. A shape, somewhere between these extremes, will probably serve best in the majority of instances, but clarity must be maintained.

31.11 Working drawings. The general principles of Chap. 28, regarding working drawings, are applicable to architectural working drawings.

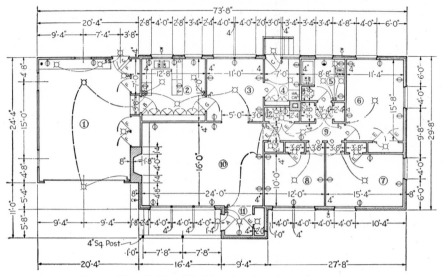

Fig. 31.12. Working drawing, floor plan.

ROOM FINISH SCHEDULE						
Rm. No.	Floor	Base	Walls	Ceiling	Trim	Remarks
1	Concrete	Concrete	Sheetrock	Sheetrock	Poplar	Built in bench w/dwrs.
2	Linoleum	Cove	Linowall	"	"	See cabinet details.
3	Concrete	Birch	Sheetrock	"	Birch	See details.
4	Linoleum	Cove	Linowall	"	Poplar	" "
5	Cer. Tile	Cer. Tile	cer. tile wnsct. sheetrock	"	"	" "
6	Concrete	Birch	Sheetrock	"	Birch	" "
7	"	"	"	"	"	" "
8	"	"	"	"	"	" "
9	"	"	"	"	"	" "
10	"	"	"	"	"	" "
11	Slate	"	"	"	"	" "
12	Concrete	Concrete	"	"	Poplar	" "

Fig. 31.13. Working drawing, room finish schedule.

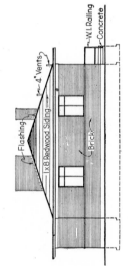

Fig. 31.14. Working drawing, right-side elevation.

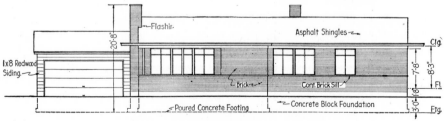

Fig. 31.15. Working drawing, front elevation.

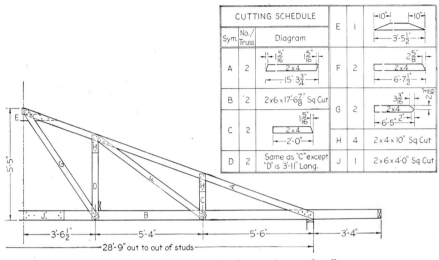

CUTTING SCHEDULE			E	1	
Sym.	No./Truss	Diagram			⊢10"⊣ ⊢10"⊣ ⎯ 3'-5½" ⎯
A	2	⊢1"⊢ 5/16" ⊢ 5/16"⊣ 2×4 ⎯ 15' 3¾" ⎯	F	2	2⅝" 2×4 ⎯ 6'-7½" ⎯
B	2	2×6 × 17'-6⅞" Sq. Cut	G	2	3 3/16" 2×4 2 3/16" ⊢ 6'-5" 2" ⊣
C	2	5/16" 2×4 ⎯ 2'-0" ⎯	H	4	2×4 × 10" Sq. Cut
D	2	Same as "C" except "D" is 3'-11" Long.	J	1	2×6 × 4'-0" Sq. Cut

⎯ 3'-6½" ⎯ ⎯ 5'-4" ⎯ ⎯ 5'-6" ⎯ ⎯ 3'-4" ⎯
⎯ 28'-9" out to out of studs ⎯

Fig. 31.16. Working drawing, roof-truss details.

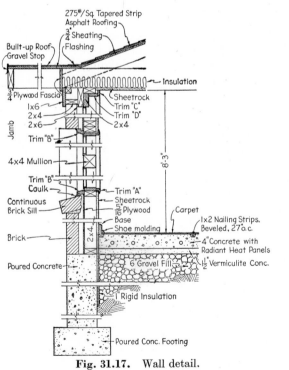

Fig. 31.17. Wall detail.

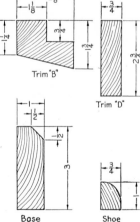

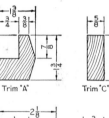

Fig. 31.18. Trim details.

As a general rule details which are related should be shown together, and information concerning each craft should be grouped whenever feasible. Many present-day buildings are so complicated that it is advantageous to draw several sets of plans, a set for each of the several crafts, that is, structural, plumbing, electrical, heating and ventilating, in addition to the architectural set.

Architectural handbooks, American Institute of Architects' fi es, Sweet's Catalogues, and other literature should be freely consulted during the preparation of all working drawings. From them, sizes for the many build ng materials and equipment are determined, together with other factual data necessary for the proper selection and specification of such items. In addition to the above, such publications as local and state building codes must be studied and adhered to in the preparation of the working drawings. Legal requirements as to approval of the plans and specifications, securement of building permits, etc., must also be accomplished.

Figures 31.12 through 31.18 are selections from a set of working drawings for a one-floor plan three-bedroom house. Omitted from reproduction here are the following working drawings: plot plan, left-side elevation, rear elevation, foundation details, radiant-heating layout, roof-framing plan, door and window schedules, doorway details, kitchen and bath elevations, fireplace details, cabinet detail, etc.

31.12 Plot plan. Before designing any structure of importance a plot plan is made giving the property line, contours, available utilities, location of trees, building lines, and other pertinent data. The building may then be designed to fit the site. This drawing is completed as one of the working drawings by locating on it the building, approaches, and finished grade contours, Fig. 31.19.

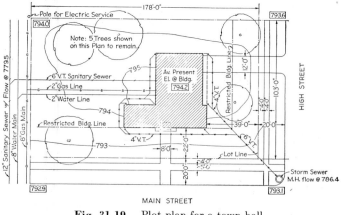

Fig. 31.19. Plot plan for a town hall.

31.13 Floor plans. A floor plan is a horizontal section taken at distances above the floor so varying as to best show all the features of the building between that floor and the next higher one. Because of their small scale, floor plans are largely made up of conventional symbols. Some of the symbols currently in use are shown in Figs. 31.20 and 31.21.

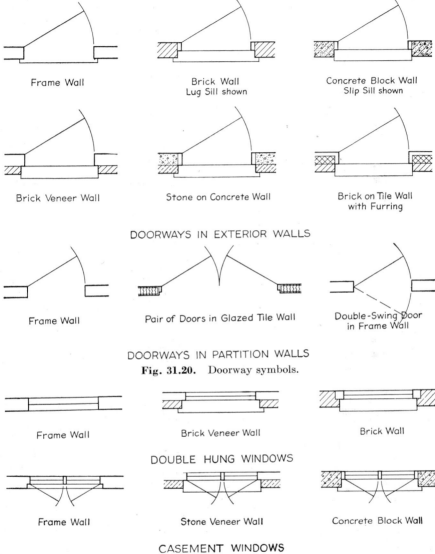

Frame Wall

Brick Wall
Lug Sill shown

Concrete Block Wall
Slip Sill shown

Brick Veneer Wall

Stone on Concrete Wall

Brick on Tile Wall
with Furring

DOORWAYS IN EXTERIOR WALLS

Frame Wall

Pair of Doors in Glazed Tile Wall

Double-Swing Door
in Frame Wall

DOORWAYS IN PARTITION WALLS
Fig. 31.20. Doorway symbols.

Frame Wall

Brick Veneer Wall

Brick Wall

DOUBLE HUNG WINDOWS

Frame Wall

Stone Veneer Wall

Concrete Block Wall

CASEMENT WINDOWS
Fig. 31.21. Window symbols.

In drawing a floor plan, the large structural grid is drawn first to serve as a guide. The entrance front is usually placed at the bottom of the sheet without regard to compass directions. Columns and walls are then positioned on the grid. Axes of communication, or route lines between the several rooms, are established. Interior doorways, stairways, elevator and service shafts, etc., are located. Exterior wall openings, however, are firmly

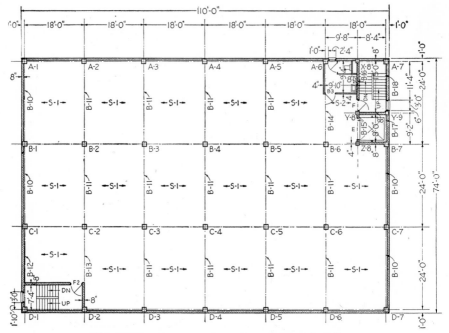

Fig. 31.22. An upper floor of a warehouse building.

positioned *only after elevation studies have been made.* A completely dimen-

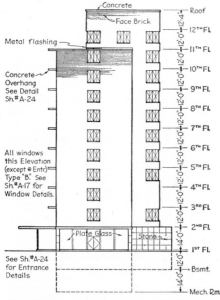

Fig. 31.23. End elevation of a hospital building.

sioned floor plan of a warehouse is shown in Fig. 31.22 (because of the simplicity of the architectural design, this drawing shows both architectural and structural information).

31.14 Elevations. An elevation is a view seen looking in a horizontal direction. For practical purposes, the elevations drawn are those showing normal views of wall surfaces.

In drawing an elevation, a wall section (that shows the grade line, floor heights, head, and sill of a typical window in each story, cornice, and roof ridge) is placed to the side of where the elevation is to be drawn, and a floor plan is secured to the top of the drawing board. The elevation is then projected from the section and plan. Figure 31.23 shows an end elevation of a hospital building.

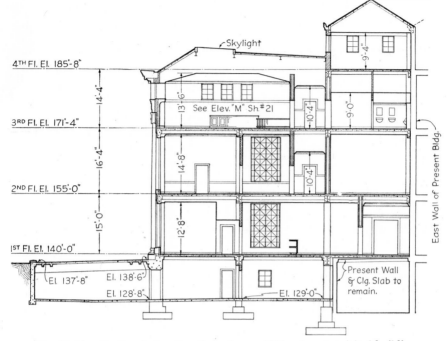

Fig. 31.24. Sectional elevation through an addition to a municipal building.

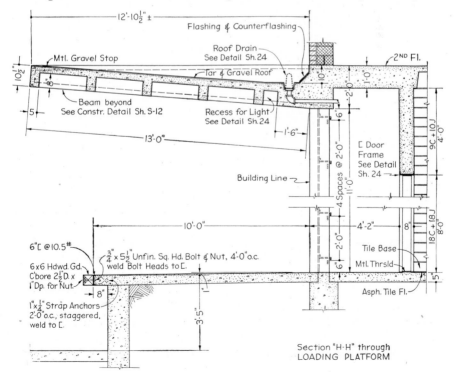

Fig. 31.25. Detail section, original scale: $\frac{3}{4}'' = 1'\text{-}0''$. (Note use of grid-referencing dimension line terminals.)

31.15   Sectional elevations.   Fig. 31.24.   Sectional elevations through the entire structure show interior construction and architectural treatment. Two such sections, called the longitudinal and transverse sections, at right angles to each other, are usually included in a set of working drawings.   The cutting planes for these sections need not be continuous, but as in the case of floor plans, may be offset to include as much information as possible.

31.16   Detail drawings.   A set of architectural drawings will contain, in addition to plans and elevations, larger scale drawings of such parts as are not indicated with sufficient definiteness on the small-scale drawings.   Stair details and detail sections of various items, that is, footings, windows, framing, etc., are required to. show details properly of both construction and architectural design.   Details are best grouped so that each sheet contains the references made on one sheet of the general drawings (a name sometimes given to the floor plans and elevations).

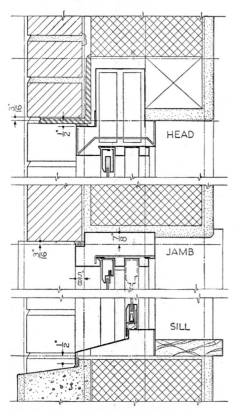

Fig. 31.26. Detail of a double-hung metal window, spring balanced. (4″ grid and referencing shown.)

As the construction progresses the drawings are supplemented by full-size details of moldings, millwork, ornamental iron, etc.   Such drawings are made *after* measurements of the building have been taken.   Revolved sections are used freely on these drawings.

Figures 31.25 and 31.26 illustrate typical detail drawings.

31.17   Lettering. There are two distinct divisions in the use of lettering by an architect; the first, office lettering, includes all titles and notes put on the drawings for information; and the second, design lettering, covers the drawing of letters to be executed in stone, bronze, or some other material, in connection with the architectural design.   Legibility is the primary consideration in both divisions.   Appearance is of equal importance in design lettering, while speed of accomplishment must be given secondary consideration in the office classification.   A pleasant appearance results from uniformity regardless of the style; accomplished speed in drafting necessarily depends upon simplicity of the letter forms.

Figures 2.46 and 2.47 show the Old Roman alphabet, generally employed in design work. Before attempting to use this letter, the designer should make himself thoroughly familiar with its construction, character, and beauty. The realization that it was designed for inscriptions in stone, together with an understanding of how letters are so carved, will assist the designer toward a sympathetic use of these classic forms.

Single-stroke letters as illustrated in Figs. 2.25, 2.29, and 2.48 are excellent for use in office lettering.

31.18 Titles. An architectural title may either be hand lettered on each sheet, or printed by some procedure, such as with a rubber stamp. In the latter instance, some bits of information will still necessarily be hand lettered to complete the title. Figure 31.27 shows several examples of architectural titles.

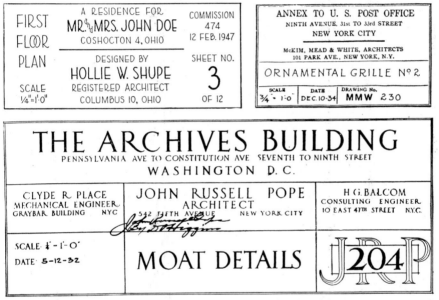

Fig. 31.27. Architectural working drawing titles.

A complete title will contain the following items of information:

1. Name and location of the building.
2. Kind of view (as "First Floor Plan") and scale.
3. Name and address of the client.
4. Name and address of the architect.
5. Sheet number.
6. Office record to include: draftsman's and checker's initials and dates.

31.19 Shop drawings. The purchase of special items of equipment for installation in a building will often result in the architect requiring that *shop drawings* be prepared by the equipment manufacturers. Such drawings will show over-all sizes, details of construction, methods for securing the equipment to the structure, and any other pertinent data the architect will need for the final positioning of that equipment.

31.20 Specifications, notes, and schedules. Architectural drawings are amplified by a document called the "specifications," a detailed account of material and workmanship, for the many parts of a completed structure. Since the workmen on the job seldom see these specifications, they should be briefed and given, as notes or schedules, on the working drawing sheets. An example of a schedule is shown in Fig. 31.28: a partial door schedule

	W.	H.	T.	TYPE	MATERIAL	GLASS	REMARKS
A	3'-0"	8'-4"	Std.	Solid	Steel	—	"Vulcan" Stor. Rm. Door
B	3'-6"	7'-6"	1¾	10 Pan.	Kalamein	—	
C	2'-6"	"	"	"	"	—	
D	3'-6"	"	"	Glaz.	"	Cl. Wr.	
E	2'-2"	7'-0"	1⅜	"	Hol. Met.	"	2 Speed Sliding
F	5'-4"	8'-4"	Std.	Tin Clad	Steel	—	"
G	3'-6"	7'-6"	1¾	Glaz.	Hol. Met.	Cl. Wr.	
H	2'-8"	6'-8"	"	1 Pan.	Kalamein	—	Stock
I	4'-0"	9'-0"	2¼	10 Pan.	Wh. Pine	Plate	2 Sp. Bi-Part. Sl.
J	2'-10"	7'-0"	"	Glaz.	"	"	
K	3'-0"	"	1¾	10 Pan.	Wood	—	
L	"	"	"	Glaz.	"	Tap.	

Fig. 31.28. Door schedule.

that was taken from the working drawings for the municipal building, whose sectional elevation is shown in Fig. 31.22.

31.21 Checking. As the architect develops the working drawings, he keeps a constant check for accuracy in his work. A tentatively final set of blueprints is then gone over by a responsible checker, who will check all correct items and mark with red pencil all mistakes. The drawings are then corrected, and another check set of blueprints is prepared.

All checking should be done in a definite order with each item followed through separately and systematically. This order will be dictated by the checker's preference, or by conditions of the problem. The following is a suggested guide:

1. Check over-all dimensions on the plans, seeing that all plans agree.
2. Check structural dimensions on the plans, seeing that column centers line up through the several stories.
3. Check location dimensions on the plans, seeing that openings line up vertically and that axes of communication are maintained by proper horizontal positioning of the openings.
4. See that detail drawings are dimensioned to correspond to the dimensions of the plan and will allow for proper fitting with adjacent features.
5. Check all doors for proper size and swing.
6. Check design and notation for all structural members.
7. Check sizes and locations of all ducts and flues.
8. Check location and notation of electrical outlets and switching for same.
9. See that several items are not indicated for the same location. For example, wiring to a switch should not share wall space with a heat duct.
10. See that all notes are complete and accurate.
11. Check the specifications with the drawings, making sure that no discrepancy exists and that the specifications are complete in every detail.
12. Check for conformity with building codes and laws.

PROBLEMS

1. Prepare a preliminary sketch plan for a vacation cottage to meet the following requirements: kitchen-dining area (approximately 140 sq ft of floor space); living-recreation area (approximately 280 sq ft); two bunk rooms (approximately 70 sq ft each);

bathroom; four closets (one for each bunk room, one for outer garments, and one for linens); and a porch. Scale: $\frac{1}{16}'' = 1'-0''$. It is recommended that the plan be developed on $\frac{1}{4}$-in. coordinate paper using sketch technique.

2. Prepare a preliminary sketch plan for a gasoline service station to be located on a corner lot (100×175 ft). Scale: $\frac{1}{16}'' = 1'-0''$. Requirements: office-salesroom; one lubrication rack; one wash rack; work space for battery charging, tire repair, etc.; two restrooms (women's restroom to be entered from the outside); two air stations; and two gasoline islands, each with three pumps.

3. Prepare a presentation perspective drawing of the house shown in Figs. 31.12 through 31.18. Scale $\frac{1}{4}'' = 1'-0''$. Picture plane to make an angle of 30° with the front wall and to contain the left front corner of the house. Perspective to show the front and left side walls. Horizon: $5'-6''$ above the finished grade.

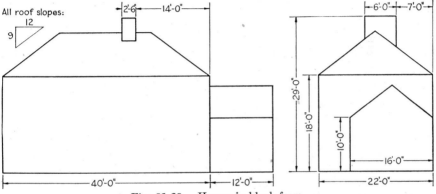

Fig. 31.29.   House, in block form.

4. Make a paper model of the house shown in block form in Fig. 31.29. Scale of model: $\frac{1}{8}'' = 1'-0''$. Mount on cardboard base. Optional requirement: Draw windows and doors on all walls, after the instructor has approved preliminary first- and second-floor plans.

5. Prepare the working drawing details for a fireplace having a 40 in. wide by 29 in. high opening. Scale of drawings: $\frac{3}{4}'' = 1'-0''$. Refer to fireplace-equipment manufacturers' catalogues and architectural handbooks for necessary data.

6. Make an isometric drawing of the piping for the house shown in Figs. 31.12 through 31.18. Scale: $\frac{1}{2}'' = 1'-0''$. Determine pipe sizes from published laws governing plumbing and drainage and from architectural handbooks; note pipe sizes on the isometric. (See Chap. 25 on Piping Drawings.)

7. Draw a completed plot plan showing the house of scheme A, Fig. 31.3, positioned on the lot shown in Fig. 31.30. Scale $\frac{1}{8}'' = 1'-0''$.

8. Complete the working drawings for the garage shown in Fig. 31.31.

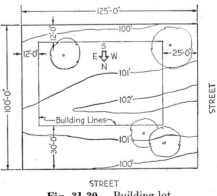

Fig. 31.30.   Building lot.

9. Prepare the working drawings for the week-end cottage shown in Fig. 31.32. Scale of elevation and plan: $\frac{1}{4}'' = 1'-0''$. Scale of wall section and fireplace details: $\frac{3}{4}'' = 1'-0''$. Scale of cornice, door, and window details: $1\frac{1}{2}'' = 1'-0''$.

10. (a) Prepare preliminary plan and elevations for a shelterhouse having a floor area approximately 24 by 40 ft. One end of the shelterhouse to have a large fireplace. Materials of constructions: stone and heavy timbers. (b) After preliminary drawings have been approved by the instructor, prepare the working drawings for the shelterhouse.

11. Complete the set of working drawings for the house shown in Figs. 31.12 through 31.18. Required views are listed in paragraph 31.11.

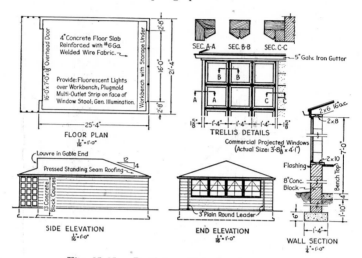

Fig. 31.31.   Partial working drawings, garage.

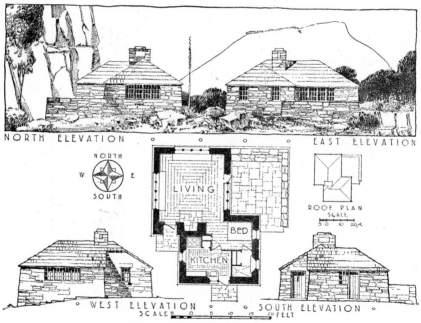

Fig. 31.32.   Week-end cottage.

32

Map and Topographic Drawing

32.1 Thus far in our consideration of drawing as a graphic language we have had to represent the three dimensions of an object either pictorially or, in the usual case, by drawing two or more views of it. In map drawing, that is, the representation of features on parts of the earth's surface, there is the distinct difference that the drawing is complete in one view, the third dimension, the height, being either represented on this view or omitted as not required for the particular purpose for which the map was made.

The surveying and mapping of the site is the first preliminary work in engineering projects, and it is desirable that all engineers should be familiar with the methods and symbols used in this branch of drawing. Without considering the practice of surveying and plotting or the various methods used by the cartographers in projecting the curved surface of the earth on a plane, we are interested in the use and details of execution of plats and topographic maps.

32.2 Classification. The content or information on maps may be classified in general under three divisions:

1. The representation of imaginary lines, such as divisions between areas subject to different authority or ownership, either public or private; or lines indicating geometric measurements on the land, on the sea, and in the air. In this division may be included plats or land maps, farm surveys, city subdivisions, plats of mineral claims, and nautical and aeronautical charts.
2. The representation of real or material features or objects within the limits of the tract, showing their relative location or size and location, depending upon the purpose of the map. When relative location only is required, the scale may be small, and symbols employed to represent objects, as houses, bridges, or even towns. When the size of the objects is an important consideration, the scale must be large and the map becomes a real orthographic top view.
3. The representation of the relative elevations of the surface of the ground. Maps with this feature are called "relief maps" or, if contours are used with elevations marked on them, "contour maps." Hydrographic maps show fathom-line depth curves.

Various combinations of these three divisions are required for different purposes. Classified according to their purpose, maps may be (*a*) geographic, (*b*) topographic, (*c*) hydrographic, (*d*) nautical, (*e*) aeronautical, (*f*) cadastral, (*g*) engineering, (*h*) photogrammetric, and (*i*) military.

a. Geographic maps include large areas and consequently must be to small scale. They show important towns and cities, streams and bodies of water, political boundaries, and relief.

b. Topographic maps are complete descriptions of certain areas and show to larger scale the geographical positions of the natural features and the works of man. The relief is usually represented by contours.

c. Hydrographic maps deal with information concerning bodies of water, as shore lines, sounding depths, subaqueous contours, navigation aids, and water control.

d. Nautical maps or charts are designed to show aids to water navigation, as buoys, beacons, lighthouses, lanes of traffic, sounding depths, shoals, and radio compass stations.

e. Aeronautical maps or charts provide prominent landmarks of the terrain and accentuate the relief by layer tints, hachures, and 500- or 1,000-ft contours as aids to air navigation.

f. Cadastral maps are very accurate control maps for cities and towns, made to large scale with all features drawn to size. They are used to control city development and operation, particularly taxation.

g. Engineering maps are working maps for engineering projects and are designed for specific purposes to aid construction. They provide accurate horizontal and vertical control data and show objects on the site or along the right of way.

h. Photogrammetric maps represent features on the earth's surface from terrestrial and aerial photographs. These photographs are perspectives from which orthographic views are obtained by stereoscopic instruments. Ground-control stations are necessary to bring the photographs to a required datum.

i. Military maps are designed to contain information of military importance in the area represented.

32.3 Plats. A map plotted from a plane survey, and having the third dimension omitted, is called a "plat" or "land map." It is used in the description of any tract of land when it is not necessary to show relief, as in such typical examples as a farm survey or a city plat.

The plotting is done from field notes by (1) latitudes and departures, (2) bearings and distances, (3) azimuths and distances, (4) deflection angles and distances, or (5) rectangular coordinates. Or the plotting is done by the total latitude and departure from some fixed origin for each separate point, which method is necessary to distribute plotting errors over the entire survey. Angles are laid off from bearing or azimuth lines by plotting the tangent of the angle or the sine of half the angle, by sine-and-cosine method, or by an accurate protractor.

The first principle to be observed in the execution of this kind of drawings is *simplicity*. Its information should be clear, concise, and direct. The lettering should be done in single stroke, and the north point and border should be of the simplest character. The day of the intricate border corner, elaborate north point, and ornamental title is, happily, past, and all such embellishments are rightly considered not only as a waste of time but as being in very bad taste.

32.4 Plat of a survey. The plat of a survey should give clearly all the information necessary for the legal description of the parcel of land. It should contain

1. Direction and length of each line.
2. Acreage.
3. Location and description of monuments found and set.
4. Location of highways, streams, rights of way, and any appurtenances required.
5. Official division lines within the tract.
6. Names of owners of abutting property.
7. Title, scale, date.

8. North point with certification of horizontal control.
9. Plat certification properly executed.
10. Reference to state plane-coordinate system.

Figure 32.1 illustrates the general treatment of this kind of drawing. It is almost always traced and blueprinted, and no water-lining of streams

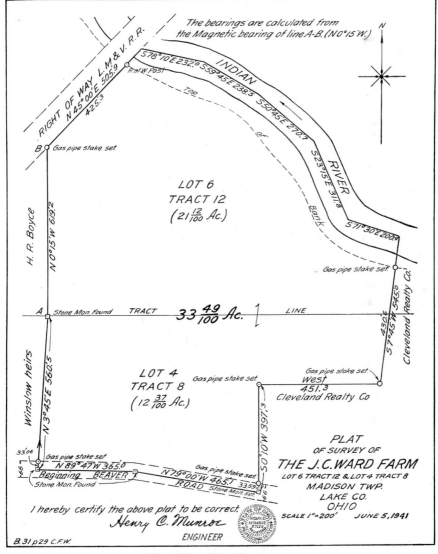

Fig. 32.1. Plat of a survey.

or other elaboration should be attempted. It is important to observe that the size of the lettering used for the several features must be in proportion to their importance.

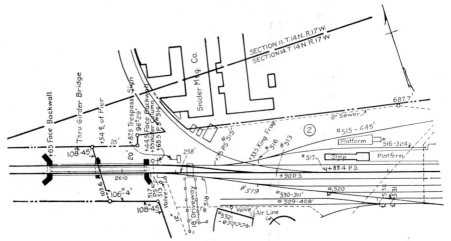

Fig. 32.2.   Part of a railroad property map.

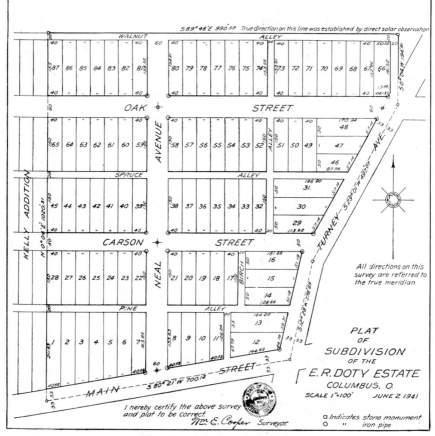

Fig. 32.3.   A city subdivision.

32.5 A railroad property map. Of the many kinds of plats used in industrial work one only is illustrated here, a portion of a railway situation or station map, Fig. 32.2. This might represent also a plant-valuation map, a type of plat often required. The information on such maps varies to meet the requirements of particular cases. In addition to the preceding list, it might include such items as pipe lines, fire hydrants, location and description of buildings, railroads and switch points, outdoor crane runways, etc.

32.6 Plats of subdivisions. The plats of subdivisions and allotments in cities are filed with the county recorder for record and must be very complete in their information concerning the location and size of the various lots and parcels composing the subdivisions, Fig. 32.3. All monuments set should be shown and all directions and distances recorded, so that it will be possible to locate any lot with precision.

Sometimes landowners desire to use these maps in display to prospective buyers and often include a blueprint or black-line print bound with the

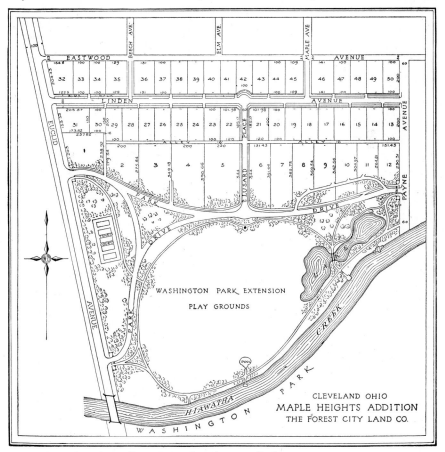

Fig. 32.4. A real-estate display map.

deed.   Some degree of embellishment is allowable, but care must be taken
not to overdo the ornamentation.   Figure 32.4 is an example showing an
acceptable style of execution and finish.

32.7   City plats.   Under this head are included chiefly maps or plats
drawn from subdivision plats or other sources for the record of city improvements.   These plats are used to record a variety of information, such as
the location of sewers, water mains, gas, power and steam lines, telephone
installations, and street improvements.

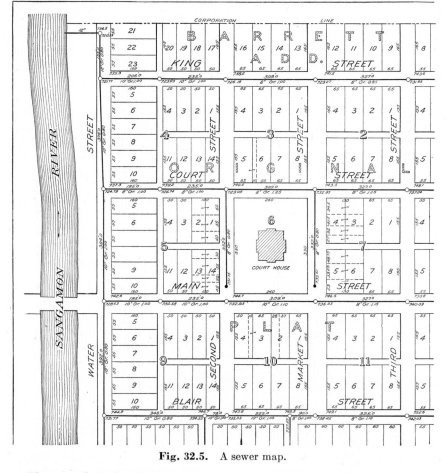

Fig. 32.5.   A sewer map.

The records maintained on these maps provide valuable data for assess-
ments and constitute progress reports on the growth of a city.   As they are
made for a definite purpose, they should not contain unnecessary information
and hence will not include all the details as to sizes of lots, which are given
on subdivision plats, but they should carry both horizontal and vertical
control points for proper location of utilities.   They are usually made on
mounted paper and should be to a scale large enough to show clearly the

features required; 100 and 200 ft to the inch are common scales, and as large as 50 ft is sometimes used.   For smaller cities the entire area may be covered by one map; for larger cities the maps are made in convenient sections so as to be filed readily.

A study of Fig. 32.5, a sewer map, will show the general treatment of such plats.   The appearance of the drawing is improved by adding shade

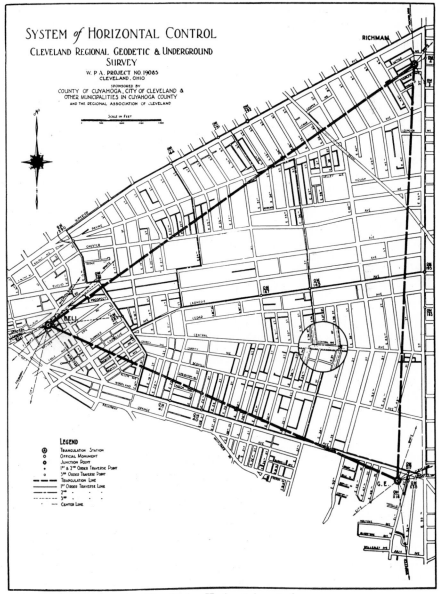

Fig. 32.6.   Horizontal control.

lines on the lower and right-hand side of the blocks, that is, treating the streets and water features as depressions. A few of the more important public buildings are shown, to facilitate reading. The various wards, subdivisions, or districts may be shown by large outline letters or numerals as illustrated in the figure. Contours are often put on these maps in red or brown ink, either on the original or sometimes on a positive print from it. Figure 32.6 shows a modern system of horizontal control used by the city of Cleveland for a geodetic and underground survey.

32.8 Topographic drawing. As before defined, a complete topographic map would contain

1. The imaginary lines indicating the divisions of authority or ownership.
2. The geographical position of both the natural features and the works of man. They may also include information in regard to the vegetation.
3. The relief, or indication of the relative elevations and depressions. The relief, which is the third dimension, is represented in general either by contours or by hill shading.

32.9 Contours. A contour is an imaginary line on the surface of the

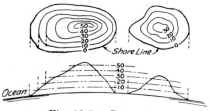

Fig. 32.7. Contours.

ground which, at every point, passes through the same elevation; thus the shore line of a body of water represents a contour. If the water should rise 1 ft, the new shore line would be another contour, with 1-ft "contour interval." A series of contours may thus be illustrated approximately as in Fig. 32.7.

Figure 32.8 is a perspective view of a tract of land. Figure 32.9 is a contour map of this area, and Fig. 32.10 is the same surface shown with hill

Fig. 32.8. Perspective view.

shading by hachures. Contours are drawn as fine full lines, with every fifth one of heavier weight and with the elevations in feet marked on them at intervals, usually with the sea level as datum. They may be drawn with a swivel pen, Fig. 35.7, or a fine pen such as Gillott's 170 or Esterbrook's 356. On paper drawings they are usually made in brown.

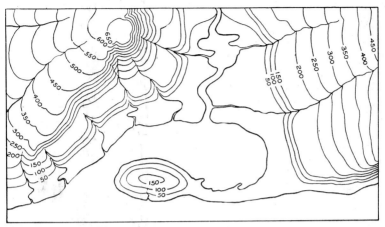

Fig. 32.9. Application of contour lines.

Figure 32.11 is a topographic map of the site of a proposed filtration plant and illustrates the use of the contour map as the necessary preliminary drawing for engineering projects. Often on the same drawing there are shown, by lines of different character, both the existing contours and the required finished grades.

Fig. 32.10. Application of hachures for hill shading.

32.10 Hill shading. The showing of relief by means of hill shading gives a pleasing effect but is very difficult of execution, does not give exact elevations, and would not be applied on maps to be used for engineering purposes. It may sometimes be used to advantage in reconnaissance maps or in small-scale maps for illustration. There are several systems, of which hachuring, as shown in Fig. 32.10, is the commonest. The contours are sketched lightly in pencil and the hachures drawn perpendicular to them, starting at the summit and grading the weight of line to the degree of slope. A scale of hachures to use for reference is often made, graded from black for 45° to white for horizontal. The rows of strokes should touch the pencil line to avoid white streaks along the contours. Two other systems in use are the horizontal, or English system, using graded hachure lines parallel to the contours, and the oblique illumination, or French system, using hachures graded to give sunlight effect as well as the degree of slope.

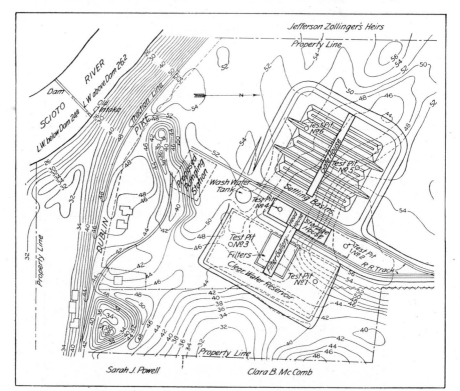

Fig. 32.11.   Contour map for an engineering project.

32.11 Water lining. On topographic maps made for display or reproduction, the water features are usually finished by "water lining," that is, by running a system of fine lines parallel to the shore lines, either in black or in blue (it must be remembered that blue will not photograph for reproduction or print well from a tracing). Poor water lining will ruin the appearance of an otherwise well-executed map, and it is better to omit it rather than do it hastily or carelessly. The shore line is drawn first, and the water lining done with a fine mapping pen, the draftsman always drawing toward his body, with the preceding line to his left. The first line should follow the shore line very closely, and the distances between the succeeding lines should be gradually increased and the irregularities lessened. Sometimes the weight of lines is graded as well as the intervals, but this is a very difficult operation and is not necessary for the effect. A common mistake is to make the lines excessively wavy or rippled.

In water-lining a stream of varying width, the lines are not to be crowded so as to be carried through the narrower portions, but corresponding lines must be brought together in the middle of the stream as illustrated in Fig. 32.10. Care should be taken to avoid spots of sudden increase or decrease in spacing.

32.12 Topographic symbols. The various symbols used in topographic drawing may be grouped under four heads:

1. Culture, or the works of man.
2. Relief—relative elevations and depressions.
3. Water features.
4. Vegetation.

When color is used the culture is done in black, the relief in brown, the water features in blue, and the vegetation in black or green.

These symbols, used to represent characteristics on the earth's surface, are made, when possible, to resemble somewhat the features or objects represented as they would appear either in plan or in elevation. No attempt is here made to give symbols for all the features that might occur in a map; indeed one may have to invent symbols for some particular locality.

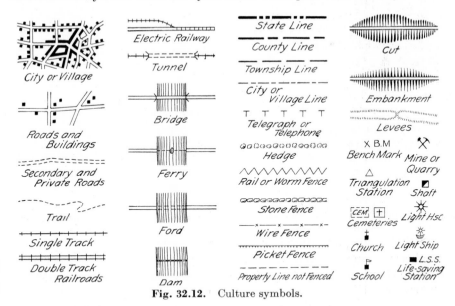

Fig. 32.12. Culture symbols.

Figure 32.12 illustrates a few of the conventional symbols used for culture, or the works of man, and no suggestion is needed as to the method of their execution. When the scale used is large, houses, bridges, roads, and even tree trunks can be plotted so that their principal dimensions can be scaled. The landscape architect is interested not only in the size of the trunk of a tree but also in the spread of its branches. A small-scale map can give by its symbols only the relative locations.

Some military symbols are shown in Fig. 32.13, symbols for aerial navigation in Fig. 32.14, and aids to water navigation in Fig. 32.15, all as adopted

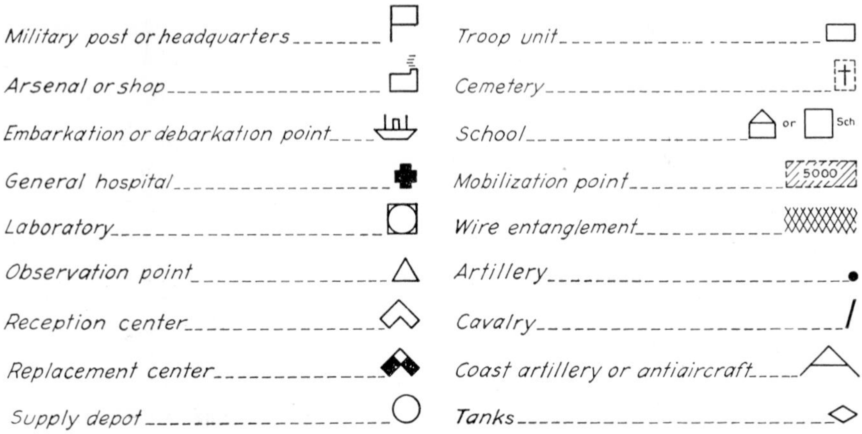

Military post or headquarters _____	⌐	Troop unit _____	▭
Arsenal or shop _____	◻	Cemetery _____	🇹
Embarkation or debarkation point ____	⛴	School _____	△ or ◻ Sch
General hospital _____	✚	Mobilization point _____	⬚5000
Laboratory _____	⬡	Wire entanglement _____	✕✕✕✕
Observation point _____	△	Artillery _____	●
Reception center _____	⬠	Cavalry _____	/
Replacement center _____	◆◆	Coast artillery or antiaircraft ____	△
Supply depot _____	◯	Tanks _____	◇

Fig. 32.13. Military symbols.

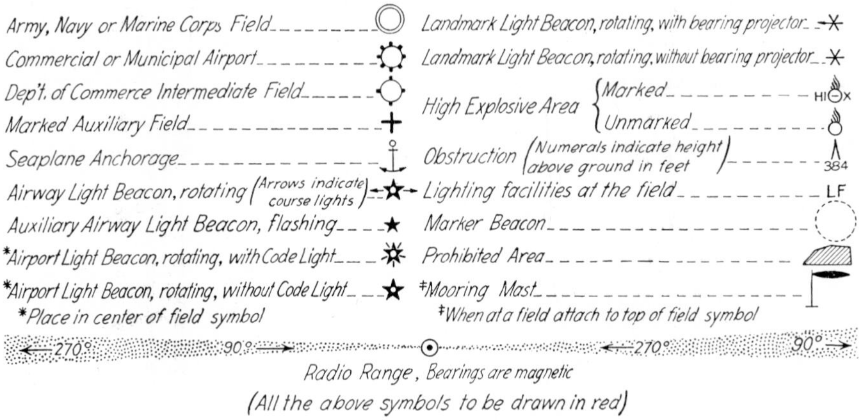

Army, Navy or Marine Corps Field _____	◎	Landmark Light Beacon, rotating, with bearing projector. ✳
Commercial or Municipal Airport _____	✵	Landmark Light Beacon, rotating, without bearing projector. ✳
Dep't. of Commerce Intermediate Field _____	◇	High Explosive Area {Marked _____ HI◯x
Marked Auxiliary Field _____	+	{Unmarked _____ ◯
Seaplane Anchorage _____	⚓	Obstruction (Numerals indicate height above ground in feet) ____ 384
Airway Light Beacon, rotating (Arrows indicate course lights)	✦	Lighting facilities at the field _____ LF
Auxiliary Airway Light Beacon, flashing ___	★	Marker Beacon _____ ◯
*Airport Light Beacon, rotating, with Code Light ___	✺	Prohibited Area _____
*Airport Light Beacon, rotating, without Code Light __	✫	‡Mooring Mast _____
*Place in center of field symbol		‡When at a field attach to top of field symbol

←270° _____ 90°→ _____ ⊙ _____ ←270° _____ 90°→

Radio Range, Bearings are magnetic

(All the above symbols to be drawn in red)

Fig. 32.14. Aviation symbols.

by the U.S. Board of Surveys and Maps. Figure 32.16 gives the standard symbols used in the development of oil and gas fields, Fig. 32.17 the symbols used to show relief, Fig. 32.18 water features, and Fig. 32.19 some of the commoner symbols for vegetation and cultivation.

The draftsman should keep in mind the purpose of the map and in some measure indicate the relative importance of the features, varying their prominence by the weights of lines used or sometimes by varying the scale of the symbol. For instance, in a map made for military maneuvering, a corn-field might be an important feature; or in maps made to show the location of special features, such as fire hydrants, these objects would be indicated

very plainly.   The map of an airport or a golf course would contain emphasized features.   This principle calls for some originality to meet various
cases.

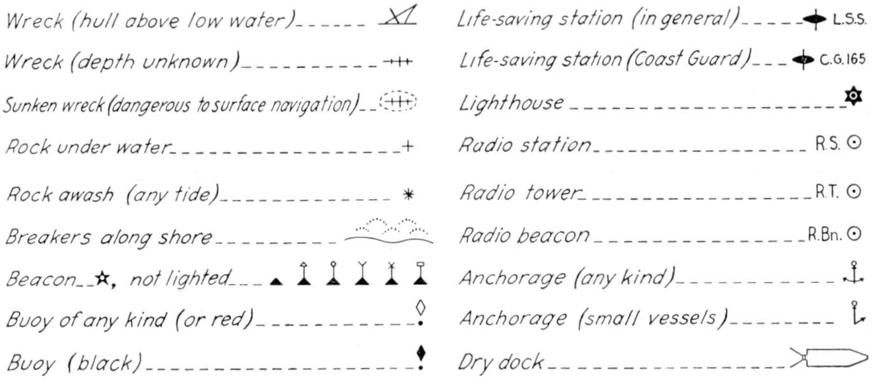

Wreck (hull above low water)_____	✗⌐	Life-saving station (in general)____◄ L.S.S.	
Wreck (depth unknown)_____ +++		Life-saving station (Coast Guard)___◄ C.G.165	
Sunken wreck (dangerous to surface navigation)_⊕		Lighthouse _____ ✿	
Rock under water_____ +		Radio station_____ R.S. ⊙	
Rock awash (any tide)_____ ✳		Radio tower_____ R.T. ⊙	
Breakers along shore_____ ⌒		Radio beacon_____ R.Bn. ⊙	
Beacon__✭, not lighted___ ▲ ⚓ ⚓ ⚓ ⚓ ⚓		Anchorage (any kind)_____ ⚓	
Buoy of any kind (or red)_____ ◊		Anchorage (small vessels)_____ ⚓	
Buoy (black)_____ ●		Dry dock _____ ▷═▭	

Fig. 32.15.   Symbols for water-navigation aids.

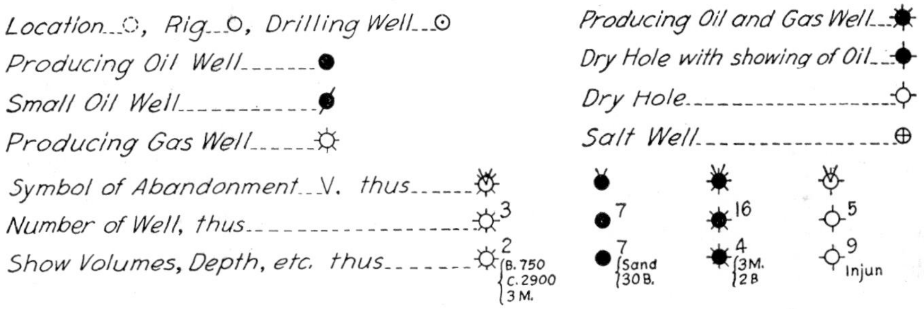

Location__○, Rig__○, Drilling Well__⊙	Producing Oil and Gas Well__✸
Producing Oil Well_____●	Dry Hole with showing of Oil__♦
Small Oil Well_____◖	Dry Hole_____○
Producing Gas Well_____✧	Salt Well_____⊕
Symbol of Abandonment__V. thus_____✻	
Number of Well, thus_____✻³	
Show Volumes, Depth, etc. thus_____✻² {B.750 {C.2900 {3 M.	

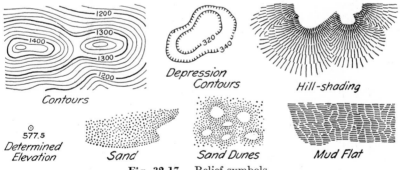

Fig. 32.16.   Oil and gas symbols.

Contours
1200
1300
1400
1300
1200

Depression
Contours
320
340

Hill-shading

⊙
577.5
Determined
Elevation

Sand

Sand Dunes

Mud Flat

Fig. 32.17.   Relief symbols.

A common fault of the beginner is to make symbols too large.   The
symbols for grass, shown under "meadow," Fig. 32.19, if not made and
spaced correctly will spoil the entire map.   This symbol is composed of
five to seven short strokes radiating from a common center and starting
along a horizontal line as shown in the enlarged form, each tuft beginning

and ending with a mere dot. Always place the tufts with the bottom parallel to the border and distribute them uniformly over the space, but not in rows. A few incomplete tufts or rows of dots improve the appear-

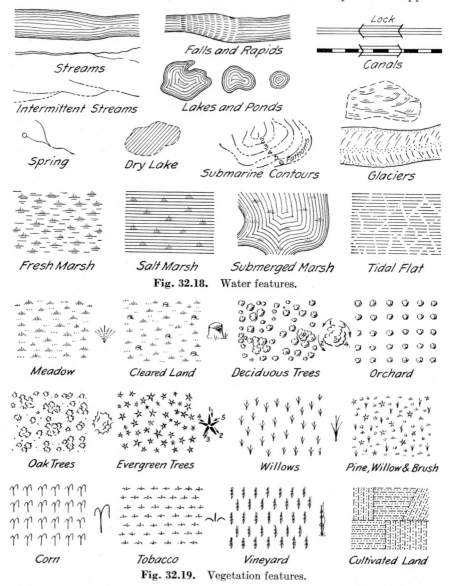

Fig. 32.18. Water features.

Fig. 32.19. Vegetation features.

ance. Grass-tuft symbols should never be as heavy as tree symbols. In drawing the symbol for deciduous trees the sequence of strokes shown should be followed.

The topographic map, Fig. 32.20, is given to illustrate the general execution and placing of symbols.

The well-known maps of the U.S. Coast and Geodetic Survey and the Geological Survey illustrate the application of topographic drawing. The *quadrangle sheets* issued by the topographic branch of the U.S. Geological Survey are excellent examples and so easily available that every draftsman should be familiar with them. These sheets represent 15 minutes of latitude and 15 minutes of longitude to the scale of 1:62,500 or approximately 1 in. to the mile. The entire United States is being mapped by the depart-

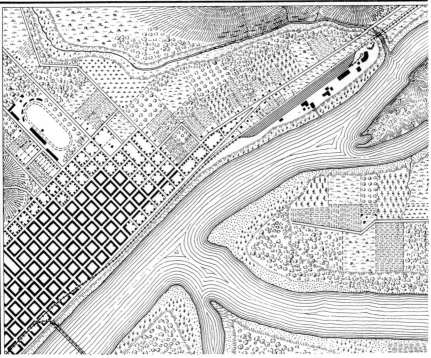

Fig. 32.20.   Part of a topographic map.

ment in cooperation with the different states. This work is now greatly facilitated through the use of aerial photography. Much territory in the West and South has been mapped ½ in. to the mile, and earlier some in the West was mapped ¼ in. to the mile. These maps may be secured by addressing The Director, U.S. Geological Survey, Washington, D.C., from whom information as to the completion of any particular locality or the progress in any state may be had.

32.13 Landscape maps.   A topographic map made to a relatively large scale and showing all details is called a "landscape map." Such maps are required by architects and landscape gardeners for use in planning buildings to fit the natural topographic features and for landscaping parks, playgrounds, and private estates. These are generally maps of small areas, and a scale of $1'' = 20'$ to $1'' = 50'$, depending upon the amount of detail, is used.

The contour interval varies from 6 in. to 2 ft according to the ruggedness of the surface. The commonest interval is 1 ft. These maps are often reproduced in black-line prints, upon which contours in different color are drawn to show the landscape treatment proposed. Natural features and culture are added in more detail than on ordinary topographic maps. Trees are designated as to size, species, and sometimes spread of branches and condition. It is often necessary to invent symbols suitable for the particular survey and to include a key or legend on the map. Roads, walks, streams, flower beds, houses, etc., should be plotted carefully to scale, so that measurements can be taken from them.

32.14 Colors. Instead of using colored inks, which are thin and unsatisfactory to handle in the pen and do not photograph or blueprint well, it is much better to use water colors for contours, streams, and other colored features in topographic mapping: for contours, burnt sienna, either straight or darkened with a drop of black, and mixed rather thick; for streams, Prussian blue; and for features in red, alizarin crimson. All work well in either crow-quill or contour pen and make good blueprints. Colors in tubes are more convenient than those in cakes or pans.

32.15 Lettering. The style of lettering on a topographic map will depend upon the purpose for which the map is made. If it is for construction purposes, such as a contour map for the study of municipal problems, street grades, plants, or railroads, the single-stroke Gothic and Reinhardt is to be preferred. For a finished map, vertical Modern Roman letters, as shown on page 24, capitals for important land features, and lower case for less-important features, such as small towns and villages; inclined Roman and stump letters, as shown on page 26, for water features, should be used. The scale should always be drawn as well as stated.

32.16 Titles. The standard letter for finished map titles is the Modern Roman. The design should be symmetrical, with the heights of the letters proportioned to the relative importance of the line. A map title should contain as many as are necessary of the following items:

1. Kind—"Map of," etc.
2. Name.
3. Location of tract.
4. Purpose, if special features are represented.
5. For whom made.
6. Engineer in charge.
7. Date (of survey).
8. Scale—stated and drawn; contour interval; datum.
9. Authorities.
10. Legend or key to symbols.
11. North point, with certification of horizontal control.
12. Certification, properly executed.
13. Reference to state plane-coordinate system.

32.17 Profiles. Perhaps no kind of drawing is used more by civil engineers than the ordinary profile, which is simply a vertical section taken along a given line, either straight or curved. Such drawings are indispensable in problems of railroad construction, highway and street improvements, sewer construction, and many other problems where a study of the surface of the ground is required. Very frequently engineers other than civil engineers are called upon to make these drawings. Several different types of profile and cross-section paper are in use, and their descriptions may be found in the catalogues of the various firms dealing in drawing materials. One type of profile paper in common use is known as "Plate A" and has 4 divisions to the inch horizontally and 20 to the inch vertically. Other divisions in use are 4 × 30 to the inch and 5 × 25 to the inch. At intervals, both horizontally and vertically, somewhat heavier lines are made in order to facilitate reading.

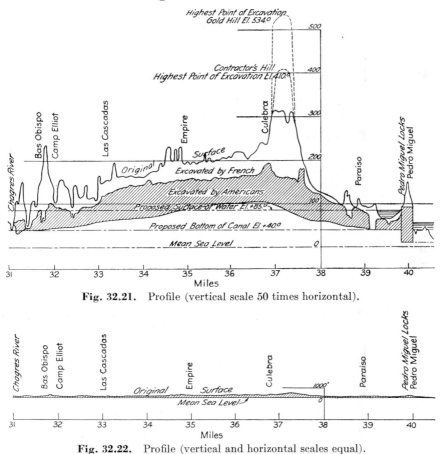

Fig. 32.21. Profile (vertical scale 50 times horizontal).

Fig. 32.22. Profile (vertical and horizontal scales equal).

Horizontal distances are plotted as abscissas and elevations as ordinates. Since the vertical distances represent elevations and are plotted to larger scale, a vertical exaggeration is obtained that is very useful in studying profiles that are to be used for establishing grades. The vertical exaggeration is sometimes confusing to the layman or inexperienced engineer, but ordinarily a profile will fail in the purpose for which it was intended if the horizontal and vertical scales are the same. Again, the profile, unless so

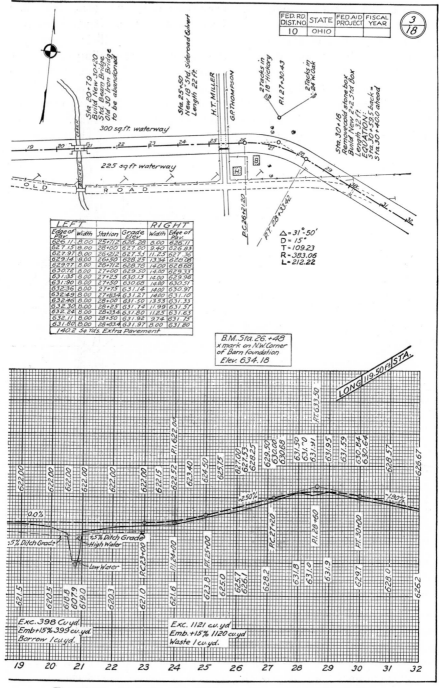

Fig. 32.23. Part of a State Highway Alignment and Profile Sheet.

distorted, would be a very long and unwieldy affair, if not entirely impossible to make.   The difference between profiles with and without vertical exaggeration is shown in Figs. 32.21 and 32.22.

Figure 32.23 is a portion of a typical State Highway Alignment and Profile Sheet, plotted to a horizontal scale of $1'' = 100'$ and a vertical scale of $1'' = 10'$.   For this type of drawing, tracing cloth is furnished with the coordinates printed in red on the back so that any changes or erasures on the profile will not damage the coordinate lines.   Lettering or other features are sometimes brought out by erasing the lines on the back.   This sheet is one of a set of drawings used for estimating cost and, by the contractor, as a working drawing during construction.   Other drawings in the set consist of a title sheet showing the location plan with detours provided, a sheet indicating conventional signs, a sheet giving an index to bound sheets, and a sheet with space reserved for declarations of approval and signatures of proper officials.

Also there are sheets of cross sections taken at each 100-ft station and all necessary intermediate stations to estimate earthwork for grading, working drawings for drainage structures, site plans for bridges, specifications for guard rails and other safety devices, standard or typical road sections for cut and fill and various other conditions; and finally summary sheets for separate tables and quantities of materials for roadway, pavement, and structures.

33

Charts, Graphs, and Diagrams

33.1 This chapter is given as an introduction to the use of graphical methods in tabulating data for analysis, solving problems, and presenting facts. It will indicate to the prospective engineer the uses and value of this application of graphics and suggest his further study of the subject.

For the purposes of presenting a series of quantitative facts quickly, the graphical chart is an excellent method. When properly constructed, charts, graphs, and diagrams constitute a powerful tool for computation, analysis of engineering data, and the presentation of statistics for comparison or prediction.

33.2 Classification. Charts, graphs, and diagrams may be divided roughly into two classes: (1) those used for purely technical purposes and (2) those used for popular appeal in advertising or the presentation of information. The engineer is concerned mainly with the first class, but he should have some acquaintance with the preparation and the influential possibilities of the second class. The aim here is to give a short study of the types with which engineers and those in allied professions should be familiar.

It is assumed that the reader is familiar with the use of rectangular coordinates and that the meaning of such terms as "axes," "ordinates," "abscissas," "coordinates," "variables," etc., is understood.

33.3 Rectilinear charts. As the greater part of chart work in experimental engineering is done on rectilinear graph paper, the student should become familiar with this form of chart early in his course. The rectilinear chart is made on a sheet ruled with equispaced horizontal lines crossing equispaced vertical lines. The spacing is optional, but commercial graph paper is divided into squares of $\frac{1}{20}$ in. with every fifth line heavier, to aid in plotting and reading. Sheets are printed with various other rulings, as 4, 6, 8, 12, and 16 divisions per inch.

It is universal practice to use the upper right-hand quadrant for plotting experimental-data curves, making the lower left-hand corner the origin. In case both positive and negative values of a function are to be plotted, as is the case with many mathematical curves, it is necessary to place the origin so as to include all desired values.

Figure 33.1 shows a usual form of rectilinear chart, such as might be made for inclusion in a written report.

33.4 Drawing the curve. In drawing graphs from experimental data, it is often a question whether the curve should pass through all the points plotted or strike a mean between them. In general, observed data not backed up by definite theory or mathematical law are shown by connecting the points plotted with straight lines as at A, Fig. 33.2. An empirical rela-

tionship between curve and plotted points may be used, as at *B*, when, in
the opinion of the engineer, the curve should exactly follow some points and
go to one side of others. Consistency of observation is indicated at *C*, in
which case the curve should closely follow a true theoretical curve.

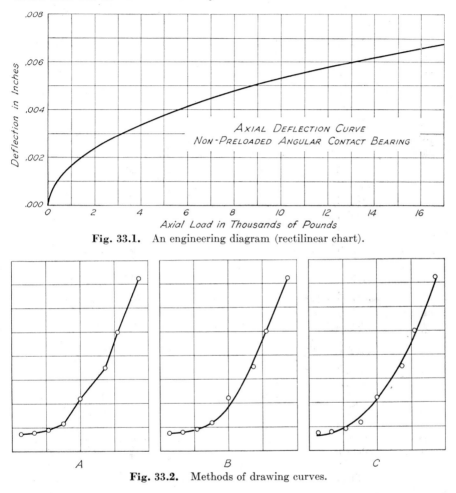

Fig. 33.1. An engineering diagram (rectilinear chart).

A   B   C

Fig. 33.2. Methods of drawing curves.

33.5 Titles and notation. The title is a very important part of a chart,
and its wording should be studied until it is clear and concise. In every case
it should contain sufficient description to tell what the chart is, the source or
authority, the name of the observer, and the date. Approved practice
places the title at the top of the sheet, arranged in phrases symmetrically
about a center line. If placed within the ruled space, a border line or box
should set it out from the sheet. Each sheet of curves should have a title,
and when more than one curve is shown on a sheet, the different curves
should be drawn so as to be easily distinguishable, by varying the character
of the lines, using full, dotted, and dot-and-dash lines, with a tabular key for

identification, or by lettering the names of the curves directly along them. When the charts are not intended for reproduction, inks of different colors may be used.

33.6 To draw a chart. In drawing a coordinate chart the general order is (1) compute and assemble all data; (2) determine size and kind of chart best adapted and whether printed or plain paper should be used; (3) determine, from the limits of the data, the scales for abscissas and ordinates to give the best effect to the resulting curve; (4) lay off the independent variable (often *time*) on the horizontal or X axis and the dependent variable on the vertical or Y axis; (5) plot points from the data and pencil the curves; (6) ink the curve; and (7) compose and letter title and coordinates.

The construction of a graphical chart requires good draftsmanship, especially for the lettering, but in engineering and scientific work the primary considerations are judgment in the proper selection of coordinates, accuracy in plotting points and drawing the graph, and an understanding of the functions and limitations of the resulting chart.

When the chart is drawn on a printed form, to be blueprinted, the curve may be drawn on the reverse side of the paper, enabling erasures to be made without injuring the ruled surface.

Green is becoming the standard color for printed forms. Blue will not print or photograph, and red is trying on the eyes.

If the curve is for purposes of computation, it should be drawn with a fine accurate line. If for demonstration, it should be fairly heavy, for contrast and effect.

The following rules are adapted from ASA Y-15 (formerly Z-15).

STANDARDS FOR GRAPHIC PRESENTATIONS

1. A graph should be free of all lines and lettering that are not essential to the reader's clear understanding of its message.

2. All lettering and numbers on a graph should be placed so as to be easily read from the bottom and from the right-hand side of the graph, not the left-hand side.

3. Standard abbreviations should be used where space is limited as, for example, in denoting the unit of measurement in scale captions.

4. The range of scales should be chosen so as to ensure effective and efficient use of the coordinate area in attaining the objective of the chart.

5. The zero line should be included if visual comparison of plotted magnitudes is desired.

6. When it is desired to show whether the rate of change of the dependent variable is increasing, constant, or decreasing, a logarithmic vertical scale should be used in conjunction with an arithmetic horizontal scale.

7. The horizontal (independent variable) scale values should usually increase from left to right and the vertical (dependent variable) scale values from bottom to top.

8. Scale values and scale captions should be placed outside the grid area, normally at the bottom for the horizontal scale and at the left side for the vertical scale. On wide graphs it may be desirable to repeat the vertical scale at the right side.

9. For arithmetic scales, the scale numbers shown on the graph and the space between coordinate rulings should preferably correspond to 1, 2, or 5 units of measurement, multiplied or divided by 1, 10, 100, etc.

10. The use of many digits in scale numbers should be avoided.

11. The scale caption should indicate both the variable measured and the unit of measurement. For example: EXPOSURE TIME IN DAYS.

12. Coordinate rulings should be limited in number to those necessary to guide the eye in making a reading to the desired degree of approximation. Closely spaced coordinate rulings are appropriate for computation charts but not for graphs intended primarily to show relationship.

13. Curves should preferably be represented by solid lines.

14. When more than one curve is presented on a graph, relative emphasis or differentiation of the curves may be secured by using different types of line, that is, solid, dashed, dotted, etc., or by different widths of line. A solid line is recommended for the most important curve.

15. The observed points should preferably be designated by circles.

16. Circles, squares, and triangles should be used rather than crosses or filled-in symbols to differentiate observed points of several curves on a graph.

17. Curves should, if practicable, be designated by brief labels placed close to the curves (horizontally or along the curves) rather than by letters, numbers, or other devices requiring a key.

18. If a key is used, it should preferably be placed within the grid in an isolated position, and enclosed by a light line border—grid lines, if convenient.

19. The title should be as clear and concise as possible. Explanatory material, if necessary to ensure clearness, should be added as a subtitle.

20. Scale captions, designations, curves, and blank spaces should, so far as practicable, be arranged to give a sense of balance around vertical and horizontal axes.

21. The appearance and the effectiveness of a graph depend in large measure on the relative widths of line used for its component parts. The widest line should be used for the principal curve. If several curves are presented on the same graph, the line width used for the curves should be less than that used when a single curve is presented.

22. A simple style of lettering, such as the gothic with its uniform line width and no serifs, should in general be used.

33.7 Logarithmic scales.

A very important type of chart is that in which the divisions, instead of being equally spaced, are made proportional to the logarithms of the numbers at the margin instead of to the numbers themselves. When ruled logarithmically in one direction with equal spacing at right angles, it is called "semilogarithmic."

Logarithmic spacing may be done directly from the graduations on one of the scales of a slide rule. Log paper is sold in various combinations of ruling. It may be had in one, two, three, or more cycles, or multiples of 10, also in part-cycle and split-cycle form. In using log paper, interpolations should be made logarithmically, not arithmetically as on rectangular coordinates, for arithmetical interpolation with coarse divisions might lead to considerable error.

33.8 Semilogarithmic chart.

This chart has equal spacing on one axis, usually the X axis, and logarithmic spacing on the other axis. Owing to a property by virtue of which the slope of the curve at any point is an exact measure of the rate of increase or decrease in the data plotted, it is frequently called a "ratio chart." Often called the "rate of change" chart as distinguished from the rectilinear or "amount of change" chart, it is extremely useful in statistical work as it shows at a glance the rate at which a variable changes. By the use of this chart it is possible to predict a trend, such as the future increase of a business, growth of population, etc.

In choosing between rectilinear ruling and semilog ruling, the important point to consider is whether the chart is to represent *numerical* increases and decreases or *percentage* increases and decreases. In many cases it is desired to emphasize the percentage or rate change, not the numerical change; hence a semilog chart should be used.

An example of the use of the semilog chart is illustrated in Fig. 33.3. This curve was drawn from data compiled for the *World Almanac*. The dash line shows the actual production by years, and the full line is the trend curve, the extension of which predicts future production.

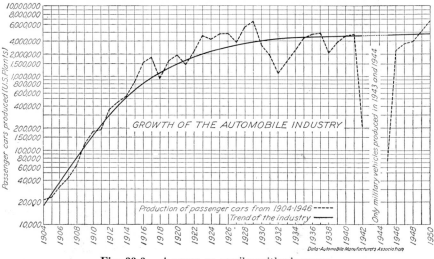

Fig. 33.3.   A curve on semilogarithmic paper.

33.9   Logarithmic charts with both abscissas and ordinates spaced logarithmically are used more for the solution of problems than for presenting facts. A property which distinguishes the logarithmic chart and accounts for its usefulness in so many cases is that the graphs of all algebraic equations representing multiplication, division, roots, and powers are straight lines. If the equation $x^2y = 16$ were plotted on ordinary rectangular coordinates, the resulting curve would be a hyperbola of the third degree with the x and y axes as asymptotes. By taking the logarithms of both sides of the given equation, it becomes $2 \log x + \log y = \log 16$. The equation now has the slope intercept form $y = mx + b$ and, if so desired, could be plotted on rectangular coordinates by substituting the logarithms of the variables. Obviously, it is easier to use logarithmic coordinates and plot the points directly than to take the logarithms of the variables and plot them on rectangular coordinates.

A feature of the logarithmic chart which makes it valuable for the study of many problems is that the exponent in the equation may be determined by measuring the slope of the graph. An inspection of the foregoing equations will show that the slope m, as given by the slope intercept form, is -2. The value of this exponent may be determined by direct measurement of the slope, using a uniformly graduated scale.

Figures 33.4 and 33.5 show an example of the use of a logarithmic chart in studying steam-engine performance. When the indicator card, Fig. 33.4,

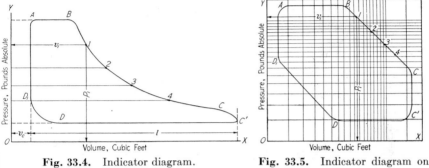

Fig. 33.4. Indicator diagram.

Fig. 33.5. Indicator diagram on log paper.

is plotted on log paper it takes the form shown in Fig. 33.5. The hyperbolas of a perfect card become straight lines, deviations from which indicate faults.

Figure 33.6 illustrates the use of multiple-cycle paper.

33.10 Polar chart. The use of polar coordinate paper for representing intensity of illumination, intensity of heat, polar forms of curves, etc., is common. Figure 33.7 shows a candle-power distribution curve for an ordinary Mazda B lamp and Fig. 33.8 the curve for a certain type of reflector. The candle power in any given direction is determined by reading off the distance from the origin to the curve. Use of these curves enables the determination of the foot-candle intensity at any point.

33.11 Trilinear chart. The trilinear chart, or "triaxial diagram" as it is sometimes called, affords a valuable means of studying the properties of

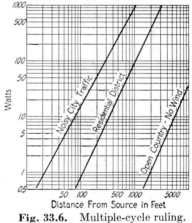

Fig. 33.6. Multiple-cycle ruling.

chemical compounds consisting of three elements, alloys of three metals or compounds, and mixtures containing three variables. The chart has the form of an equilateral triangle, the altitude of which represents 100 per cent of each of the three constituents. Figure 33.9, showing the ultimate tensile strength of copper-tin-zinc alloys, is a typical example of its application. The usefulness of such diagrams depends upon the geometrical principle that the sum of the perpendiculars to the sides from any point within an equilateral triangle is a constant and is equal to the altitude.

33.12   Choice of type and presentation.   The function of a chart is to reveal facts.   It may be entirely misleading if a wrong choice of paper or coordinates is taken.   The growth of an operation plotted on a rectilinear chart might, for example, entirely mislead an owner analyzing the trend of

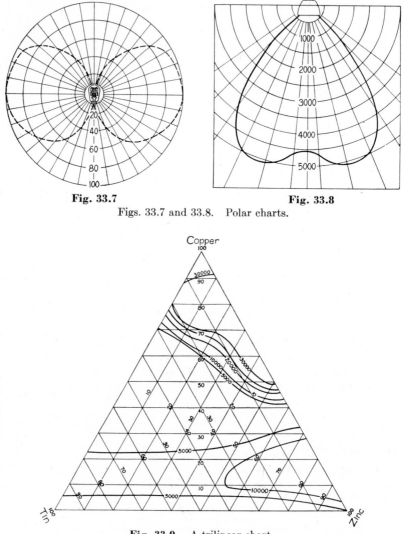

Fig. 33.7   Fig. 33.8

Figs. 33.7 and 33.8.   Polar charts.

Fig. 33.9.   A trilinear chart.

his business, while if plotted on a semilog chart it would give a true picture of conditions.   Intentionally misleading charts have been used many times in advertising matter, the commonest form being the chart with a greatly exaggerated vertical scale.   Naturally, in engineering work the facts must be presented honestly and with scientific accuracy.

33.13   Classification charts, route charts, and flow sheets.   The uses to which these three classes of charts may be put are widely different, but their underlying principles are similar and they have thus been grouped together for convenience.

A *classification chart,* as illustrated in Fig. 33.10, is intended to show the subdivisions of a whole and the interrelation of its parts to each other.   Such

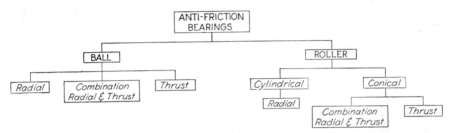

Fig. 33.10.   A classification chart.

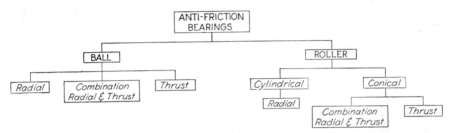

Fig. 33.11.   A flow sheet.

a chart often takes the place of a written outline, since it gives a better visualization of the facts than words alone would convey.   A common application is an organization chart of a corporation or business.   It is customary to enclose the names of the divisions in rectangles, although circles or other shapes may be used.   The rectangle has the advantage of being more convenient for lettering, while the circle may be drawn more quickly and possesses a greater popular appeal.   Often a combination of both is used.

The *route chart* is used mainly for the purpose of showing the various steps in a process, either of manufacturing or other business.   The *flow sheet* given in Fig. 33.11 is an example of a route chart applied to a chemical process.   Charts of this type show in a dynamic way facts which might require considerable study to compre-

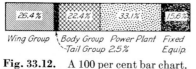

Fig. 33.12.   A 100 per cent bar chart.

hend from a written description.   A different form of route chart is that of Fig. 19.1, showing the course of a drawing through the shops.

33.14   Popular   charts.   Engineers and draftsmen are frequently called upon to prepare charts and diagrams which will be understood by diversified and nontechnical readers.   In many cases it is not advisable to present the facts by means of curves drawn on coordinate paper, although for the sake of greater effectiveness the resulting chart may suffer somewhat in accuracy. In preparing charts for popular use, particular care must be taken to make them so that the impression produced will be both quick and accurate.   It is to be remembered that such charts are seldom studied critically but are taken in at a glance; hence the method of presentation requires the exercise of careful judgment and the application of a certain amount of psychology.

33.15   Bar charts.   The bar chart is a very easily understood type for the nontechnical reader.   One of its simplest forms is the 100 *per cent bar* for showing the relations of the constituents to a given total.   Figure 33.12 is an example of this form of chart.   The different segments should be crosshatched, shaded, or distinguished in some effective man-ner,   the   percentage   represented placed on the diagram or directly opposite, and the meaning of each

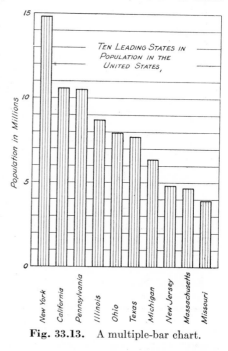

Fig. 33.13.   A multiple-bar chart.

segment clearly stated.   These bars may be placed either vertically or horizontally, the vertical position giving an advantage for lettering, and the horizontal position an advantage in readability, as the eye judges horizontal distances readily.

Figure 33.13 is an example of a *multiple-bar chart* in which the length of each bar is proportional to the magnitude of the quantity represented. Means should be provided for reading numerical values represented by the bars. If it is necessary to give the exact value represented by the individual bars, these values should not be lettered at the ends of the bars, since the apparent length would be increased. This type is made both horizontally, with the description at the base, and vertically. The vertical form is sometimes called the "pipe-organ chart." When vertical bars are drawn close together so as to touch along the sides, the diagram is called a "staircase chart." This is made oftener as the "staircase curve," a line plotted on coordinate paper representing the profile of the tops of the bars.

A *compound-bar chart* is made when it is desired to show two or more components in each bar. It is really a set of 100 per cent bars of different lengths set together either in pipe-organ or horizontal form.

33.16 Pie charts. The "pie diagram" or 100 per cent circle, Fig. 33.14, is much inferior to the bar chart but is used constantly because of its insistent popular appeal. It is a simple form of chart and, with the exception of the lettering, is easily constructed. It may be regarded as a 100 per cent bar bent into circular form. The circumference of the circle is divided into 100 parts, and sectors are used to represent per-

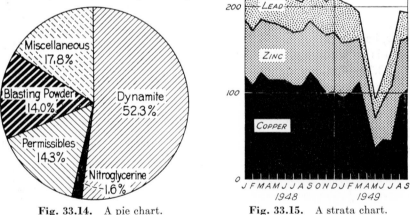

Fig. 33.14. A pie chart.   Fig. 33.15. A strata chart.

centages of the total. To be effective, this diagram must be carefully lettered and the percentages marked on the sectors or at the circumference opposite the sectors. For contrast it is best to crosshatch or shade the individual sectors. If the original drawing is to be displayed, the sectors may be colored and the diagram supplied with a key showing the meaning of each color. In every case the percentage notation should be placed where it can be read without removing the eyes from the diagram.

33.17 Strata and volume diagrams. The use of strata and volume diagrams has been very common, although they are usually the most deceptive of the graphic methods of representation. Figure 33.15 shows a strata chart showing a change in amounts over a period of time. The area between the curves is shaded to emphasize each variable represented. However, in reading it should be remembered that the areas *between* curves have no significance.

33.18 Pictorial charts. Pictorial charts were formerly much used for comparisons, such as costs, populations, standing armies, livestock, and various products. It was customary to represent the data by human or other figures, whose heights were proportional to the numerical values, or by silhouettes of the animals or products concerned, whose heights or sometimes areas were proportional. Since volumes vary as the cubes of the linear dimensions, such charts are grossly misleading. For such compari-

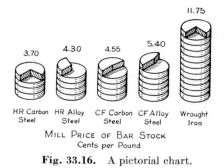

Fig. 33.16. A pictorial chart.

sons, bar charts or charts such as Fig. 33.16, where the diameter of the column is constant, should be used.

33.19 Charts for reproduction. Charts for reproduction by the zinc-etching process should be carefully penciled to about twice the size of the required cut (see Drawing for Reproduction, paragraph 34.13). In inking, first ink circles around plotted points, second, ink the curves with strong lines. A border pen is useful for heavy lines, and a Payzant pen may be used to advantage, particularly with dotted lines. Third, ink the title box and all lettering; fourth, ink the coordinates with fine black lines, putting in only as many as are necessary for easy reading, and breaking them wherever they interfere with title or lettering or where they cross plotted points.

33.20 Charts for display. Large charts for demonstration purposes are sometimes required. These may be drawn on sheets 22 by 28 in. or 28 by 44 in. known as "printer's blanks." The quickest way to make them is with the show-card colors and single-stroke sign-writer's brushes. Large bar charts may be made with strips of black adhesive tape. Lettering may be done with the brush or with gummed letters.

PROBLEMS

The following problems are given as suggestive of various types for both technical and popular presentation.

1. In a tension test of a machine-steel bar the following data were obtained:

Applied Load, Pounds per Square Inch	Elongation per Inch of Length
0	0
3,000	0.00011
5,000	0.00018
10,000	0.00033
15,000	0.00051
20,000	0.00067
25,000	0.00083
30,000	0.00099
35,000	0.00115
40,000	0.00134
42,000	0.00142

Plot the foregoing data on rectangular coordinates using the elongation as the independent variable and the applied load as the dependent variable.

2. A test of the corrosive effect of 5 per cent sulphuric acid, both air-free and air-saturated, on 70 per cent nickel 30 per cent copper alloy (Monel) over a temperature range from 20 to 120°C resulted in the data tabulated below. Plot this data on rectangular coordinates with corrosion rate as ordinate versus temperature as abscissa.

Temperature, °C	Corrosion rate in MDD (mg/sq decimeter/day)	
	Acid saturated with air	Acid air free, saturated with N_2
20	195	35
30	240	45
40	315	50
50	425	63
60	565	70
70	670	74
80	725	72
83	715	70
85	700	68
92	580	57
95	470	42
101	60	12

3. In testing a small 1-kw transformer for efficiency at various loads, the following data were obtained:

Watts Delivered	Losses
948	73
728	62
458	53
252	49
000	47

Plot curves on rectangular coordinate paper showing the relation between percentage of load and efficiency, using watts delivered as the independent variable and remembering that efficiency = output ÷ (output + losses).

4. The following data were obtained from a test of an automobile engine:

Rpm	Length of run, min	Fuel per run, lb	Brake horsepower
1,006	11.08	1.0	5.5
1,001	4.25	0.5	8.5
997	7.53	1.0	13.0
1,000	5.77	1.0	16.3
1,002	2.38	0.5	21.1

Plot curves on rectangular coordinate paper showing the relation between fuel used per brake horsepower-hour and brake horsepower developed. Show also the relation between thermal efficiency and brake horsepower developed, assuming the heat value of the gasoline to be 19,000 British thermal units per pound.

5. During the year 1950, the consumption of wood pulp by various grades in the United States was as follows:

Grade of Pulp	Consumption in Paper and Board Manufacture, Tons
Sulphate......................	8,380,864
Sulphite......................	3,331,668
Groundwood...................	2,483,980
Defibrated, exploded, etc.........	971,912
Soda..........................	564,355
All other......................	754,331
Total (all grades)..............	16,487,110

Show these facts by means of a 100 per cent bar, a pie diagram, and a multiple bar chart.

6. Put the data of Fig. 33.14 into 100 per cent bar form.

7. Put the data of Fig. 33.12 into pie chart form.

8. A test of the resistance of alloy steels to high-temperature steam resulted in the data tabulated below. Represent the results of the test graphically by means of a multiple bar chart.

Corrosion of Steel Bars in Contact with Steam at 1100°F for 2000 Hr

Steel	Average Penetration, In.
SAE 1010..............	0.001700
1.25 Cr-Mo............	0.001169
4.6 Cr-Mo.............	0.000956
9 Cr 1.22 Mo...........	0.000694
12 Cr.................	0.000045
18-8-Cb...............	0.000012

9. From the data below plot curves showing the "thinking distance" and "braking distance." From these curves plot the sum curve "total distance." Title "Automobile Minimum Travel Distances When Stopping—Average Driver."

Mph	Ft per sec	Thinking distance, ft	Braking distance, ft
20	29	22	18
30	44	33	40
40	59	44	71
50	74	55	111
60	88	66	160
70	103	77	218

10. Make a semilogarithmic chart showing the comparative rate of growth of the five largest American cities from 1880 to 1950. Data for this chart are given below:

Population

City	1880	1890	1900	1910
New York, N.Y.	1,911,698	2,507,414	3,437,202	4,766,883
Chicago, Ill.	503,185	1,099,850	1,698,575	2,185,283
Philadelphia, Pa.	847,170	1,046,964	1,293,697	1,549,008
Los Angeles, Calif.	11,181	50,395	102,479	319,198
Detroit, Mich.	116,340	205,876	285,704	465,766

City	1920	1930	1940	1950
New York, N.Y.	5,620,048	6,930,446	7,454,995	7,835,099
Chicago, Ill.	2,701,705	3,376,438	3,396,808	3,606,436
Philadelphia, Pa	1,823,779	1,950,961	1,931,334	2,064,794
Los Angeles, Calif	576,673	1,238,048	1,504,277	1,957,692
Detroit, Mich.	993,678	1,568,662	1,623,452	1,838,517

11. On polar coordinate paper plot a curve for the first set of data given below as a solid line (Fig. 33.8) and a curve for the second set as a broken line (Fig. 33.7). The lower end of the vertical center line is to be taken as the zero-degree line. The curves will be symmetrical about this line, two points being plotted for each angle, one to the left and one to the right. Mark the candle power along this center line also.

Angle, °	(1) Mazda lamp and porcelain enameled reflector, candlepower	(2) Type S-1 sun lamp, candle-power	Angle, °	(1) Mazda lamp and porcelain enameled reflector, candlepower	(2) Type S-1 sun lamp, candle-power	Angle, °	(1) Mazda lamp and porcelain enameled reflector, candlepower	(2) Type S-1 sun lamp, candle-power
0	600	1000	35	825	205	65	485	—
5	655	925	40	830	170	70	330	—
10	695	790	45	815	150	75	200	—
15	725	640	50	785	130	80	90	—
20	760	460	55	740	120	85	25	—
25	800	350	60	640	0	90	0	—
30	815	260						

12. On trilinear coordinate paper plot the data below. Complete the chart, identifying the curves and lettering the title below the coordinate lines (Fig. 33.9).

Freezing Points of Solutions of Glycerol and Methanol in Water

Water	Weight, per cent Meth-anol	Gly-cerol	Freez-ing points, °F	Water	Weight, per cent Meth-anol	Gly-cerol	Freez-ing points, °F	Water	Weight, per cent Meth-anol	Gly-cerol	Freez-ing points, °F
86	14	0	+14	62	23	15	−22	50	20	30	−40
82	8	10	+14	60	40	0	−40	47	31	22	−58
78	6	16	+14	58	5	37	− 4	45	0	55	−22
76	24		− 4	57	17	26	−22	42	7	51	−40
74	2	24	+14	55	0	45	− 4	39	12	49	−58
71	17	12	− 4	54	28	18	−40	37	0	63	−40
70	0	30	+14	53	47	0	−58	36	8	56	−58
68	32	0	−22	52	10	38	−22	33	0	67	−58
65	10	25	− 4								

34

Illustration

34.1   As applied to the graphic language, illustration means a clarification in the readability of a drawing through the use of shading and special methods of projection and representation.   Often, the drawing may be made so clear that the layman is able to read it quite as readily as one experienced in graphical methods.   Any drawing, orthographic, diagrammatic, or pictorial, made either freehand or with instruments in pencil or ink, may be illustrated.   Figure 34.1 is an example of an illustrated drawing.

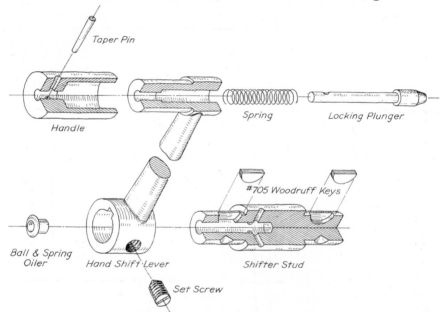

Fig. 34.1.   An illustrated drawing.

34.2   Types of illustrated drawings.   Illustrated drawings are used for many purposes and in many different fields of endeavor.   The following examples are typical:

Advertising illustrations are usually rendered pictorial drawings, often having color added to make the presentation as forceful as possible.

Catalogue illustrations, either orthographic or pictorial, are often rendered in pencil, ink, by stippling, air brush, etc.

Operation, service, and repair charts are drawings showing the working parts of a machine with appropriate directions for the purpose intended.   These drawings are very effective in shaded pictorial form.

Piping, wiring, and installation diagrams are very easy to read when made in shaded pictorial form.

Architectural and engineering presentation drawings, sometimes rendered in pencil or ink, often in water color, show the building or structure as it will appear when completed.

Textbook illustrations in pictorial form, usually in black and white but sometimes in two colors or full color, add visual clarity and give emphasis not possible by words alone.

Patent drawings are usually shaded to bring out and clarify every feature of the invention.

Production drawings from original design sketches to the final details, subassemblies, and assemblies are frequently made in pictorial form, often shaded. Such drawings are particularly useful when persons not trained in reading orthographic drawings are employed.

34.3   Orthographic illustration. The general practice on working drawings is to use a uniform bold full line for visible outlines. In some special kinds of work, an effective appearance of relief and finish is given, and the legibility of the drawing increased, by using two weights of lines, light and heavy, and by the use of line shading on the surfaces of the object. These methods, singly or together, are used to advantage in technical illustrations, advertising matter, etc., where the definition of *shape* needs emphasis. In any case where an increase in readability is desired, the advantage gained will probably justify the increased cost.

34.4   Shade lines. The shade-line system is based on the principle that the object is illuminated by one source of light, with rays coming from the left and downward so that both projections of any ray make an angle of 45° with horizontal-frontal lines. Part of the object is thus illuminated and part is in shade. A *shade line* is a line separating a light face from a dark face, Fig. 34.2. The light lines should be comparatively fine and the shade

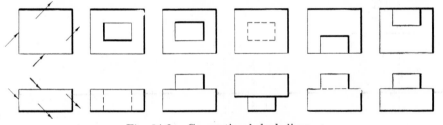

Fig. 34.2.   Conventional shade lines.

lines about three times wider. The width of the shade line is added outside the outline of the view. Hidden lines are never shaded.

A circle may be shaded by shifting the center on a 45° line toward the shade line an amount equal to the thickness of the shade line and drawing another semicircular arc with the same radius, Fig. 34.3; or it may be done by keeping the needle in the center and gradually springing the legs out and back to form the shade line, Fig. 34.4.

34.5   Line shading. Line shading is a method of representing the effect of light and shade by means of ruled lines. Often the simple shading of a shaft or other round member will add greatly to the effectiveness of a drawing and may even save making another view; or a few lines of "surface shading" on a flat surface will show its position and character.

The theoretical direction of the light is considered to be in the direction
of the body diagonal of a cube whose faces are parallel to the planes of pro-

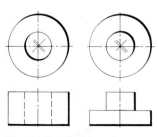

Fig. 34.3.   Shifting the center.   **Fig. 34.4.**   Springing the legs.

jection.   Thus the two projections of a ray of light would be as A_T and A_F,
Fig. 34.5, and two visible faces of the hexagonal prism would be illuminated
while one is in shade.   The figure illustrates the rule that *an inclined
illuminated surface is lightest nearest the eye and an inclined surface in shade is
darkest nearest the eye.*

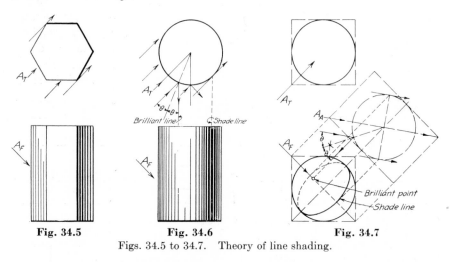

Fig. 34.5   **Fig. 34.6**   **Fig. 34.7**
Figs. 34.5 to 34.7.   Theory of line shading.

A cylinder would be illuminated as in Fig. 34.6.   The darkest place is
at the tangent or "shade line" and the lightest part at the "brilliant line"
where the light is reflected directly to the eye.

A method of finding the brilliant point and shade line of a sphere is
shown in Fig. 34.7.   A right auxiliary view of the sphere and circumscribing
cube is taken on the body diagonal plane of the cube, and the angle (2θ)
between the auxiliary view of the ray of light and the auxiliary view of the
center line to the eye bisected, giving the brilliant point.   Tangents to the
auxiliary view of the sphere parallel to the auxiliary view of a ray of light
locate the shade line.

Flat and graded tints are shown in Fig. 34.8. In these the pitch, or distance from center to center of lines, is equal. In graded tints, the setting of the pen is not changed for every line, but several lines are drawn, the pen is changed, and several more are drawn.

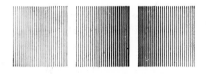

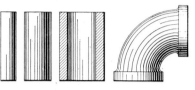

Fig. 34.8. Flat and graded tints.   **Fig. 34.9.** Cylinder shading.

Figure 34.9 shows the shading technique for cylinders. A conical surface may be shaded with lines pointing toward the apex A, toward a point on the extension of the side B, or with lines parallel to the sides C, Fig. 34.10. Three methods of shading a sphere are shown in Fig. 34.11.

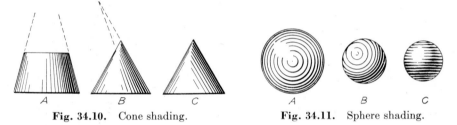

Fig. 34.10. Cone shading.   **Fig. 34.11.** Sphere shading.

To execute shading rapidly and effectively requires practice, some artistic ability, and as much as anything else, good judgment in knowing when to stop. Applications of line shading on flat and curved surfaces are shown in Fig. 34.12.

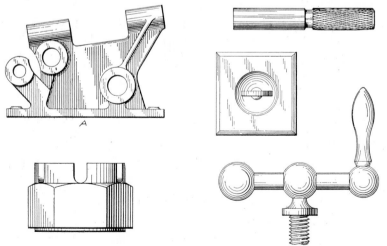

Fig. 34.12. Applications of line shading.

34.6 Pictorial illustration. Pictorial illustration combines any one of the regular pictorial methods with some method of shading or "rendering." In considering a specific problem, the pictorial form—axonometric, oblique, or perspective—should be decided upon, and then a method of shading chosen which is suited to the method of reproduction and the general effect desired. The chapters on pictorial representation, perspective, and sketching are prerequisite to the study of pictorial illustration.

34.7 Light and shade. The conventional position of the light for light-and-shade drawing is the same as that used for orthographic line shading, that is, a position to the left, in front of, and above the object. Any surface or portion of a surface perpendicular to the light direction and directly illuminated by the light would receive the greatest amount of light and be lightest in tone on the drawing; any face not illuminated by the light source would be "in shade" and be darkest on the drawing. Other surfaces, receiving less light than the "high" light but more than a shade portion, would be intermediate in tone.

One must have, at the outset, an understanding of the simple one-light method of illumination and, in addition, have some artistic appreciation for the illumination on various surfaces of the object. Figure 34.13 shows

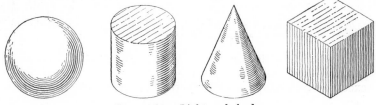

Fig. 34.13.   Light and shade.

a sphere, cylinder, cone, and cube illuminated as described and shaded accordingly. Study the tone values in this illustration.

34.8 Shade lines—pictorial. Shade lines, by their contrast, add some effect of light and shade to the drawing. These lines used alone, without

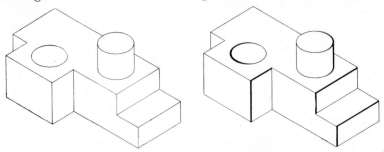

Fig. 34.14.   Outline and shade lines.

other shading, give the simplest possible shading method. Usually, the best effect is had by using heavy lines for only the left vertical and upper horizontal edges of the dark faces, Fig. 34.14. Holes and other circular features are drawn with heavy lines on the shade side. Shade lines should be used sparingly as the inclusion of too many heavy lines simply adds weight to the drawing and does not give the best effect.

34.9 Pencil rendering. There are two general methods of pencil shading—continuous tone and line tone. Continuous-tone shading is done with a fairly soft pencil with its point flattened. A medium-rough paper is best to use for the purpose. Start with a light over-all tone and then build the middle tones and shade portions gradually. Figure 34.15 is an example. High lights may be cleaned out with an eraser.

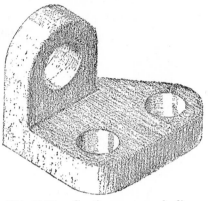

Fig. 34.15. Continuous-tone shading.

Line-tone shading requires a little more skill, as the tones are produced by line spacing and weight. Light lines at wide spacing produce the lightest tone and heavy lines at close spacing make the darkest shade. High lights are left perfectly white, and pure black may be used sparingly for deep shade or shadow. Figure 34.16 is an example, drawn with only a very light outline.

Usually, complete over-all shading is somewhat heavy, and a lighter, more "open" treatment is desired. In this method light portions of the object are left with little or no shading, and middle tones and shade are

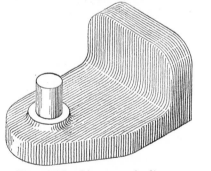

Fig. 34.16. Line-tone shading.

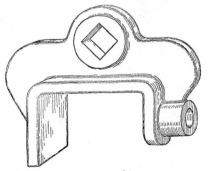

Fig. 34.17. Line technique.

lined sparingly. The few lines used, however, strongly suggest light and shade and surface finish, Fig. 34.17. There are many variations in this type of rendering.

34.10 Pen-and-ink rendering. Pen-and-ink methods follow the same general pattern as work in pencil, with the exception that no continuous tone is possible. There are, however, some variations not usually used in pencil work. Figure 28.56 indicates line techniques. As in pencil work, the common, and usually the most pleasing, method is the partially shaded, suggestive system.

34.11   Special shading methods.   Several unique methods may be used as occasion demands for the representation of special textures and for rapid work.

Smudge shading is a rapid method often used for the representation of smooth surfaces, Fig. 34.18.   Graphite from a soft pencil, powdered graph-

Fig. 34.18.   Smudge shading.

ite, charcoal, or crayon sauce is rubbed first on a piece of paper, then picked up with a piece of cotton or an artist's stump and applied to the drawing.

High lights are easily cleaned out with a sharpened eraser.   Be careful in shading over an erased portion, however, as the abrading of the paper will cause the shading medium to "take" more heavily.

Stippling with pen, pencil, brush, or sponge is a very effective method for indicating rough-texture surfaces.   With pen or pencil, a multitude of dots widely spaced for light surfaces and closer for dark surfaces give a good effect of light and shade.   In brush or sponge stippling, printer's ink or artist's oil color (drier added) is first worked out smoothly on a palette; the medium is then picked up from the palette with a bristle brush or a sponge and applied to the drawing with a dabbing motion.   Sharp edges of shaded areas may be maintained by the use of masks.

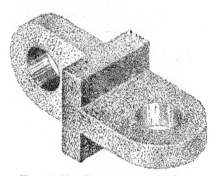

Fig. 34.19.   Brush-stipple shading.

Small areas are easily cleaned up with a razor blade or "scratcher." High lights may be cleaned out with an eraser after the ink is dry.   Figure 34.19 is an example of brush stippling with the smooth surfaces rendered by smudging.

Prepared papers are popular for a wide variety of commercial drawings. Craftint[1] papers are made in two varieties, single-tone and double-tone, and have a shading pattern in the paper that is brought out by a special developer.

[1] Craftint Manufacturing Co., Cleveland, Ohio.

In using these papers the drawing is penciled and the solid blacks inked in with waterproof drawing ink. The shading tones are then brought out by brushing on the developer in the areas where shading is wanted. These papers are available in a wide variety of shading patterns. Figure 34.21 is drawn on Craftint paper.

Shading screens of clear cellulose with printed line or dot pattern provide a simple and effective shading method. Craftint shading film is an overlay sheet containing a pattern printed in either black or white. The shading pattern is easily rubbed off with a smooth wood stick wherever the shading is not wanted. Any part of the white pattern may be converted to black with a special developer.

Zip-a-tone screens[1] are clear cellulose printed with a shading pattern and backed with a special adhesive. In use, the screen is applied to the drawing and rubbed down lightly wherever shading is wanted. The shaded sections are then outlined with a cutting needle and the unwanted pieces stripped off. The portions left on the drawing are then rubbed down firmly with a burnisher. High lights may be painted out with opaque white if the area is too small to strip off in the regular way. A variety of shading patterns are available. Figure 4.36 is shaded with a Zip-a-tone screen.

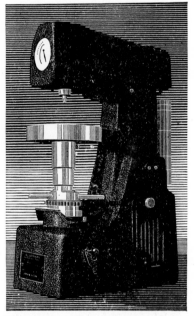

Scratchboard. Drawing paper having a chalky surface is much used for commercial illustrations because of the ease with which white lines may be produced on a black background, as well as black lines on a white background. Rossboard,[2] obtainable in many surface textures for both pencil and ink drawings, is popular among illustrators.

For ink work, the drawing is penciled on the board in the usual way, and then inked in by line-shading the lighter areas, working gradually to the darker areas. The darker areas are painted in with a

Fig. 34.20. A scratchboard drawing. (*Courtesy of Wilson Mechanical Instrument Co.*)

brush, and, when dry, white lines, dots, etc., are easily produced by scratching off the ink with a sharp-pointed knife, sharp stylus, or a needle point. Corrections are easily made by scratching off unwanted ink. Scratched areas may be reinked if necessary. Figure 34.20 is an example of scratchboard technique.

[1] The Para-tone Company, Chicago, Ill.

[2] The Charles J. Ross Co., Philadelphia, Pa.

34.12 Illustrated working drawings. Modern mass-production methods demand simplification and breakdown of the multitude of manufacturing operations. By the use of illustrated drawings, complex and difficult jobs are brought within the grasp of workers not trained in reading complicated orthographic drawings. Illustrated drawings are used in every phase of production, from the original design to the final operating instructions.

Actual practice will vary somewhat within an industry, and vary widely between industries, but in general, illustrated drawings may be classified as (1) *design*, (2) *manufacturing*, and (3) *operation and maintenance*.

Design drawings include a variety of pictorial illustrations that first break down the machine or structure into small workable units, and second, give details of construction, location of equipment, structural features, function of parts and equipment, tooling methods, etc. These drawings are used to study the complete production job and to plan and correlate the work. As the design progresses these drawings are altered, corrected, or redrawn. The preliminary production breakdown, Fig. 34.21, is an example of the type of illustration used in the design stage of the work.

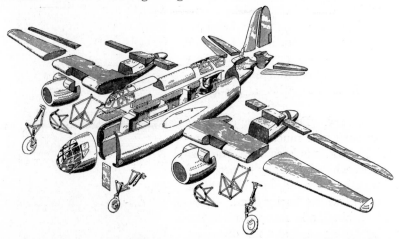

Fig. 34.21. A design illustration. (*Redrawn from Aviation Sketchbook.*)

Manufacturing illustrations give detailed information regarding the breakdown of the structure or machine from which a multitude of separate illustrations are made to show the location of subassemblies, parts, and equipment, give directions for performing operations, give detailed information for the manufacture of parts, and give directions for assembly. Figure 34.22 is an example of a manufacturing illustration taken from the set of details, Fig. 28.34.

Operation and maintenance illustrations give directions for disassembly, repair and replacement of parts, directions for lubrication, inspection and care of equipment, etc. In many cases the same drawings that were originally made for manufacturing can be used in a service manual. Figure 34.23 is an example.

34.13 Drawing for reproduction. Drawings required for the illustrations in books, periodicals, catalogues, or other printed materials are reproduced by one of the photomechanical processes, that is, by zinc or copper etching, halftone, or one of the methods of photolithography.

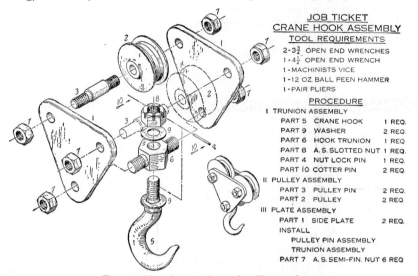

JOB TICKET
CRANE HOOK ASSEMBLY
TOOL REQUIREMENTS

2 - 3¾ OPEN END WRENCHES
1 - 4½ OPEN END WRENCH
1 - MACHINISTS VICE
1 - 12 OZ. BALL PEEN HAMMER
1 - PAIR PLIERS

PROCEDURE

I TRUNION ASSEMBLY

PART 5	CRANE HOOK	1 REQ.
PART 9	WASHER	2 REQ.
PART 6	HOOK TRUNION	1 REQ
PART 8	A.S. SLOTTED NUT	1 REQ.
PART 4	NUT LOCK PIN	1 REQ.
PART 10	COTTER PIN	2 REQ.

II PULLEY ASSEMBLY

PART 3	PULLEY PIN	2 REQ.
PART 2	PULLEY	2 REQ

III PLATE ASSEMBLY

PART 1	SIDE PLATE	2 REQ.

INSTALL
    PULLEY PIN ASSEMBLY
    TRUNION ASSEMBLY
    PART 7 A.S. SEMI-FIN. NUT 6 REQ

Fig. 34.22. A manufacturing illustration.

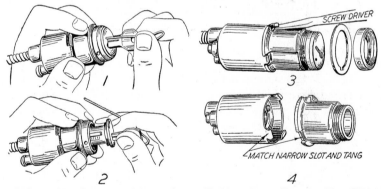

Fig. 34.23. A maintenance illustration. *(Redrawn from Chevrolet Shop Manual.)*

The drawings are usually made larger than the final printed size and are reduced photographically in the reproduction process; consequently the work must be done with visualization of the line weights, contrast, size of lettering, and general effect in reduced size.

If it is desired to preserve the hand-drawn character of the original, the reduction should be slight; but if a very smooth effect is wanted, the drawing may be as much as 3 or 4 times larger than the reproduction. The best general size is 1½ (for one-third reduction) to 2 times (for one-half reduction) the linear size of the cut.

The reduction is usually some even proportion as one-fourth, one-third, one-half, etc., although odd reductions may be used. For a drawing marked "Reduce ⅓," the reproduction will be two-thirds the linear size of the

Fig. 34.24.   A drawing for one-half reduction.

original. Figure 34.24 illustrates the appearance of an original drawing, and Fig. 34.25 is the same drawing reduced one-half. The coarse appearance, open shading, and lettering size of the original should be noticed. The line work must be kept fairly "open," for if lines are drawn close together the space between them may choke in the reproduction and mar the effect. A reducing glass, a concave lens mounted like a reading glass, is sometimes used to aid in judging the appearance of a drawing on reduction.

Fig. 34.25.   One-half reduction.

Drawings for reproduction may be altered and corrected in ways not permissible in other work. Irregularities may be painted out with opaque white. A sharp blade or "scratcher" may be used to clean off small errors. If it is desired to shift a figure after it has been inked, it may be cut out and pasted on in the required position. A portion of the drawing may be pasted over with a piece of paper for blocking out or for redrawing. Reference letters and numbers, notes, and other lettering are often cut out of a sheet printed from type of proper size and pasted on the drawing. The edges of pasted pieces will not show on the final reproduction as they will be eliminated by the engraver when the plate is finished.

Line drawings are usually reproduced by the process known as "zinc etching" in which the drawing is photographed on a prepared zinc plate (when a particularly fine result is desired, a copper plate is used); then this plate is etched with acid, leaving the lines in relief and giving, when mounted, a block which can be printed along with type in an ordinary printing press. Drawings for zinc etching should be made on smooth white paper or tracing cloth in black drawing ink. The finest lines should be black and definite—weak thin lines will not reproduce well.

Wash drawings and photographs are reproduced in a similar way on copper by the halftone process in which a ruled screen is placed in front of the plate, which breaks up the tones into a series of dots of varying size. Screens of different fineness are used for different kinds of paper, from the newspaper halftone of 80 to 100 lines to the inch, the ordinary commercial and magazine halftone of 133 lines, to the fine 150- and 175-line halftones for printing on very smooth coated paper.

The photolithographic processes may be used to reproduce line drawings, wash drawings, or photographs. The drawing is photographed on a thin sheet of sensitized zinc and chemically processed to use in a lithographic press in which the zinc plate prints on a rubber blanket, which in turn prints on the paper.

34.14 Patent-office drawings. In an application for letters patent on an invention or discovery a written description, called the "specification," is required, and for a machine or device a drawing showing every feature of the invention must also be supplied. A high standard of execution and conformity to the rules of the Patent Office must be observed. A pamphlet called the *Rules of Practice*, giving full information and rules governing Patent-office procedure in applying for a patent, may be had by addressing the *Commissioner of Patents, Washington, D.C.*

The drawings are made on smooth white paper, 10 by 15 in., with a border line 1 in. from the edges. A space not less than $1\frac{1}{4}$ in. inside the top border must be left blank for the printed title added by the Patent Office. Drawings must be made in India ink and drawn for reproduction to a reduced size. As many sheets as are necessary may be used.

Patent-office drawings are not working drawings. They are descriptive and pictorial rather than structural; hence they will have no center lines, dimensions, notes, or names of views. The views are lettered with figure numbers and the parts designated by reference numbers through which the invention is described in the specification.

The drawings may be made in orthographic, axonometric, oblique, or perspective. The pictorial system is used extensively, for either all or part of the views. Surface shading is used whenever it will aid legibility.

Figure 34.26 is an example of a Patent-office drawing.

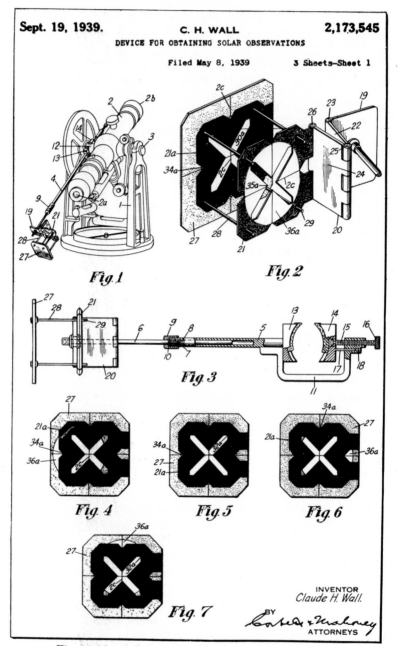

Sept. 19, 1939.   C. H. WALL   2,173,545
                    DEVICE FOR OBTAINING SOLAR OBSERVATIONS

                         Filed May 8, 1939   3 Sheets—Sheet 1

                    Fig. 1   Fig. 2

                              Fig. 3

        Fig. 4   Fig. 5   Fig. 6

              Fig. 7

                                              INVENTOR
                                           Claude H. Wall.
                                         BY
                                              ATTORNEYS

Fig. 34.26.   A Patent-office drawing (reduced one-half).

PROBLEMS

The problems in other chapters may be used for problems of illustration as well as their originally assigned purpose. Some previously drawn orthographic problem may be redrawn as an illustration in either orthographic or pictorial, or some problem not previously worked on may be used. The following are suggested:

Group I. Orthographic illustrations

Select one of the pictorial drawings of Chap. 9 and make an orthographic drawing. Use shade lines and line shading to bring out the surface features.

Group II. Isometric illustrations

Select one of the isometric problems of Chap. 16 and make an isometric illustration. Use any appropriate shading method.

Group III. Oblique illustrations

Select one of the oblique problems in Chap. 16 and make an oblique illustration. Use any appropriate shading method.

Group IV. Axonometric illustrations

Select one of the problems in Chap. 16 and make an axonometric illustration by projection from the orthographic views.

Group V. Perspective illustrations

Select one of the problems in Chap. 16 or 17, make a perspective drawing, and shade.

Group VI. Design illustrations

Select one of the problems in Chap. 28, either an assembly or set of details, and redesign for (a) different size, (b) some different method of manufacture (castings changed to forgings or welded construction, etc.), (c) simplification of construction, (d) changed appearance. Make first design freehand in pictorial form, then make finished drawings in axonometric or perspective, shaded.

Group VII. Manufacturing illustrations

Select one of the problems in Chap. 28, either an assembly or set of details, and make (a) an illustrated detail drawing of a single part, (b) a job-sheet illustration for a group of parts, giving directions for assembly, tools used, etc., (c) an "exploded" assembly, with piece numbers and parts list.

Group VIII. Operation and maintenance illustrations

Select one of the problems in Chap. 28 and make, (a) diagram for oiling, etc., (b) exploded assembly with order and directions for assembly.

Group IX. Freehand illustrations

Make any of the illustrations in Groups I to III freehand.

Group X. Illustrations for reduction

Make a shaded pictorial drawing of one of the problems described in Groups I to V for catalogue or advertising illustration.

35

Notes on Commercial Practice

35.1 There are many items of practical information of value to the student and draftsman which are not included in the ordinary course in drawing but are learned through experience. A few miscellaneous points are given here as suggestions of kinds of information which are worth collecting and preserving in notebook form.

35.2 Stretching paper. If a drawing is to be tinted, the paper should be stretched on the board. First, dampen it on both sides until limp, either with a sponge or under the faucet, then lay it on the drawing board face down, take up the excess water from the edges with a blotter, brush a strip of glue or paste about $\frac{1}{2}$ in. wide around the edge, turn the paper over and rub its edges down on the board until set, and allow to dry horizontally.

Drawings or maps on which much work is to be done, even though not to be tinted, may be made advantageously on stretched paper; but Bristol or calendered paper should not be stretched.

35.3 Tinting is done with washes made with water colors. The drawing may be inked (with waterproof ink) either before or, preferably, after tinting. The drawing should be cleaned and the unnecessary pencil marks removed with a very soft rubber, the tint being mixed in a saucer and applied with a camel-hair or sable brush. Incline the board and flow the color with horizontal strokes, leading the pool of color down over the surface, taking up the surplus at the bottom by wiping the brush out quickly and picking up with it the excess color. Stir the color each time the brush is dipped into the saucer. Tints should be made in light washes, depth of color being obtained if necessary by repeating the wash. To get an even color it is well to go over the surface first with a wash of clear water. Diluted colored inks may be used for washes instead of water color.

35.4 Methods of copying drawings—pricking. Drawings are often copied on opaque paper by laying the drawing over the paper and pricking through with a needle point, turning the upper sheet back frequently, and connecting the points. Prickers may be purchased or may be made easily by forcing a fine needle into a softwood handle. They may be used to advantage also in accurate drawing, in transferring measurements from scale to paper.

35.5 Transfer by rubbing. This method, known as *frotté*, is very useful, particularly in architectural drawing, in transferring any kind of sketch or design to the paper on which it is to be rendered.

The original is made on any paper and may be worked over, changed, and marked up until the design is satisfactory. Lay a piece of tracing paper over the original and trace the outline carefully. Turn the tracing over and retrace the outline just as carefully on the other side, using a medium soft pencil with a *sharp* point.   Turn back to first position and tack down smoothly over the paper on which the drawing is to be made, registering the tracing to proper position by center or reference lines on both tracing and drawing.   Now transfer the drawing by rubbing the tracing with the rounded edge of a knife handle or other instrument (a smooth-edged coin held between thumb and forefinger and scraped back and forth is commonly used), holding a small piece of tracing cloth with smooth side up between the rubbing instrument and the paper, to protect the paper.   Do not rub too hard and be sure that neither the cloth nor the paper moves while rubbing. Transfers in ink instead of pencil, useful on wash drawings, may be made by tracing with *encre à poncer*, a rubbing ink made for this purpose.

If the drawing is symmetrical about any axis, the reversed tracing need not be made, as the rubbing can be done from the first tracing by reversing it about the axis of symmetry.

Several rubbings can be made from one tracing, and when the same figure or detail must be repeated several times on a drawing, much time can be saved by drawing it on tracing paper and rubbing it in the several positions.

35.6   Glass drawing board.   Drawing tables with glass tops and with lights in reflecting boxes underneath are successful devices for copying drawings on opaque paper.   Even pencil drawings may be copied readily on the heaviest paper or Bristol board by the use of a transparent drawing board.

35.7   Proportional methods—the pantograph.   The principle of the pantograph, used for reducing or enlarging drawings in any proportion, is well known.   The instrument consists essentially of four bars, which for any setting must form a parallelogram and have the pivot, tracing point, and marking point in a straight line; and any arrangement of four arms conforming to this requirement will work in true proportion.   For reduction the tracing point and marking point are interchanged.   A suspended pantograph with metal arms, for accurate engineering work, is shown in Fig. 35.1.

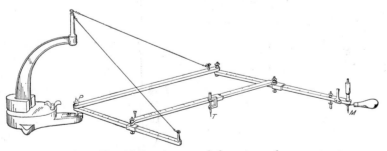

Fig. 35.1.   A suspended pantograph.

Drawings may be copied to reduced or enlarged scale by using the proportional dividers, illustrated in Fig. 35.2.   The divisions marked "lines" are linear proportions, those marked "circles" give the setting for dividing a circle into a desired number of equal parts when the large end is opened to the diameter of the circle.

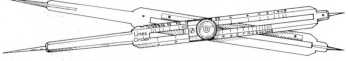

Fig. 35.2. Proportional dividers.

The well-known method of *proportional squares* is often used for reduction or enlargement. The drawing to be copied is ruled in squares of convenient size, or, if it is undesirable to mark on the drawing, a sheet of ruled tracing cloth or celluloid is laid over it and the copy made freehand on the paper, which has been ruled in corresponding squares, larger or smaller, Fig. 35.3.

Fig. 35.3. Enlargement by squares (craticulation).

35.8 Special instruments. There are some instruments not in the usual assortment that are occasionally needed. Beam compasses are used for circles larger than the capacity of ordinary compasses with lengthening bar. A good form is illustrated in Fig. 35.4. A tubular beam compass is shown in Fig. 3.9.

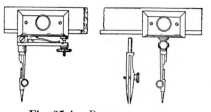

Fig. 35.4. Beam compasses.

With the drop pen or rivet pen, Fig. 35.5, smaller circles can be made much faster than with the bow pen. It is held as shown, the needle point is stationary, and the pen is revolved around it. It is of particular convenience in bridge and structural work and in topographic drawing.

Several instruments for drawing ellipses have been made. The ellipsograph, Fig. 35.6, is a very satisfactory one.

Three special pens are shown in Fig. 35.7. The *railroad pen A* is used for double lines. A better pen for double lines up to $\frac{1}{4}$ in. apart is the *border pen B,* as it can be held down to the paper more satisfactorily. It may be used for very wide solid lines by inking the middle space as well as the two pens. The *contour pen* or curve pen *C,* made with a swivel, is used in map work for freehand curves.

A *protractor* is a necessity in map and topographical work. A semi-circular brass or nickel-silver one, 6 in. in diameter, will read to half degrees. They may be had with an arm and vernier reading to minutes. Large circular paper protractors 8 and 14 in. in diameter reading to half and quarter degrees are used and preferred by some map draftsmen. Others prefer the Brown and Sharpe protractor, Fig. 35.8, reading to 5 minutes.

A combination of triangle and protractor popular with architects and draftsmen is shown

Fig. 35.5. A drop pen.

in Fig. 35.9. Numerous different forms of combination "triangles" have been devised, of which several are usually carried by the dealers.

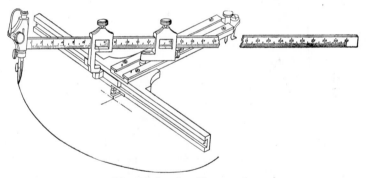

Fig. 35.6. An ellipsograph.

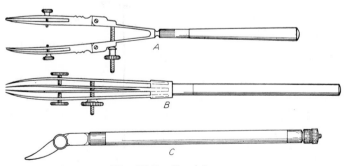

Fig. 35.7. Special pens.

Drafting machines. Since the expiration of the patent on the Universal drafting machine several makers have come into competition with varied

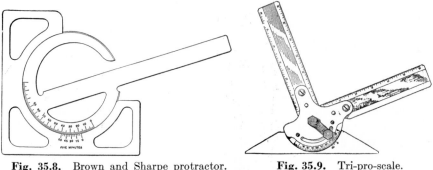

Fig. 35.8. Brown and Sharpe protractor.   **Fig. 35.9.** Tri-pro-scale.

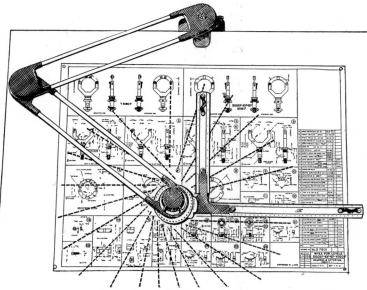

Fig. 35.10. A drafting machine.

designs of this important instrument, which combines the functions of

Fig. 35.11. Alteneder bottleholder.

T square, triangles, scale, and protractor, and which is used very extensively in commercial drafting rooms (it is estimated that 35 per cent of time in machine drawing and over 50 per cent in structural drawing is saved by its use). Figure 35.10 shows a band-type drafting machine. Special drafting machines are made for left-handed draftsmen.

Vertical drawing boards with sliding parallel straightedges are preferred by some for large work.

Figure 35.11 shows a special *bottleholder* made by the Alteneder Company, with which the pen may be filled with one hand and time saved thereby.

Curves. Some irregular curves were illustrated in Fig. 3.18. Many others are sold. Sometimes for special or recurring curves it is advisable for the draftsman to make his own template. These may be cut out of thin holly or basswood, sheet lead, celluloid, or even cardboard or pressboard. To make a paper curve, sketch the desired shape on the paper, cut out with scissors, and sandpaper the edge. For inking, use it over a triangle or another piece of paper. Flexible curves of different kinds are sold. A copper wire or piece of wire solder can be used as a homemade substitute.

The curve illustrated in Fig. 35.12 has been found particularly useful for engineering diagrams, steam curves, etc.

Fig. 35.12. A diagram curve.	Fig. 35.13. A spline and "ducks."

If the glaze is removed from a celluloid irregular curve by rubbing with fine sandpaper, pencil marks that facilitate the drawing of symmetrical curves may be made on it.

Splines are flexible curve rulers, which are adjusted to the points of the curve to be drawn and held in place by lead weights, called by the draftsmen "ducks." They come in various lengths and are part of the regular equipment of all aircraft drawing rooms, Fig. 35.13.

35.9 Various devices. In making a drawing or map so large that it extends over the bottom edge of the board, a piece of half round should be fastened to the board, as in Fig. 35.14, to prevent creasing the paper.

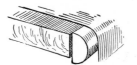

Fig. 35.14. Rounded edge for large drawings.

Fig. 35.15. Starrett edge.

A steel edge for a drawing board may be made of an angle iron planed straight and set flush with the edge. A well-liked adjustable metal edge is made by L. S. Starrett & Company, Fig. 35.15. With a steel edge and steel T square, very accurate plotting may be done. These are often used in bridge offices.

Section lining or "crosshatching" is a difficult operation for the beginner but is done almost automatically by the experienced draftsman. A number of instruments for mechanical spacing have been devised.

Section liners are mechanical spacers for use in crosshatching or other evenly spaced line work. One type is shown in Fig. 35.16.

Erasing shields of metal or celluloid permit an erasure to be made in a small space.   Slots for the same purpose may be cut from sheet celluloid or tough paper.

The *K and E isometric drawing kit*[1] is a set of special triangles with special templates and paper, designed to speed and simplify the making of isometric drawings.   Full details may be obtained from the manufacturer.

Mechanical lettering devices are being much used in drafting rooms. Several forms are on the market, including the Wrico, Edco, Normograph, and Leroy, all based on the principle of a stylographic pen guided by a sliding master plate.   With their use very satisfactory display lettering can

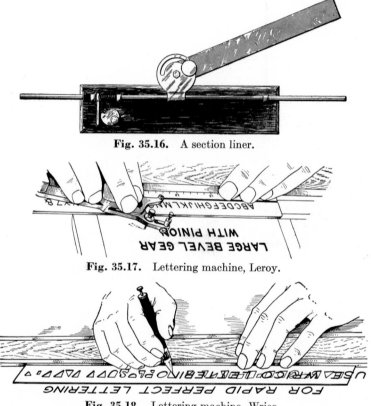

Fig. 35.16.   A section liner.

Fig. 35.17.   Lettering machine, Leroy.

Fig. 35.18.   Lettering machine, Wrico.

be done by unskilled labor.   Figures 35.17 and 35.18 illustrate two of these instruments, and Figs. 27.10 and 27.11 show examples of their use.

There are many other devices designed for labor saving and convenience in drafting rooms.   The Bostich tacker is used instead of thumbtacks. Many draftsmen like to fasten paper to the board with scotch tape.   For this *drafting tape* should be used in preference to masking tape or other varieties of scotch tape.   The Dexter "Draftsmen's Special" pencil sharpener removes the wood only, leaving a long exposure of lead.   Electric erasing machines are popular.

[1] Keuffel & Esser Co., Hoboken, N.J.

36

Bibliography of Allied Subjects

The following short classified list of books is given to supplement this book, whose scope as a general treatise on the language of engineering drawing permits only the mention or brief explanation of some subjects.

Abbreviations used for publishers' names:
  Harper—Harper & Brothers, New York.
  Int. T.—International Textbook Company, Scranton, Pa.
  McGH.—McGraw-Hill Book Company, Inc., New York.
  Macm.—The Macmillan Company, New York.
  PH.—Prentice-Hall, Inc., New York.
  PP.—Pencil Points Library (Reinhold Publishing Corporation, New York).
  Pitm.—Pitman Publishing Corporation, New York.
  Van N.—D. Van Nostrand Company, Inc., New York.
  Wiley—John Wiley & Sons, Inc., New York.

Aeronautical Drafting and Design

ANDERSON, NEWTON.—Aircraft Layout and Detail Design. McGH.
KATZ, H. H.—Aircraft Drafting. Macm.
LIMING, ROY.—Practical Analytic Geometry with Application to Aircraft. Macm.
LISTON, JOSEPH.—Power Plants for Aircraft. McGH.
MEADOWCROFT, NORMAN.—Aircraft Detail Drafting. McGH.
NELSON, W.—Airplane Lofting. McGH.
TITTERTON, G. F.—Aircraft Materials and Processes. Pitm.

Architectural Drawing

CRANE, T.—Architectural Construction. Wiley.
FIELD, W. B.—An Introduction to Architectural Drawing. McGH.
————. Architectural Drawing. McGH.
————. House Planning. McGH.
MARTIN, C. L.—Architectural Graphics. Macm.
MORGAN, S. W.—Architectural Drawing. McGH.
RAMSEY and SLEEPER.—Architectural Graphic Standards. Wiley.
SAYLOR, H. H.—Dictionary of Architecture. Wiley.
SLEEPER, H. R.—Architectural Specifications. Wiley.

Cams

FURMAN, F. DER.—Cams, Elementary and Advanced. Wiley.

Charts, Graphs, and Diagrams

DOUGLAS and ADAMS.—Elements of Nomography. McGH.
HASKELL, A. C.—How to Make and Use Graphic Charts. Codex Book Co., New York.
KARSTEN, K. G.—Charts and Graphs. PH.
KULMANN, C. A.—Nomographic Charts. McGH.
LEVENS, A. S.—Nomography. Wiley.
MAVIS, F. T.—The Construction of Nomographic Charts. Int. T.

Descriptive Geometry

GRANT, H.—Practical Descriptive Geometry. McGH.
HIGBEE, F. G.—Drawing-board Geometry. Wiley.
HOOD, G. J.—Geometry of Engineering Drawing. McGH.
LEVENS and EGGERS.—Descriptive Geometry. Harper.
ROWE, C. E.—Engineering Descriptive Geometry. Van N.
WARNER, F. M.—Applied Descriptive Geometry. McGH.
WELLMAN, B. L.—Technical Descriptive Geometry. McGH.

Drawing Instruments (Catalogues)

THEO. ALTENEDER AND SONS, Philadelphia.
EUGENE DIETZGEN COMPANY, Chicago.
GRAMERCY IMPORT COMPANY, INC., New York.
KEUFFEL & ESSER COMPANY, Hoboken, N.J.
THE FREDERICK POST COMPANY, Chicago.
V. AND E. MANUFACTURING COMPANY, Pasadena, Calif.

Engineering Drawing Problem Sheets

HIGBEE and RUSS.—Engineering Drawing Problems, $8\frac{1}{2}'' \times 11''$. Wiley.
LEVENS and EDSTROM.—Problems in Engineering Drawing, $8\frac{1}{2}'' \times 11''$. McGH.
VIERCK, COOPER, MACHOVINA.—Engineering Drawing Problems, Series Two, $11'' \times 17''$. McGH.
———, ———, ———. Engineering Drawing—Basic Problems, Series A, $8\frac{1}{2}'' \times 11''$. McGH.

Gears and Gearing

BEALE, O. J.—Practical Treatise on Gearing. Brown and Sharpe Mfg. Co., Providence, R. I.
BUCKINGHAM, E.—Spur Gears—Design, Operation and Production. McGH.
FELLOWS GEAR SHAPER Co.—Treatise on Commercial Gear Cutting. Springfield, Vt.

Graphical Solutions

HOELSCHER, ARNOLD, and PIERCE.—Graphic Aids in Engineering Computation. McGH.
LIPKA, JOSEPH.—Graphical and Mechanical Computation. Wiley.
MACKEY, C. O.—Graphic Solutions. Wiley.
MALCOLM, C. W.—A Textbook on Graphic Statics. McGH.
RULE and WATTS.—Engineering Graphics. McGH.

Handbooks

A great many handbooks, with tables, formulas, and information, are published for the different branches of the engineering profession, and draftsmen keep the ones pertaining to their particular line at hand for ready reference. Attention is called, however, to the danger of using handbook formulas and figures without understanding the principles upon which they are based. "Handbook designer" is a term of reproach applied not without reason to one who depends wholly upon these aids without knowing their theory or limitations.

Among the best known of these reference books are the following:

American Machinists' Handbook, Colvin and Stanley. McGH.
American Society of Heating and Ventilating Engineers' Guide (annual).
Architects' and Builders' Handbook, Kidder-Parker. Wiley.
Chemical Engineers' Handbook, J. H. Perry. McGH.
Civil Engineering Handbook, L. C. Urquhart. McGH.

Civil Engineers' Reference Book.   Trautwine Co., Ithaca, N.Y.
General Engineering Handbook, C. E. O'Rourke.   McGH.
Handbook of Building Construction, Hool and Johnson.   McGH.
Handbook of Engineering Fundamentals, Eshbach.   Wiley.
Handbooks of various steel and other material companies, such as Bethlehem, Carnegie,
    Aluminum Co. of America, Portland Cement Assoc., etc.
Machinery's Handbook, Industrial Press, New York.
Mechanical Engineers' Handbook, L. S. Marks.   McGH.
Mechanical Engineers' Handbook, William Kent.   2v.   Wiley.
Pencil Points Data Sheets.   PP.
Standard Handbook for Electrical Engineers.   A. E. Knowlton.   McGH.
Steel Construction.   Am. Inst. of Steel Const., Inc., New York.
Structural Drafting Manual.   Am. Inst. of Steel Const., Inc., New York.
Tool Engineers' Handbook.   Am. Soc. of Tool Engineers.   McGH.

Illustration

HOELSCHER, SPRINGER, and POHLE.—Industrial Production Illustration.   McGH.
TREACY, JOHN.—Production Illustration.   Wiley.

Lettering

FRENCH and TURNBULL.—Lessons in Lettering.   Books I and II.   McGH.
OGG, OSCAR.—An Alphabet Source Book.   Harper.
REINHARDT, C. W.—Lettering for Draftsmen, etc.   Van N.
SVENSEN, C. L.—The Art of Lettering.   Van N.

Machine Design

ALBERT, C. D.—Machine Design Drawing Room Problems.   Wiley.
BERARD and WATERS.—The Elements of Machine Design.   Van N.
BRADFORD and EATON.—Machine Design.   Wiley.
FAIRES, V. M.—Design of Machine Elements.   Macm.
MALEEV, V. L.—Machine Design.   Int. T.
NORMAN, AULT, and ZAROBSKY.—Fundamentals of Machine Design.   Macm.
VALLANCE and DOUGHTIE.—Design of Machine Members.   McGH.

Map and Topographical Drawing

DEETZ, CHARLES H.—Cartography.   U.S. Government Printing Office.
SLOANE and MONTZ.—Elements of Topographic Drawing.   McGH.

Mechanism and Kinematics

GUILLET, G. L.—Kinematics of Machines.   Wiley.
HAM and CRANE.—Mechanics of Machinery.   McGH.
KEOWN and FAIRES.—Mechanism.   McGH.
PRAGEMAN, I. H.—Mechanism.   Int. T.
SCHWAMB, MERRILL, JAMES, and DOUGHTIE.—Elements of Mechanism.   Wiley.
SLOANE, ALVIN.—Engineering Kinematics.   Macm.
VALLANCE and FARRIS.—Principles of Mechanism.   Macm.

Perspective

FREESE, E. I.—Perspective Projection.   PP.
LAWSON, P. J.—Practical Perspective Drawing.   McGH.
LUBCHEZ, B.—Perspective.   Van N.

Piping

CRANE & Co., Chicago; catalogue.
CROCKER, S.—Piping Handbook. McGH.
PLUM, S.—Plumbing Practice and Design. Wiley.
WALWORTH COMPANY, Boston; catalogue.
See also Handbooks.

Rendering

GUPTIL, A. L.—Drawing with Pen and Ink. PP.
———. Sketching and Rendering in Pencil. PP.
KAUTSKY, T.—Pencil Broadsides. PP.
MAGONIGLE, H. V.—Architectural Rendering in Wash. Charles Scribner's Sons, New York.

Sheet-metal Drafting

GIACHINO, J. W.—Basic Sheet-metal Practice. Int. T.
KIDDER, F. S.—Triangulation Applied to Sheet Metal Pattern Cutting. Sheet Metal Publishing Co., New York.
O'ROURKE, F. J.—Sheet-metal Pattern Drafting. McGH.

Shop Practice and Tools

BENEDICT, O. J., JR.—Manual of Foundry and Pattern Shop Practice. McGH.
BOSTON, O. W.—Metal Processing. Wiley.
BURGHARDT, H. D.—Machine Tool Operations. 2v. McGH.
CAMPBELL, J. S.—Casting and Forming Processes in Manufacturing. McGH.
CINCINNATI MILLING MACHINE Co.—A Treatise on Milling and Milling Machines, Cincinnati.
CLAPP and CLARK.—Engineering Materials and Processes. Int. T.
COLVIN and HAAS.—Jigs and Fixtures. McGH.
DOE, E. W.—Foundry Work. Wiley.
HINE, C. R.—Machine Tools for Engineers. McGH.
KILEY and PAUSTIAN.—Pattern Design. Int. T.
SCHALLER, G. S.—Engineering Manufacturing Methods. McGH.

Slide Rule

CAJORI, F.—A History of the Logarithmic Slide Rule. Eng. News Pub. Co., N.Y.
COOPER, H. O.—Slide Rule Calculations. Oxford University Press.
MACHOVINA, P. E.—A Manual for the Slide Rule. McGH.
MACKEY, C. O.—Graphic Solutions. Wiley.
STROHM and DEGROOT.—The Slide Rule. Int. T.

Structural Drawing and Design

BISHOP, C. T.—Structural Drafting. Wiley.
MORRIS, C. T.—Designing and Detailing of Simple Steel Structures. McGH.
SHEDD and VAWTER.—Theory of Simple Structures. Wiley.
URQUHART and O'ROURKE.—Design of Concrete Structures. McGH.
———, ———. Design of Steel Structures. McGH.

Tool Drafting and Design

BLOOM, R. R.—Principles of Tool Engineering. McGH.

Welding

ELZEA, L. S.—Aircraft Welding. McGH.
FISH, G. D.—Arc Welded Steel Frame Structures. McGH.

Fox and Bloor.—Welding Technology and Design. J. B. Lippincott Company, Philadelphia.

Lincoln Electric Co.—Simple Blueprint Reading with Particular Reference to Welding, Cleveland.

———. Procedure Handbook of Arc Welding Design and Practice, Cleveland.

Moon, A. R.—Design of Welded Steel Structures. Pitm.

Rossi, B. E.—Welding and Its Application. McGH.

AMERICAN STANDARDS

The American Standards Association is working continually on standardization projects. Of its many publications the following standards having to do with the subjects in this book are available at the time of this printing. A complete list of American Standards will be sent by the association on application to its offices, 29 West Thirty-ninth Street, New York.

Civil Engineering and Construction

Drain Tile, Specifications for	A6
Cast-iron Soil Pipe and Fittings	A40.1
Threaded Cast-iron Pipe for Drainage, Vent, and Waste Services	A40.5
Steel Reinforcing Bars	A47

Mechanical Engineering

Screw Threads

Unified and American Screw Threads for Screws, Bolts, Nuts, and Other Threaded Parts	B1.1
Screw Threads for High-strength Bolting	B1.4
Acme Threads	B1.5
Nomenclature, Definitions, and Letter Symbols for Screw Threads	B1.7
Stub Acme Screw Threads	B1.8
Pipe Threads	B2.1

Dimensioning

Limits and Fits for Engineering and Manufacturing (Part I)	B4.1

Machine Elements and Tools

T-slots—Their Bolts, Nuts, Tongues, and Cutters	B5.1
Milling Cutters, Nomenclature, Principal Dimensions, etc	B5.3
Taps, Cut and Ground Threads	B5.4
Jig Bushings	B5.6
Machine Tapers, Self-holding and Steep Taper Series	B5.10
Twist Drills, Straight Shank and Taper Shank	B5.12
Reamers	B5.14

Gears

Involute Splines, Side Bearing	B5.15
Spur Gear Tooth Form	B6.1
Letter Symbols for Gear Engineering	B6.5
20-Degree Involute Fine-pitch System for Spur and Helical Gears	B6.7
Fine-pitch Straight Bevel Gears	B6.8
Gear Nomenclature, Terms, Definitions, and Illustrations	B6.10

Pipe and Fittings

Cast-iron Pipe Flanges and Flanged Fittings, Class 250	B16b
Cast-iron Pipe Flanges and Flanged Fittings	B16b1

Appendix

CONTENTS

Length of Chord for Circle Arcs of One Inch Radius

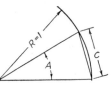

Deg	Minutes					
	0′	10′	20′	30′	40′	50′
0	0.0000	0.0029	0.0058	0.0087	0.0116	0.0145
1	0.0175	0.0204	0.0233	0.0262	0.0291	0.0320
2	0.0349	0.0378	0.0407	0.0436	0.0465	0.0494
3	0.0524	0.0553	0.0582	0.0611	0.0640	0.0669
4	0.0698	0.0727	0.0756	0.0785	0.0814	0.0843
5	0.0872	0.0901	0.0931	0.0960	0.0989	0.1018
6	0.1047	0.1076	0.1105	0.1134	0.1163	0.1192
7	0.1221	0.1250	0.1279	0.1308	0.1337	0.1366
8	0.1395	0.1424	0.1453	0.1482	0.1511	0.1540
9	0.1569	0.1598	0.1627	0.1656	0.1685	0.1714
10	0.1743	0.1772	0.1801	0.1830	0.1859	0.1888
11	0.1917	0.1946	0.1975	0.2004	0.2033	0.2062
12	0.2091	0.2119	0.2148	0.2177	0.2206	0.2235
13	0.2264	0.2293	0.2322	0.2351	0.2380	0.2409
14	0.2437	0.2466	0.2495	0.2524	0.2553	0.2582
15	0.2611	0.2639	0.2668	0.2697	0.2726	0.2755
16	0.2783	0.2812	0.2841	0.2870	0.2899	0.2927
17	0.2956	0.2985	0.3014	0.3042	0.3071	0.3100
18	0.3129	0.3157	0.3186	0.3215	0.3244	0.3272
19	0.3301	0.3330	0.3358	0.3387	0.3416	0.3444
20	0.3473	0.3502	0.3530	0.3559	0.3587	0.3616
21	0.3645	0.3673	0.3702	0.3730	0.3759	0.3788
22	0.3816	0.3845	0.3873	0.3902	0.3930	0.3959
23	0.3987	0.4016	0.4044	0.4073	0.4101	0.4130
24	0.4158	0.4187	0.4215	0.4244	0.4272	0.4300
25	0.4329	0.4357	0.4386	0.4414	0.4442	0.4471
26	0.4499	0.4527	0.4556	0.4584	0.4612	0.4641
27	0.4669	0.4697	0.4725	0.4754	0.4782	0.4810
28	0.4838	0.4867	0.4895	0.4923	0.4951	0.4979
29	0.5008	0.5036	0.5064	0.5092	0.5120	0.5148
30	0.5176	0.5204	0.5233	0.5261	0.5289	0.5317
31	0.5345	0.5373	0.5401	0.5429	0.5457	0.5485
32	0.5513	0.5541	0.5569	0.5597	0.5625	0.5652
33	0.5680	0.5708	0.5736	0.5764	0.5792	0.5820
34	0.5847	0.5875	0.5903	0.5931	0.5959	0.5986
35	0.6014	0.6042	0.6070	0.6097	0.6125	0.6153
36	0.6180	0.6208	0.6236	0.6263	0.6291	0.6319
37	0.6346	0.6374	0.6401	0.6429	0.6456	0.6484
38	0.6511	0.6539	0.6566	0.6594	0.6621	0.6649
39	0.6676	0.6704	0.6731	0.6758	0.6786	0.6813
40	0.6840	0.6868	0.6895	0.6922	0.6950	0.6977
41	0.7004	0.7031	0.7059	0.7086	0.7113	0.7140
42	0.7167	0.7195	0.7222	0.7249	0.7276	0.7303
43	0.7330	0.7357	0.7384	0.7411	0.7438	0.7465
44	0.7492	0.7519	0.7546	0.7573	0.7600	0.7627
45	0.7654	0.7681	0.7707	0.7734	0.7761	0.7788

For angles between 45° and 90°, draw 90° angle and lay off complement from 90° line.

Decimal Equivalents of Inch Fractions

Fraction	Equiv.	Fraction	Equiv.	Fraction	Equiv.	Fraction	Equiv.
$\frac{1}{64}$	0.015625	$\frac{17}{64}$	0.265625	$\frac{33}{64}$	0.515625	$\frac{49}{64}$	0.765625
$\frac{1}{32}$	0.03125	$\frac{9}{32}$	0.28125	$\frac{17}{32}$	0.53125	$\frac{25}{32}$	0.78125
$\frac{3}{64}$	0.046875	$\frac{19}{64}$	0.296875	$\frac{35}{64}$	0.546875	$\frac{51}{64}$	0.796875
$\frac{1}{16}$	0.0625	$\frac{5}{16}$	0.3125	$\frac{9}{16}$	0.5625	$\frac{13}{16}$	0.8125
$\frac{5}{64}$	0.078125	$\frac{21}{64}$	0.328125	$\frac{37}{64}$	0.578125	$\frac{53}{64}$	0.828125
$\frac{3}{32}$	0.09375	$\frac{11}{32}$	0.34375	$\frac{19}{32}$	0.59375	$\frac{27}{32}$	0.84375
$\frac{7}{64}$	0.109375	$\frac{23}{64}$	0.359375	$\frac{39}{64}$	0.609375	$\frac{55}{64}$	0.859375
$\frac{1}{8}$	0.1250	$\frac{3}{8}$	0.3750	$\frac{5}{8}$	0.6250	$\frac{7}{8}$	0.8750
$\frac{9}{64}$	0.140625	$\frac{25}{64}$	0.390625	$\frac{41}{64}$	0.640625	$\frac{57}{64}$	0.890625
$\frac{5}{32}$	0.15625	$\frac{13}{32}$	0.40625	$\frac{21}{32}$	0.65625	$\frac{29}{32}$	0.90625
$\frac{11}{64}$	0.171875	$\frac{27}{64}$	0.421875	$\frac{43}{64}$	0.671875	$\frac{59}{64}$	0.921875
$\frac{3}{16}$	0.1875	$\frac{7}{16}$	0.4375	$\frac{11}{16}$	0.6875	$\frac{15}{16}$	0.9375
$\frac{13}{64}$	0.203125	$\frac{29}{64}$	0.453125	$\frac{45}{64}$	0.703125	$\frac{61}{64}$	0.953125
$\frac{7}{32}$	0.21875	$\frac{15}{32}$	0.46875	$\frac{23}{32}$	0.71875	$\frac{31}{32}$	0.96875
$\frac{15}{64}$	0.234375	$\frac{31}{64}$	0.484375	$\frac{47}{64}$	0.734375	$\frac{63}{64}$	0.984375
$\frac{1}{4}$	0.2500	$\frac{1}{2}$	0.5000	$\frac{3}{4}$	0.7500	1	1.0000

Metric Equivalents

Millimeters to inches				Inches to millimeters			
Mm	In.*	Mm	In.	In.	Mm†	In.	Mm
1 = 0.0394		17 = 0.6693		$\frac{1}{32}$ = 0.794		$\frac{17}{32}$ = 13.493	
2 = 0.0787		18 = 0.7087		$\frac{1}{16}$ = 1.587		$\frac{9}{16}$ = 14.287	
3 = 0.1181		19 = 0.7480		$\frac{3}{32}$ = 2.381		$\frac{19}{32}$ = 15.081	
4 = 0.1575		20 = 0.7874		$\frac{1}{8}$ = 3.175		$\frac{5}{8}$ = 15.875	
5 = 0.1969		21 = 0.8268		$\frac{5}{32}$ = 3.968		$\frac{21}{32}$ = 16.668	
6 = 0.2362		22 = 0.8662		$\frac{3}{16}$ = 4.762		$\frac{11}{16}$ = 17.462	
7 = 0.2756		23 = 0.9055		$\frac{7}{32}$ = 5.556		$\frac{23}{32}$ = 18.256	
8 = 0.3150		24 = 0.9449		$\frac{1}{4}$ = 6.349		$\frac{3}{4}$ = 19.050	
9 = 0.3543		25 = 0.9843		$\frac{9}{32}$ = 7.144		$\frac{25}{32}$ = 19.843	
10 = 0.3937		26 = 1.0236		$\frac{5}{16}$ = 7.937		$\frac{13}{16}$ = 20.637	
11 = 0.4331		27 = 1.0630		$\frac{11}{32}$ = 8.731		$\frac{27}{32}$ = 21.431	
12 = 0.4724		28 = 1.1024		$\frac{3}{8}$ = 9.525		$\frac{7}{8}$ = 22.225	
13 = 0.5118		29 = 1.1418		$\frac{13}{32}$ = 10.319		$\frac{29}{32}$ = 23.018	
14 = 0.5512		30 = 1.1811		$\frac{7}{16}$ = 11.112		$\frac{15}{16}$ = 23.812	
15 = 0.5906		31 = 1.2205		$\frac{15}{32}$ = 11.906		$\frac{31}{32}$ = 24.606	
16 = 0.6299		32 = 1.2599		$\frac{1}{2}$ = 12.699		1 = 25.400	

* Calculated to *nearest* fourth decimal place.
† Calculated to *nearest* third decimal place.

Sizes of Numbered and Lettered Drills

Number	Size	Number	Size	Number	Size	Letter	Size
80	0.0135	53	0.0595	26	0.1470	A	0.2340
79	0.0145	52	0.0635	25	0.1495	B	0.2380
78	0.0160	51	0.0670	24	0.1520	C	0.2420
77	0.0180	50	0.0700	23	0.1540	D	0.2460
76	0.0200	49	0.0730	22	0.1570	E	0.2500
75	0.0210	48	0.0760	21	0.1590	F	0.2570
74	0.0225	47	0.0785	20	0.1610	G	0.2610
73	0.0240	46	0.0810	19	0.1660	H	0.2660
72	0.0250	45	0.0820	18	0.1695	I	0.2720
71	0.0260	44	0.0860	17	0.1730	J	0.2770
70	0.0280	43	0.0890	16	0.1770	K	0.2810
69	0.0292	42	0.0935	15	0.1800	L	0.2900
68	0.0310	41	0.0960	14	0.1820	M	0.2950
67	0.0320	40	0.0980	13	0.1850	N	0.3020
66	0.0330	39	0.0995	12	0.1890	O	0.3160
65	0.0350	38	0.1015	11	0.1910	P	0.3230
64	0.0360	37	0.1040	10	0.1935	Q	0.3320
63	0.0370	36	0.1065	9	0.1960	R	0.3390
62	0.0380	35	0.1100	8	0.1990	S	0.3480
61	0.0390	34	0.1110	7	0.2010	T	0.3580
60	0.0400	33	0.1130	6	0.2040	U	0.3680
59	0.0410	32	0.1160	5	0.2055	V	0.3770
58	0.0420	31	0.1200	4	0.2090	W	0.3860
57	0.0430	30	0.1285	3	0.2130	X	0.3970
56	0.0465	29	0.1360	2	0.2210	Y	0.4040
55	0.0520	28	0.1405	1	0.2280	Z	0.4130
54	0.0550	27	0.1440				

Acme and Stub Acme Threads[1]

ASA PREFERRED DIAMETER-PITCH COMBINATIONS

Nominal (major) diam.	Threads per in.	Nominal (major) diam.	Threads per in.	Nominal (major) diam.	Threads per in.	Nominal (major) diam.	Threads per in.
$\frac{1}{4}$	16	$\frac{3}{4}$	6	$1\frac{1}{2}$	4	3	2
$\frac{5}{16}$	14	$\frac{7}{8}$	6	$1\frac{3}{4}$	4	$3\frac{1}{2}$	2
$\frac{3}{8}$	12	1	5	2	4	4	2
$\frac{7}{16}$	12	$1\frac{1}{8}$	5	$2\frac{1}{4}$	3	$4\frac{1}{2}$	2
$\frac{1}{2}$	10	$1\frac{1}{4}$	5	$2\frac{1}{2}$	3	5	2
$\frac{5}{8}$	8	$1\frac{3}{8}$	4	$2\frac{3}{4}$	3		

[1] ASA B1.5 and B1.8—1952. Diameters in inches.

American Standard Unified and American Thread Series[1]

THREADS PER INCH FOR COARSE, FINE, EXTRA FINE, 8-THREAD, 12-THREAD, AND 16-THREAD SERIES[4]

Tap-drill Sizes for Approximately 75% Depth of Thread (Not American Standard)

Nominal size (basic major diam.)	Coarse thd series UNC and NC[2] in classes 1A, 1B, 2A, 2B, 3A, 3B, 2, 3		Fine thd series UNF and NF[2] in classes 1A, 1B, 2A, 2B, 3A, 3B, 2, 3		Extra-fine thd series UNEF and NEF[3] in classes 2A, 2B, 2, 3		8-thd series 8N[2] in classes 2A, 2B, 2, 3		12-thd series 12UN and 12N[3] in classes 2A, 2B, 2, 3		16-thd series 16UN and 16N[3] in classes 2A, 2B, 2, 3	
	Thds per in.	Tap drill	Thds per in.	Tap drill	Thds per in.	Tap drill	Thds per in.	Tap drill	Thds per in.	Tap drill	Thds per in.	Tap drill
0(0.060)			80	$\frac{3}{64}$								
1(0.073)	64	No. 53	72	No. 53								
2(0.086)	56	No. 50	64	No. 50								
3(0.099)	48	No. 47	56	No. 45								
4(0.112)	40	No. 43	48	No. 42								
5(0.125)	40	No. 38	44	No. 37								
6(0.138)	32	No. 36	40	No. 33								
8(0.164)	32	No. 29	36	No. 29								
10(0.190)	24	No. 25	32	No. 21								
12(0.216)	24	No. 16	28	No. 14	32	No. 13						
$\frac{1}{4}$	20	No. 7	28	No. 3	32	$\frac{7}{32}$						
$\frac{5}{16}$	18	Let. F	24	Let. I	32	$\frac{9}{32}$						
$\frac{3}{8}$	16	$\frac{5}{16}$	24	Let. Q	32	$\frac{11}{32}$						
$\frac{7}{16}$	14	Let. U	20	$\frac{25}{64}$	28	$\frac{13}{32}$						
$\frac{1}{2}$	13	$\frac{27}{64}$	20	$\frac{29}{64}$	28	$\frac{15}{32}$			12	$\frac{27}{64}$		
$\frac{9}{16}$	12	$\frac{31}{64}$	18	$\frac{33}{64}$	24	$\frac{33}{64}$			12	$\frac{31}{64}$		
$\frac{5}{8}$	11	$\frac{17}{32}$	18	$\frac{37}{64}$	24	$\frac{37}{64}$			12	$\frac{35}{64}$		
$\frac{11}{16}$					24	$\frac{41}{64}$			12	$\frac{39}{64}$		
$\frac{3}{4}$	10	$\frac{21}{32}$	16	$1\frac{1}{16}$	20	$\frac{45}{64}$			12	$\frac{43}{64}$	16	$1\frac{1}{16}$
$\frac{13}{16}$					20	$\frac{49}{64}$			12	$\frac{47}{64}$	16	$\frac{3}{4}$
$\frac{7}{8}$	9	$\frac{49}{64}$	14	$1\frac{3}{16}$	20	$\frac{53}{64}$			12	$\frac{51}{64}$	16	$1\frac{3}{16}$
$\frac{15}{16}$					20	$\frac{57}{64}$			12	$\frac{55}{64}$	16	$\frac{7}{8}$
1			14	$\frac{15}{16}$			8	$\frac{7}{8}$				
1	8	$\frac{7}{8}$	12	$\frac{59}{64}$	20	$\frac{61}{64}$			12	$\frac{59}{64}$	16	$\frac{15}{16}$
1 $\frac{1}{16}$					18	1			12	$\frac{63}{64}$	16	1
1 $\frac{1}{8}$	7	$\frac{63}{64}$	12	$1\frac{3}{64}$	18	$1\frac{5}{64}$	8	1	12	$1\frac{3}{64}$	16	$1\frac{1}{16}$
1 $\frac{3}{16}$					18	$1\frac{9}{64}$			12	$1\frac{7}{64}$	16	$1\frac{1}{8}$
1 $\frac{1}{4}$	7	$1\frac{7}{64}$	12	$1\frac{11}{64}$	18	$1\frac{3}{16}$	8	$1\frac{1}{8}$	12	$1\frac{11}{64}$	16	$1\frac{3}{16}$
1 $\frac{5}{16}$					18	$1\frac{17}{64}$			12	$1\frac{15}{64}$	16	$1\frac{1}{4}$
1 $\frac{3}{8}$	6	$1\frac{7}{32}$	12	$1\frac{19}{64}$	18	$1\frac{5}{16}$	8	$1\frac{1}{4}$	12	$1\frac{19}{64}$	16	$1\frac{5}{16}$
1 $\frac{7}{16}$					18	$1\frac{3}{8}$			12	$1\frac{23}{64}$	16	$1\frac{3}{8}$
1 $\frac{1}{2}$	6	$1\frac{11}{32}$	12	$1\frac{27}{64}$	18	$1\frac{7}{16}$	8	$1\frac{3}{8}$	12	$1\frac{27}{64}$	16	$1\frac{7}{16}$
1 $\frac{9}{16}$					18	$1\frac{1}{2}$					16	$1\frac{1}{2}$
1 $\frac{5}{8}$					18	$1\frac{9}{16}$	8	$1\frac{1}{2}$	12	$1\frac{35}{64}$	16	$1\frac{9}{16}$

American Standard Unified and American Thread Series[1]—*(Continued)*

Nominal size (basic major diam.)	Coarse thd series UNC and NC[2] in classes 1A, 1B, 2A, 2B, 3A, 3B, 2, 3.		Fine thd series UNF and NF[2] in classes 1A, 1B, 2A, 2B, 3A, 3B, 2, 3.		Extra-fine thd series UNEF and NEF[3] in classes 2A, 2B, 2, 3		8-thd series 8N[2] in classes 2A, 2B, 2, 3		12-thd series 12UN and 12N[3] in classes 2A, 2B, 2, 3		16-thd series 16UN and 16N[3] in classes 2A, 2B, 2, 3	
	Thds per in.	Tap drill	Thds per in.	Tap drill	Thds per in.	Tap drill	Thds per in.	Tap drill	Thds per in.	Tap drill	Thds per in.	Tap drill
$1\frac{11}{16}$	....	....	..	.....	**18**	$1\frac{5}{8}$	..	....	..	.....	**16**	$1\frac{5}{8}$
$1\frac{3}{4}$	**5**	$1\frac{9}{16}$	..	.....	**16**	$1\frac{11}{16}$	8*	$1\frac{5}{8}$	**12**	$1\frac{43}{64}$	**16**	$1\frac{11}{16}$
$1\frac{13}{16}$	....	.....	..	.....	..	...	..	.....	..	.....	**16**	$1\frac{3}{4}$
$1\frac{7}{8}$	....	.....	..	.....	..	.....	8	$1\frac{3}{4}$	**12**	$1\frac{51}{64}$	**16**	$1\frac{13}{16}$
$1\frac{15}{16}$	....	.....	..	.....	..	.....	..	...	..	.....	**16**	$1\frac{7}{8}$
2	**4½**	$1\frac{25}{32}$	..	.....	**16**	$1\frac{15}{16}$	8*	$1\frac{7}{8}$	**12**	$1\frac{59}{64}$	**16**	$1\frac{15}{16}$
$2\frac{1}{16}$	....	.....	..	.....	..	.....	..	.....	..	.....	**16**	2
$2\frac{1}{8}$	....	.....	..	.....	..	.....	8	2	**12**	$2\frac{3}{64}$	**16**	$2\frac{1}{16}$
$2\frac{3}{16}$	....	.....	..	.....	..	.....	..	...	..	.....	**16**	$2\frac{1}{8}$
$2\frac{1}{4}$	**4½**	$2\frac{1}{32}$	..	.....	..	.....	8*	$2\frac{1}{8}$	**12**	$2\frac{11}{64}$	**16**	$2\frac{3}{16}$
$2\frac{5}{16}$	....	.....	..	.....	..	.....	..	.....	..	.....	**16**	$2\frac{1}{4}$
$2\frac{3}{8}$	....	.....	..	.....	..	.....	..	...	**12**	$2\frac{19}{64}$	**16**	$2\frac{5}{16}$
$2\frac{7}{16}$	....	.....	..	.....	..	.....	..	...	..	.....	**16**	$2\frac{3}{8}$
$2\frac{1}{2}$	**4**	$2\frac{1}{4}$	..	.....	..	.....	8*	$2\frac{3}{8}$	**12**	$2\frac{27}{64}$	**16**	$2\frac{7}{16}$
$2\frac{5}{8}$	....	.....	..	.....	..	.....	..	...	**12**	$2\frac{35}{64}$	**16**	$2\frac{9}{16}$
$2\frac{3}{4}$	**4**	$2\frac{1}{2}$	..	.....	..	.....	8*	$2\frac{5}{8}$	**12**	$2\frac{43}{64}$	**16**	$2\frac{11}{16}$
$2\frac{7}{8}$	....	.....	..	.....	..	.....	..	...	**12**	$2\frac{51}{64}$	**16**	$2\frac{13}{16}$
3	**4**	$2\frac{3}{4}$	..	.....	..	.....	8*	$2\frac{7}{8}$	**12**	$2\frac{59}{64}$	**16**	$2\frac{15}{16}$
$3\frac{1}{8}$	....	.....	..	.....	..	.....	..	...	**12**	$3\frac{3}{64}$	**16**	$3\frac{1}{16}$
$3\frac{1}{4}$	**4**	3	..	.....	..	.....	8*	$3\frac{1}{8}$	**12**	$3\frac{11}{64}$	**16**	$3\frac{3}{16}$
$3\frac{3}{8}$	....	.....	..	.....	..	.....	..	...	**12**	$3\frac{19}{64}$	**16**	$3\frac{5}{16}$
$3\frac{1}{2}$	**4**	$3\frac{1}{4}$	..	.....	..	.....	8*	$3\frac{3}{8}$	**12**	$3\frac{27}{64}$	**16**	$3\frac{7}{16}$
$3\frac{5}{8}$	....	.....	..	.....	..	.....	..	...	**12**	$3\frac{35}{64}$	**16**	$3\frac{9}{16}$
$3\frac{3}{4}$	**4**	$3\frac{1}{2}$	..	.....	..	.....	8*	$3\frac{5}{8}$	**12**	$3\frac{43}{64}$	**16**	$3\frac{11}{16}$
$3\frac{7}{8}$	....	.....	..	.....	..	.....	..	...	**12**	$3\frac{51}{64}$	**16**	$3\frac{13}{16}$
4	**4**	$3\frac{3}{4}$	..	.....	..	.....	8*	$3\frac{7}{8}$	**12**	$3\frac{59}{64}$	**16**	$3\frac{15}{16}$
$4\frac{1}{4}$	....	.....	..	.....	..	.....	8*	$4\frac{1}{8}$	**12**	$4\frac{11}{64}$	**16**	$4\frac{3}{16}$
$4\frac{1}{2}$	....	.....	..	.....	..	.....	8*	$4\frac{3}{8}$	**12**	$4\frac{27}{64}$	**16**	$4\frac{7}{16}$
$4\frac{3}{4}$	....	.....	..	.....	..	.....	8*	$4\frac{5}{8}$	**12**	$4\frac{43}{64}$	**16**	$4\frac{11}{16}$
5	....	.....	..	.....	..	.....	8*	$4\frac{7}{8}$	**12**	$4\frac{59}{64}$	**16**	$4\frac{15}{16}$
$5\frac{1}{4}$	....	.....	..	.....	..	.....	8*	$5\frac{1}{8}$	**12**	$5\frac{11}{64}$	**16**	$5\frac{3}{16}$
$5\frac{1}{2}$	....	.....	..	.....	..	.....	8*	$5\frac{3}{8}$	**12**	$5\frac{27}{64}$	**16**	$5\frac{7}{16}$
$5\frac{3}{4}$	....	.....	..	.....	..	.....	8*	$5\frac{5}{8}$	**12**	$5\frac{43}{64}$	**16**	$5\frac{11}{16}$
6	....	.....	..	.....	..	.....	8*	$5\frac{7}{8}$	**12**	$5\frac{59}{64}$	**16**	$5\frac{15}{16}$

[1] ASA B1.1—1949. Dimensions are in inches.

[2] Limits of size for classes are based on a length of engagement equal to the nominal diameter.

[3] Limits of size for classes are based on a length of engagement equal to nine times the pitch.

[4] Bold type indicates unified combinations.

* These sizes, with specified limits of size, based on a length of engagement of 9 threads in classes 2A and 2B, are designated "UN."

NOTE: If a thread is in both the 8-, 12-, or 16-thread series and the coarse, fine, or extra-fine thread series, the symbols and tolerances of the latter series apply.

American Standard Square and Hexagon Bolts and Hexagon Cap Screws[1]

Nominal size (basic major diameter)	Regular bolts			Heavy bolts		
	Width across flats W, sq[2] and hex	Height H		Width across flats W	Height H	
		Unfin sq and hex	Semifin hex and hex screw[3]		Unfin hex	Semifin hex and hex screw
$\frac{1}{4}$	$\frac{3}{8}$(sq), $\frac{7}{16}$(hex)	$\frac{11}{64}$	$\frac{5}{32}$			
$\frac{5}{16}$	$\frac{1}{2}$	$\frac{7}{32}$	$\frac{13}{64}$			
$\frac{3}{8}$	$\frac{9}{16}$	$\frac{1}{4}$	$\frac{15}{64}$			
$\frac{7}{16}$	$\frac{5}{8}$	$\frac{19}{64}$	$\frac{9}{32}$			
$\frac{1}{2}$	$\frac{3}{4}$	$\frac{11}{32}$	$\frac{5}{16}$	$\frac{7}{8}$	$\frac{7}{16}$	$\frac{13}{32}$
$\frac{9}{16}$	$\frac{13}{16}$	$\frac{25}{64}$	$\frac{23}{64}$	$\frac{15}{16}$	$\frac{15}{32}$	$\frac{7}{16}$
$\frac{5}{8}$	$\frac{15}{16}$	$\frac{27}{64}$	$\frac{25}{64}$	$1\frac{1}{16}$	$\frac{17}{32}$	$\frac{1}{2}$
$\frac{3}{4}$	$1\frac{1}{8}$	$\frac{1}{2}$	$\frac{15}{32}$	$1\frac{1}{4}$	$\frac{5}{8}$	$\frac{19}{32}$
$\frac{7}{8}$	$1\frac{5}{16}$	$\frac{37}{64}$	$\frac{35}{64}$	$1\frac{7}{16}$	$\frac{23}{32}$	$\frac{11}{16}$
1	$1\frac{1}{2}$	$\frac{43}{64}$	$\frac{39}{64}$	$1\frac{5}{8}$	$\frac{13}{16}$	$\frac{3}{4}$
$1\frac{1}{8}$	$1\frac{11}{16}$	$\frac{3}{4}$	$\frac{11}{16}$	$1\frac{13}{16}$	$\frac{29}{32}$	$\frac{27}{32}$
$1\frac{1}{4}$	$1\frac{7}{8}$	$\frac{27}{32}$	$\frac{25}{32}$	2	1	$\frac{15}{16}$
$1\frac{3}{8}$	$2\frac{1}{16}$	$\frac{29}{32}$	$\frac{27}{32}$	$2\frac{3}{16}$	$1\frac{3}{32}$	$1\frac{1}{32}$
$1\frac{1}{2}$	$2\frac{1}{4}$	1	$\frac{15}{16}$	$2\frac{3}{8}$	$1\frac{3}{16}$	$1\frac{1}{8}$
$1\frac{5}{8}$	$2\frac{7}{16}$	$1\frac{1}{16}$	1	$2\frac{9}{16}$	$1\frac{9}{32}$	$1\frac{7}{32}$
$1\frac{3}{4}$	$2\frac{5}{8}$	$1\frac{5}{32}$	$1\frac{3}{32}$	$2\frac{3}{4}$	$1\frac{3}{8}$	$1\frac{5}{16}$
$1\frac{7}{8}$	$2\frac{13}{16}$	$1\frac{7}{32}$	$1\frac{5}{32}$	$2\frac{15}{16}$	$1\frac{15}{32}$	$1\frac{13}{32}$
2	3	$1\frac{11}{32}$	$1\frac{7}{32}$	$3\frac{1}{8}$	$1\frac{9}{16}$	$1\frac{7}{16}$
$2\frac{1}{4}$	$3\frac{3}{8}$	$1\frac{1}{2}$	$1\frac{3}{8}$	$3\frac{1}{2}$	$1\frac{3}{4}$	$1\frac{5}{8}$
$2\frac{1}{2}$	$3\frac{3}{4}$	$1\frac{21}{32}$	$1\frac{17}{32}$	$3\frac{7}{8}$	$1\frac{15}{16}$	$1\frac{13}{16}$
$2\frac{3}{4}$	$4\frac{1}{8}$	$1\frac{13}{16}$	$1\frac{11}{16}$	$4\frac{1}{4}$	$2\frac{1}{8}$	2
3	$4\frac{1}{2}$	2	$1\frac{7}{8}$	$4\frac{5}{8}$	$2\frac{5}{16}$	$2\frac{3}{16}$
$3\frac{1}{4}$	$4\frac{7}{8}$	$2\frac{3}{16}$	2			
$3\frac{1}{2}$	$5\frac{1}{4}$	$2\frac{5}{16}$	$2\frac{1}{8}$			
$3\frac{3}{4}$	$5\frac{5}{8}$	$2\frac{1}{2}$	$2\frac{5}{16}$			
4	6	$2\frac{11}{16}$	$2\frac{1}{2}$			

[1] ASA B18—1951. All dimensions in inches.

[2] Square bolts in (nominal) size from $\frac{1}{4}$ to $1\frac{1}{2}$ only.

[3] Hexagon-head cap screw, automotive hexagon-head bolt, and close-tolerance regular bolt; lengths from $\frac{1}{4}$ to 3 in. only.

For bolt length increments see table page 657.

Threads are coarse series, class 2A except with hexagon screw which is coarse, fine, or 8-pitch series, class 2A.

Minimum thread length $\begin{cases} \text{2D} + \frac{1}{4} \text{ in. for bolts 6 in. or less in length.} \\ \text{2D} + \frac{1}{2} \text{ in. for bolts over 6 in. in length.} \\ \text{Bolts too short for formula, thread entire length.} \end{cases}$

American Standard Square and Hexagon Nuts[1]

Nominal size (basic major diameter)	Regular nuts						Heavy nuts					Slot	
	Width across flats W, sq and hex	Thickness T					Width across flats W, sq and hex	Thickness T					
		Unfin sq and hex	Unfin hex jam	Semifin hex and hex slotted[2]	Semifin hex jam	Semifin hex thick, thick slotted,[2] and castle		Unfin sq and hex	Unfin hex jam	Semifin hex and hex slotted	Semifin hex jam	Width	Depth
1/4	7/16	15/64	11/64	7/32	5/32	9/32	1/2	1/4	3/16	15/64	11/64	5/64	3/32
5/16	1/2	9/32	13/64	17/64	3/16	21/64	9/16	5/16	7/32	19/64	13/64	3/32	3/32
3/8	9/16	11/32	15/64	21/64	7/32	13/32	11/16	3/8	1/4	23/64	15/64	1/8	1/8
7/16	11/16	25/64	17/64	3/8	1/4	29/64	3/4	7/16	9/32	27/64	17/64	1/8	5/32
1/2	3/4	29/64	21/64	7/16	5/16	9/16	7/8	1/2	5/16	31/64	19/64	5/32	5/32
9/16	7/8	1/2	21/64	31/64	5/16	39/64	15/16	9/16	11/32	35/64	21/64	5/32	3/16
5/8	15/16	9/16	25/64	35/64	3/8	23/32	1 1/16	5/8	3/8	39/64	23/64	3/16	7/32
3/4	1 1/8	21/32	7/16	41/64	27/64	13/16	1 1/4	3/4	7/16	47/64	27/64	3/16	1/4
7/8	1 5/16	49/64	1/2	3/4	31/64	29/32	1 7/16	7/8	1/2	55/64	31/64	3/16	1/4
1	1 1/2	7/8	9/16	55/64	35/64	1	1 5/8	1	9/16	63/64	35/64	1/4	9/32
1 1/8	1 11/16	1	5/8	31/32	39/64	1 5/32	1 13/16	1 1/8	5/8	1 7/64	39/64	1/4	11/32
1 1/4	1 7/8	1 3/32	3/4	1 1/16	23/32	1 1/4	2	1 1/4	3/4	1 7/32	23/32	5/16	3/8
1 3/8	2 1/16	1 13/64	13/16	1 11/64	25/32	1 3/8	2 3/16	1 3/8	13/16	1 11/32	25/32	5/16	3/8
1 1/2	2 1/4	1 5/16	7/8	1 9/32	27/32	1 1/2	2 3/8	1 1/2	7/8	1 15/32	27/32	3/8	7/16
1 5/8	2 7/16	....	....	1 25/64	29/32	.....	2 9/16	1 5/8	15/16	1 19/32	29/32	3/8	7/16
1 3/4	2 5/8	....	....	1 1/2	31/32	.....	2 3/4	1 3/4	1	1 23/32	31/32	7/16	1/2
1 7/8	2 13/16	....	....	1 39/64	1 1/32	.....	2 15/16	1 7/8	1 1/16	1 27/32	1 1/32	7/16	9/16
2	3	....	....	1 23/32	1 3/32	.....	3 1/8	2	1 1/8	1 31/32	1 3/32	7/16	9/16
2 1/4	3 3/8	....	....	1 59/64	1 13/64	.....	3 1/2	2 1/4	1 1/4	2 13/64	1 13/64	7/16	9/16
2 1/2	3 3/4	....	....	2 9/64	1 29/64	.....	3 7/8	2 1/2	1 1/2	2 29/64	1 29/64	9/16	11/16
2 3/4	4 1/8	....	....	2 23/64	1 37/64	.....	4 1/4	2 3/4	1 5/8	2 45/64	1 37/64	9/16	11/16
3	4 1/2	....	....	2 37/64	1 45/64	.....	4 5/8	3	1 3/4	2 61/64	1 45/64	5/8	3/4
3 1/4	....	....	....	....	....	.....	5	3 1/4	1 7/8	3 3/16	1 13/16	5/8	3/4
3 1/2	....	....	....	....	....	.....	5 3/8	3 1/2	2	3 7/16	1 15/16	5/8	3/4
3 3/4	....	....	....	....	....	.....	5 3/4	3 3/4	2 1/8	3 11/16	2 1/16	5/8	3/4
4	....	....	....	....	....	.....	6 1/8	4	2 1/4	3 15/16	2 3/16	5/8	3/4

[1] ASA B18—1951. All dimensions in inches.

[2] Slot dimensions for regular slotted nuts are same as for heavy slotted nuts.

Thread—unfinished nuts: coarse series, class 2B; semifinished nuts: coarse, fine, or 8-pitch series, class 2B.

American Standard Round-head Bolts[1]

PROPORTIONS FOR DRAWING PURPOSES

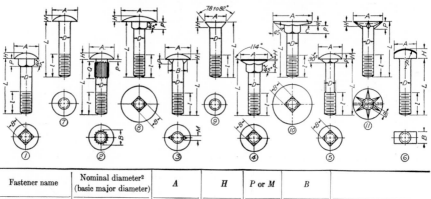

	Fastener name	Nominal diameter[2] (basic major diameter)	A	H	P or M	B	
Carriage bolts	① Round-head square-neck bolt[3]	No. 10, ¼″ to ½″ by (¹⁄₁₆″), ⅝″ to 1″ by (⅛″)	$2D + \frac{1}{16}$	$\frac{D}{2}$	$\frac{D}{2}$	D	
	② Round-head ribbed-neck bolt[4]	No. 10, ¼″ to ½″ by (¹⁄₁₆″), ⅝″ and ¾″	$2D + \frac{1}{16}$	$\frac{D}{2}$	¹⁄₁₆	$D + \frac{1}{16}$	Q $\begin{cases} \text{³⁄₁₆″ for } L = \text{⅞″ or less} \\ \text{⁵⁄₁₆″ for } L = 1″ \text{ and } 1⅛″ \\ \text{½″ for } L = 1¼″ \text{ or more} \end{cases}$
	③ Round-head fin-neck bolt[3]	No. 10, ¼″ to ½″ by (¹⁄₁₆″)	$2D + \frac{1}{16}$	$\frac{D}{2}$	$⅜D$	$1½D + \frac{1}{16}$	[1] The proportions in this table are in some instances approximate and are intended for drawing purposes only. For exact dimensions see ASA B18.5—1951, from which this table was compiled. Dimensions are in inches.
	④ 114° countersunk square-neck bolt[3]	No. 10, ¼″ to ½″ by (¹⁄₁₆″), ⅝″ and ¾″	$2D + ⅛$	$¹⁄₃₂$	$D + \frac{1}{32}$	D	[2] Fractions in parentheses show diameter increments, *e.g.*, ¼″ to ½″ by (¹⁄₁₆″) includes the diameters ¼″, ⁵⁄₁₆″, ⅜″, ⁷⁄₁₆″, and ½″. Threads are coarse series, class 2A.
⑤	Round-head short square-neck bolt[5]	¼″ to ½″ by (¹⁄₁₆″), ⅝″ and ¾″	$2D + \frac{1}{16}$	$\frac{D}{2}$	$\frac{D}{4} + \frac{1}{32}$	D	Minimum thread length (l) $\begin{cases} 2D + ¼″ \text{ for bolts 6″ or less in length.} \\ 2D + ½″ \text{ for bolts over 6″ in length.} \end{cases}$
⑥	T-head bolt[4]	¼″ to ½″ by (¹⁄₁₆″), ⅝″ to 1″ by (⅛″)	$2D$	$⅞D$	$1⅝D$	D	For bolt length increments see table page 657. [3] Full-size body bolts furnished unless undersize body is specified. [4] Only full-size body bolts furnished. [5] Undersize body bolts furnished unless full-size body is specified.
⑦	Round-head bolt[3] (Button-head bolt)	No. 10, ¼″ to ½″ by (¹⁄₁₆″), ⅝″ to 1″ by (⅛″)	$2D + \frac{1}{16}$	$\frac{D}{2}$			
⑧	Step bolt[3]	No. 10, ¼″ to ½″ by (¹⁄₁₆″)	$3D + \frac{1}{16}$	$\frac{D}{2}$	$\frac{D}{2}$	D	
⑨	Countersunk bolt[3] (may be slotted if so specified)	¼″ to ½″ by (¹⁄₁₆″), ⅝″ to 1½″ by (⅛″)	$1.8D$	Obtain by projection			
⑩	Elevator bolt, flat head, countersunk[3]	No. 10, ¼″ to ½″ by (¹⁄₁₆″)	$2½D + ⁵⁄₁₆$	$\frac{D}{3}$	$\frac{D}{2} + \frac{1}{16}$	D	Angle $C = 16D + 5°$ (approx.)
⑪	Elevator bolt, ribbed head[4] (slotted or unslotted as specified)	¼″, ⁵⁄₁₆″, ⅜″	$2D + \frac{1}{16}$	$\frac{D}{2} - \frac{1}{32}$	$\frac{D}{2} + \frac{3}{64}$	$\frac{D}{8} + \frac{1}{16}$	

Bolt Length Increments[1]

Bolt diameter	1/4	5/16	3/8	7/16	1/2	5/8	3/4	7/8	1
Length increments 1/4	3/4–3	3/4–4	3/4–6	1–3	1–6	1–6	1–6	1–4½	
1/2	3–4	4–5	6–9	3–6	6–13	6–10	6–15	4½–6	3–6
1	4–5	...	9–12	6–8	13–24	10–22	15–24	6–20	6–12
2	...	...	....	...	.....	22–30	24–30	20–30	12–30

Example: 1/4" bolt lengths increase by 1/4" increments from 3/4" to 3" length. 1/2" bolt lengths increase by 1/2" increments from 6" to 13" length. 1" bolt lengths increase by 2" increments from 12" to 30" length.

[1] Compiled from manufacturers' catalogues.

American Standard Cap Screws[1]—Socket[2] and Slotted Heads[3]
FOR HEXAGON-HEAD SCREWS, SEE PAGE 654

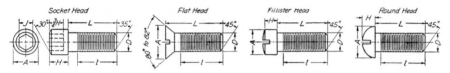

Nominal diameter	Socket head[4] A	H	J	Flat head[5] A	Fillister head[5] A	H	Round head[5] A	H
2	0.140	0.086	1/16					
3	0.161	0.099	5/64					
4	0.183	0.112	5/64					
5	0.205	0.125	3/32					
6	0.226	0.138	3/32					
8	0.270	0.164	1/8					
10	5/16	0.190	5/32					
12	11/32	0.216	5/32					
1/4	3/8	1/4	3/16	1/2	3/8	11/64	7/16	3/16
5/16	7/16	5/16	7/32	5/8	7/16	13/64	9/16	15/64
3/8	9/16	3/8	5/16	3/4	9/16	1/4	5/8	17/64
7/16	5/8	7/16	5/16	13/16	5/8	19/64	3/4	5/16
1/2	3/4	1/2	3/8	7/8	3/4	21/64	13/16	11/32
9/16	13/16	9/16	3/8	1	13/16	3/8	15/16	13/32
5/8	7/8	5/8	1/2	1 1/8	7/8	27/64	1	7/16
3/4	1	3/4	9/16	1 3/8	1	1/2	1 1/4	17/32
7/8	1 1/8	7/8	9/16	1 5/8	1 1/8	19/32		
1	1 5/16	1	5/8	1 7/8	1 5/16	21/32		
1 1/8	1 1/2	1 1/8	3/4					
1 1/4	1 3/4	1 1/4	3/4					
1 3/8	1 7/8	1 3/8	3/4					
1 1/2	2	1 1/2	1					

[1] Dimensions in inches.
[2] ASA B18.3—1947.
[3] ASA B18.6—1947.
[4] Body length increments { for screw lengths 1/4" to 1" = 1/8". for screw lengths, 1" to 4" = 1/4". for screw lengths 4" to 6" = 1/2".
[4] Thread length (l) { coarse thread: 2D + 1/2". fine thread: 1½D + 1/2".
[5] Thread either coarse or fine, class 3.
Thread length (l): 2D + 1/4.
Slot proportions vary with size of screw; draw to look well.
Body length increments may be taken the same as for socket-head screws.

American Standard Machine Screws[1]

HEADS MAY BE SLOTTED OR RECESSED

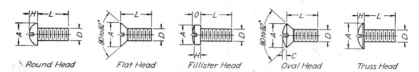

Round Head   Flat Head   Fillister Head   Oval Head   Truss Head

Nominal diameter	Round head		Flat head	Fillister head			Oval head		Truss head	
	A	H	A	A	H	O	A	C	A	H
0	0.113	0.053	0.119	0.096	0.045	0.059	0.119	0.021		
1	0.138	0.061	0.146	0.118	0.053	0.071	0.146	0.025	0.194	0.053
2	0.162	0.069	0.172	0.140	0.062	0.083	0.172	0.029	0.226	0.061
3	0.187	0.078	0.199	0.161	0.070	0.095	0.199	0.033	0.257	0.069
4	0.211	0.086	0.225	0.183	0.079	0.107	0.225	0.037	0.289	0.078
5	0.236	0.095	0.252	0.205	0.088	0.120	0.252	0.041	0.321	0.086
6	0.260	0.103	0.279	0.226	0.096	0.132	0.279	0.045	0.352	0.094
8	0.309	0.120	0.332	0.270	0.113	0.156	0.332	0.052	0.384	0.102
10	0.359	0.137	0.385	0.313	0.130	0.180	0.385	0.060	0.448	0.118
12	0.408	0.153	0.438	0.357	0.148	0.205	0.438	0.068	0.511	0.134
1/4	0.472	0.175	0.507	0.414	0.170	0.237	0.507	0.079	0.573	0.150
5/16	0.590	0.216	0.635	0.518	0.211	0.295	0.635	0.099	0.698	0.183
3/8	0.708	0.256	0.762	0.622	0.253	0.355	0.762	0.117	0.823	0.215
7/16	0.750	0.328	0.812	0.625	0.265	0.368	0.812	0.122	0.948	0.248
1/2	0.813	0.355	0.875	0.750	0.297	0.412	0.875	0.131	1.073	0.280
9/16	0.938	0.410	1.000	0.812	0.336	0.466	1.000	0.150	1.198	0.312
5/8	1.000	0.438	1.125	0.875	0.375	0.521	1.125	0.169	1.323	0.345
3/4	1.250	0.547	1.375	1.000	0.441	0.612	1.375	0.206	1.573	0.410

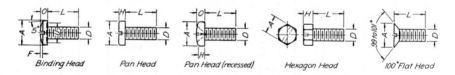

Binding Head   Pan Head   Pan Head (recessed)   Hexagon Head   100° Flat Head

Nominal diameter	Binding head				Pan head			Hexagon head		100° flat head
	A	O	F	U	A	H	O	A	H	A
2	0.181	0.046	0.018	0.141	0.167	0.053	0.062	0.125	0.050	
3	0.208	0.054	0.022	0.162	0.193	0.060	0.071	0.187	0.055	
4	0.235	0.063	0.025	0.184	0.219	0.068	0.080	0.187	0.060	0.225
5	0.263	0.071	0.029	0.205	0.245	0.075	0.089	0.187	0.070	
6	0.290	0.080	0.032	0.226	0.270	0.082	0.097	0.250	0.080	0.279
8	0.344	0.097	0.039	0.269	0.322	0.096	0.115	0.250	0.110	0.332
10	0.399	0.114	0.045	0.312	0.373	0.110	0.133	0.312	0.120	0.385
12	0.454	0.130	0.052	0.354	0.425	0.125	0.151	0.312	0.155	
1/4	0.513	0.153	0.061	0.410	0.492	0.144	0.175	0.375	0.190	0.507
5/16	0.641	0.193	0.077	0.513	0.615	0.178	0.218	0.500	0.230	0.635
3/8	0.769	0.234	0.094	0.615	0.740	0.212	0.261	0.562	0.295	0.762

[1] ASA B18.6—1947. Dimensions given are maximum values, all in inches.

Thread length { screws 2 in. long or less, thread entire length.

{ screws over 2 in. long, thread length (l) = 1¾ in.

Threads are coarse or fine series, class 2.

Heads may be slotted or recessed as specified, excepting hexagon form which is plain or may be slotted if so specified.

Slot and recess proportions vary with size of fastener; draw to look well.

American Standard Machine-screw[2] and Stove-bolt[3] Nuts[1]

Nominal size	0	1	2	3	4	5	6	8	10	12	¼	5/16	3/8
"W"	5/32	5/32	3/16	3/16	¼	5/16	5/16	11/32	3/8	7/16	7/16	9/16	5/8
"T"	3/64	3/64	1/16	1/16	3/32	7/64	7/64	1/8	1/8	5/32	3/16	7/32	¼

[1] ASA B18—1951. Dimensions are in inches.
[2] Machine-screw nuts are hexagonal and square.
[3] Stove-bolt nuts are square.
Thread is coarse series for square nuts, coarse or fine series for hexagon nuts; class 2B.

American Standard Hexagon Socket,[1] Slotted Headless,[2] and Square-head[3] Setscrews

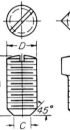

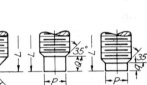

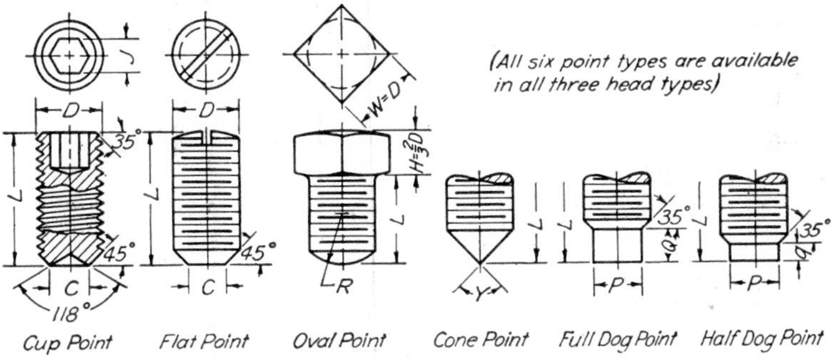

(All six point types are available in all three head types)

Cup Point   Flat Point   Oval Point   Cone Point   Full Dog Point   Half Dog Point

Diameter D	Cup and flat-point diameter C	Oval-point radius R	Cone-point angle Y		Full and half dog points			Socket width J
			118° for these lengths and shorter	90° for these lengths and longer	Diameter P	Length Full Q	Length Half q	
5	1/16	3/32	1/8	3/16	0.083	0.06	0.03	1/16
6	0.069	7/64	1/8	3/16	0.092	0.07	0.03	1/16
8	5/64	1/8	3/16	¼	0.109	0.08	0.04	5/64
10	3/32	9/64	3/16	¼	0.127	0.09	0.04	3/32
12	7/64	5/32	3/16	¼	0.144	0.11	0.06	3/32
¼	1/8	3/16	¼	5/16	5/32	1/8	1/16	1/8
5/16	11/64	15/64	5/16	3/8	13/64	5/32	5/64	5/32
3/8	13/64	9/32	3/8	7/16	¼	3/16	3/32	3/16
7/16	15/64	21/64	7/16	½	19/64	7/32	7/64	7/32
½	9/32	3/8	½	9/16	11/32	¼	1/8	¼
9/16	5/16	27/64	9/16	5/8	25/64	9/32	9/64	¼
5/8	23/64	15/32	5/8	¾	15/32	5/16	5/32	5/16
¾	7/16	9/16	¾	7/8	9/16	3/8	3/16	3/8
7/8	33/64	21/32	7/8	1	21/32	7/16	7/32	½
1	19/32	¾	1	1⅛	¾	½	¼	9/16
1⅛	43/64	27/32	1⅛	1¼	27/32	9/16	9/32	9/16
1¼	¾	15/16	1¼	1½	15/16	5/8	5/16	5/8
1⅜	53/64	1 1/32	1⅜	1⅝	1 1/32	11/16	11/32	5/8
1½	29/32	1 1/8	1½	1¾	1 1/8	¾	3/8	¾
1¾	1 1/16	1 5/16	1¾	2	1 5/16	7/8	7/16	1
2	1 7/32	1 ½	2	2¼	1 ½	1	½	1

Dimensions are in inches. Threads are coarse or fine series, classes 2 or 2A.
[1] ASA B18.3—1947.
Length increments: ¼" to 5/8" by (1/16"); 5/8" to 1" by (⅛"); 1" to 4" by (¼"); 4" to 6" by (½"). Fractions in parentheses show length increments; for example, 5/8" to 1" by ⅛" includes the lengths 5/8", ¾", 7/8" and 1".
[2] ASA B18.6—1947.
Slotted headless screws standardized in sizes No. 5 to ¾" only. Slot proportions vary with diameter. Draw to look well.
[1] ASA B18—1951.
Square head set screws are standardized in sizes No. 10 to 1½" only.

American Standard Socket-head Shoulder Screws[1]

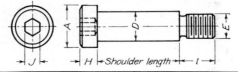

Shoulder diameter D			Head[2]			Thread		Shoulder lengths[4]
Nominal	Max	Min	Diameter A	Height H	Hexagon[3] J	Specification E	Length l	
$\frac{1}{4}$	0.2480	0.2460	$\frac{3}{8}$	$\frac{3}{16}$	$\frac{1}{8}$	10-24NC-3	$\frac{3}{8}$	$\frac{3}{4}$–$2\frac{1}{2}$
$\frac{5}{16}$	0.3105	0.3085	$\frac{7}{16}$	$\frac{7}{32}$	$\frac{5}{32}$	$\frac{1}{4}$-20NC-3	$\frac{7}{16}$	1 –3
$\frac{3}{8}$	0.3730	0.3710	$\frac{9}{16}$	$\frac{1}{4}$	$\frac{3}{16}$	$\frac{5}{16}$-18NC-3	$\frac{1}{2}$	1 –4
$\frac{1}{2}$	0.4980	0.4960	$\frac{3}{4}$	$\frac{5}{16}$	$\frac{1}{4}$	$\frac{3}{8}$-16NC-3	$\frac{5}{8}$	$1\frac{1}{4}$–5
$\frac{5}{8}$	0.6230	0.6210	$\frac{7}{8}$	$\frac{3}{8}$	$\frac{5}{16}$	$\frac{1}{2}$-13NC-3	$\frac{3}{4}$	$1\frac{1}{2}$–6
$\frac{3}{4}$	0.7480	0.7460	1	$\frac{1}{2}$	$\frac{3}{8}$	$\frac{5}{8}$-11NC-3	$\frac{7}{8}$	$1\frac{1}{2}$–8
1	0.9980	0.9960	$1\frac{5}{16}$	$\frac{5}{8}$	$\frac{1}{2}$	$\frac{3}{4}$-10NC-3	1	$1\frac{1}{2}$–8
$1\frac{1}{4}$	1.2480	1.2460	$1\frac{3}{4}$	$\frac{3}{4}$	$\frac{5}{8}$	$\frac{7}{8}$-9NC-3	$1\frac{1}{8}$	$1\frac{1}{2}$–8

[1] ASA B18.3—1947. Dimensions are in inches.
[2] Head chamfer is 30°.
[3] Socket depth = $\frac{3}{4}H$.

[4] Shoulder length increments
- shoulder lengths from $\frac{3}{4}''$ to $1''$, $\frac{1}{8}''$ intervals.
- shoulder lengths from $1''$ to $5''$, $\frac{1}{4}''$ intervals.
- shoulder lengths from $5''$ to $7''$, $\frac{1}{2}''$ intervals.
- shoulder lengths from $7''$ to $8''$, $1''$ intervals.

Shoulder length tolerance ± 0.005.

American Standard Wood Screws[1]

Round Head   Flat Head   Oval Head

Nominal size	Basic diameter of screw D	No. of threads per in.[2]	Slot width[3] J (all heads)	Round head		Flat head	Oval head	
				A	H	A	A	C
0	0.060	32	0.023	0.113	0.053	0.119	0.119	0.021
1	0.073	28	0.026	0.138	0.061	0.146	0.146	0.025
2	0.086	26	0.031	0.162	0.069	0.172	0.172	0.029
3	0.099	24	0.035	0.187	0.078	0.199	0.199	0.033
4	0.112	22	0.039	0.211	0.086	0.225	0.225	0.037
5	0.125	20	0.043	0.236	0.095	0.252	0.252	0.041
6	0.138	18	0.048	0.260	0.103	0.279	0.279	0.045
7	0.151	16	0.048	0.285	0.111	0.305	0.305	0.049
8	0.164	15	0.054	0.309	0.120	0.332	0.332	0.052
9	0.177	14	0.054	0.334	0.128	0.358	0.358	0.056
10	0.190	13	0.060	0.359	0.137	0.385	0.385	0.060
12	0.216	11	0.067	0.408	0.153	0.438	0.438	0.068
14	0.242	10	0.075	0.457	0.170	0.491	0.491	0.076
16	0.268	9	0.075	0.506	0.187	0.544	0.544	0.084
18	0.294	8	0.084	0.555	0.204	0.597	0.597	0.092
20	0.320	8	0.084	0.604	0.220	0.650	0.650	0.100
24	0.372	7	0.094	0.702	0.254	0.756	0.756	0.116

Dimensions given are maximum values, all in inches.
[1] ASA B18.6—1947.
Heads may be slotted or recessed as specified.
[2] Thread length (l) = $\frac{2}{3}L$.
[3] Slot depths and recesses vary with type and size of screw; draw to look well.

Widths and Heights of Standard Square- and Flat-stock Keys with Corresponding Shaft Diameters

APPROVED BY AMERICAN STANDARDS ASSOCIATION[1]

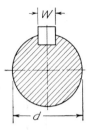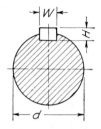

Shaft diameter d (inclusive)	Square-stock keys W	Flat-stock keys, W × H	Shaft diameter d (inclusive)	Square-stock keys W	Flat-stock keys, W × H
1/2 – 9/16	1/8	1/8 × 3/32	2 7/8–3 1/4	3/4	3/4 × 1/2
5/8 – 7/8	3/16	3/16 × 1/8	3 3/8–3 3/4	7/8	7/8 × 5/8
15/16–1 1/4	1/4	1/4 × 3/16	3 7/8–4 1/2	1	1 × 3/4
1 5/16–1 3/8	5/16	5/16 × 1/4			
1 7/16–1 3/4	3/8	3/8 × 1/4	4 3/4–5 1/2	1 1/4	1 1/4 × 7/8
1 13/16–2 1/4	1/2	1/2 × 3/8	5 3/4–6	1 1/2	1 1/2 × 1
2 5/16–2 3/4	5/8	5/8 × 7/16			

Dimensions in inches.
[1] ASA B17.1 1934.

Dimensions of Standard Gib-head Keys, Square and Flat

APPROVED BY AMERICAN STANDARDS ASSOCIATION[1]

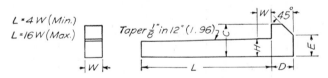

L = 4 W (Min.)
L = 16 W (Max.)

Taper 1/8″ in 12″ (1.96)

Diameters of shafts	Square type					Flat type				
	Key		Gib head			Key		Gib head		
	W	H	C	D	E	W	H	C	D	E
1/2 – 9/16	1/8	1/8	1/4	7/32	5/32	1/8	3/32	3/16	1/8	1/8
5/8 – 7/8	3/16	3/16	5/16	9/32	7/32	3/16	1/8	1/4	3/16	5/32
15/16–1 1/4	1/4	1/4	7/16	11/32	11/32	1/4	3/16	5/16	1/4	3/16
1 5/16–1 3/8	5/16	5/16	9/16	13/32	13/32	5/16	1/4	3/8	5/16	1/4
1 7/16–1 3/4	3/8	3/8	11/16	15/32	15/32	3/8	1/4	7/16	3/8	5/16
1 13/16–2 1/4	1/2	1/2	7/8	19/32	5/8	1/2	3/8	5/8	1/2	7/16
2 5/16–2 3/4	5/8	5/8	1 1/16	23/32	3/4	5/8	7/16	3/4	5/8	1/2
2 7/8 –3 1/4	3/4	3/4	1 1/4	7/8	7/8	3/4	1/2	7/8	3/4	5/8
3 3/8 –3 3/4	7/8	7/8	1 1/2	1	1	7/8	5/8	1 1/16	7/8	3/4
3 7/8 –4 1/2	1	1	1 3/4	1 3/16	1 3/16	1	3/4	1 1/4	1	1 3/16
4 3/4 –5 1/2	1 1/4	1 1/4	2	1 7/16	1 7/16	1 1/4	7/8	1 1/2	1 1/4	1
5 3/4 –6	1 1/2	1 1/2	2 1/2	1 3/4	1 3/4	1 1/2	1	1 3/4	1 1/2	1 1/4

Dimensions in inches.
[1] ASA B17.1 1934

Woodruff Key Dimensions

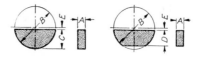

Key[1] No.	Nominal size $A \times B$	Maximum width of key A	Maximum diameter of key B	Maximum height of key		Distance below center E
				C	D	
204	$\frac{1}{16} \times \frac{1}{2}$	0.0635	0.500	0.203	0.194	$\frac{3}{64}$
304	$\frac{3}{32} \times \frac{1}{2}$	0.0948	0.500	0.203	0.194	$\frac{3}{64}$
305	$\frac{3}{32} \times \frac{5}{8}$	0.0948	0.625	0.250	0.240	$\frac{1}{16}$
404	$\frac{1}{8} \times \frac{1}{2}$	0.1260	0.500	0.203	0.194	$\frac{3}{64}$
405	$\frac{1}{8} \times \frac{5}{8}$	0.1260	0.625	0.250	0.240	$\frac{1}{16}$
406	$\frac{1}{8} \times \frac{3}{4}$	0.1260	0.750	0.313	0.303	$\frac{1}{16}$
505	$\frac{5}{32} \times \frac{5}{8}$	0.1573	0.625	0.250	0.240	$\frac{1}{16}$
506	$\frac{5}{32} \times \frac{3}{4}$	0.1573	0.750	0.313	0.303	$\frac{1}{16}$
507	$\frac{5}{32} \times \frac{7}{8}$	0.1573	0.875	0.375	0.365	$\frac{1}{16}$
606	$\frac{3}{16} \times \frac{3}{4}$	0.1885	0.750	0.313	0.303	$\frac{1}{16}$
607	$\frac{3}{16} \times \frac{7}{8}$	0.1885	0.875	0.375	0.365	$\frac{1}{16}$
608	$\frac{3}{16} \times 1$	0.1885	1.000	0.438	0.428	$\frac{1}{16}$
609	$\frac{3}{16} \times 1\frac{1}{8}$	0.1885	1.125	0.484	0.475	$\frac{5}{64}$
807	$\frac{1}{4} \times \frac{7}{8}$	0.2510	0.875	0.375	0.365	$\frac{1}{16}$
808	$\frac{1}{4} \times 1$	0.2510	1.000	0.438	0.428	$\frac{1}{16}$
809	$\frac{1}{4} \times 1\frac{1}{8}$	0.2510	1.125	0.484	0.475	$\frac{5}{64}$
810	$\frac{1}{4} \times 1\frac{1}{4}$	0.2510	1.250	0.547	0.537	$\frac{5}{64}$
811	$\frac{1}{4} \times 1\frac{3}{8}$	0.2510	1.375	0.594	0.584	$\frac{3}{32}$
812	$\frac{1}{4} \times 1\frac{1}{2}$	0.2510	1.500	0.641	0.631	$\frac{7}{64}$
1008	$\frac{5}{16} \times 1$	0.3135	1.000	0.438	0.428	$\frac{1}{16}$
1009	$\frac{5}{16} \times 1\frac{1}{8}$	0.3135	1.125	0.484	0.475	$\frac{5}{64}$
1010	$\frac{5}{16} \times 1\frac{1}{4}$	0.3135	1.250	0.547	0.537	$\frac{5}{64}$
1011	$\frac{5}{16} \times 1\frac{3}{8}$	0.3135	1.375	0.594	0.584	$\frac{3}{32}$
1012	$\frac{5}{16} \times 1\frac{1}{2}$	0.3135	1.500	0.641	0.631	$\frac{7}{64}$
1210	$\frac{3}{8} \times 1\frac{1}{4}$	0.3760	1.250	0.547	0.537	$\frac{5}{64}$
1211	$\frac{3}{8} \times 1\frac{3}{8}$	0.3760	1.375	0.594	0.584	$\frac{3}{32}$
1212	$\frac{3}{8} \times 1\frac{1}{2}$	0.3760	1.500	0.641	0.631	$\frac{7}{64}$

Dimensions in inches.

[1] Key numbers indicate the nominal key dimensions. The last two digits give the nominal diameter B in eighths of an inch and the digits preceding the last two give the nominal width A in thirty-seconds of an inch. Thus, 204 indicates a key $\frac{3}{32}$ by $\frac{5}{8}$, or $\frac{1}{16}$ by $\frac{1}{2}$ inch.

Woodruff Key-seat Dimensions

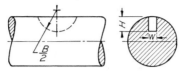

Key[1] No.	Nominal size	Key slot			
		Width W		Depth H	
		Maximum	Minimum	Maximum	Minimum
204	$\frac{1}{16} \times \frac{1}{2}$	0.0630	0.0615	0.1718	0.1668
304	$\frac{3}{32} \times \frac{1}{2}$	0.0943	0.0928	0.1561	0.1511
305	$\frac{3}{32} \times \frac{5}{8}$	0.0943	0.0928	0.2031	0.1981
404	$\frac{1}{8} \times \frac{1}{2}$	0 1255	0.1240	0.1405	0.1355
405	$\frac{1}{8} \times \frac{5}{8}$	0.1255	0.1240	0.1875	0.1825
406	$\frac{1}{8} \times \frac{3}{4}$	0.1255	0.1240	0.2505	0.2455
505	$\frac{5}{32} \times \frac{5}{8}$	0.1568	0.1553	0.1719	0.1669
506	$\frac{5}{32} \times \frac{3}{4}$	0.1568	0.1553	0.2349	0.2299
507	$\frac{5}{32} \times \frac{7}{8}$	0.1568	0.1553	0.2969	0.2919
606	$\frac{3}{16} \times \frac{3}{4}$	0 1880	0.1863	0.2193	0.2143
607	$\frac{3}{16} \times \frac{7}{8}$	0.1880	0.1863	0.2813	0.2763
608	$\frac{3}{16} \times 1$	0.1880	0.1863	0.3443	0.3393
609	$\frac{3}{16} \times 1\frac{1}{8}$	0.1880	0.1863	0.3903	0.3853
807	$\frac{1}{4} \times \frac{7}{8}$	0.2505	0.2487	0.2500	0.2450
808	$\frac{1}{4} \times 1$	0.2505	0.2487	0.3130	0.3080
809	$\frac{1}{4} \times 1\frac{1}{8}$	0.2505	0.2487	0.3590	0.3540
810	$\frac{1}{4} \times 1\frac{1}{4}$	0 2505	0.2487	0.4220	0.4170
811	$\frac{1}{4} \times 1\frac{3}{8}$	0.2505	0.2487	0.4690	0.4640
812	$\frac{1}{4} \times 1\frac{1}{2}$	0.2505	0.2487	0.5160	0.5110
1008	$\frac{5}{16} \times 1$	0.3130	0.3111	0.2818	0.2768
1009	$\frac{5}{16} \times 1\frac{1}{8}$	0.3130	0.3111	0.3278	0.3228
1010	$\frac{5}{16} \times 1\frac{1}{4}$	0.3130	0.3111	0.3908	0.3858
1011	$\frac{5}{16} \times 1\frac{3}{8}$	0.3130	0.3111	0.4378	0.4328
1012	$\frac{5}{16} \times 1\frac{1}{2}$	0.3130	0.3111	0.4848	0.4798
1210	$\frac{3}{8} \times 1\frac{1}{4}$	0.3755	0.3735	0.3595	0.3545
1211	$\frac{3}{8} \times 1\frac{3}{8}$	0.3755	0.3735	0.4060	0.4015
1212	$\frac{3}{8} \times 1\frac{1}{2}$	0.3755	0.3735	0.4535	0.4485

Dimensions in inches.

[1] Key numbers indicate the nominal key dimensions. The last two digits give the nominal diameter B in eighths of an inch and the digits preceding the last two give the nominal width A in thirty-seconds of an inch. Thus, 204 indicates a key $\frac{3}{32}$ by $\frac{5}{8}$, or $\frac{1}{16}$ by $\frac{1}{2}$ inch.

Dimensions of Pratt and Whitney Keys

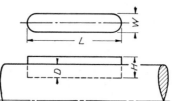

Key No.	L	W	H	D	Key No.	L	W	H	D
1	1/2	1/16	3/32	1/16	22	1 3/8	1/4	3/8	1/4
2	1/2	3/32	9/64	3/32	23	1 3/8	5/16	15/32	5/16
3	1/2	1/8	3/16	1/8	F	1 3/8	3/8	9/16	3/8
4	5/8	3/32	9/64	3/32	24	1 1/2	1/4	3/8	1/4
5	5/8	1/8	3/16	1/8	25	1 1/2	5/16	15/32	5/16
6	5/8	5/32	15/64	5/32	G	1 1/2	3/8	9/16	3/8
7	3/4	1/8	3/16	1/8	51	1 3/4	1/4	3/8	1/4
8	3/4	5/32	15/64	5/32	52	1 3/4	5/16	15/32	5/16
9	3/4	3/16	9/32	3/16	53	1 3/4	3/8	9/16	3/8
10	7/8	5/32	15/64	5/32	26	2	3/16	9/32	3/16
11	7/8	3/16	9/32	3/16	27	2	1/4	3/8	1/4
12	7/8	7/32	21/64	7/32	28	2	5/16	15/32	5/16
A	7/8	1/4	3/8	1/4	29	2	3/8	9/16	3/8
13	1	3/16	9/32	3/16	54	2 1/4	1/4	3/8	1/4
14	1	7/32	21/64	7/32	55	2 1/4	5/16	15/16	5/16
15	1	1/4	3/8	1/4	56	2 1/4	3/8	9/16	3/8
B	1	5/16	15/32	5/16	57	2 1/4	7/16	21/32	7/16
16	1 1/8	3/16	9/32	3/16	58	2 1/2	5/16	15/32	5/16
17	1 1/8	7/32	21/64	7/32	59	2 1/2	3/8	9/16	3/8
18	1 1/8	1/4	3/8	1/4	60	2 1/2	7/16	21/32	7/16
C	1 1/8	5/16	15/32	5/16	61	2 1/2	1/2	3/4	1/2
19	1 1/4	3/16	9/32	3/16	30	3	3/8	9/16	3/8
20	1 1/4	7/32	21/64	7/32	31	3	7/16	21/32	7/16
21	1 1/4	1/4	3/8	1/4	32	3	1/2	3/4	1/2
D	1 1/4	5/16	15/32	5/16	33	3	9/16	27/32	9/16
E	1 1/4	3/8	9/16	3/8	34	3	5/8	15/16	5/8

Dimensions in inches.
Key is 2/3 in shaft; 1/3 in hub.
Keys are 0.001 inch oversize in width to ensure proper fitting in keyway.
Keyway size: width = W; depth = $H - D$.
Length L should never be less than $2W$.

Small Rivets[1]

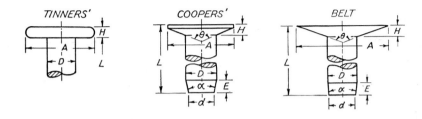

	Tinner's			Cooper's			Belt	
	D	**L**		**D**	**L**		**D**	**L**
Size No.[2]	Diam body	Length	Size No.[2]	Diam body	Length	Size No.[3]	Diam body	Length
8 oz	0.089	0.16	1 lb	0.109	0.219	7	0.180	
12	0.105	0.19	1½	0.127	0.256	8	0.165	
1 lb	0.111	0.20	2	0.141	0.292	9	0.148	From ⅜ to ¾ by ⅛″ increments
1½	0.130	0.23	2½	0.148	0.325	10	0.134	
2	0.144	0.27	3	0.156	0.358	11	0.120	
2½	0.148	0.28	4	0.165	0.392	12	0.109	
3	0.160	0.31	6	0.203	0.466	13	0.095	
4	0.176	0.34	8	0.238	0.571			
6	0.203	0.39	10	0.250	0.606			
8	0.224	0.44	12	0.259	0.608			
10	0.238	0.47	14	0.271	0.643			
12	0.259	0.50	16	0.281	0.677			
14	0.284	0.52						
16	0.300	0.53						

Belt — Approximate proportions:

$A = 2.8 \times D, d = 0.9 \times D$
$E = 0.4 \times D, H = 0.3 \times D$

Tolerances on the nominal diameter:

$+0.002$
-0.004

Finished rivets shall be free from injurious defects.

Cooper's — Approximate proportions:
$A = 2.25 \times D, d = 0.90 \times D$
$E = 0.40 \times D, H = 0.30 \times D$
Included $\angle \theta = 144°$
$\angle \alpha = 18°$

Tinner's — Approximate proportions:
$A = 2.25 \times D, H = 0.30 \times D$

All dimensions given in inches.

[1] ASA B18g1 1942.

[2] Size numbers refer to the "Trade Name" or weight of 1,000 rivets.

[3] Size number refers to the Stubs iron wire gage number of the stock used in the body of the rivet.

American Standard Plain Washers[1]

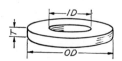

Size	Light			Medium			Heavy			Extra heavy		
	ID	OD	Thickness	ID	OD	Thickness	ID	OD	Thickness	ID	OD	Thickness
0	5/64	3/16	0.020									
1	3/32	7/32	0.020									
2	3/32	1/4	0.020									
3	1/8	1/4	0.022									
4	1/8	1/4	0.022	1/8	5/16	0.032						
5	5/32	5/16	0.035	5/32	3/8	0.049						
6	5/32	5/16	0.035	5/32	3/8	0.049						
7	11/64	13/32	0.049	3/16	3/8	0.049						
8	3/16	3/8	0.049	3/16	7/16	0.049						
9	13/64	15/32	0.049	7/32	1/2	0.049						
3/16	7/32	7/16	0.049	7/32	1/2	0.049	1/4	9/16	0.049			
10	7/32	7/16	0.049	1/4	9/16	0.049	1/4	9/16	0.065			
11	15/64	17/32	0.049	1/4	9/16	0.049	1/4	9/16	0.065			
12	1/4	1/2	0.049	1/4	9/16	0.049	1/4	9/16	0.065			
14	17/64	5/8	0.049	5/16	3/4	0.065	5/16	7/8	0.065			
1/4	9/32	5/8	0.065	5/16	3/4	0.065	5/16	3/4	0.065	5/16	7/8	0.065
16	9/32	5/8	0.065	5/16	3/4	0.065	5/16	7/8	0.065	5/16	7/8	0.065
18	5/16	3/4	0.065	5/16	3/4	0.065	3/8	7/8	0.083	3/8	1 1/8	0.065
5/16	11/32	11/16	0.065	3/8	3/4	0.065	3/8	7/8	0.083	3/8	1 1/8	0.065
20	11/32	11/16	0.065	3/8	3/4	0.065	3/8	7/8	0.083	3/8	1 1/8	0.065
24	13/32	13/16	0.065	7/16	7/8	0.083	7/16	1	0.083	7/16	1 3/8	0.083
3/8	13/32	13/16	0.065	7/16	7/8	0.083	7/16	1	0.083	7/16	1 3/8	0.083
7/16	15/32	59/64	0.065	1/2	1 1/8	0.083	1/2	1 1/4	0.083	1/2	1 5/8	0.083
1/2	17/32	1 1/16	0.095	9/16	1 1/4	0.109	9/16	1 3/8	0.109	9/16	1 7/8	0.109
9/16	19/32	1 3/16	0.095	5/8	1 3/8	0.109	5/8	1 1/2	0.109	5/8	2 1/8	0.134
5/8	21/32	1 5/16	0.095	11/16	1 1/2	0.134	11/16	1 3/4	0.134	11/16	2 3/8	0.165
3/4	13/16	1 1/2	0.134	13/16	1 3/4	0.148	13/16	2	0.148	13/16	2 7/8	0.165
7/8	15/16	1 3/4	0.134	15/16	2	0.165	15/16	2 1/4	0.165	15/16	3 3/8	0.180
1	1 1/16	2	0.134	1 1/16	2 1/4	0.165	1 1/16	2 1/2	0.165	1 1/16	3 7/8	0.238
1 1/8	. . . .	. . . .	. . . .	1 3/16	2 1/2	0.165	1 1/4	2 3/4	0.165			
1 1/4	. . . .	. . . .	. . . .	1 5/16	2 3/4	0.165	1 3/8	3	0.165			
1 3/8	. . . .	. . . .	. . . .	1 7/16	3	0.180	1 1/2	3 1/4	0.180			
1 1/2	. . . .	. . . .	. . . .	1 9/16	3 1/4	0.180	1 5/8	3 1/2	0.180			
1 5/8	. . . .	. . . .	. . . .	1 11/16	3 1/2	0.180	1 3/4	3 3/4	0.180			
1 3/4	. . . .	. . . .	. . . .	1 13/16	3 3/4	0.180	1 7/8	4	0.180			
1 7/8	. . . .	. . . .	. . . .	1 15/16	4	0.180	2	4 1/4	0.180			
2	. . . .	. . . .	. . . .	2 1/16	4 1/4	0.180	2 1/8	4 1/2	0.180			
2 1/4	. . . .	. . . .	. . . .	. . . .	. . . .	. . . .	2 3/8	4 3/4	0.220			
2 1/2	. . . .	. . . .	. . . .	. . . .	. . . .	. . . .	2 5/8	5	0.238			
2 3/4	. . . .	. . . .	. . . .	. . . .	. . . .	. . . .	2 7/8	5 1/4	0.259			
3	. . . .	. . . .	. . . .	. . . .	. . . .	. . . .	3 1/8	5 1/2	0.284			

[1] ASA B27.2—1949. All dimensions in inches.

American Standard Lock Washers[1]

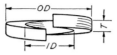

Nominal size	Inside diam, min	Light		Medium		Heavy		Extra heavy	
		Min thick-ness	Outside diam, max	Min thick-ness	Outside diam, max	Min thick-ness	Outside diam, max	Min thick-ness	Outside diam, max
0.086 (No. 2)	0.088	0.015	0.165	0.020	0.175	0.025	0.185	0.027	0.211
0.099 (No. 3)	0.102	0.020	0.188	0.025	0.198	0.031	0.212	0.034	0.242
0.112 (No. 4)	0.115	0.020	0.202	0.025	0.212	0.031	0.226	0.034	0.256
0.125 (No. 5)	0.128	0.025	0.225	0.031	0.239	0.040	0.255	0.045	0.303
0.138 (No. 6)	0.141	0.025	0.239	0.031	0.253	0.040	0.269	0.045	0.317
0.164 (No. 8)	0.168	0.031	0.280	0.040	0.296	0.047	0.310	0.057	0.378
0.190 (No. 10)	0.194	0.040	0.323	0.047	0.337	0.056	0.353	0.068	0.437
0.216 (No. 12)	0.221	0.047	0.364	0.056	0.380	0.063	0.394	0.080	0.500
1/4	0.255	0.047	0.489	0.062	0.493	0.077	0.495	0.084	0.539
5/16	0.319	0.056	0.575	0.078	0.591	0.097	0.601	0.108	0.627
3/8	0.382	0.070	0.678	0.094	0.688	0.115	0.696	0.123	0.746
7/16	0.446	0.085	0.780	0.109	0.784	0.133	0.792	0.143	0.844
1/2	0.509	0.099	0.877	0.125	0.879	0.151	0.889	0.162	0.945
9/16	0.573	0.113	0.975	0.141	0.979	0.170	0.989	0.182	1.049
5/8	0.636	0.126	1.082	0.156	1.086	0.189	1.100	0.202	1.164
11/16	0.700	0.138	1.178	0.172	1.184	0.207	1.200	0.221	1.266
3/4	0.763	0.153	1.277	0.188	1.279	0.226	1.299	0.241	1.369
13/16	0.827	0.168	1.375	0.203	1.377	0.246	1.401	0.261	1.473
7/8	0.890	0.179	1.470	0.219	1.474	0.266	1.504	0.285	1.586
15/16	0.954	0.191	1.562	0.234	1.570	0.284	1.604	0.308	1.698
1	1.017	0.202	1.656	0.250	1.672	0.306	1.716	0.330	1.810
1 1/16	1.081	0.213	1.746	0.266	1.768	0.326	1.820	0.352	1.922
1 1/8	1.144	0.224	1.837	0.281	1.865	0.345	1.921	0.375	2.031
1 3/16	1.208	0.234	1.923	0.297	1.963	0.364	2.021	0.396	2.137
1 1/4	1.271	0.244	2.012	0.312	2.058	0.384	2.126	0.417	2.244
1 5/16	1.335	0.254	2.098	0.328	2.156	0.403	2.226	0.438	2.350
1 3/8	1.398	0.264	2.183	0.344	2.253	0.422	2.325	0.458	2.453
1 7/16	1.462	0.273	2.269	0.359	2.349	0.440	2.421	0.478	2.555
1 1/2	1.525	0.282	2.352	0.375	2.446	0.458	2.518	0.496	2.654

[1] ASA B27.1—1950. All dimensions in inches.

Tapers. Taper means the difference in diameter or width in 1 ft of length, see figure below. *Taper pins*, much used for fastening cylindrical parts and for doweling, have a standard taper of $\frac{1}{4}$ in. per ft.

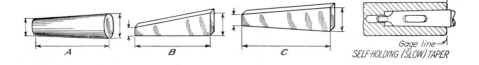

A   *B*   *C*   Gage line —| SELF-HOLDING (SLOW) TAPER

Machine tapers. The American Standard for self-holding (slow) machine tapers is designed to replace the various former standards. The table below shows its derivation. Detailed dimensions and tolerances for taper tool shanks and taper sockets will be found in ASA B5.10 1937.

Dimensions of Taper Pins

TAPER $\frac{1}{4}''$ PER FOOT

Size No.	Diameter, large end	Drill size for reamer	Max length
000000	0.072	53	$\frac{5}{8}$
00000	0.092	47	$\frac{5}{8}$
0000	0.108	42	$\frac{3}{4}$
000	0.125	37	$\frac{3}{4}$
00	0.147	31	1
0	0.156	28	1
1	0.172	25	$1\frac{1}{4}$
2	0.193	19	$1\frac{1}{2}$
3	0.219	12	$1\frac{3}{4}$
4	0.250	3	2
5	0.289	$\frac{1}{4}$	$2\frac{1}{4}$
6	0.341	$\frac{9}{32}$	$3\frac{1}{4}$
7	0.409	$1\frac{1}{32}$	$3\frac{3}{4}$
8	0.492	$1\frac{3}{32}$	$4\frac{1}{2}$
9	0.591	$3\frac{1}{64}$	$5\frac{1}{4}$
10	0.706	$1\frac{9}{32}$	6
11	0.857	$2\frac{3}{32}$	$7\frac{1}{4}$
12	1.013	$5\frac{5}{64}$	$8\frac{3}{4}$
13	1.233	$1\frac{1}{64}$	$10\frac{3}{4}$

All dimensions in inches.

American Standard Machine Tapers[1] Self-holding (Slow) Taper Series

BASIC DIMENSIONS

Origin of series	No. of taper	Taper per foot	Diameter at gage line	Means of driving and holding
Brown and Sharpe taper series	0.239	0.500	0.239	
	0.299	0.500	0.299	
	0.375	0.500	0.375	Tongue drive with shank held in by friction
Morse taper series	1	0.600	0.475	
	2	0.600	0.700	
	3	0.602	0.938	Tongue drive with shank held in by key
	4	0.623	1.231	
	$4\frac{1}{2}$	0.623	1.500	
	5	0.630	1.748	
$\frac{3}{4}''$ per foot taper series	200	0.750	2.000	
	250	0.750	2.500	
	300	0.750	3.000	
	350	0.750	3.500	Key drive with shank held in by key
	400	0.750	4.000	
	500	0.750	5.000	
	600	0.750	6.000	Key drive with shank held in by drawbolt
	800	0.750	8.000	
	1,000	0.750	10.000	
	1,200	0.750	12.000	

All dimensions in inches
[1] ASA B5.10 1937.

Wire and Sheet-metal Gages

DIMENSIONS IN DECIMAL PARTS OF AN INCH

Number of gage	American or Brown and Sharpe[1]	Washburn & Moen or American Steel & Wire Co.[2]	Birming-ham or Stubs iron wire[3]	Music wire[4]	Imperial wire gage[5]	U.S. Std. for plate[6]
0000000	.....	0.4900	.....	.....	0.5000	0.5000
000000	0.5800	0.4615	.....	0.004	0.4640	0.4688
00000	0.5165	0.4305	0.500	0.005	0.4320	0.4375
0000	0.4600	0.3938	0.454	0.006	0.4000	0.4063
000	0.4096	0.3625	0.425	0.007	0.3720	0.3750
00	0.3648	0.3310	0.380	0.008	0.3480	0.3438
0	0.3249	0.3065	0.340	0.009	0.3240	0.3125
1	0.2893	0.2830	0.300	0.010	0.3000	0.2813
2	0.2576	0.2625	0.284	0.011	0.2760	0.2656
3	0.2294	0.2437	0.259	0.012	0.2520	0.2500
4	0.2043	0.2253	0.238	0.013	0.2320	0.2344
5	0.1819	0.2070	0.220	0.014	0.2120	0.2188
6	0.1620	0.1920	0.203	0.016	0.1920	0.2031
7	0.1443	0.1770	0.180	0.018	0.1760	0.1875
8	0.1285	0.1620	0.165	0.020	0.1600	0.1719
9	0.1144	0.1483	0.148	0.022	0.1440	0.1563
10	0.1019	0.1350	0.134	0.024	0.1280	0.1406
11	0.0907	0.1205	0.120	0.026	0.1160	0.1250
12	0.0808	0.1055	0.109	0.029	0.1040	0.1094
13	0.0720	0.0915	0.095	0.031	0.0920	0.0938
14	0.0641	0.0800	0.083	0.033	0.0800	0.0781
15	0.0571	0.0720	0.072	0.035	0.0720	0.0703
16	0.0508	0.0625	0.065	0.037	0.0640	0.0625
17	0.0453	0.0540	0.058	0.039	0.0560	0.0563
18	0.0403	0.0475	0.049	0.041	0.0480	0.0500
19	0.0359	0.0410	0.042	0.043	0.0400	0.0438
20	0.0320	0.0348	0.035	0.045	0.0360	0.0375
21	0.0285	0.0317	0.032	0.047	0.0320	0.0344
22	0.0253	0.0286	0.028	0.049	0.0280	0.0313
23	0.0226	0.0258	0.025	0.051	0.0240	0.0281
24	0.0201	0.0230	0.022	0.055	0.0220	0.0250
25	0.0179	0.0204	0.020	0.059	0.0200	0.0219
26	0.0159	0.0181	0.018	0.063	0.0180	0.0188
27	0.0142	0.0173	0.016	0.067	0.0164	0.0172
28	0.0126	0.0162	0.014	0.071	0.0148	0.0156
29	0.0113	0.0150	0.013	0.075	0.0136	0.0141
30	0.0100	0.0140	0.012	0.080	0.0124	0.0125
31	0.0089	0.0132	0.010	0.085	0.0116	0.0109
32	0.0080	0.0128	0.009	0.090	0.0108	0.0102
33	0.0071	0.0118	0.008	0.095	0.0100	0.0094
34	0.0063	0.0104	0.007	0.100	0.0092	0.0086
35	0.0056	0.0095	0.005	0.106	0.0084	0.0078
36	0.0050	0.0090	0.004	0.112	0.0076	0.0070
37	0.0045	0.0085	.....	0.118	0.0068	0.0066
38	0.0040	0.0080	.....	0.124	0.0060	0.0063
39	0.0035	0.0075	.....	0.130	0.0052	
40	0.0031	0.0070	.....	0.138	0.0048	

[1] Recognized standard in the United States for wire and sheet metal of copper and other metals except steel and iron.

[2] Recognized standard for steel and iron wire. Called the "U.S. steel wire gage."

[3] Formerly much used, now nearly obsolete.

[4] American Steel & Wire Company's music or piano wire gage. Recommended by U.S. Bureau of Standards.

[5] Official British Standard.

[6] Legalized U.S. Standard for iron and steel plate, although plate is now always specified by its thickness in decimals of an inch.

Preferred thicknesses for uncoated thin flats metals (under 0.250 in.), ASA B32 1941, gives recommended sizes for sheets.

Table of Limits for Cylindrical Fits[1]

Size of hole or external member inclusive[2]	Clearance fits							
	Class 1　Loose fit				Class 2　Free fit			
	Hole or external member		Shaft or internal member		Hole or external member		Shaft or internal member	
	+		−	−	+		−	−
$0-\frac{3}{16}$	0.001	0.000	0.001	0.002	0.0007	0.0000	0.0004	0.0011
$\frac{3}{16}-\frac{5}{16}$	0.002	0.000	0.001	0.003	0.0008	0.0000	0.0006	0.0014
$\frac{5}{16}-\frac{7}{16}$	0.002	0.000	0.001	0.003	0.0009	0.0000	0.0007	0.0016
$\frac{7}{16}-\frac{9}{16}$	0.002	0.000	0.002	0.004	0.0010	0.0000	0.0009	0.0019
$\frac{9}{16}-1\frac{1}{16}$	0.002	0.000	0.002	0.004	0.0011	0.0000	0.0010	0.0021
$1\frac{1}{16}-1\frac{3}{16}$	0.002	0.000	0.002	0.004	0.0012	0.0000	0.0012	0.0024
$1\frac{3}{16}-1\frac{5}{16}$	0.002	0.000	0.002	0.004	0.0012	0.0000	0.0013	0.0025
$1\frac{5}{16}-1\frac{7}{16}$	0.003	0.000	0.003	0.006	0.0013	0.0000	0.0014	0.0027
$1\frac{7}{16}-1\frac{3}{16}$	0.003	0.000	0.003	0.006	0.0014	0.0000	0.0015	0.0029
$1\frac{3}{16}-1\frac{3}{8}$	0.003	0.000	0.003	0.006	0.0014	0.0000	0.0016	0.0030
$1\frac{3}{8}-1\frac{5}{8}$	0.003	0.000	0.003	0.006	0.0015	0.0000	0.0018	0.0033
$1\frac{5}{8}-1\frac{7}{8}$	0.003	0.000	0.004	0.007	0.0016	0.0000	0.0020	0.0036
$1\frac{7}{8}-2\frac{1}{8}$	0.003	0.000	0.004	0.007	0.0016	0.0000	0.0022	0.0038
$2\frac{1}{8}-2\frac{3}{8}$	0.003	0.000	0.004	0.007	0.0017	0.0000	0.0024	0.0041
$2\frac{3}{8}-2\frac{3}{4}$	0.003	0.000	0.005	0.008	0.0018	0.0000	0.0026	0.0044
$2\frac{3}{4}-3\frac{1}{4}$	0.004	0.000	0.005	0.009	0.0019	0.0000	0.0029	0.0048
$3\frac{1}{4}-3\frac{3}{4}$	0.004	0.000	0.006	0.010	0.0020	0.0000	0.0032	0.0052
$3\frac{3}{4}-4\frac{1}{4}$	0.004	0.000	0.006	0.010	0.0021	0.0000	0.0035	0.0056
$4\frac{1}{4}-4\frac{3}{4}$	0.004	0.000	0.007	0.011	0.0021	0.0000	0.0038	0.0059
$4\frac{3}{4}-5\frac{1}{2}$	0.004	0.000	0.007	0.011	0.0022	0.0000	0.0041	0.0063
$5\frac{1}{2}-6\frac{1}{2}$	0.005	0.000	0.008	0.013	0.0024	0.0000	0.0046	0.0070
$6\frac{1}{2}-7\frac{1}{2}$	0.005	0.000	0.009	0.014	0.0025	0.0000	0.0051	0.0076
$7\frac{1}{2}-8\frac{1}{2}$	0.005	0.000	0.010	0.015	0.0026	0.0000	0.0056	0.0082

Size	Class 3　Medium fit				Class 4　Snug fit			
	Hole or external member		Shaft or internal member		Hole or external member		Shaft or internal member	
	+		−	−	+			−
$0-\frac{3}{16}$	0.0004	0.0000	0.0002	0.0006	0.0003	0.0000	0.0000	0.0002
$\frac{3}{16}-\frac{5}{16}$	0.0005	0.0000	0.0004	0.0009	0.0004	0.0000	0.0000	0.0003
$\frac{5}{16}-\frac{7}{16}$	0.0006	0.0000	0.0005	0.0011	0.0004	0.0000	0.0000	0.0003
$\frac{7}{16}-\frac{9}{16}$	0.0006	0.0000	0.0006	0.0012	0.0005	0.0000	0.0000	0.0003
$\frac{9}{16}-1\frac{1}{16}$	0.0007	0.0000	0.0007	0.0014	0.0005	0.0000	0.0000	0.0003
$1\frac{1}{16}-1\frac{3}{16}$	0.0007	0.0000	0.0007	0.0014	0.0005	0.0000	0.0000	0.0004
$1\frac{3}{16}-1\frac{5}{16}$	0.0008	0.0000	0.0008	0.0016	0.0006	0.0000	0.0000	0.0004
$1\frac{5}{16}-1\frac{7}{16}$	0.0008	0.0000	0.0009	0.0017	0.0006	0.0000	0.0000	0.0004
$1\frac{7}{16}-1\frac{3}{16}$	0.0008	0.0000	0.0010	0.0018	0.0006	0.0000	0.0000	0.0004
$1\frac{3}{16}-1\frac{3}{8}$	0.0009	0.0000	0.0010	0.0019	0.0006	0.0000	0.0000	0.0004
$1\frac{3}{8}-1\frac{5}{8}$	0.0009	0.0000	0.0012	0.0021	0.0007	0.0000	0.0000	0.0005
$1\frac{5}{8}-1\frac{7}{8}$	0.0010	0.0000	0.0013	0.0023	0.0007	0.0000	0.0000	0.0005
$1\frac{7}{8}-2\frac{1}{8}$	0.0010	0.0000	0.0014	0.0024	0.0008	0.0000	0.0000	0.0005
$2\frac{1}{8}-2\frac{3}{8}$	0.0010	0.0000	0.0015	0.0025	0.0008	0.0000	0.0000	0.0005
$2\frac{3}{8}-2\frac{3}{4}$	0.0011	0.0000	0.0017	0.0028	0.0008	0.0000	0.0000	0.0005
$2\frac{3}{4}-3\frac{1}{4}$	0.0012	0.0000	0.0019	0.0031	0.0009	0.0000	0.0000	0.0006
$3\frac{1}{4}-3\frac{3}{4}$	0.0012	0.0000	0.0021	0.0033	0.0009	0.0000	0.0000	0.0006
$3\frac{3}{4}-4\frac{1}{4}$	0.0013	0.0000	0.0023	0.0036	0.0010	0.0000	0.0000	0.0006
$4\frac{1}{4}-4\frac{3}{4}$	0.0013	0.0000	0.0025	0.0038	0.0010	0.0000	0.0000	0.0007
$4\frac{3}{4}-5\frac{1}{2}$	0.0014	0.0000	0.0026	0.0040	0.0010	0.0000	0.0000	0.0007
$5\frac{1}{2}-6\frac{1}{2}$	0.0015	0.0000	0.0030	0.0045	0.0011	0.0000	0.0000	0.0007
$6\frac{1}{2}-7\frac{1}{2}$	0.0015	0.0000	0.0033	0.0048	0.0011	0.0000	0.0000	0.0008
$7\frac{1}{2}-8\frac{1}{2}$	0.0016	0.0000	0.0036	0.0052	0.0012	0.0000	0.0000	0.0008

All dimensions in inches.
[1] Compiled from American Standard ASA B4a 1925.
[2] When nominal value is one of sizes given, use upper line in table.

Table of Limits for Cylindrical Fits[1]—(Continued)

Size of hole or external member inclusive[2]	Class 5 Wringing fit				Class 6 Tight fit			
	Hole or external member		Shaft or internal member		Hole or external member		Shaft or internal member	
	+		+		+		+	+
0–3/16	0.0003	0.0000	0.0002	0.0000	0.0003	0.0000	0.0003	0.0000
3/16–5/16	0.0004	0.0000	0.0003	0.0000	0.0004	0.0000	0.0005	0.0001
5/16–7/16	0.0004	0.0000	0.0003	0.0000	0.0004	0.0000	0.0005	0.0001
7/16–9/16	0.0005	0.0000	0.0003	0.0000	0.0005	0.0000	0.0006	0.0001
9/16–11/16	0.0005	0.0000	0.0003	0.0000	0.0005	0.0000	0.0007	0.0002
11/16–13/16	0.0005	0.0000	0.0004	0.0000	0.0005	0.0000	0.0007	0.0002
13/16–15/16	0.0006	0.0000	0.0004	0.0000	0.0006	0.0000	0.0008	0.0002
15/16–1 1/16	0.0006	0.0000	0.0004	0.0000	0.0006	0.0000	0.0009	0.0003
1 1/16–1 3/16	0.0006	0.0000	0.0004	0.0000	0.0006	0.0000	0.0009	0.0003
1 3/16–1 3/8	0.0006	0.0000	0.0004	0.0000	0.0006	0.0000	0.0009	0.0003
1 3/8–1 5/8	0.0007	0.0000	0.0005	0.0000	0.0007	0.0000	0.0011	0.0004
1 5/8–1 7/8	0.0007	0.0000	0.0005	0.0000	0.0007	0.0000	0.0011	0.0004
1 7/8–2 1/8	0.0008	0.0000	0.0005	0.0000	0.0008	0.0000	0.0013	0.0005
2 1/8–2 3/8	0.0008	0.0000	0.0005	0.0000	0.0008	0.0000	0.0014	0.0006
2 3/8–2 3/4	0.0008	0.0000	0.0005	0.0000	0.0008	0.0000	0.0014	0.0006
2 3/4–3 1/4	0.0009	0.0000	0.0006	0.0000	0.0009	0.0000	0.0017	0.0008
3 1/4–3 3/4	0.0009	0.0000	0.0006	0.0000	0.0009	0.0000	0.0018	0.0009
3 3/4–4 1/4	0.0010	0.0000	0.0006	0.0000	0.0010	0.0000	0.0020	0.0010
4 1/4–4 3/4	0.0010	0.0000	0.0007	0.0000	0.0010	0.0000	0.0021	0.0011
4 3/4–5 1/2	0.0010	0.0000	0.0007	0.0000	0.0010	0.0000	0.0023	0.0013
5 1/2–6 1/2	0.0011	0.0000	0.0007	0.0000	0.0011	0.0000	0.0026	0.0015
6 1/2–7 1/2	0.0011	0.0000	0.0008	0.0000	0.0011	0.0000	0.0029	0.0018
7 1/2–8 1/2	0.0012	0.0000	0.0008	0.0000	0.0012	0.0000	0.0032	0.0020

Size of hole or external member inclusive	Class 7 Medium force fit				Class 8 Heavy force and shrink fit			
	Hole or external member		Shaft or internal member		Hole or external member		Shaft or internal member	
	+		+	+	+		+	+
0–3/16	0.0003	0.0000	0.0004	0.0001	0.0003	0.0000	0.0004	0.0001
3/16–5/16	0.0004	0.0000	0.0005	0.0001	0.0004	0.0000	0.0007	0.0003
5/16–7/16	0.0004	0.0000	0.0006	0.0002	0.0004	0.0000	0.0008	0.0004
7/16–9/16	0.0005	0.0000	0.0008	0.0003	0.0005	0.0000	0.0010	0.0005
9/16–11/16	0.0005	0.0000	0.0008	0.0003	0.0005	0.0000	0.0011	0.0006
11/16–13/16	0.0005	0.0000	0.0009	0.0004	0.0005	0.0000	0.0013	0.0008
13/16–15/16	0.0006	0.0000	0.0010	0.0004	0.0006	0.0000	0.0015	0.0009
15/16–1 1/16	0.0006	0.0000	0.0010	0.0005	0.0006	0.0000	0.0016	0.0010
1 1/16–1 3/16	0.0006	0.0000	0.0012	0.0006	0.0006	0.0000	0.0017	0.0011
1 3/16–1 3/8	0.0006	0.0000	0.0012	0.0006	0.0006	0.0000	0.0019	0.0013
1 3/8–1 5/8	0.0007	0.0000	0.0015	0.0008	0.0007	0.0000	0.0022	0.0015
1 5/8–1 7/8	0.0007	0.0000	0.0016	0.0009	0.0007	0.0000	0.0025	0.0018
1 7/8–2 1/8	0.0008	0.0000	0.0018	0.0010	0.0008	0.0000	0.0028	0.0020
2 1/8–2 3/8	0.0008	0.0000	0.0019	0.0011	0.0008	0.0000	0.0031	0.0023
2 3/8–2 3/4	0.0008	0.0000	0.0021	0.0013	0.0008	0.0000	0.0033	0.0025
2 3/4–3 1/4	0.0009	0.0000	0.0024	0.0015	0.0009	0.0000	0.0039	0.0030
3 1/4–3 3/4	0.0009	0.0000	0.0027	0.0018	0.0009	0.0000	0.0044	0.0035
3 3/4–4 1/4	0.0010	0.0000	0.0030	0.0020	0.0010	0.0000	0.0050	0.0040
4 1/4–4 3/4	0.0010	0.0000	0.0033	0.0023	0.0010	0.0000	0.0055	0.0045
4 3/4–5 1/2	0.0010	0.0000	0.0035	0.0025	0.0010	0.0000	0.0060	0.0050
5 1/2–6 1/2	0.0011	0.0000	0.0041	0.0030	0.0011	0.0000	0.0071	0.0060
6 1/2–7 1/2	0.0011	0.0000	0.0046	0.0035	0.0011	0.0000	0.0081	0.0070
7 1/2–8 1/2	0.0012	0.0000	0.0052	0.0040	0.0012	0.0000	0.0092	0.0080

All dimensions in inches.
[1] Compiled from American Standard ASA B4a 1925.
[2] When nominal value is one of sizes given, use upper line in table.

Standard Jig

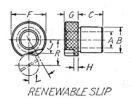
RENEWABLE SLIP

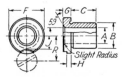
RENEWABLE FIXED

RENEWABLE SLIP TYPE AND RENEWABLE FIXED TYPE

Slip type Hole size A	Fixed type Hole size A	Tolerance on hole	Body diameter limits B	Lengths available C	F	G Slip type	G Fixed type	H	J	L	R	Lock screw No.
0.052 to 0.089	0.055 to 0.089	+0.0004	0.3125	$\frac{5}{16}$, $\frac{1}{2}$ $\frac{3}{4}$, 1	$\frac{35}{64}$	$\frac{3}{8}$	$\frac{1}{4}$	$\frac{1}{8}$	$\frac{11}{64}$	65°	$\frac{1}{2}$	
0.0935 to 0.1562	0.0935 to 0.1562	+0.0001	0.3123	$\frac{5}{16}$, $\frac{1}{2}$ $\frac{3}{4}$, 1								
0.1406 to 0.3437	0.1570 to 0.3125	Incl $\frac{1}{4}$ +0.0004 +0.0001 Over $\frac{1}{4}$ +0.0005 +0.0001	0.5000 0.4998	$\frac{5}{16}$, $\frac{1}{2}$, $\frac{3}{4}$ 1, $1\frac{3}{8}$, $1\frac{3}{4}$	$\frac{51}{64}$	$\frac{7}{16}$	$\frac{1}{4}$	$\frac{1}{8}$	$\frac{19}{64}$	65°	$\frac{5}{8}$	1
0.2812 to 0.5312	0.3160 to 0.5000	+0.0005	0.7500 0.7498	$\frac{1}{2}$, $\frac{3}{4}$, 1 $1\frac{3}{8}$, $1\frac{3}{4}$, $2\frac{1}{8}$	$1\frac{3}{64}$	$\frac{7}{16}$	$\frac{1}{4}$	$\frac{1}{8}$	$\frac{27}{64}$	50°	$\frac{3}{4}$	
0.4687 to 0.7812	0.5156 to 0.750	+0.0001	1.0000 0.9998	$\frac{3}{4}$, 1, $1\frac{3}{8}$ $1\frac{3}{4}$, $2\frac{1}{8}$, $2\frac{1}{2}$	$1\frac{27}{64}$	$\frac{7}{16}$	$\frac{3}{8}$	$\frac{3}{16}$	$\frac{19}{32}$	35°	$\frac{59}{64}$	2
0.7817 to 1.0312	0.7656 to 1.0000	+0.0006	1.3750 1.3747	$\frac{3}{4}$, 1, $1\frac{3}{8}$ $1\frac{3}{4}$, $2\frac{1}{8}$, $2\frac{1}{2}$	$1\frac{51}{64}$	$\frac{7}{16}$	$\frac{3}{8}$	$\frac{3}{16}$	$\frac{25}{32}$	30°	$1\frac{7}{64}$	
0.9687 to 1.4062	1.0156 to 1.3750	+0.0002	1.7500 1.7497	1, $1\frac{3}{8}$, $1\frac{3}{4}$ $2\frac{1}{8}$, $2\frac{1}{2}$, 3	$2\frac{19}{64}$	$\frac{5}{8}$	$\frac{3}{8}$	$\frac{3}{16}$	1	30°	$1\frac{25}{64}$	
1.3437 to 1.7812	1.3906 to 1.750	Incl $1\frac{1}{2}$ +0.0006 +0.0002 Over $1\frac{1}{2}$ +0.0007 +0.0003	2.2500 2.2496	1, $1\frac{3}{8}$, $1\frac{3}{4}$ $2\frac{1}{8}$, $2\frac{1}{2}$, 3	$2\frac{51}{64}$	$\frac{5}{8}$	$\frac{3}{8}$	$\frac{3}{16}$	$1\frac{1}{4}$	25°	$1\frac{41}{64}$	3

Dimensions in inches.
[1] ASA B5.6 1941.
Head design in accordance with manufacturer's practice; slip type usually knurled.

Lock Screws

Screw No.	A	B	C	D	E	F	ASA thd
1	$\frac{5}{8}$	$\frac{3}{8}$	$\frac{5}{8}$	$\frac{1}{16}$	$\frac{1}{4}$	.138 .132	$\frac{5}{16}$–18
2	$\frac{7}{8}$	$\frac{3}{8}$	$\frac{5}{8}$	$\frac{3}{32}$	$\frac{3}{8}$	.200 .194	$\frac{5}{16}$–18
3	1	$\frac{7}{16}$	$\frac{3}{4}$	$\frac{1}{8}$	$\frac{3}{8}$	.200 .194	$\frac{3}{8}$–16

Bushings[1]

LINER
(used with Renewable Type bushings)

PRESS FIT
HEADLESS TYPE

PRESS FIT
HEAD TYPE

LINERS			PRESS FIT HEADLESS AND PRESS FIT HEAD TYPES					
Hole limits A	OD limits B	Lengths	Hole size A	Tolerance on hole	OD limits B	Lengths available C	Head type dimension	
							F	G
0.3126 0.3129	0.5017 0.5014		0.055 to 0.0995		0.2046 0.2043	5/16, 1/2	1 9/64	3/32
			0.1015 to 0.1360	+0.0004	0.2516 0.2513	5/16, 1/2	2 3/64	3/32
0.5002 0.5005	0.7518 0.7515		0.1405 to 0.1875	+0.0001	0.3141 0.3138	5/16, 1/2 3/4, 1	2 7/64	1/8
			0.1890 to 0.2500		0.4078 0.4075	5/16, 1/2, 3/4, 1,	1/2	5/32
0.7503 0.7506	1.0015 1.0018	Same as the bushing	0.2570 to 0.3125		0.5017 0.5014	1 3/8, 1 3/4	3 9/64	7/32
1.0004 1.0007	1.3772 1.3768		0.316 to 0.4219		0.6267 0.6264	1/2, 3/4 1, 1 3/8	5 1/64	7/32
1.3756 1.3760	1.7523 1.7519		0.4375 to 0.500	+0.0005 +0.0001	0.7518 0.7515	1 3/4, 2 1/8	5 9/64	7/32
1.7508 1.7512	2.2521 2.2525		0.5156 to 0.625		0.8768 0.8765	3/4, 1	1 7/64	1/4
2.2510 2.2515	2.7526 2.7522		0.6406 to 0.7500		1.0018 1.0015	1 3/8, 1 3/4	1 15/64	5/16
			0.7656 to 1.0000	+0.0006	1.3772 1.3768	2 1/8, 2 1/2	1 39/64	3/8
			1.0156 to 1.3750	+0.0002	1.7523 1.7519	1, 1 3/8	1 63/64	3/8
			1.3906 to 1.7500	Incl. 1 1/2 +0.0006 +0.0002 Over 1 1/2 +0.0007 +0.0003	2.2525 2.2521	1 3/4, 2 1/8 2 1/2, 3	2 31/64	3/8

American Standard Pipe[1,5]

WELDED WROUGHT IRON

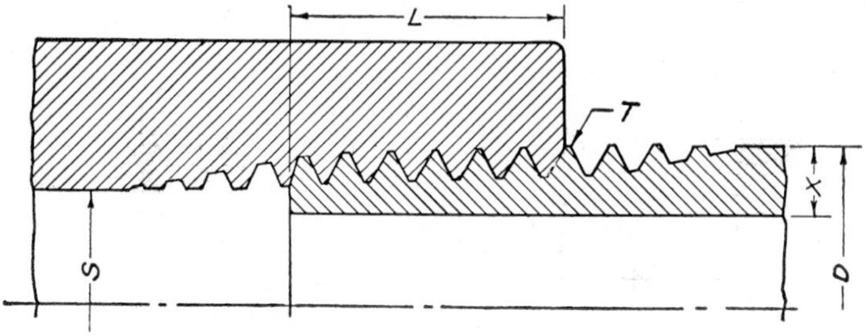

Nominal pipe size	Actual outside diam D	Tap-drill size S	Thds per in. T	Distance pipe enters fittings L	Wall thickness X			Weight—pounds per foot[6]		
					Standard 40[2]	Extra strong 80[3]	Double extra strong[4]	Standard 40[2]	Extra strong 80[3]	Double extra strong[4]
$\frac{1}{8}$	0.405	$\frac{11}{32}$	27	$\frac{3}{16}$	0.070	0.098	.....	0.25	0.32	
$\frac{1}{4}$	0.540	$\frac{7}{16}$	18	$\frac{9}{32}$	0.090	0.122	.....	0.43	0.54	
$\frac{3}{8}$	0.675	$\frac{37}{64}$	18	$\frac{19}{64}$	0.093	0.129	.....	0.57	0.74	
$\frac{1}{2}$	0.840	$\frac{23}{32}$	14	$\frac{3}{8}$	0.111	0.151	0.307	0.86	1.09	1.714
$\frac{3}{4}$	1.050	$\frac{59}{64}$	14	$\frac{13}{32}$	0.115	0.157	0.318	1.14	1.48	2.440
1	1.315	1 $\frac{5}{32}$	$11\frac{1}{2}$	$\frac{1}{2}$	0.136	0.183	0.369	1.68	2.18	3.659
$1\frac{1}{4}$	1.660	1 $\frac{1}{2}$	$11\frac{1}{2}$	$\frac{35}{64}$	0.143	0.195	0.393	2.28	3.00	5.214
$1\frac{1}{2}$	1.900	$1\frac{47}{64}$	$11\frac{1}{2}$	$\frac{9}{16}$	0.148	0.204	0.411	2.72	3.64	6.408
2	2.375	2 $\frac{7}{32}$	$11\frac{1}{2}$	$\frac{37}{64}$	0.158	0.223	0.447	3.66	5.03	9.029
$2\frac{1}{2}$	2.875	2 $\frac{5}{8}$	8	$\frac{7}{8}$	0.208	0.282	0.565	5.80	7.67	13.695
3	3.5	3 $\frac{1}{4}$	8	$\frac{15}{16}$	0.221	0.306	0.615	7.58	10.3	18.583
$3\frac{1}{2}$	4.0	3 $\frac{3}{4}$	8	1	0.231	0.325	.....	9.11	12.5	......
4	4.5	4 $\frac{1}{4}$	8	1 $\frac{1}{16}$	0.242	0.344	0.690	10.8	15.0	27.451
5	5.563	5 $\frac{5}{16}$	8	1 $\frac{5}{32}$	0.263	0.383	0.768	14.7	20.8	38.552
6	6.625	6 $\frac{5}{16}$	8	1 $\frac{1}{4}$	0.286	0.441	0.884	19.0	28.6	53.160
8	8.625	.....	8	$1\frac{15}{32}$	0.329	0.510	0.895	28.6	43.4	72.424
10	10.75	.....	8	$1\frac{43}{64}$	0.372	0.606	.....	40.5	64.4	
12	12.75	.....	8	1 $\frac{7}{8}$	0.414	0.702	.....	53.6	88.6	
14 OD	14.0	.....	8	2	0 437	0.750	.....	62.2	104.	
16 OD	16.0	.....	8	$2\frac{13}{64}$	0.500	.....	.....	81.2		
18 OD	18.0	.....	8	$2\frac{13}{32}$	0.562	.....	.....	103.		
20 OD	20.0	.....	8	$2\frac{19}{32}$	0.562	.....	.....	115.		
24 OD	24.0	.....	8	3						

Dimensions in inches.

[1] For welded and seamless steel pipe—see ASA B36.10 1939.

[2] Refers to American Standard schedule numbers, approximate values for the expression 1,000 × *P/S*. Schedule 40—standard weight.

[3] Schedule 80—extra strong.

[4] Not American Standard, but commercially available in both wrought iron and steel.

[5] A pipe size may be designated by giving the nominal pipe size and wall thickness, or by giving the nominal pipe size and weight per linear foot.

[6] Plain ends.

American Standard 150-lb Malleable-iron Screwed Fittings[1]

90°ELBOW TEE CROSS 45°ELL Y BRANCH PLUG

90°STREET ELBOW 45°STREET ELBOW STREET TEE COUPLING REDUCING COUPLING CAP

Nominal pipe size	A	B	C	E	F	G	H	J	K	L	M
1/8	0.69	0.25	....	0.200	0.405	0.090	0.693	1.00[2]	....	0.264	
1/4	0.81	0.32	0.73	0.215	0.540	0.095	0.844	1.19	0.94	0.402	1.00
3/8	0.95	0.36	0.80	0.230	0.675	0.100	1.015	1.44	1.03	0.408	1.13
1/2	1.12	0.43	0.88	0.249	0.840	0.105	1.197	1.63	1.15	0.534	1.25
3/4	1.31	0.50	0.98	0.273	1.050	0.120	1.458	1.89	1.29	0.546	1.44
1	1.50	0.58	1.12	0.302	1.315	0.134	1.771	2.14	1.47	0.683	1.69
1¼	1.75	0.67	1.29	0.341	1.660	0.145	2.153	2.45	1.71	0.707	2.06
1½	1.94	0.70	1.43	0.368	1.900	0.155	2.427	2.69	1.88	0.724	2.31
2	2.25	0.75	1.68	0.422	2.375	0.173	2.963	3.26	2.22	0.757	2.81
2½	2.70	0.92	1.95	0.478	2.875	0.210	3.589	3.86	2.57	1.138	3.25
3	3.08	0.98	2.17	0.548	3.500	0.231	4.285	4.51	3.00	1.200	3.69
3½	3.42	1.03	2.39	0.604	4.000	0.248	4.843	5.09[2]	....	1.250	4.00
4	3.79	1.08	2.61	0.661	4.500	0.265	5.401	5.69	3.70	1.300	4.38
5	4.50	1.18	3.05	0.780	5.563	0.300	6.583	6.86[2]	....	1.406	5.12
6	5.13	1.28	3.46	0.900	6.625	0.336	7.767	8.03[2]	....	1.513	5.86

Nominal pipe size	N	P	T	U	V	W	X	Y	Z[3]	O[4]	Thickness of ribs on caps, couplings
1/8	0.20	....	....	....	....	0.96	0.37	0.24	9/32	....	0.090
1/4	0.26	....	....	....	....	1.06	0.44	0.28	3/8	....	0.095
3/8	0.37	....	0.50	1.43	1.93	1.16	0.48	0.31	7/16	....	0.100
1/2	0.51	0.87	0.61	1.71	2.32	1.34	0.56	0.38	9/16	0.16	0.105
3/4	0.69	0.97	0.72	2.05	2.77	1.52	0.63	0.44	5/8	0.18	0.120
1	0.91	1.16	0.85	2.43	3.28	1.67	0.75	0.50	13/16	0.20	0.134
1¼	1.19	1.28	1.02	2.92	3.94	1.93	0.80	0.56	15/16	0.22	0.145
1½	1.39	1.33	1.10	3.28	4.38	2.15	0.83	0.62	1 1/8	0.24	0.155
2	1.79	1.45	1.24	3.93	5.17	2.53	0.88	0.68	1 5/16	0.26	0.173
2½	2.20	1.70	1.52	4.73	6.25	2.88	1.07	0.74	1 1/2	0.29	0.210
3	2.78	1.80	1.71	5.55	7.26	3.18	1.13	0.80	1 11/16	0.31	0.231
3½	3.24	1.90	....	....	....	3.43	1.18	0.86	1 7/8	0.34	0.248
4	3.70	2.08	2.01	6.97	8.98	3.69	1.22	1.00	2 1/8	0.37	0.265
5	4.69	2.32	....	....	....	....	1.31	1.00	2 5/16	0.46	0.300
6	5.67	2.55	....	....	....	....	1.40	1.25	2 1/2	0.52	0.336

Dimensions in inches. Left-hand couplings have four or more ribs. Right-hand couplings have two ribs.
[1] ASA B16c 1939. Street tee not made in 1/8" size. [2] Street ell only. [3] These dimensions are the nominal size of wrench (ASA B18.2 1941). Square-head plugs are designed to fit these wrenches. [4] Solid plugs are provided in sizes 1/8 to 3½ in. incl.; cored plugs 1/2 to 3½ in., inclusive. Cored plugs have minimum metal thickness at all points equal to dimension O except at the end of the thread.

American Standard Cast-iron Screwed Fittings[1]

FOR MAXIMUM WORKING SATURATED STEAM PRESSURE OF 125 AND 250 PSI

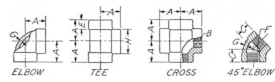

ELBOW   TEE   CROSS   45°ELBOW

Nominal pipe size	A	B min	C	E min	F Min	F Max	G min	H min
$\frac{1}{4}$	0.81	0.32	0.73	0.38	0.540	0.584	0.110	0.93
$\frac{3}{8}$	0.95	0.36	0.80	0.44	0.675	0.719	0.120	1.12
$\frac{1}{2}$	1.12	0.43	0.88	0.50	0.840	0.897	0.130	1.34
$\frac{3}{4}$	1.31	0.50	0.98	0.56	1.050	1.107	0.155	1.63
1	1.50	0.58	1.12	0.62	1.315	1.385	0.170	1.95
$1\frac{1}{4}$	1.75	0.67	1.29	0.69	1.660	1.730	0.185	2.39
$1\frac{1}{2}$	1.94	0.70	1.43	0.75	1.900	1.970	0.200	2.68
2	2.25	0.75	1.68	0.84	2.375	2.445	0.220	3.28
$2\frac{1}{2}$	2.70	0.92	1.95	0.94	2.875	2.975	0.240	3.86
3	3.08	0.98	2.17	1.00	3.500	3.600	0.260	4.62
$3\frac{1}{2}$	3.42	1.03	2.39	1.06	4.000	4.100	0.280	5.20
4	3.79	1.08	2.61	1.12	4.500	4.600	0.310	5.79
5	4.50	1.18	3.05	1.18	5.563	5.663	0.380	7.07
6	5.13	1.28	3.46	1.28	6.625	6.725	0.430	8.28
8	6.56	1.47	4.28	1.47	8.625	8.725	0.550	10.63
10	8.08	1.68	5.16	1.68	10.750	10.850	0.690	13.12
12	9.50	1.88	5.97	1.88	12.750	12.850	0.800	15.47

Dimensions in inches.
[1] ASA B16d 1941.

Globe, Angle-globe, and Gate Valves[1]

Size	A (globe only)	B (open)	C	D (angle only)	E	F (open)	G
$\frac{1}{8}$	2	4	$1\frac{3}{4}$	1			
$\frac{1}{4}$	2	4	$1\frac{3}{4}$	1	$1\frac{7}{8}$	$5\frac{1}{8}$	$1\frac{3}{4}$
$\frac{3}{8}$	$2\frac{1}{4}$	$4\frac{1}{2}$	2	$1\frac{1}{8}$	2	$5\frac{1}{8}$	$1\frac{3}{4}$
$\frac{1}{2}$	$2\frac{3}{4}$	$5\frac{1}{4}$	$2\frac{1}{2}$	$1\frac{1}{4}$	$2\frac{1}{8}$	$5\frac{1}{2}$	2
$\frac{3}{4}$	$3\frac{3}{16}$	6	$2\frac{3}{4}$	$1\frac{1}{2}$	$2\frac{3}{8}$	$6\frac{5}{8}$	$2\frac{1}{2}$
1	$3\frac{3}{4}$	$6\frac{3}{4}$	3	$1\frac{3}{4}$	$2\frac{7}{8}$	$7\frac{7}{8}$	$2\frac{3}{4}$
$1\frac{1}{4}$	$4\frac{1}{4}$	$7\frac{1}{4}$	$3\frac{5}{8}$	2	$3\frac{1}{4}$	$9\frac{1}{2}$	3
$1\frac{1}{2}$	$4\frac{3}{4}$	$8\frac{1}{4}$	4	$2\frac{1}{4}$	$3\frac{1}{2}$	$10\frac{7}{8}$	$3\frac{5}{8}$
2	$5\frac{3}{4}$	$9\frac{1}{2}$	$4\frac{3}{4}$	$2\frac{3}{4}$	$3\frac{7}{8}$	$13\frac{1}{8}$	4
$2\frac{1}{2}$	$6\frac{3}{4}$	11	6	$3\frac{1}{4}$	$4\frac{1}{2}$	$15\frac{3}{8}$	$4\frac{3}{4}$
3	8	$12\frac{1}{4}$	7	$3\frac{3}{4}$	5	$17\frac{7}{8}$	$5\frac{3}{8}$

Dimensions in inches.
[1] Dimensions compiled from manufacturers' catalogues for drawing purposes.

Pipe Bushings[1]

DIMENSIONS OF OUTSIDE-HEAD, INSIDE-HEAD, AND FACE BUSHINGS IN INCHES

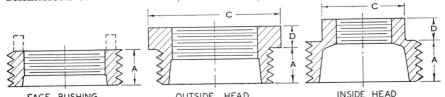

FACE BUSHING OUTSIDE HEAD INSIDE HEAD

Size	Length of external thread[2] min A	Height of head, min D	Width of head,[3] min C Outside	Inside
1/4 × 1/8	0.44	0.14	0.64	....
3/8 × 1/4	0.48	0.16	0.68	....
3/8 × 1/8	0.48	0.16	0.68	....
1/2 × 3/8	0.56	0.19	0.87	....
1/2 × 1/4	0.56	0.19	0.87	....
1/2 × 1/8	0.56	0.19	0.87	....
3/4 × 1/2	0 63	0.22	1.15	...
3/4 × 3/8	0.63	0.22	1.15	....
3/4 × 1/4	0.63	0.22	1.15	....
3/4 × 1/8	0.63	0.22	1.15	....
1 × 3/4	0.75	0.25	1.42	....
1 × 1/2	0.75	0.25	1.42	....
1 × 3/8	0.75	0.30	....	1.12
1 × 1/4	0.75	0.30	....	1.12
1 × 1/8	0.75	0.30	....	1.12
1¼ × 1	0.80	0.28	1.76	....
1¼ × 3/4	0.80	0.28	1.76	....
1¼ × 1/2	0.80	0.34	....	1.34
1¼ × 3/8	0.80	0.34	....	1.12
1¼ × 1/4	0.80	0.34	..	1.12
1½ × 1¼	0.83	0.31	2.00	....
1½ × 1	0.83	0.31	2.00	....
1½ × 3/4	0.83	0.37	....	1.63
1½ × 1/2	0.83	0.37	....	1.34
1½ × 3/8	0.83	0.37	....	1.12
1½ × 1/4	0.83	0.37	...	1.12

Size	Length of external thread[2] min A	Height of head, min D	Width of head,[3] min C Outside	Inside
2 × 1½	0.88	0.34	2.48	
2 × 1¼	0.88	0.34	2.48	
2 × 1	0.88	0.41	....	1.95
2 × 3/4	0.88	0.41	....	1.63
2 × 1/2	0.88	0.41	....	1.34
2 × 3/8	0.88	0.41	....	1.12
2 × 1/4	0.88	0.41	....	1.12
2½ × 2	1.07	0.37	2.98	
2½ × 1½	1.07	0.44	2.68	
2½ × 1¼	1.07	0.44	....	2.39
2½ × 1	1.07	0.44	....	1.95
2½ × 3/4	1.07	0.44	....	1.63
2½ × 1/2	1.07	0.44	....	1.34
3 × 2½	1.13	0.40	3.86	
3 × 2	1.13	0.48	3.28	
3 × 1½	1.13	0.48	....	2.68
3 × 1¼	1.13	0.48	....	2.39
3 × 1	1.13	0.48	....	1.95
3 × 3/4	1.13	0.48	....	1.63
3 × 1/2	1.13	0.48	....	1.34

[1] ASA B16.14—1949.
[2] In the case of outside-head bushings, length A includes provisions for imperfect threads.
[3] Heads of bushings shall be hexagonal or octagonal, except that on the larger sizes of outside-head bushings the heads may be made round with lugs instead of hexagonal or octagonal.

Lengths of Pipe Nipples[1]

Size	Length Close	Short	Size	Length Close	Short	Size	Length Close	Short	Size	Length Close	Short
1/8	3/4	1½	1/2	1⅛	1½	1¼	1⅝	2½	2½	2½	3
1/4	7/8	1½	3/4	1⅜	2	1½	1¾	2½	3	2⅝	3
3/8	1	1½	1	1½	2	2	2	2½			

Long nipple lengths { from short nipple lengths to 6" in ½" increments.
from 6" nipple lengths to 12" in 1" increments.
from 12" nipple lengths to 24" in 2" increments.

[1] Compiled from manufacturer's catalogues.
Dimensions in inches.

Lengths of Malleable-iron Unions[1]

GROUND JOINT

Nom. size	1/8	1/4	3/8	1/2	3/4	1	1¼	1½	2	2½	3
End to end	1½	1 9/16	1⅝	1 13/16	2 1/16	2¼	2½	2⅝	3	3 9/16	3 15/16

[1] Compiled from manufacturer's catalogues.
Dimensions in inches.

American Standard Cast-iron Pipe Flanges and Flanged Fittings[1]

FOR MAXIMUM WORKING SATURATED STEAM PRESSURE OF 125 PSI (GAGE)

90°ELL   LONG RAD.ELL 45°ELL REDUCING ELL SIDE OUTLET ELL TRUE "Y"   TEE

SIDE OUTLET TEE CROSS   LATERAL   REDUCER   ECCENTRIC REDUCER   FLANGES

Nominal pipe size N	A	B	C	D	E	F	G	H	K min
1	$3\frac{1}{2}$	5	$1\frac{3}{4}$	$7\frac{1}{2}$	$5\frac{3}{4}$	$1\frac{3}{4}$	....	$4\frac{1}{4}$	$\frac{7}{16}$
$1\frac{1}{4}$	$3\frac{3}{4}$	$5\frac{1}{2}$	2	8	$6\frac{1}{4}$	$1\frac{3}{4}$	....	$4\frac{5}{8}$	$\frac{1}{2}$
$1\frac{1}{2}$	4	6	$2\frac{1}{4}$	9	7	2	....	5	$\frac{9}{16}$
2	$4\frac{1}{2}$	$6\frac{1}{2}$	$2\frac{1}{2}$	$10\frac{1}{2}$	8	$2\frac{1}{2}$	5	6	$\frac{5}{8}$
$2\frac{1}{2}$	5	7	3	12	$9\frac{1}{2}$	$2\frac{1}{2}$	$5\frac{1}{2}$	7	$\frac{11}{16}$
3	$5\frac{1}{2}$	$7\frac{3}{4}$	3	13	10	3	6	$7\frac{1}{2}$	$\frac{3}{4}$
$3\frac{1}{2}$	6	$8\frac{1}{2}$	$3\frac{1}{2}$	$14\frac{1}{2}$	$11\frac{1}{2}$	3	$6\frac{1}{2}$	$8\frac{1}{2}$	$\frac{13}{16}$
4	$6\frac{1}{2}$	9	4	15	12	3	7	9	$\frac{15}{16}$
5	$7\frac{1}{2}$	$10\frac{1}{4}$	$4\frac{1}{2}$	17	$13\frac{1}{2}$	$3\frac{1}{2}$	8	10	$\frac{15}{16}$
6	8	$11\frac{1}{2}$	5	18	$14\frac{1}{2}$	$3\frac{1}{2}$	9	11	1
8	9	14	$5\frac{1}{2}$	22	$17\frac{1}{2}$	$4\frac{1}{2}$	11	$13\frac{1}{2}$	$1\frac{1}{8}$
10	11	$16\frac{1}{2}$	$6\frac{1}{2}$	$25\frac{1}{2}$	$20\frac{1}{2}$	5	12	16	$1\frac{3}{16}$
12	12	19	$7\frac{1}{2}$	30	$24\frac{1}{2}$	$5\frac{1}{2}$	14	19	$1\frac{1}{4}$

Nominal pipe size N	L	M	Number of bolts	Diam of bolts	Length of bolts	X min	Y min	Wall thickness	V
1	$3\frac{1}{8}$	$\frac{5}{8}$	4	$\frac{1}{2}$	$1\frac{3}{4}$	$1\frac{15}{16}$	$1\frac{1}{16}$	$\frac{5}{16}$	$\frac{3}{8}$
$1\frac{1}{4}$	$3\frac{1}{2}$	$\frac{5}{8}$	4	$\frac{1}{2}$	2	$2\frac{5}{16}$	$1\frac{3}{16}$	$\frac{5}{16}$	$\frac{7}{16}$
$1\frac{1}{2}$	$3\frac{7}{8}$	$\frac{5}{8}$	4	$\frac{1}{2}$	2	$2\frac{9}{16}$	$\frac{7}{8}$	$\frac{5}{16}$	$\frac{1}{2}$
2	$4\frac{3}{4}$	$\frac{3}{4}$	4	$\frac{5}{8}$	$2\frac{1}{4}$	$3\frac{1}{16}$	1	$\frac{5}{16}$	$\frac{9}{16}$
$2\frac{1}{2}$	$5\frac{1}{2}$	$\frac{3}{4}$	4	$\frac{5}{8}$	$2\frac{1}{2}$	$3\frac{9}{16}$	$1\frac{1}{8}$	$\frac{5}{16}$	$\frac{5}{8}$
3	6	$\frac{3}{4}$	4	$\frac{5}{8}$	$2\frac{1}{2}$	$4\frac{1}{4}$	$1\frac{3}{16}$	$\frac{3}{8}$	$1\frac{1}{16}$
$3\frac{1}{2}$	7	$\frac{3}{4}$	8	$\frac{5}{8}$	$2\frac{3}{4}$	$4\frac{13}{16}$	$1\frac{1}{4}$	$\frac{7}{16}$	$\frac{3}{4}$
4	$7\frac{1}{2}$	$\frac{3}{4}$	8	$\frac{5}{8}$	3	$5\frac{5}{16}$	$1\frac{5}{16}$	$\frac{1}{2}$	$\frac{7}{8}$
5	$8\frac{1}{2}$	$\frac{7}{8}$	8	$\frac{3}{4}$	3	$6\frac{7}{16}$	$1\frac{7}{16}$	$\frac{1}{2}$	$\frac{7}{8}$
6	$9\frac{1}{2}$	$\frac{7}{8}$	8	$\frac{3}{4}$	$3\frac{1}{4}$	$7\frac{9}{16}$	$1\frac{9}{16}$	$\frac{9}{16}$	$1\frac{5}{16}$
8	$11\frac{3}{4}$	$\frac{7}{8}$	8	$\frac{3}{4}$	$3\frac{1}{4}$	$9\frac{11}{16}$	$1\frac{3}{4}$	$\frac{5}{8}$	$1\frac{1}{16}$
10	$14\frac{1}{4}$	1	12	$\frac{7}{8}$	$3\frac{3}{4}$	$11\frac{15}{16}$	$1\frac{15}{16}$	$\frac{3}{4}$	$1\frac{1}{8}$
12	17	1	12	$\frac{7}{8}$	$3\frac{3}{4}$	$14\frac{7}{16}$	$2\frac{3}{16}$	$1\frac{3}{16}$	

Dimensions in inches.
[1] ASA B16a 1939.

American Standard Steel Butt-welding Fittings[1,2]

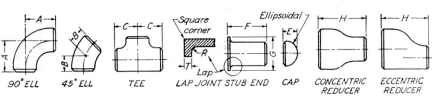

| 90° ELL | 45° ELL | TEE | LAP JOINT STUB END | CAP | CONCENTRIC REDUCER | ECCENTRIC REDUCER |

ELBOWS, TEES, CAPS, AND STUB ENDS

Nominal pipe size	Outside diameter at bevel	Center to end			Welding caps	Lapped-joint stub ends		
		90-deg welding elbow A	45-deg welding elbow B	of run, welding tee C	E	Lengths F	Radius of fillet R	Diameter of lap G
1	1.310	1½	⅞	1½	1½	4	⅛	2
1¼	1.660	1⅞	1	1⅞	1½	4	3/16	2½
1½	1.900	2¼	1⅛	2¼	1½	4	¼	2⅞
2	2.375	3	1⅜	2½	1½	6	5/16	3⅝
2½	2.875	3¾	1¾	3	1½	6	5/16	4⅛
3	3.500	4½	2	3⅜	2	6	⅜	5
3½	4.000	5¼	2¼	3¾	2½	6	⅜	5½
4	4.500	6	2½	4⅛	2½	6	7/16	6 3/16

BUTT-WELDING REDUCERS

Nominal pipe size	Outside diameter at bevel		End to end H	Nominal pipe size	Outside diameter at bevel		End to end H
	Large end	Small end			Large end	Small end	
1 × ¾	1.315	1.050	2	3 × 2½	3.500	2.875	3½
1 × ½		0.840		3 × 2		2.375	
1 × ⅜		0.675		3 × 1½		1.900	
				3 × 1¼		1.660	
1¼ × 1	1.660	1.315	2				
1¼ × ¾		1.050		3½ × 3	4.000	3.500	4
1¼ × ½		0.840		3½ × 2½		2.875	
				3½ × 2		2.375	
1½ × 1¼	1.900	1.660	2½	3½ × 1½		1.900	
1½ × 1		1.315		3½ × 1¼		1.660	
1½ × ¾		1.050					
1½ × ½		0.840		4 × 3½	4.500	4.000	4
				4 × 3		3.500	
2 × 1½	2.375	1.900	3	4 × 2½		2.875	
2 × 1¼		1.660		4 × 2		2.375	
2 × 1		1.315		4 × 1½		1.900	
2 × ¾		1.050					
				5 × 4	5.563	4.500	5
2½ × 2	2.875	2.375	3½	5 × 3½		4.000	
2½ × 1½		1.900		5 × 3		3.500	
2½ × 1¼		1 660		5 × 2½		2.875	
2½ × 1		1.315					

Dimensions in inches.
[1] For larger sizes see ASA B16.
[2] ASA B16.9 1940.

Threaded Cast-iron Pipe[1]

DIMENSION OF PIPE AND DRAINAGE HUBS

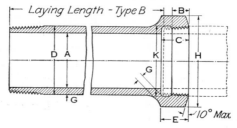

Pipe size	Pipe				Drainage hubs					Nominal weights	
	Nominal diameter		Wall thick-ness min	Thread length[1]	Diameter of groove max	End to shoulder[2]	Minimum band			Type A and barrel of type B per ft	Addi-tional wt of hubs for type B
	Outside	Inside					Diam-eter	Length			
	D	A	G	B	K	C	H	E			
1¼	1.66	1.23	0.187	0.42	1.73	0.71	2.39	0.71	3.033	0.60
1½	1.90	1.45	0.195	0.42	1.97	0.72	2.68	0.72	3.666	0.90
2	2.38	1.89	0.211	0.43	2.44	0.76	3.28	0.76	5.041	1.00
2½	2.88	2.32	0.241	0.68	2.97	1.14	3.86	1.14	7.032	1.35
3	3.50	2.90	0.263	0.76	3.60	1.20	4.62	1.20	9.410	2.80
4	4.50	3.83	0.294	0.84	4.60	1.30	5.79	1.30	13.751	3.48
5	5.56	4.81	0.328	0.93	5.66	1.41	7.05	1.41	19.069	5.00
6	6.63	5.76	0.378	0.95	6.72	1.51	8.28	1.51	26.223	6.60
8	8.63	7.63	0.438	1.06	8.72	1.71	10.63	1.71	39.820	10.00
10	10.75	9.75	0.438	1.21	10.85	1.92	13.12	1.93	50.234	
12	12.75	11.75	0.438	1.36	12.85	2.12	15.47	2.13	60.036	

All dimensions are given in inches, except where otherwise stated. Type A has external threads both ends. Type B as shown. [1] ASA A40.5 1943. [2] The length of thread B and the end to shoulder C shall not vary from the dimensions shown by more than plus or minus the equivalent of the pitch of one thread.

Beam Connections

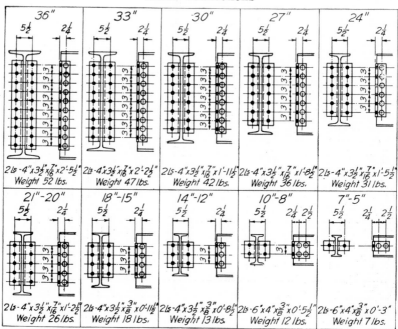

Selected Structural Shapes

DIMENSIONS FOR DETAILING[1]

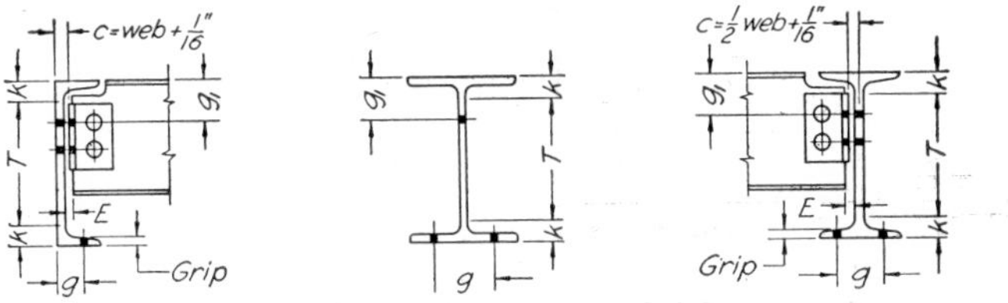

CHANNEL WF SHAPE BEAM

Name	Depth of section, in.	Weight per ft, lb	Flange: Width, in.	Flange: Mean thickness, in.	Web: Thickness, in.	Web: Half thickness, in.	Distances: T, in.	Distances: k, in.	Distances: g_1, in.	Distances: c, in.	Grip, in.	Max flange rivet, in.	Usual gage g, in.
Channels	18	58.0	4 1/4	5/8	11/16	3/8	15 3/8	1 5/16	2 3/4	3/4	5/8	1	2 1/2
	15	40.0	3 1/2	5/8	9/16	1/4	12 3/8	1 5/16	2 3/4	5/8	5/8	1	2
	12	30.0	3 1/8	1/2	1/2	1/4	9 7/8	1 1/16	2 1/2	9/16	1/2	7/8	1 3/4
	10	15.3	2 5/8	7/16	1/4	1/8	8 1/8	15/16	2 1/2	5/16	7/16	3/4	1 1/2
	9	13.4	2 3/8	7/16	1/4	1/8	7 1/4	7/8	2 1/2	5/16	3/8	3/4	1 3/8
	8	18.75	2 1/2	3/8	1/2	1/4	6 3/8	13/16	2 1/4	9/16	3/8	3/4	1 1/2
	7	12.25	2 1/4	3/8	5/16	3/16	5 3/8	13/16	2	3/8	3/8	5/8	1 1/4
	6	10.5	2	3/8	5/16	3/16	4 1/2	3/4	2	3/8	3/8	5/8	1 1/8
	5	9.0	1 7/8	5/16	5/16	3/16	3 5/8	11/16	2	3/8	5/16	1/2	1 1/8
	4	7.25	1 3/4	5/16	5/16	3/16	2 3/4	5/8	2	3/8	5/16	1/2	1
	3	6.0	1 5/8	1/4	3/8	3/16	1 3/4	5/8	...	7/16	5/16	1/2	7/8
WF shapes	21[2] (21 1/4)	127	13	1	9/16	5/16	17 3/4	1 3/4	3	3/8	.....	.....	5 1/2
	16 (16 3/8)	96	11 1/2	7/8	9/16	5/16	13 1/8	1 5/8	2 3/4	3/8	.....	.....	5 1/2
	14 (14 1/8)	84	12	3/4	7/16	1/4	11 3/8	1 3/8	2 3/4	5/16	.....	.....	5 1/2
	14 (13 3/4)	48	8	9/16	3/8	3/16	11 3/8	1 3/16	2 1/2	1/4	.....	.....	5 1/2
	12 (12 1/4)	50	8 1/8	5/8	3/8	3/16	9 3/4	1 1/4	2 1/2	1/4	.....	.....	5 1/2
	10 (10)	49	10	9/16	3/8	3/16	7 7/8	1 1/16	2 1/2	1/4	.....	.....	5 1/2
	10 (9 3/4)	33	8	7/16	5/16	3/16	7 7/8	15/16	2 1/4	1/4	.....	.....	5 1/2
	8 (8)	28	6 1/2	7/16	5/16	1/8	6 3/8	13/16	2 1/4	3/16	.....	.....	3 1/2
Beams	24	120.0	8	1 1/8	13/16	7/16	20 1/8	1 15/16	3 1/4	1/2	1 1/8	1	4
	20	85.0	7	15/16	11/16	5/16	16 1/2	1 3/4	3 1/4	3/8	7/8	1	4
	18	70.0	6 1/4	11/16	3/4	3/8	15 1/4	1 3/8	2 3/4	7/16	11/16	7/8	3 1/2
	15	50.0	5 5/8	5/8	9/16	5/16	12 1/2	1 1/4	2 3/4	3/8	9/16	3/4	3 1/2
	12	31.8	5	9/16	3/8	3/16	9 3/4	1 1/8	2 1/2	1/4	1/2	3/4	3
	10	35.0	5	1/2	5/8	5/16	8	1	2 1/2	3/8	1/2	3/4	2 3/4
	8	23.0	4 1/8	7/16	7/16	1/4	6 1/4	7/8	2 1/4	5/16	7/16	3/4	2 1/4
	7	20.0	3 7/8	3/8	7/16	1/4	5 3/8	13/16	2	5/16	3/8	5/8	2 1/4
	6	17.25	3 5/8	3/8	1/2	1/4	4 1/2	3/4	2	5/16	3/8	5/8	2
	5	10.0	3	5/16	1/4	1/8	3 5/8	11/16	2	3/16	5/16	1/2	1 3/4
	4	9.5	2 3/4	5/16	5/16	3/16	2 3/4	5/8	2	1/4	5/16	1/2	1 1/2
	3	7.5	2 1/2	1/4	3/8	3/16	1 7/8	9/16	..	1/4	1/4	3/8	1 1/2

[1] From Steel Construction Handbook.

[2] Nominal depth; ( ) indicates actual depth.

Driving Clearances for Riveting

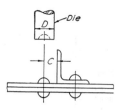

	Diameter of rivet								
	$\frac{1}{2}$	$\frac{5}{8}$	$\frac{3}{4}$	$\frac{7}{8}$	1	$1\frac{1}{8}$	$1\frac{1}{4}$	$1\frac{3}{8}$	$1\frac{1}{2}$
D	$1\frac{3}{4}$	2	$2\frac{1}{4}$	$2\frac{1}{2}$	$2\frac{3}{4}$	3	$3\frac{1}{4}$	$3\frac{1}{2}$	$3\frac{3}{4}$
C	1	$1\frac{1}{8}$	$1\frac{1}{4}$	$1\frac{3}{8}$	$1\frac{1}{2}$	$1\frac{5}{8}$	$1\frac{3}{4}$	$1\frac{7}{8}$	2

Dimensions in inches.

Gage and Maximum Rivet Size for Angles

Leg	8	7	6	5	4	$3\frac{1}{2}$	3	$2\frac{1}{2}$	2	$1\frac{3}{4}$	$1\frac{1}{2}$	$1\frac{3}{8}$	$1\frac{1}{4}$	1
G	$4\frac{1}{2}$	4	$3\frac{1}{2}$	3	$2\frac{1}{2}$	2	$1\frac{3}{4}$	$1\frac{3}{8}$	$1\frac{1}{8}$	1	$\frac{7}{8}$	$\frac{7}{8}$	$\frac{3}{4}$	$\frac{5}{8}$
G_1	3	$2\frac{1}{2}$	$2\frac{1}{4}$	2										
G_2	3	3	$2\frac{1}{2}$	$1\frac{3}{4}$										
Max rivet	$1\frac{1}{8}$	$1\frac{1}{8}$	1	1	$\frac{7}{8}$	$\frac{7}{8}$	$\frac{7}{8}$	$\frac{3}{4}$	$\frac{5}{8}$	$\frac{1}{2}$	$\frac{3}{8}$	$\frac{3}{8}$	$\frac{3}{8}$	$\frac{1}{4}$

Dimensions in inches.

SAE Standard Cotter Pins

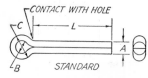

Pin diameter, A			Eye diameter, min		Recommended hole diameter, drill size
Nominal	Max	Min	Inside, B	Outside, C	
$\frac{1}{32}$ (.031)	.032	.028	$\frac{1}{32}$	$\frac{1}{16}$	$\frac{3}{64}$ (.0469)
$\frac{3}{64}$ (.047)	.048	.044	$\frac{3}{64}$	$\frac{3}{32}$	$\frac{1}{16}$ (.0625)
$\frac{1}{16}$ (.062)	.060	.056	$\frac{1}{16}$	$\frac{1}{8}$	$\frac{5}{64}$ (.0781)
$\frac{5}{64}$ (.078)	.076	.072	$\frac{5}{64}$	$\frac{5}{32}$	$\frac{3}{32}$ (.0937)
$\frac{3}{32}$ (.094)	.090	.086	$\frac{3}{32}$	$\frac{3}{16}$	$\frac{7}{64}$ (.1094)
$\frac{1}{8}$ (.125)	.120	.116	$\frac{1}{8}$	$\frac{1}{4}$	$\frac{9}{64}$ (.1406)
$\frac{5}{32}$ (.156)	.150	.146	$\frac{5}{32}$	$\frac{5}{16}$	$\frac{11}{64}$ (.1719)
$\frac{3}{16}$ (.188)	.176	.172	$\frac{3}{16}$	$\frac{3}{8}$	$\frac{13}{64}$ (.2031)
$\frac{7}{32}$ (.219)	.207	.202	$\frac{7}{32}$	$\frac{7}{16}$	$\frac{15}{64}$ (.2344)
$\frac{1}{4}$ (.250)	.225	.220	$\frac{1}{4}$	$\frac{1}{2}$	$\frac{17}{64}$ (.2656)
$\frac{5}{16}$ (.312)	.280	.275	$\frac{5}{16}$	$\frac{5}{8}$	$\frac{5}{16}$ (.3125)
$\frac{3}{8}$ (.375)	.335	.329	$\frac{3}{8}$	$\frac{3}{4}$	$\frac{3}{8}$ (.3750)
$\frac{1}{2}$ (.500)	.473	.467	$\frac{1}{2}$	1	$\frac{1}{2}$ (.5000)

American Standard Graphical Symbols[1]

PIPING

Piping, in general	(Lettered with name of material conveyed)
Non-intersecting Pipes	

(To differentiate lines of piping on a drawing the following symbols may be used)

Air	Cold Water	Steam
Gas	Hot Water	Condensate
Oil	Vacuum	Refrigerant

PIPE FITTINGS AND VALVES

	Flanged	Screwed	Bell and Spigot	Welded	Soldered
Joint					
Elbow—90 deg					
Elbow—45 deg					
Elbow—Turned Up					
Elbow—Turned Down					
Elbow—Long Radius					
Side Outlet Elbow Outlet Down					
Side Outlet Elbow Outlet Up					
Base Elbow					
Double Branch Elbow					
Reducing Elbow					
Reducer					
Eccentric Reducer					
Tee-Outlet Up					
Tee-Outlet Down					
Tee					
Side Outlet Tee Outlet Up					
Side Outlet Tee Outlet Down					
Single Sweep Tee					
Double Sweep Tee					
Cross					
Lateral					
Gate Valve					

[1] ASA Z14.2—1935.

American Standard Graphical Symbols[1]

PIPING

	Flanged	Screwed	Bell and Spigot	Welded	Soldered
Globe Valve					
Angle Globe Valve					
Angle Gate Valve					
Check Valve					
Angle Check Valve					
Stop Cock					
Safety Valve					
Quick Opening Valve					
Float Operating Valve					
Motor Operated Gate Valve					
Motor Operated Globe Valve					
Expansion Joint Flanged					
Reducing Flange					
Union	(See Joint)				
Sleeve					
Bushing					

HEATING AND VENTILATING

Lock and Shield Valve	Tube Radiator	(Plan) (Elev.)	Exhaust Duct, Section	
Reducing Valve	Wall Radiator	(Plan) (Elev.)	Butterfly Damper	(Plan or Elev.) (Elev or Plan)
Diaphragm Valve	Pipe Coil	(Plan) (Elev.)	Deflecting Damper Rectangular Pipe	
Thermostat				
Radiator Trap	(Plan) (Elev.)	Indirect Radiator	(Plan) (Elev.)	Vanes
	Supply Duct, Section		Air Supply Outlet	
			Exhaust Inlet	

HEAT-POWER APPARATUS

Flue Gas Reheater (Intermediate Superheater)	Steam Turbine	Automatic By pass Valve	
Steam Generator (Boiler)	Condensing Turbine	Automatic Valve Operated by Governor	
Live Steam Superheater	Open Tank	Pumps Air Service Boiler Feed Condensate Circulating Water Reciprocating	
Feed Heater With Air Outlet	Closed Tank		
Surface Condenser	Automatic Reducing Valve	Dynamic Pump (Air Ejector)	

[1] ASA Z14.2—1935.

American Standard Plumbing Symbols[1]

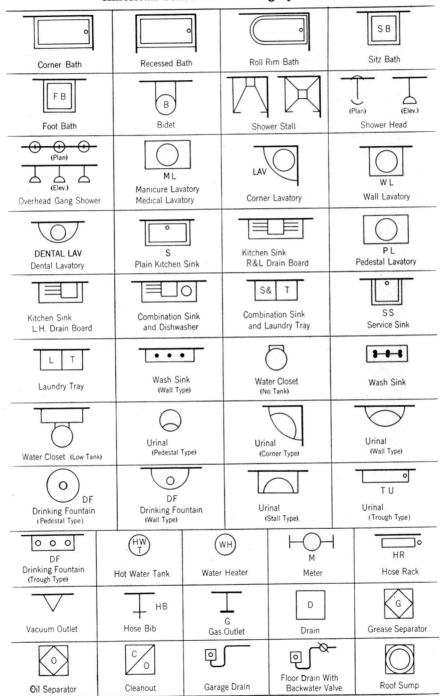

[1] A Z14.2—1935.

American Standard Wiring Symbols[1]

Ceiling Outlet.. -Ø-

      "   "   for Extensions............ -Ⓔ-

      "   Lamp Receptacle, Specifications   Ⓡ

    to describe type, as Key, Keyless or Pull Chain

Ceiling Fan Outlet.................................. ∞⊕

Pull Switch.. ⊕PS

Drop Cord.. Ⓓ

Wall Bracket....................................... -Ø.

      "   Outlet for Extensions............... Ⓔ-

      "   Lamp Receptacle, as specified........ -Ⓡ

      "   Fan Outlet............................. ⚇

Single Convenience Outlet............ ⊏⊖

Double   "   "   " .... ⊖₂

Junction Box....................................... Ⓙ

Special Purpose Outlets............ ⎰ ▲

   Lighting, Heating and Power ⎱ ◓

    as described in specifications   ◑

Exit Light.. -⊗

Floor Outlet... -⊙,

Floor Elbow..... Oᴱ, Floor Tee......... Oᵀ

Local Switch, Single Pole.................. S¹

     Double Pole.... S², 3-Way..S³, 4-Way..... S⁴

Automatic Door Switch.................. Sᴰ

Key Push Button Switch.................. Sᴷ

Electrolier Switch............................ Sᴱ

Push Button Switch and Pilot.......... Sᴾ

Remote Control Push Button Switch...Sᴿ

Tank Switch............................. T.S.

Motor.... ⊕, Motor Controller.... M.C.

Lighting Panel............................ ▬

Power Panel............................ ▨

Heating Panel............................ ◣

Pull Box.................................... ▩

Cable Supporting Box........ ⊞⊞⊞

Meter.................................... ⊡

Transformer............................... ⏛

Push Button.............................. ⊡

Pole Line. .... -o-o-

Buzzer..... ⊏/, Bell..... ⌂

Annunciator............................. ◇-

Branch Circuit, Run Exposed   -----

   Run Concealed Under Floor   ----

    "   "   "   Floor Above   ———

Feeder Run Exposed   -----

   Run Concealed Under Floor   ----

    "   "   "   Floor Above   ———

Telephone, Interior....◁, Public.... ◀

Clock, Secondary ..🕒, Master..... Ⓒ

Time Stamp............................. ⊕

Electric Door Opener.............. 🔲

Local Fire Alarm Gong............. Ⓕ

City Fire Alarm Station........ ◪

Local   "   "   " .... Ⓕ

Fire Alarm Central Station..... ◁ᶠᴬ

Speaking Tube............................. ▶

Nurse's Signal Plug................. Ⓝ

Maid's Plug............................. Ⓜ

Horn Outlet............................. ◁

District Messenger Call......... D-

Watchman Station............... Ⓦ

Watchman Central Station Detector...... ◫

Public Telephone-P.B.X. Switchboard.... ◪

Interior Telephone Central Switchboard........ ◫

Interconnection Cabinet............ ▭

Telephone Cabinet................ ⊠

Telegraph   "   .... ◄►

Special Outlet for Signal System as Specified.... ⊠

Battery............................. |¦|¦|¦|¦|

Signal Wires in Conduit Under Floor———–

   "   "   "   "   "   Floor Above ————

This Character Marked on Tap Circuits Indicates

2 No. 14 Conductors in $\frac{1}{2}$" Conduit   .ll

3   " 14   "   " $\frac{1}{2}$"   "   lll

4   " 14   "   " $\frac{3}{4}$" " $\left(\substack{\text{Unless} \\ \text{Marked} \frac{1}{2}}\right)$ llll

5   " 14   "   " $\frac{3}{4}$" "   lllll

6   " 14   "   " 1" "$\left(\substack{\text{Unless} \\ \text{Marked} \frac{3}{4}}\right)$ llllll

7   " 14   "   " 1" "   lllllll

8   " 14   "   " 1" "   llllllll

(Radio Outlet.......................... Ⴑ)

(Public Speaker Outlet .... ⊲)

[1] ASA C10.

Electric Symbols[1]

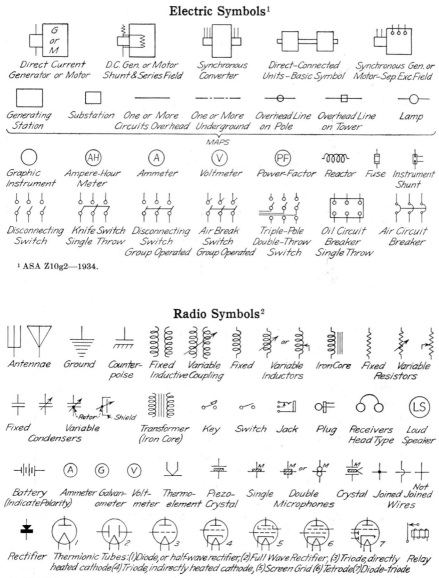

| Direct Current Generator or Motor | D.C. Gen. or Motor Shunt & Series Field | Synchronous Converter | Direct-Connected Units – Basic Symbol | Synchronous Gen. or Motor-Sep Exc. Field |

| Generating Station | Substation | One or More Circuits Overhead | One or More Underground | Overhead Line on Pole | Overhead Line on Tower | Lamp |

MAPS

| Graphic Instrument | Ampere-Hour Meter | Ammeter | Voltmeter | Power-Factor | Reactor | Fuse | Instrument Shunt |

| Disconnecting Switch | Knife Switch Single Throw | Disconnecting Switch Group Operated | Air Break Switch Group Operated | Triple-Pole Double-Throw Switch | Oil Circuit Breaker Single Throw | Air Circuit Breaker |

[1] ASA Z10g2—1934.

Radio Symbols[2]

| Antennae | Ground | Counter-poise | Fixed Inductive Coupling | Variable | Fixed | Variable Inductors | IronCore | Fixed Resistors | Variable |

| Fixed Condensers | Variable | Transformer (Iron Core) | Key | Switch | Jack | Plug | Receivers Head Type | Loud Speaker |

| Battery (Indicate Polarity) | Ammeter | Galvan-ometer | Volt-meter | Thermo-element | Piezo-Crystal | Single Microphones | Double | Crystal | Joined Wires | Not Joined |

Rectifier Thermionic Tubes:(1)Diode, or half-wave rectifier,(2)Full Wave Rectifier,(3)Triode, directly Relay
heated cathode(4)Triode, indirectly heated cathode,(5)Screen Grid (6)Tetrode(7)Diode-triode

[2] ASA Z10g3—1933.

Symbols for Materials (Exterior)

Brick

Stone

Transparent Material
Glass, Celluloid, Etc.

Wood

Symbols for Materials (Section)

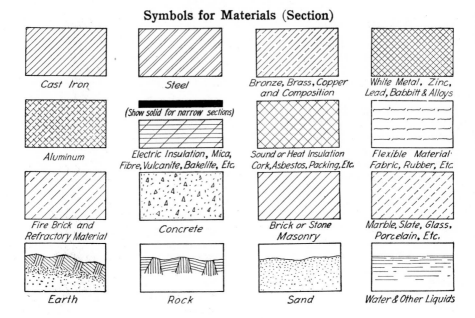

Weights of Materials

METALS

	lb/cu in.
Aluminum alloy, cast	0.099
Aluminum, cast	0.094
Aluminum, wrought	0.097
Babbitt metal	0.267
Brass, cast or rolled	0.303–0.313
Brass, drawn	0.323
Bronze, aluminum cast	0.277
Bronze, phosphor	0.315–0.321
Chromium	0.256
Copper, cast	0.311
Copper, rolled, drawn or wire	0.322
Dowmetal A	0.065
Duralumin	0.101

	lb/cu in.
Gold	0.697
Iron, cast	0.260
Iron, wrought	0.283
Lead	0.411
Magnesium	0.063
Mercury	0.491
Monel metal	0.323
Silver	0.379
Steel, cast or rolled	0.274–0.281
Steel, tool	0.272
Tin	0.263
Zinc	0.258

WOOD

	lb/cu in.
Ash	0.024
Balsa	0.0058
Cedar	0.017
Cork	0.009
Hickory	0.0295
Maple	0.025
Oak (white)	0.028
Pine (white)	0.015
Pine (yellow)	0.025
Poplar	0.018
Walnut (black)	0.023

MISCELLANEOUS MATERIALS

	lb/cu ft
Asbestos	175
Bakelite	79.5
Brick, common	112
Brick, fire	144
Celluloid	86.4
Earth, packed	100
Fiber	89.9
Glass	163
Gravel	109
Limestone	163
Plexiglass	74.3
Sandstone	144
Water	62.4

Abbreviations and Word Symbols to Be Used on Drawings

Alternating current	a-c	Fillister	fil
Angle (structural shape)	∟	Fine (screw threads)	F
American Standard	Am Std	Foot, Feet	ft or ′
American Standards Association	ASA	Finish	**V** or fin or *f*
American wire gage (B & S gage)	Awg	Gage	ga
		Gallon	gal
Approved (by)	App	Galvanized iron	GI
Birmingham wire gage	Bwg	Grind	gr
Brown & Sharpe gage	B & S	H Beam	**H**
Babbitt metal (specified by number)	bab #——	Head	hd
		Hexagonal	hex
Brass, SAE (specified by number)	br #——	Harden	hdn
		Horsepower	hp or **HP**
Bronze, SAE (specified by number)	bro #——	Heat-treatment, SAE (specified by number)	htr #——
Brinell hardness number	Bhn	I beam	I
Cast iron	CI	Impregnate	impreg
Center line	₵ or CL	Inside diameter	ID
Center to center	c to c	Inch (es)	″ or in.
Centimeter (s)	cm	Insulate, insulated	insl
Chamfer	chfr	Kilowatt	kw
Channel	⊔	Kip	k
Checked (by)	Ch	Left hand	LH
Circular	cir	Laminate	lam
Circular pitch (gear drawings)	CP	Lateral	lat
		Longitudinal	long
Coarse (screw threads)	C	Lubricate, lubrication	lub
Copper	cop	Machine	mach
Cold rolled steel	CRS	Magnetic	mag
Counterbore	c'bore	Malleable iron	Mal I
Countersink	csk	Maximum	max
Cubic inches (feet; yards)	cu in. (ft; yd)	Meter (s)	m
		Millimeter (s)	mm
Cylinder, cylindrical	cyl	Minute (s), (time)	′ or min
Degree (s) (angular measurement)	° or deg	Minute (s) (angular measure)	′
Diameter	D	Minimum	min
Direct current	d-c	National form (screw threads)	N
Diagonal	diag	National Electrical Code	NEC
Diametral pitch (gear drawings)	DP	Number	# or no.
Drawing (s)	Dwg, Dwgs	On center—(center to center)	oc
Drawn (by)	Dr	Outside diameter	OD
Drop forging	D forg	Oxidize	ox
Detail drawing	Dtl dwg	Parallel to	‖
Die casting	D cast	Patent	pat
Die stamping	D st	Pattern	patt
External	ext	Perforate	perf
Extra fine (screw threads)	EF	Perpendicular to	⊥
Fabricate	fab	Phosphor bronze	phos bro

Piece (s)..............	pc, pcs	Square bar...........	⊕
Pitch.................	P	Square bar, deformed..	⊏f⊐
Pitch diameter........	PD	Square foot, feet.......	sq ft or □′
Plate.................	pl	Square inch (es).......	sq in. or □″
Pound.................	# or lb	Standard.............	Std
Pratt and Whitney (key)	P & W	Steel.................	Stl
Propeller............	prop	Steel casting.........	Stl C
Quart.................	qt	Tee (structural shape)..	T
Radius...............	R	Teeth (on gear draw-	
Required............	req	ings)..............	T
Revolutions per minute	rpm	Thread (s)............	thd, thds
Revolutions per second.	rps	Traced (by)..........	Tr
Right hand...........	RH	Unified (screw threads)	U
Round...............	rd	United States Standard	
Round bar...........	ϕ	(old)..............	USS
Round bar deformed...	ƒ	Wide flange section	
Screw...............	sc	(structural)........	W⌐
Section..............	sec	Woodruff (key).......	spell out or Wdrf
Society of Automotive		Wrought iron.........	WI
Engineers..........	SAE	Yard (s).............	yd, yds
Special (screw threads)	S	Zee (structural shape)..	Z
Square..............	□ or sq		

Greek Alphabet

While Greek is not a required study in most engineering curricula, the engineer often uses letters of the Greek alphabet, both capitals and lower case, as symbols and reference letters. He should therefore be able to draw them readily and to read them without hesitation when encountered in equations or formulas.

There is a variety in Greek alphabets, just as there is in Roman alphabets. The one given below is a legible form with accented and unaccented strokes in the capitals that follow closely the rules for shading Roman letters. The lower case has good historical precedent in form, shading, and comparative size.

$A\alpha$	$B\beta$	$\Gamma\gamma$	$\Delta\delta$	$E\varepsilon$	$Z\zeta$	$H\eta$	$\Theta\vartheta$
ALPHA	BETA	GAMMA	DELTA	EPSILON	ZETA	ETA	THETA

$I\iota$	$K\kappa$	$\Lambda\lambda$	$M\mu$	$N\nu$	$\Xi\xi$	Oo	$\Pi\pi$
IOTA	KAPPA	LAMBDA	MU	NU	XI	OMICRON	PI

$P\rho$	$\Sigma\sigma$	$T\tau$	$Y\upsilon$	$\Phi\phi$	$X\chi$	$\Psi\psi$	$\Omega\omega$
RHO	SIGMA	TAU	UPSILON	PHI	CHI	PSI	OMEGA

Glossary of Technical Terms

PART I. SHOP TERMS

Anneal (*v*)—To soften a metal piece and remove internal stresses by heating to its critical temperature and allowing to cool very slowly.

Arc-weld (*v*)—To weld by electric-arc process.

Bore (*v*)—To enlarge a hole with a boring tool as in a lathe or boring mill. Distinguished from *drill*.

Boss (*n*)—A projection of circular cross section, as on a casting or forging.

Boss.

Braze (*v*)—To join by the use of hard solder.

Broach (*v*)—To finish the inside of a hole to a shape usually other than round. (*n*) A tool with serrated edges, pushed or pulled through a hole to enlarge it to a required shape.

Buff (*v*)—To polish with abrasive on a cloth wheel or other soft carrier.

Burnish (*v*)—To smooth or polish by a rolling or sliding tool under pressure.

Bushing (*n*)—A removable sleeve or liner for a bearing; also a guide for a tool in a jig or fixture.

Bushing.

Carburize (*v*)—To prepare a low-carbon steel for heat-treatment by packing in a box with carbonizing material, such as wood charcoal, and heating to about 2000°F for several hours, then allowing to cool slowly.

Caseharden (*v*)—To harden the surface of carburized steel by heating to critical temperature and quenching, as in an oil or lead bath.

Castellate (*v*)—To form into a shape resembling a castle battlement, as castellated nut. Often applied to a shaft with multiple integral keys milled on it.

Chamfer (*v*)—To bevel a sharp external edge. (*n*) A beveled edge.

Chase (*v*)—To cut threads in a lathe, as distinguished from cutting threads with a die. (*n*) A slot or groove.

Chamfer.

Chill (*v*)—To harden the surface of cast iron by sudden cooling against a metal mold.

Chip (*v*)—To cut or clean with a chisel.

Coin (*v*)—To stamp and form a metal piece in one operation, usually with a surface design.

Cold-work (*v*)—To deform metal stock by hammering, forming, drawing, etc., while the metal is at ordinary room temperature.

Color-harden (*v*)—To caseharden to a very shallow depth, chiefly for appearance.

Core (*v*)—To form the hollow part of a casting, using a solid form made of sand, shaped in a core box, baked and placed in the mold. After cooling the core is easily broken up leaving the casting hollow.

Counterbore (*v*)—To enlarge a hole to a given depth. (*n*) 1. The cylindrical enlargement of the end of a drilled or bored hole. 2. A cutting tool for counterboring, having a piloted end of the size of the drilled hole.

Counterbore.

Countersink(*v*)—To form a depression to fit the conical head of a screw, or the thickness of a plate, so the face will be level with the surface. (*n*) A conical tool for countersinking.

Countersink.

Crown (*n*)—Angular or rounded contour, as on the face of a pulley.

Die (*n*)—1. One of a pair of hardened metal blocks for forming, impressing, or cutting out a desired shape. 2 (thread). A tool for cutting external threads. Opposite of *tap*.

Die casting (*n*)—A very accurate and smooth casting made by pouring a molten alloy (or composition, as Bakelite) usually under pressure into a metal mold or die. Distinguished from a casting made in sand.

Die stamping (*n*)—A piece, usually of sheet metal, formed or cut out by a die.

Draw (*v*)—1. To form by a distorting or stretching process. 2. To temper steel by gradual or intermittent quenching.

Drill (*v*)—To sink a hole with a drill, usually a twist drill. (*n*) A pointed cutting tool rotated under pressure.

Drop forging (*n*)—A wrought piece formed hot between dies under a drop hammer, or by pressure.

Face (*v*)—To machine a flat surface perpendicular to the axis of rotation on a lathe. Distinguished from *turn*.

Feather (*n*)—A flat sliding key, usually fastened to the hub.

Fettle (*v*)—To remove fins and smooth the corners on unfired ceramic products.

File (*v*)—To finish or trim with a file.

Fillet (*n*)—A rounded filling of the internal angle between two surfaces.

Fillet.

Fin (*n*)—A thin projecting rib. Also, excess ridge of material.

Fit (*n*)—The kind of contact between two machined surfaces, as (1) *drive, force*, or *press*—when the shaft is slightly larger than the hole and must be forced in with sledge or power press.

    (2) *shrink*—when the shaft is slightly larger than the hole, the piece containing the hole is heated, thereby expanding the hole sufficiently to slip over the shaft. On cooling, the shaft will be seized firmly if the fit allowances have been correctly proportioned.

    (3) *running* or *sliding*—when sufficient allowance has been made between sizes of shaft and hole to allow free running without seizing or heating.

    (4) *wringing*—when the allowance is smaller than a running fit and the shaft will enter the hole by twisting it by hand.

Flange (*n*)—A projecting rim or edge for fastening or stiffening.

Flange.

Forge (*v*)—To shape metal while hot and plastic by a hammering or forcing process either by hand or by machine.

Galvanize (*v*)—To treat with a bath of lead and zinc to prevent rusting.

Graduate (*v*)—To divide a scale or dial into regular spaces.

Grind (*v*)—To finish or polish a surface by means of an abrasive wheel.

Harden (*v*)—To heat hardenable steel above the critical temperature and quench in a bath.

Hot-work (*v*)—To deform metal stock by hammering, forming, drawing, etc., while the metal is heated to a plastic state.

Kerf (*n*)—The channel or groove cut by a saw or other tool.

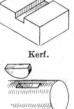

Kerf.

Key (*n*)—A small block or wedge inserted between shaft and hub to prevent circumferential movement.

Key and Seat.

Keyway or **key seat** (*n*) A groove or slot cut to fit a key. A key fits into a key seat and slides in a keyway.

Knurl (*v*)—To roughen or indent a turned surface, as a knob or handle.

Keyway.

Lap (*n*)—A piece of soft metal, wood, or leather charged with abrasive material, used for obtaining an accurate finish. (*v*) To finish by lapping.

Lug (*n*)—A projecting "ear" usually rectangular in cross section. Distinguished from *boss*.

Lug.

Malleable casting (*n*)—An ordinary casting toughened by annealing. Applicable to small castings with uniform metal thicknesses.

Mill (*v*)—To machine with rotating toothed cutters on a milling machine.

Neck (*v*)—To cut a groove around a shaft, usually near the end or at a change in diameter. (*n*) A portion reduced in diameter between the ends of a shaft.

Neck.

Normalize (*v*)—To remove internal stresses by heating a metal piece to its critical temperature and allowing to cool very slowly.

Pack-harden(*v*)—To carburize and caseharden.

Pad (*n*)—A shallow projection. Distinguished from *boss* by shape or size.

Pad.

Peen (*v*)—To stretch, rivet, or clinch over by strokes with the peen of a hammer. (*n*) The end of a hammer head opposite the face, as *ball peen.*

Pickle (*v*)—To clean castings or forgings in a hot weak sulphuric acid bath.

Plane (*v*)—To machine work on a planer having a fixed tool and reciprocating bed.

Planish (*v*)—To finish sheet metal by hammering with polished-faced hammers.

Plate (*v*)—The electrochemical coating of a metal piece with a different metal.

Polish (*v*)—To make smooth or lustrous by friction with a very fine abrasive.

Profile (*v*)—To machine an outline with a rotary cutter usually controlled by a master cam or die.

Punch (*v*)—To perforate by pressing a non-rotating tool through the work.

Ream (*v*)—To finish a drilled or punched hole very accurately with a rotating fluted tool of the required diameter.

Relief (*n*)—The amount one plane surface of a piece is set below or above another plane, usually for clearance or for economy in machining.

Rivet (*v*)—1. To fasten with rivets. 2. To batter or upset the headless end of a pin used as a permanent fastening.

Round (*n*)—A rounded exterior corner between two surfaces. Compare with *Fillet.*

Sandblast (*v*)—To clean

Round.

castings or forgings by means of sand driven through a nozzle by compressed air.

Shape (*v*)—To machine with a shaper, a machine tool differing from a planer in that the work is stationary and the tool reciprocating.

Shear (*v*)—To cut off sheet or bar metal between two blades.

Sherardize (*v*)—To galvanize with zinc by a dry heating process.

Shim (*n*)—A thin spacer of sheet metal used for adjusting.

Shoulder (*n*)—A plane surface on a shaft, normal to the axis and formed by a difference in diameter.

Spin (*v*)—To shape sheet metal by forcing it against a form as it revolves.

Spline (*n*)—A long keyway. Sometimes also a flat key.

Splines

Spot-face (*v*)—To finish a round spot on a rough surface, usually around a drilled hole, to give a good seat to a screw or bolthead, cut, usually $\frac{1}{16}$ in. deep, by a rotating milling cutter.

Spot-face.

Spot-weld (*v*)—To weld in spots by means of the heat of resistance to an electric current. Not applicable to sheet copper or brass.

Steel casting (*n*)—Material used in machine construction. It is ordinary cast iron into which varying amounts of scrap steel have been added in the melting.

Swage (*v*)—To shape metal by hammering or pressure with the aid of a form or anvil called a "swage block."

Sweat (*v*)—To join metal pieces by clamping together with solder between and applying heat.

Tack-weld (*v*)—To join at the edge by welding in short intermittent sections.

Tap (*v*)—To cut threads in a hole with a rotating tool called a "tap," having threads on it and fluted to give cutting edges.

Temper (*v*)—To change the physical characteristics of hardened steel by reheating to a temperature below the critical point and allowing to cool.

Template, templet (*n*)—A flat pattern for laying out shapes, location of holes, etc.

Trepan (*v*)—To cut an outside annular groove around a hole.

Trepan

Tumble (*v*)—To clean, smooth, or polish castings or forgings in a rotating barrel or drum by friction with each other, assisted by added mediums, as scraps, "jacks," balls, sawdust, etc.

Turn (*v*)—To machine on a lathe. Distinguished from *face*.

Undercut (*v*)—To cut, leaving an overhanging edge. (*n*) A cut having inwardly sloping sides.

Upset (*v*)—To forge a larger diameter or shoulder on a bar.

Undercut.

Weld (*v*)—To join two pieces by heating them to the fusing point and pressing or hammering together.

PART II.　STRUCTURAL TERMS

Batten plate—A small plate used to hold two parts in their proper position when made up as one member.

Batter—A deviation from the vertical in upright members.

Bar—Square or round rod; also flat steel up to 6 in. in width.

Bay—The distance between two trusses or transverse bents.

Beam—A horizontal member forming part of the frame of a building or structure.

Bearing plate—A steel plate, usually at the base of a column, used to distribute a load over a larger area.

Bent—A vertical framework usually consisting of a truss or beam supported at the ends on columns.

Brace—A diagonal member used to stiffen a framework.

Buckle plate—A flat plate with dished depression pressed into it to give transverse strength.

Built-up member—A member built from standard shapes to give one single stronger member.

Camber—Slight upward curve given to trusses and girders to avoid effect of sag.

Cantilever—A beam, girder, or truss overhanging one or both supports.

Chord—The principal member of a truss on either the top or bottom.

Clearance—Rivet driving clearance is distance from center of rivet to obstruction. Erection clearance is amount of space left between members for ease in assembly.

Clevis—U-shaped shackle for connecting a rod to a pin.

Clip angle—A small angle used for fastening various members together.

Column—A vertical compression member.

Cope—To cut out top or bottom of flanges and web so that one member will frame into another.

Coping—A projecting top course of concrete or stone.

Counters—Diagonal members in a truss to provide for reversal of shear due to live load.

Cover plate—A plate used in building up flanges, in a built-up member to give greater strength and area, or for protection.

Crimp—To offset the end of a stiffener to fit over the leg of an angle.

Diagonals—Diagonal members used for stiffening and wind bracing.

Dowel—An iron or wooden pin extending into but not through two timbers to connect them.

Driftpin—A tapered steel pin used to bring rivet holes fair in assembling steel work.

Edge distance—The distance from center of rivet to edge of plate or flange.

Fabricate—To cut, punch, and subassemble members in the shop.

Fillers—Either plate or ring fills used to take up space in riveting two members where a gusset is not used.

Flange—The projecting portion of a beam, channel, or column.

Gage line—The center line for rivet holes.

Gin pole—A guyed mast with block at the top for hoisting.

Girder—A horizontal member, either single or built up, acting as a principal beam.

Girt—A beam usually bolted to columns to support the side covering or serve as window lintels.

Gusset plate—A plate used to connect various members, such as in a truss.

Hip—The intersection between two sloping surfaces forming an exterior angle.

Knee brace—A corner brace used to prevent angular movement.

Lacing or lattice bars—Bars used diagonally to space and stiffen two parallel members, such as in a built-up column.

Laterals—Members used to prevent lateral deflection.

Lintel—A horizontal member used to carry a wall over an opening.

Louvers—Metal slats either movable or fixed, as in a monitor ventilator.

Monitor ventilator—A framework that carries fixed or movable louvers at the top of the roof.

Panel—The space between adjacent floor supports or purlins in a roof.

Pitch—Center distance between rivets parallel to axis of member. Also for roofs, the ratio of rise to span.

Plate—Flat steel over 6 in. in width and $\frac{1}{4}$ in. or more in thickness.

Purlins—Horizontal members extending between trusses, used as beams for supporting the roof.

Rafters—Beams or truss members supporting the purlins.

Sag ties—Tie rods between purlins in the plane of the roof to carry the component of the roof load parallel to the roof.

Separator—Either a cast-iron spacer or wrought-iron pipe on a bolt for the purpose of holding members a fixed distance apart.

Sheet—Flat steel over 6 in. in width and less than $\frac{1}{4}$ in. in thickness.

Shim—A thin piece of wood or steel placed under a member to bring it to a desired elevation.

Sleeve nut—A long nut with right and left threads for connecting two rods to make an adjustable member.

Span—Distance between centers of supports of a truss, beam, or girder.

Splice—A longitudinal connection between the parts of a continuous member.

Stiffener—Angle, plate, or channel riveted to a member to prevent buckling.

Stringer—A longitudinal member used to support loads directly.

Strut—A compression member in a framework.

Truss—A rigid framework for carrying loads, formed in a series of triangles.

Turnbuckle—A coupling, threaded right and left or swiveled on one end, for adjustably connecting two rods.

Valley—The intersection between two sloping surfaces, forming a reentrant angle.

Web—The part of a channel, I beam, or girder between the flanges.

PART III. ARCHITECTURAL TERMS

Apron—The finished board placed against the wall surface, immediately below a window stool.

Ashlar—Thin, squared, and dressed stone facing of a masonry wall.

Backing—The inner portion of a wall; that which is used behind the facing.

Batten—A strip of wood used for nailing across two other pieces of wood to hold them together and cover a crack.

Batter boards—Boards set up at the corners of a proposed building from which the lines marking off the walls are stretched.

Bearing wall—A wall that supports loads other than its own weight.

Bond—The joining together of building materials to ensure solidity.

Bridging—The braces, or system of bracing, used between joists or other structural members to stiffen them and to distribute the load.

Centering—A substructure of temporary nature, usually of timber or planks, on which a masonry arch or vault is built.

Coffer—An ornamental panel deeply recessed, usually in a dome or portico ceiling.

Corbel—A bracket formed on a wall by building out successive courses of masonry.

Curtain wall—A wall that carries no building load other than its own weight.

Fenestration—The arrangement and proportioning of window and door openings.

Flashing—The sheet metal built into the joints of a wall, or covering the valleys, ridges, and hips of a roof for the purpose of preventing leakage.

Footing—A course or series of courses projecting at the base of a wall, for the purpose of distributing the load from above over a greater area, thereby preventing excessive settlement.

Furring—The application of thin wood, metal, or other building material to a wall, beam, ceiling, or the like to level a surface for lathing, boarding, etc., or to make an air space within a wall.

Glazing—The act of furnishing or fitting with glass.

Ground—Strips of wood, flush with the plastering, to which moldings, etc., are attached. Grounds are usually installed first and the plastering floated flush with them.

Grout—A thin mortar used for filling up spaces where heavier mortar will not penetrate.

Head—The horizontal piece forming the top of a wall opening, as a door or window.

Hip—The intersection of two roof surfaces, which form on the plan an external angle.

Jamb—The vertical piece forming the side of a wall opening.

Lintel—The horizontal structural member that supports the wall over an opening.

Millwork—The finish woodwork, machined and in some cases partly assembled at the mill.

Miter—To match together, as two pieces of molding, on a line bisecting the angle of junction.

Mullion—A vertical division of a window opening.

Muntin—The thin members that separate the individual lights of glass in a window frame.

Party wall—A division wall common to two adjacent pieces of property.

Plate—A horizontal member that carries other structural members; usually the top timber of a wall that carries the roof trusses or rafters directly.

Rail—A horizontal piece in a frame or paneling.

Return—The continuation in a different direction, most often at right angles, of the face of a building or any member, as a colonnade or molding; applied to the shorter in contradistinction to the longer.

Reveal—The side of a wall opening; the whole thickness of the wall; the jamb.

Riser—The upright piece of a step, from tread to tread.

Saddle—A small double-sloping roof to carry water away from behind chimneys, etc.

Scratch coat—The first coat in plastering, roughened by scratching or scoring so that the next coat may firmly adhere to it.

Screeds—A strip of plaster of the thickness proposed for the work, applied to the wall at intervals of 4 or 5 ft, to serve as guides.

Shoring—A prop, as a timber, placed against the side of a structure; a prop placed beneath anything, as a beam, to prevent sinking or sagging.

Sill—The horizontal piece, as a timber, which forms the lowest member of a frame.

Sleepers—The timbers laid on a firm foundation to carry and secure the superstructure.

Soffit—The underside of subordinate parts and members of buildings, such as staircases, beams, arches, etc.

Stile—A vertical piece in a frame or paneling.

Stool—The narrow shelf fitted on the inside of a window against the actual sill.

Threshold—The stone, wood, or metal piece which lies directly under a door.

Trap—A water seal in a sewage system to prevent sewer gas from entering the building.

Tread—The upper horizontal piece of a step, on which the foot is placed.

Valley—The intersection of two roof surfaces which form, on the plan, a re-entrant angle.

Supplementary Visual Materials

In addition to the McGraw-Hill Text-Films that are specifically correlated with certain chapters in this book and are listed at the end of these chapters, the following list of visual aids may be used to supplement some of the material in the book. It is suggested that each film and filmstrip be previewed before using as some may contain information that is too advanced while others may contain information that is too elementary.

These films and filmstrips can be obtained from the producer or distributor listed with each title. (The addresses of these producers and distributors are given at the end of this listing.) In many cases these films can also be obtained from your local film library or distributor; also, many universities have large film libraries from which they can be borrowed.

The running time (min), whether it is silent (si) or sound (sd), and whether it is a motion picture (MP) or filmstrip (FS) are listed with each title. All the motion pictures are 16mm; filmstrips are 35mm.

All the U. S. Office of Education films have coordinated silent filmstrips and instructor's manuals. In many cases other films also have accompanying instructor's manuals.

Each film and filmstrip has been listed only once in connection with the chapter to which it is most applicable. However, many of them can be used advantageously in connection with other chapters.

CHAPTER 1—INTRODUCTORY

The Draftsman (VGF 11min sd MP).
Behind the Shop Drawing (JH 20min sd MP).

CHAPTER 2—LETTERING

Capital Letters (Purdue 20min sd MP).
Lower Case Letters (Purdue 13min sd MP).
Basic Standards in Mechanical Drafting (Eberhard Faber 16- by 24-in. wall chart)

CHAPTER 3—THE SELECTION OF INSTRUMENTS
and
CHAPTER 4—THE USE OF INSTRUMENTS

T Squares and Triangles, Part 1 (JH FS).
T Squares and Triangles, Part 2 (JH FS).
Use of T Square and Triangles (Purdue 11min sd MP).
Testing of T Square and Triangles (Purdue 13min si MP).
Instruments and Materials (IIT 18min si MP).
Drafting Tips (PSC 28min sd MP).
Ink Work and Tracing (Purdue 30min si MP).

CHAPTER 5—APPLIED GEOMETRY

Applied Geometry (Purdue 16min si MP).
Geometric Construction, Part 1 (JH FS).
Geometric Construction, Part 2 (JH FS).

CHAPTERS 6 TO 9 INCLUSIVE—ORTHOGRAPHIC PROJECTION

Orthographic Projection (Purdue 30min si MP).
Introduction to Mechanical Drawing (Cocking 20min si MP).

CHAPTER 10—AUXILIARY VIEWS

Auxiliary Views (Purdue 15min si MP).

CHAPTER 13—SECTIONS AND CONVENTIONS

Sectional Views, Projections, Finish Marks (USOE 15min sd **MP).**
Shop Drawing, Part 1 **(IIT 11min sd MP).**

CHAPTER 14—INTERSECTIONS
and
CHAPTER 15—DEVELOPMENTS

Development of Surfaces (**Purdue** 15min si MP).
Intersection of Surfaces (Purdue 15min si MP).
How to Develop an Intersection: Part 1 (Castle si FS).
How to Develop an Intersection: Part 2 (Castle si FS).

CHAPTER 18—PICTORIAL SKETCHING

Pictorial Drawing (Purdue 30min si MP).
Freehand Drawing (Purdue 13min si MP).

CHAPTER 19—THE DRAWINGS AND THE SHOP

Shop Drawing, Part 2 (IIT 11min sd MP).
Basic Machines: The Lathe (USOE 15min sd MP).
Machine Tools: The Lathe (Army sd FS).
The Turret Lathe: An Introduction (USOE 17min sd MP).
Turret Lathes (Gisholt 45min sd MP).
Specialized Machines: Turret Lathe (JH FS).
Basic Machines: The Milling Machine (USOE 15min sd MP).
Machine Tools: The Milling Machine (Army sd FS).
The Milling Machine (USOE 18min sd MP).
Basic Machines: The Shaper (USOE 15min sd MP).
Machine Tools: The Shaper (Army sd FS).
Machine Tools: Planers (Army sd FS).
Planer and Shaper Operations (FiPr 10min sd MP).
Basic Machines: The Drill Press (USOE 10min sd MP).

CHAPTER 20—DIMENSIONS AND NOTES
and
CHAPTER 21—PRECISION AND LIMIT DIMENSIONING

Principal Dimensions, Reference Surfaces and Tolerances (USOE 12min sd MP).
Visualizing an Object (USOE 9min sd MP).
Reading a Three-view Drawing (USOE 10min sd MP).
Reading a Drawing of a Valve Bonnet (USOE 20min sd MP).
Drawing an Anchor Plate (JH FS).

CHAPTER 22—SCREW THREADS

Screw Threads (Purdue 23min si MP).

CHAPTER 30—THE ELEMENTS OF STRUCTURAL DRAWING

Structural Drawing (Purdue 20min si MP).

CHAPTER 31—THE ELEMENTS OF ARCHITECTURAL DRAWING

Basic Standards for Architectural Drawing (Eberhard Faber 16- by 24-in. wall chart).
Architectural and Engineering Symbols (Fredrick Post 23- by 35-in. wall chart).
Standard Woodworking Joints (Eberhard Faber 16- by 24-in. wall chart).

CHAPTER 33—CHARTS, GRAPHS, AND DIAGRAMS

Plotting Graphs (JH FS).
Graph Uses (JH FS).
Analytic Geometry (JH FS).
Rectilinear Co-ordinates (United 12min sd MP).
Frequency Curves (Wisconsin 11min sd MP).

CHAPTER 34—ILLUSTRATION

Broad Stroke Drawing (Ideal 10min sd MP).

GENERAL

Shop Terms and Methods (NYU 30min si MP).
Scales and Models (JH FS).
The Slide Rule: Multiplication and Division (USOE 24min sd MP).
The Slide Rule: Percentage, Proportion, Squares and Square Roots (USOE 21min sd MP).

SOURCES OF FILMS LISTED ABOVE

Army—U.S. Army (obtainable from Castle Films, Inc.).
Castle Films, 30 Rockefeller Plaza, New York 20.
Cocking, Floyd W., 4757 Constance Dr., San Diego, Calif.
Eberhard Faber Co., Education Department, 37 Greenpoint Ave., Brooklyn 27, N.Y.
FiPr—Film Production Co., 3650 N. Fremont Ave., Minneapolis, Minn.
Gisholt Machine Co., 1245 E. Washington Ave., Madison 3, Wis.
Ideal Pictures Corp., 28 E. Eighth St., Chicago 5.
IIT—Illinois Institute of Technology, 3300 Federal St., Chicago.
JH—Jam Handy Organization, 2900 E. Grand Blvd., Detroit 11, Mich.
NYU—New York University Film Library, 26 Washington Sq., New York 3.
PSC—Pennsylvania State College, Film Library, State College, Pa.
Post Co., Fredrick, 3635 N. Hamilton Ave., Chicago.
Purdue University, General Engineering Dept., Lafayette, Ind.
United World Films, Inc., 1250 Sixth Ave., New York 20.
USOE—U.S. Office of Education (obtainable from Castle Films, Inc.).
Wisconsin, University of, Bureau of Visual Instruction, Madison 6, Wis.

Index